WEEDS

OF CALIFORNIA

By

W. W. ROBBINS,[1] MARGARET K. BELLUE,[2] and
WALTER S. BALL[3]

[1] Professor of Botany and Botanist in the Experiment Station, University of California.
[2] Weed and Seed Botanist, State Department of Agriculture.
[3] Chief, Bureau of Rodent and Weed Control and Seed Inspection, State Department of Agriculture

For Sale by
DOCUMENTS AND PUBLICATIONS
P.O. Box 20191
Sacramento, California 95820

A. A. BROCK
DIRECTOR

Earl Warren
Governor

OFFICE OF THE DIRECTOR
STATE OFFICE BUILDING NO. 1
SACRAMENTO 14

STATE OF CALIFORNIA
Department of Agriculture

FOREWORD

The year 1922 marked the beginning of a real and active interest in weeds and weed control on the part of official agencies in California. Although several weed laws had been enacted, the earliest in 1872, there was a dearth of information on control procedures, and descriptive data on weeds themselves were even less available. The State Department of Agriculture, recognizing the need, issued a bulletin entitled "Weeds of California and Methods of Control," by F. J. Smiley, Collaborator, with contributions by members of the department. That document served admirably as a weed manual and control handbook from 1922 to 1930. However, the demand soon depleted the supply, resulting in constantly increasing requests for material of a similar character.

A keener interest in weed suppression among growers and regulatory officials led to a coordination of research and field practice efforts between the Division of Botany of the College of Agriculture at Davis and that bureau of the State Department of Agriculture engaged in correlating the activities of county agricultural officers responsible by law for weed cleanup work. Thus, an ideal combination of investigational, educational and procedural effort was established which resulted in a rapid development in information relating to weeds, particularly the control features, and indicating the necessity for small periodical and timely publications on control phases. This further emphasized the necessity for a more permanent manual giving descriptions of weeds, their life histories and habits of growth, as represented by this volume.

The original publication represented the results of painstaking endeavor on the part of the authors, each a recognized authority in his line, and was the culmination of years of planning and pooling of resources. This revision fortunately could be undertaken by those same people and brings about a much needed, up-to-date document. To the many who have participated in supplying data, particularly those officially associated with the authors in this work, the department and the authors express deep appreciation.

W. C. JACOBSEN, Assistant to the Director
California State Department of Agriculture

(3)

TABLE OF CONTENTS

———

LIST OF COLOR PLATES

INTRODUCTION

This publication is designed for those who do not have a technical knowledge of botanical terms and plant structures. Its primary aim is to assist the user to independently identify and recognize our common weeds. Accordingly, numerous photographs and drawings are included; keys have been made simple and are illustrated; and descriptions are as free of technical terms as is possible.

Since 1922, many weeds new to the State have made their appearance, and the relative importance of others has been modified. Further, greater activity in weed surveys has given us considerable additional data concerning the distribution and significance of numerous weed species.

In 1931, the California Agricultural Extension Service issued Circular 54, The Control of Weeds, By W. S. Ball, B. A. Madson, and W. W. Robbins. This was revised and superseded by Extension Circular 97, Weed Control, by W. S. Ball, A. S. Crafts, B. A. Madson, and W. W. Robbins, issued in 1936 and revised in 1940. The circulars cited above are rather exhaustive in their discussion of weed control methods, but they do not include descriptions of our weed species. Accordingly, this publication does not aim at a detailed discussion of weed control; the reader is referred to California Agricultural Extension Service Circulars, listed below, for control measures. The reader is also referred to Bulletin No. 637 of the California Agricultural Experiment Station entitled "Alien Plants Growing Without Cultivation in California," by W. W. Robbins. This gives the approximate dates and places of introduction of our alien species, and their behavior in the State following introduction.

A majority of the weeds of California, and usually the most pernicious, are aliens; however, many natives have become troublesome. Of the total number of species cited in this publication, 437, or 63 percent, are aliens, and 256, or 37 percent, are natives. Weeds of minor importance and of limited distribution are given attention, for experience shows that many such may become widespread and of major importance.

Stock-poisoning plants are included, but are treated in less detail than the strictly weedy species of cultivated areas.

The authors wish to acknowledge the assistance of Wanda Coover who has made most of the drawings, and to Edna Willis Gaskill for assistance in the reading of proof.

LIST OF PUBLICATIONS
on Specific Weeds, Weed Control, and Weed Problems in California

Akesson, N. B., and W. A. Harvey
  1948. Equipment for the application of herbicides. Agr. Engr. 29 (9) : 384-389, September.
Ball, W. E., and O. C. French
  1935. Sulfuric acid for control of weeds. California Agr. Expt. Sta. Bul. 596. 29 p.
Ball, Walter S.
  1933. Weed control. California State Dept. Agr. Bul. 22 : 252-257.
  1933. Artichoke thistle. California State Dept. Agr. Bul. 22 : 269-272.
  1935-48. 16th to 29th Annual Reports, California Dept. Agr. Bul. Vol. 24-Vol. 37.
  1938. Note on *Hypericum perforatum.* California State Dept. Agr. Bul. 27 : 295.
  1939. Creeping sow thistle in Santa Clara County. California State Dept. Agr. Bul. 28 : 415.
  1944. Germination of buried weed seed. California State Dept. Agr. Bul. 33 : 105-107.
Ball, Walter S., and M. K. Bellue
  1934. Nut grasses. California State Dept. Agr. Bul. 23 : 182-184.
  1935. A new means of dissemination of nut grass. California State Dept. Agr. Bul. 24 : 235-237.
Ball, Walter S., and W. W. Robbins
  1931. Russian knapweed. California State Dept. Agr. Bul. 20 : 666-668.
  1932. Puncture vine. California State Dept. Agr. Bul. 21 : 211-213.
  1932. Johnson grass (*Holcus halepensis* L.). California State Dept. Agr. Bul. 21 : 287-289.
  1932. Bermuda grass (*Cynodon dactylon*). California State Dept. Agr. Bul. 21 : 322-323.
  1932. White horse nettle (*Solanum elaeagnifolium* Cav.). California State Dept. Agr. Bul. 21 : 348-349.
  1932. Canada thistle (*Cirsium arvense* Scop.). California State Dept. Agr. Bul. 21 : 394-395.
  1932. Quack grass (*Agropyron repens* Beauv.). California State Dept. Agr. Bul. 21 : 414-415.
  1933. Camel thorn. California State Dept. Agr. Bul. 22 : 258-260.
  1933. Spiny clotbur (*Xanthium spinosum* L.). California State Dept. Agr. Bul. 22 : 278.
  1933. Perennial sow thistle (*Sonchus arvensis* L.). California State Dept. Agr. Bul. 22 : 286.
  1933. Poverty weed (*Iva axillaris* Pursh.). Calfiornia State Dept. Agr. Bul. 22 : 305.
  1933. Sandbur. California State Dept. Agr. Bul. 22 : 318.
  1933. Heliotrope (*Heliotropium curassavicum* L.). California State Dept. Agr. Bul. 22 : 379.
Ball, Walter S., and W. W. Robbins
  1934. Klamath weed. California State Dept. Agr. Bul. 23 : 103-108.
  1935. Wild morning-glory (*Convolvulus arvensis* L.). California State Dept. Agr. Bul. 24 : 192-194.
  1935. Mexican whorled or narrow-leaf milkweed (*Asclepias mexicana* Cav.). California State Dept. Agr. Bul. 24 : 219-220.
  1935. Alkali mallow (*Sida hederacea* [Dougl.] Torr.). California State Dept. Agr. Bul. 24 : 232.
  1935. Pignut (*Hoffmannseggia densiflora* Benth.). California State Dept. Agr. Bul. 24 : 260.
  1941. Status of weed problems in California. California State Dept. Agr. Bul. 30 : 184 195.
Ball, Walter S., W. W. Robbins, and Margaret K. Bellue
  1933. The star thistles. California State Dept. Agr. Bul. 22 : 294-298.

Bellue, Margaret K.
1933. New weeds confused with hoary cress. California State Dept. Agr. Bul. 22: 288-293.
1933. Austrian field cress—new and noxious (*Rorippa austriaca*). California State Dept. Agr. Bul. 22: 385-386.
1934. *Carduus neglectus* Ten., Italian thistle. California State Dept. Agr. Bul. 23: 195.
1934. Silver-sheathed knotweed as a pest in southwestern alfalfa (*Polygonum argyrocoleon* Steud.). California State Dept. Agr. Bul. 24: 238-241.
1935. Knotweed or kelp, *Polygonum muhlenbergii* Wats. California State Dept. Agr. Bul. 24: 191.
1935. Again—Italian thistle, *Carduus neglectus* Ten. California State Dept. Agr. Bul. 24: 300.
1935. Lily-of-the-Valley Vine (*Salpichroa rhomboidea* Miers.) is difficult to eradicate. California State Dept. Agr. Bul. 24: 345.
1936. Kelp or swamp knotweed. California State Dept. Agr. Bul. 25: 273.
1936. Garden rocket (*Eruca sativa* Mill.), a new flax weed. California State Dept. Agr. Bul. 25: 280.
1936. *Lepidium latifolium* L., a new perennial peppergrass. California State Dept. Agr. Bul. 25: 359.
1936. A new and spiny nightshade (*Solanum pyracanthum* Jacq.). California State Dept. Agr. Bul. 25: 377.
1936. Leafy Spurge (*Euphorbia Esula* L.). California State Dept. Agr. Bull. 25: 384-387.
1937. Bladder campion (*Silene latifolia* Britton and Rend.) established near Santa Rosa. California State Dept. Agr. Bul. 26: 176.
1937. Blueweed (*Helianthus ciliaris* DC.) is established in five counties. California State Dept. Agr. Bul. 26: 247-252.
1937. Matrimony vine (*Lycium halimifolium* Mill.) forms spiny thickets in neglected areas. California State Dept. Agr. Bul. 26: 293.
1937. Lily-of-the-Valley Vine (*Salpichroa rhomboidea* Miers.) a frequent garden escape. California State Dept. Agr. Bul. 26: 310.
1938. The bristlegrasses, *Setaria* spp., in California. California State Dept. Agr. Bul. 27: 210-214.
1938. Perennial peppercress, *Lepidium latifolium* L. California State Dept. Agr. Bul. 22: 287.
1938. Matrimony vine and lily-of-the-valley vine as weed pests. California State Dept. Agr. Bul. 28: 293-297.
1938. Carolina horse nettle (*Solanum carolinense* L.) and other weedy solanums in California. California State Dept. Agr. Bul. 28: 471-478.
1940. Italian thistles, *Carduus tenuiflorus* Curt. and *C. pycnocephalus* L. not serious on cultivated lands. California State Dept. Agr. Bul. 29: 128-131.
1945-47. Weed Seed Handbook. Series I-VIII. California State Dept. Agr. Bul. 34: 27-34, 76-83, 116-123. 35: 13-20, 87-94, 159-166. 36: 27-30, 31-38.
1947. Rough-seed bulrush, *Scirpus mucronatus* L., a menace to rice production. California State Dept. Agr. Bul. 36: 91-96.
1948. Bladderflower, *Arauja sericifera* Brot., an escaped ornamental in California. California State Dept. Agr. Bul. 37: 20-22.
1949. Halogeton invades California. California State Dept. Agr. Bul. 38: 44-48.
1950. Mediterranean sage moves. California State Dept. Agr. Bul. 39: 43.

Bellue, Margaret K., and Walter S. Ball
1933. Hoary cress, *Lepidium draba* L., California State Dept. Agr. Bul. 22: 287.

Bellue, Margaret K., and C. E. Berry
1941. Additional sites for Leafy Spurge, *Euphorbia Esula* L. California State Dept. Agr. Bul. 30: 286-289.

Bottell, A. E.
1933. Introduction and control of camel thorn. California State Dept. Agr. Bul. 22: 261-263.

Bruce, H. D.
1939. Chemical killing of sprouting stumps. Calif. Forest & Range Expt. Sta., U.S.D.A., Research Note No. 23. 10 p.

Buhn, Norman G.
1938. Wild gorse in Mendocino County. California State Dept. Agr. Bul. 27: 425.

Bunting, Leatha
  1933. Noxious weed seeds found in crop seeds. California State Dept. Agr. Bul. 22: 283-285.
Cook, J. B. Pocket gophers spread Canada thistle. California State Dept. Agr. Bul. 28: 142-143.
Crafts, A. S.
  1933. The use of arsenical compounds in the control of deep-rooted perennial weeds. Hilgardia 7: 361-372.
  1933. Progress in chemical weed control. California State Dept. Agr. Bul 22: 264-268.
  1933. Sulfuric acid as a penetrating agent in arsenical sprays for weed control. Hilgardia 8: 125-147.
  1935. Plot tests with sodium arsenite and sodium chlorate as soil sterilants in California. California State Dept. Agr. Bul. 24: 247-259.
  1935. Physiological problems connected with the use of sodium chlorate in weed control. Plant Physiology 10: 699-711.
  1937. The acid-arsenical method in weed control. Jour. Amer. Soc. of Agronomy 29: 934-943.
  1939. The relation of nutrients to toxicity of arsenic, borax, and chlorate in soils. Jour. Agr. Research 58: 637-671.
  1939. Toxicity studies with sodium chlorate in eighty California soils. Hilgardia 12: 233-247.
  1945. A new herbicide, 2,4-dinitro 6 secondary butyl phenol. Science 101: 417-418.
  1945. Toxicity of certain herbicides in soils. Hilgardia 16: 459-483.
  1945. Control of aquatic weeds. California Agr. Expt. Sta. Bot. Div. Mimeog. 6 p.
  1946. The 2,4-D weed killers: A warning. California State Dept. Agr. Bul. 35: 34-36.
  1946. Selectivity of herbicides. Plant Physiology 21: 345-361.
  1947. Oil sprays for weeding carrots and related crops. California Agr. Ext. Serv. Circ. 136. 12 p.
  1947. General contact weed killers. California Agr. Ext. Serv. Circ. 137. 16 p.
  1948. Weed control in the Tropics. Science 107: 196-197.
  1948. Results of soil treatment vs. contact sprays in corn and cane weed control. Agr. Chemicals 3: 25-27, 81-85.
  1948. A theory of herbicidal action. Science 108: 85-86.
  1949. Toxicity of 2,4-D in California soils. Hilgardia 19(5): 141-158.
  1949. Toxicity of ammonium dinitro-o-sec-butyl phenolate in California soils. Hilgardia 19(5): 159-169.
  1949. Control of aquatic weeds. Calif. Agr. Ext. Serv. Circ. 158, October. 16 p.
  1949. General-contact weed killers. Calif. Agr. Ext. Serv. Circ. 137 Rev., October. 15 p.
Crafts, A. S., H. D. Bruce and R. N. Raynor
  1941. Plot tests with chemical soil sterilants in California. California Agr. Expt. Sta. Bul. 648.
Crafts, A. S., and C. W. Cleary
  1936. Toxicity of arsenic, borax, chlorate, and their combinations in three California soils. Hilgardia 10: 401-413.
Crafts, A. S., and A. Emanuelli
  1948. Combination of 2,4-D with fortified oil-emulsion contact herbicides. Bot. Gaz. 110: 148-154.
Crafts, A. S., and W. A. Harvey.
  1949. Selective weed killers. Calif. Agr. Ext. Serv. Circ. 157, September. 16 p.
  1949. Weed Control. Advances in Agronomy, V.1: 289-320.
Crafts, A. S., and P. B. Kennedy
  1930. The physiology of Convolvulus arvensis (morning-glory or bindweed) in relation to its control by chemical sprays. Plant Physiology 5: 329-344.
Crafts, A. S., and R. N. Raynor
  1936. The herbicidal properties of boron compounds. Hilgardia 10: 343-374.
  1940. Principles of chemical weed control. Herbage Publ. Series, Imperial Bur. of Pastures and Forage Crops, Gt. Brit. Bul. 27: 38-54.
  1944. Experiments in chemical weed control of onions. Western Grower and Shipper 25: 10-11, 26-28.

Crafts, A. S., and H. G. Reiber
  1945. Studies on the activation of herbicides. Hilgardia 16 : 487-500.
  1946. Herbicidal properties of oils. California State Dept. Agr. Bul. 35 : 34-36.
  1948. Herbicidal properties of oils. Hilgardia 18 : 77-156.
Crafts, A. S., and R. S. Rosenfels
  1939. Toxicity studies with arsenic in eighty California soils. Hilgardia 12 :
          177-200.
Currier, H. B., and A. S. Crafts
  1950. Maleic hydrazide, a selective herbicide. Science 111 (2876) : 152-153.
Fix, Ernest E.
  1946. Leafy spurge (*Euphorbia Esula* L.). California State Dept. Agr. Bul. 35 :
          122-123.
French, O. C., and A. S. Crafts
  1936. Spray nozzles for vegetable and weed spraying. Jour. Agr. Engineering 17 :
          115-119.
Goodwin, Paul M.
  1933. Weed control by means of soil sterilization. California State Dept. Agr. Bul.
          22 : 299-301.
Hannesson, H. A., R. N. Raynor, and A. S. Crafts
  1945. Herbicidal use of carbon disulfide. California Agr. Expt. Sta. Bul. 693. 57 p.
Harvey, W. A.
  1948. Control of weeds on fence lines and ditch banks. Spreckels Sugar Beet Bul.
          12 :43, 46.
  1948. Chemical weed killers. Calif. Citrograph 33 : 381, 403-405.
Harvey, W. A., and O. C. Riddle
  1946. Controlling alfalfa weeds with chemical sprays. California Agr. Expt. Sta.
          Bot. Div. Mimeog. 7 p.
Harvey, W. A., and W. W. Robbins
  1947. 2,4-D as a weed killer. California Agr. Ext. Serv. Circ. 133 Revised. 33 p.
Johnson, E.
  1932. The puncture vine in California. California Agr. Expt. Sta. Bul. 528 : 1-42.
  1939. Five-hook Bassia, *Bassia hyssopifolia* (Pall.) Kuntze, a host of Say's plant
          bug, *Chlorochroa sayi* Stal. California State Dept. Agr. Bul. 28 : 139.
  1940. The storage of sodium chlorate and white arsenic mixture a dangerous prac-
          tice. California State Dept. Agr. Bul. 29 : 110-111.
Johnston, J. C., and Wallace Sullivan
  1949. Eliminating tillage in citrus soil management. Calif. Agr. Ext. Serv. Circ. 150,
          March. 16 p.
Kennedy, P. B., and A. S. Crafts
  1927. The application of physiological methods to weed control. Plant Physiology
          2 : 503-506.
  1931. The anatomy of *Convolvulus arvensis*, wild morning-glory or bindweed. Hil-
          gardia 5 : 591-622.
Pryor, Murray R.
  1948. Observations of weed control in California rice fields with 2,4-D. California
          State Dept. Agr. Bul. 37 : 14-18.
Raynor, R. N.
  1937. The chemical control of St. Johnswort. California Agr. Expt. Sta. Bul. 615,
          38 p.
  1945. Experiments on controlling hoary cress by cultivation, searing and spraying.
          California State Dept. Agr. Bul. 34 : 17-26.
Robbins, W. W.
  1931. Weed control in California. California State Dept. Agr. Bul. 20 : 461-466.
  1934. Weed investigations in California. California State Dept. Agr. Bul. 23 :
          307-312.
  1939. The alien plant population of California. California State Dept. Agr. Bul.
          28 : 163-165.
  1940. Alien plants growing without cultivation in California. California Agr. Expt.
          Sta. Bul. 637. 128 p.
  1941. Weeds in orchards. Reclamation Era 31 : 147-150.

Robbins, W. W., and Roy Bainer
　1947.　Pre-emergence spray for weed control in sugar beets seeded in undisturbed soil successful. California Agr. 1 : 1, 2.

Robbins, W. W., A. S. Crafts, and R. N. Raynor
　1942.　Weed Control—A Textbook and Manual. McGraw Hill Book Co., New York. 543 p.

Rosenfels, R. S., and A. S. Crafts
　1939.　Arsenic fixation in relation to the sterilization of soils with sodium arsenite. Hilgardia 12 : 203-209.

Sampson, A. W., and H. E. Malmsten
　1935.　Stock-poisoning plants of California. California Agr. Expt. Sta. Bul. 593 90 p.

Stout, Gilbert L.
　1936.　A rare case of dodder (*Cuscuta indecora* Choisy) attacking olive in California. California State Dept. Agr. Bul. 25 : 213.
　1938.　A recurrence of broomrape, *Orobanche ramosa* L., on tomato plants in California. California State Dept. Agr. Bul. 27 : 166-171.
　1940.　A case of dodder (*Cuscuta subinclusa* Durand & Hilgard) on Valencia orange (*Citrus sinensis* Osbeck) in Southern California. California State Dept. Agr. Bul. 29 : 121-124.

Stroup, B. F.
　1945.　A report on Klamath weed control in Shasta. California State Dept. Agr. Bul. 25 : 148-150.

Sullivan, Wallace, Paul W. Moore, J. C. Johnston, and H. E. Wahlberg
　1947.　Oil spray for weed control in noncultivated citrus orchards. California Agr. Expt. Sta. Reprint 3m. 7 p.

Westgate, W. A., and R. N. Raynor
　1940.　A new selective spray for the control of certain weeds. California Agr. Expt. Sta. Bul. 634. 35 p.

PRINCIPLES OF WEED CONTROL *

The methods used in controlling any weed must be related to its habits of growth and reproduction. Since these vary widely, as already indicated, control practices differ. The first problem, always, is to determine the mode of attack best suited to the weed and to the conditions in question. Sound judgment is needed for often success depends upon adapting the methods to the situation.

Annuals

Annual weeds live but one year; they produce seed but once and then die down entirely, root and all. Having no parts underground by means of which they can spread, they propagate themselves by seeds alone. Obviously, all methods of controlling them have one principal object—*the prevention of seeding*—which may be attained by mowing, cultivating, burning, or spraying. If seed production is consistently prevented over a series of years, and if the introduction of weed seeds from neighboring areas is largely eliminated, the annual weed population will gradually decrease. Of course, weed seeds of many annuals may live for years in the soil and may then be brought by cultural operations to the surface, where conditions for their growth are favorable. The germination of such seeds should be encouraged by irrigation or cultivation before or soon after the crop is planted, to insure killing of the young plants before they injure the crop. Annuals in the early stages are easily and cheaply destroyed by cultivation, plowing, or chemicals; and, once the top has been killed, the root has no power of rejuvenation.

Summer and *winter annuals* differ considerably in their habits. The seeds of summer annuals germinate in the spring; and the plants grow to maturity during the same season, develop a crop of seeds, and die during the winter. Shallow cultivation and sprays, either oil, or 2,4-D or a preparation of sodium dinitro-cresol or dinitro-phenol,** afford the best control. It is to check summer annuals that an intertilled summer crop is usually placed in a crop-rotation plan.

Winter annuals usually start in the fall or early winter when soil-moisture conditions are favorable. The young plants live throughout the winter in a vegetative condition, often forming a rosette-like growth. In the spring they grow rapidly, flower, and produce seed. Such plants are more difficult to control in California. The seeds usually germinate throughout the winter; and shallow cultivation, to be effective, would have to be repeated several times—a procedure often impossible during the rainy season. Two effective methods, however, are available.

---
* This section is taken from California Agricultural Extension Service Circular No. 97, *Weed Control*, by W. S. Ball, A. S. Crafts, R. N. Raynor and W. W. Robbins, (revised by R. N. Raynor).
** California Agricultural Extension Service Bulletin No. 634, *A New Selective Spray for the Control of Certain Weeds*, by W. A. Westgate and R. N. Raynor.

The first method is plowing. If plowed under fairly early in the spring, these weeds are effectively controlled, leaving the land free for crops. Plowing which is done primarily for the control of annual weeds should be shallow, in order that seeds be kept in the surface layers of soil where they will germinate readily. Spring plowing is common practice in California, both in cereal production and in preparing the land for later summer crops. In cereal production a good job of plowing often means the difference between a clean, heavy crop and a weedy unprofitable one.

The second means of checking winter annuals, principally used in growing cereals, is a selective spray such as 2,4-D. This method will be described in detail in the next section.

Annuals often grow luxuriantly during the mild winters in California and are sometimes used for pasturage. In this case they are usually plowed under in the spring, and they serve the two-fold purpose of providing green feed for cattle or sheep and a soiling crop for the land. They should be turned under before seed is produced, and the plowing should be clean and thorough. Some annuals are similarly used in orchards, providing a valuable covercrop at minimum cost. Where used in this way, they are perpetuated by allowing the seeds to ripen before plowing. This practice always presents the hazard of severe competition for moisture if irrigation water is not available and it also may menace surrounding fields if seeds scatter. Where such a program is followed, the orchardist should be extremely careful that troublesome annuals or noxious perennials do not invade his land and spread undetected. Great caution should also be exercised in the planting of screenings for covercrop production.

Although mowing will prevent some annual weeds from seeding, certain species, such as wild lettuce, wild radish and yellow star thistle, will send up new shoots from buds in the axils of the lower leaves and may produce a second crop of flowers and seed. Such operations as mowing and spraying must be done at the proper time; delay may mean failure. The easiest way to dispose of annual weeds is to kill them in their early stages.

Common California annuals are mustards, wild radish, tumbleweed, pigweeds, wild oats, shepherd's purse, barnyard grass, chess or cheat, lamb's-quarters, Russian thistle, puncture vine, dodder, spiny sow thistle, yellow star thistle, sunflower, cocklebur, and crabgrass.

Biennials

A biennial weed lives for two years, passing through the first year in a low rosette form and producing seed the second summer. In California the biennials do not form a distinct or important group. Many weeds that are annuals in regions of freezing winters have a biennial habit in this State. True biennials are few, examples being purple star thistle and burdock. They are controlled like annuals, the treatment being made during the first year.

Perennials

The most troublesome weeds are perennials, which require special methods and systematic, painstaking endeavor for control. Plants in this group, as contrasted with annuals and biennials, live three years or more and spread not only by seed but also by underground roots or stems.

Perennials fall into three classes, according to their methods of reproduction:

The simple perennials have either a large taproot, like the dandelion, or a fibrous root system, like certain bunch grasses; in either case there is a well-developed perennial crown. Under natural conditions these perennials propagate only by seed; but if the roots of such plants as the dandelion, or the crowns of the bunch grasses, are broken into pieces, each piece is capable of rejuvenating the plant.

The creeping perennials are the most difficult type to control because they reproduce by creeping underground stems (rootstocks or rhizomes) as well as by seed. Among the most common are Johnson grass, hoary cress, morning-glory, Canada thistle, and Russian knapweed. These not only spread horizontally for appreciable distances underground but have deeply penetrating roots. Morning-glory roots have been found over 20 feet deep in the soil.

Bulbous perennials reproduce by bulbs or nut-like structures and by seeds as well. Their reproductive organs are often but weakly attached to the mother plant and are easily dragged loose and scattered through the soil during plowing and cultivation. Some common bulbous perennials of California are wild onion, and the nutgrasses.

METHODS OF CONTROLLING PERENNIAL WEEDS

In combating perennial weeds, two problems are involved. First, to check spread of reinfestation by seedlings, the old plants must be prevented from ripening seed, and seedlings developing from seed already present in the soil must be killed. Second, the existing stand of old established plants must be eradicated.

In handling the seedling situation, one may use methods similar to those already described for annuals, except that the greater hazard involved makes it much more important to prevent the spread of seed. Mowing in the blossoming stages, spraying with contact sprays, or burning will accomplish this purpose. Probably early spraying or mowing, followed by spraying of the stubble after removal of top growth, is the best way to prevent seed formation. Plowing or shallow cultivation, if done early enough, will kill seedlings of perennials. Morning-glory seedlings may be controlled in the two to five-leaf stage by two cultivations to a depth of 3 inches on unirrigated land or four cultivations after each irrigation on irrigated land. If allowed to become more mature, the plans assume a perennial habit, and eradication becomes much more difficult.

In controlling or eradicating established perennial weeds, several methods are effective. Certain requirements limit the vigor of such plants and their ability to perpetuate themselves. All, for example, need sunlight, oxygen, water, and certain mineral nutrients from the soil. If any one of these factors is limited, either by cultivation, smothering, or immersion under water, or by competition with other plants, the vigor of the plant is reduced; and if any one is rendered permanently unavailable, the plant must ultimately die.

In addition, the perennial plant goes through a more or less normal annual cycle of vegetation, reproduction, storage, and dormancy; and any disturbance of this cycle lowers its vigor. A plant may be induced, furthermore, under certain limited conditions, to take up a chemical through cut or injured tops; the poison is then translocated to the roots, killing all tissue with which it comes in contact. And finally a plant, under other conditions, may absorb toxic chemicals from the soil and die when these accumulate sufficiently.

The usual practice in combating deep-rooted perennials by clean cultivation has been to cut the plants below the soil surface with a weed knife just as soon as any growth appears above-ground. The theory behind this has been that the new green growth, unless destroyed, would immediately begin the manufacture of food and this food would move into the roots and stems underground and add to the store of reserves, thus replenishing that required to form the new growth. Working on this principle, it was usually necessary for the farmer to cultivate the infested area at least one a week for two or more years. Recent field studies with morning-glory at several stations in the middle west have indicated that such frequent clean cultivations are not only unnecessary but undesirable. It appears that during the first four to eight days after emergence, the new shoots above ground use more food reserves than they manufacture. Consequently, by postponing cultivation and allowing the new growth to develop for a number of days, there is a tendency during this period for the plant to exhaust itself of reserves rather than add to them. The practical application of this principle in a clean cultivation program is a material reduction in the number of cultivations necessary to attain results. Cultivation must begin in the spring as soon as growth starts and must continue until growth definitely stops in the late fall or early winer. On shallow soils or soils with a high water table, where all root development is near the surface, less time is required to eradicate morning-glory than on soils that permit deep root penetration. Under the former condition, some farmers have reported eradication in a single season. At Davis, however, on a Yolo sandy loam soil, plants were still thriving and producing vigorous shoots after three years of clean cultivation. On the latter type of soil, morning-glory grows more luxuriantly, and eradication by cultivating is obviously slow.

The implement most suitable for cultivating morning-glory is the straight-blade weeder, kept sharp and in good cutting condition. Duck-foot shovels on a field cultivator are also satisfactory providing they are lapped sufficiently to cut all of the weed shoots. The field should be plowed rather deep in the early spring, and the soil worked down thoroughly. If a deep layer of loose soil is thus provided at the start, the week cutter can be run at the necessary depth more easily than if the plowing had not been done. When weed-cutting the field, the weeder must be lapped at least 18 inches to 2 feet to insure the cutting of all the shoots. Care and eternal vigilance are the price of success in controlling morning-glory by cultivation.

Summer fallowing, so commonly practiced in dry-land areas accomplishes the same results as clean cultivation if followed by conscientious weed cutting.

Extra deep plowing, 14 inches in same cases, in preparing a seed bed is sometimes used as a method of retarding perennial weeds and getting the crop well established before the weed shoots reach the surface.

Although pasturing of fallowed lands tends to check such perennials as morning-glory, it does not appreciably reduce the stand.

Flooding

A practice in California for controlling perennial weeds is flooding. This is accomplished by surrounding the areas with dikes and covering them with 6 to 10 inches of water for several weeks in the summer. The infested area should be plowed before immersing, and no growth should be allowed to appear above the water.

Flooding first attracted attention when areas infested with morning-glory and other noxious perennials were planted to rice. Such weeds were usually eradicated. This method has been used rather extensively with camel thorn and hoary cress and yields excellent results in sandy soils. In heavy soils flooding has not been so satisfactory. White horse nettle occurring in several of the camel thorn areas has been killed in nearly every instance. In Stanislaus County a 13-acre area of Russian knapweed, flooded for 60 days, was completely killed. In several other places knapweed has given the same response. Occasionally submergence for three to five weeks has given satisfactory control.

As results of flooding have varied on different soils, soil type is evidently a factor. Flooding is effective only where the area is completely immersed for the whole time of treatment. Many failures have resulted from allowing the water level to lower so that regrowth occurred. Not all weeds react in the same way to flooding and our information is not yet complete enough to warrant general recommendations.

As flooding kills plants by excluding the air, it is effective only when the plant is covered and the roots completely surrounded with water. Under certain soil conditions some plants apparently become dormant and thus, through lowered oxygen consumption, are enabled to survive.

Cropping Methods

In several cases recently noted in California, morning-glory, creeping mallow, and other perennial weeds have disappeared in certain crops. After the serious outbreak of curly top in the sugar beet area of the Salinas Valley in 1925, lettuce culture was inaugurated; within three years the extent and vigor of morning-glory infestation markedly decreased. Two years ago the Agronomy Division at the University Farm, Davis, found that morning-glory had almost disappeared in certain of their alfalfa plots. A series of alfalfa plots plowed in 1934 proved to be almost free of this pest, although the area had been heavily infested four years previously when it was planted. A grain sorghum crop grown there during the summer of 1934 was practically free of weeds. Encouraged by these results the Agronomy Division, which had previously spent hundreds of dollars annually in spraying and hoeing morning-glory, has initiated a 5- to 6-year plan of crop rotation, with alfalfa serving the dual role of legume for soil improvement and competitor for weed control.

Studies now under way explain the effectiveness of alfalfa as a weed control crop under California conditions. Though no definite report is yet possible, several factors are apparently involved in this response. In the first place, alfalfa grows vigorously and competes effectively with the weed for soil moisture and nutrients. Above ground it shades the sun loving morning-glory. Furthermore, it takes the available nitrates from the soil rapidly in the spring and then utilizes nitrogen fixed by the bacteria in its root nodules. Thus it can maintain a low nitrate level in the soil and yet thrive in competition with a nonlegume. By the second crop in the summer following spring planting of alfalfa at Davis, morning-glory becomes spindling and light green, evidencing nitrogen deficiency. This condition progresses throughout the season and, although less apparent in the first crop of the following season, becomes very pronounced during the second summer. Meanwhile, if the alfalfa is vigorous, the stand of morning-glory becomes notably weaker and thinner. By the third season only a fraction of the original infestation remains and by the fourth it is practically gone. Finally, morning-glory likes to grow vigorously without competition in the spring; blossom, fruit, and mature seed during the summer; and then, with the depletion of soil moisture, die down and go into dormancy until the next spring. When this cycle is disturbed the plant suffers. In both lettuce and alfalfa culture, in addition to frequent cutting, which tends to keep the plant vegetative, the soil is kept moist, inducing continued growth. This long vegetative period reduces starch reserves in the roots to a minimum and then fails to provide for replenishment. The roots consequently start the winter in a depleted condition and fail to survive, especially if the rainy season is long and wet. Apparently, then, several factors operate in this cropping method; and when they favor the crop in comparison with the weed, excellent results are obtained. The benefits are three-fold: Not only are the weeds eliminated, but the soil is improved in fertility and physical condition, and a valuable crop is produced.

Besides alfalfa, ladino clover offers some promise as a control crop for weeds. Although it does not provide so much shade or such keen root competition, it may be grown on a wide variety of soils not suited to alfalfa. It may take longer, but it should eventually give the same results.

In addition to these two legumes, several combinations will be tested for their value in weed control. Most of them consist of an annual legume and a nonleguminous truck or field crop. Crop rotation has not been sufficiently stressed in this State, where large areas of the most fertile lands are still under a system of bonanza farming.

Smothering

The control of perennials by smothering with straw, manure, or paper, though not practicable for large infestations, may be successful on small patches. Weeds with indeterminate growth, like morning-glory, are extremely difficult to keep under cover. On others more easily managed, like Bermuda and Johnson grass and Russian knapweed, smothering has proved successful. If continued long enough, it should be effective on any plant that can be successfully covered.

Smother crops are not so generally useful in California as elsewhere. Millet, Sudan grass, sweet clover, sunflowers, rape, rye, and sorghums, unless combined with some other agency, can do little except hold the weed in check. Any crop that offers competition, however, tends to reduce the vigor of perennial weeds and to check their spread; and it is always advisable, if nothing else can be done, to plant one of the crops just listed rather than let noxious weeds thrive undisturbed.

Biological Method

In recent years insect enemies of Klamath weed have been introduced into California, and released in those counties where the weed occurs. In certain areas, the insects have multiplied and are effectively controlling the stand of Klamath weed. Present results are encouraging.

METHODS OF CHEMICAL WEED CONTROL

Within the past few years, progress has been made in chemical weed control. Not only have new chemicals been added to the list of herbicides, but research has increased our knowledge of the reagents previously used. Recent information permits a much more intelligent application of chemicals than was possible in the past.

A classification of different types of herbicides follows:

These fall into four groups: (A) general contact herbicides, (B) selective contact herbicides, (C) translocated herbicides, and (D) soil sterilants.

A. GENERAL CONTACT HERBICIDES

As with all contact herbicides, these chemicals kill only the tissues of the plant which they contact. Thus good coverage of the plants sprayed is essential for a satisfactory kill. There are three general requirements for use of these materials:

1. Sufficient toxicant to kill all the vegetation on the area.
2. Sufficient volume to cover all the vegetation on the area.
3. Excess volume for grasses to permit creeping of the solution into the crown and to the protected growing point.

Volume and toxicity must then be balanced so that enough of the killing agent is applied in enough volume to wet all the plants. The amount of excess volume will depend on the proportion of the plants that are grasses. We can divide these herbicides into four general groups: (1) inorganic compounds, (2) organic compounds, (3) oils, and (4) emulsions.

1. Inorganic Compounds

This group consists of water soluble chemicals and includes some of our earliest herbicides. Almost any soluble inorganic salt could be included in this group since high concentrations of most salts will plasmolyze plant cells. Cost and convenience determine which may be used. Few, if any, are very important today. All have certain disadvantages which limit their use.

(a) Sodium arsenite (Na_3AsO_3)

Still widely sold as a weed killer. Cheap, used as a 1% solution. Poison hazard is serious where people or livestock may contact the sprayed vegetation. Safer as a soil sterilant.

(b) Sodium chlorate ($NaClO_3$)

High toxicity to most plants, 2 to 5% solution. May be a serious fire hazard. More widely used as a soil sterilant.

(c) Sulphuric acid (H_2SO_4)

Somewhat selective, used as a 5 to 10% solution. Cheap but highly corrosive requiring special spray equipment. Will burn skin.

(d) Sodium hydroxide (NaOH)

Ordinary household lye is the type ordinarily used. Rather expensive at rates required, 5% solution, and also corrosive. Will burn skin.

(e) Sodium chloride (NaCl)

Salt—cheap but large amount required. Usually 10% solution; will sterilize soil to some extent.

2. Organic Compounds

This group is not water soluble but will dissolve in oil and can then be emulsified. Used as oil *fortifiers* either with straight oil or in emulsion.

(a) Pentachlorophenal (PCP)

Of considerable interest at the present time. Several brands available. Difficultly soluble in cold diesel oil, highly soluble in aromatic oils. Best handled as a concentrate.

(b) Dinitro-o-cresal (DNOC)

Similar to (c) and (d) but less toxic, probably not available at present.

(c) Dinitro-o-secondary butyl phenol (DNOSBP)

Commercial products are concentrates used at about 1 qt. per 100 gallons of oil or emulsion.

(d) Dinitro-o-secondary amyl phenol (DNOSAP)

Very similar to (c).

3. Oils

These, too, are organic compounds but form such a distinct group that they may be listed separately. Oils have been widely used as weed killers because of the low cost. In countries where oils are relatively cheap they will find wide use as weed killers. In general, oils are good grass killers and will kill most broad-leaved weeds except certain oil resistant ones in the carrot and thistle families.

(a) Smudge pot oil

Common in Southern California. Cheap, heavy oil with high toxicity.

(b) Diesel oil

Commonest oil herbicide for many years. Present high price and low toxicity because of new refining processes may limit its use. Most diesels now need fortifying to give sufficient toxicity.

(c) Commercial weed oils

With the reduced toxicity of diesel fuel, many oil companies are selling special weed killing oils which are high in toxicity, and should ultimately replace diesel, particularly if the price can be reduced. For further information on oil herbicides see Crafts and Reiber, Herbicidal Properties of Oils, Hilgardia 18(2) :77-156, 1948.

4. Emulsions

Because of the high cost of oils, there is increasing interest in emulsions.

(a) Oil + water

Where oils of high toxicity are available, they may frequently be mixed with water to give sufficient volume for coverage at a low rate of the oil.

(b) Oil + water + fortifier

It is possible to increase the toxicity of an emulsion by the addition of one of the fortifiers previously discussed. This is particularly useful where the oil is low in toxicity. Thus the toxicity may be balanced against the volume by changing the amount of fortifier.

B. SELECTIVE CONTACT HERBICIDES

Selectivity of contact herbicides is based on two principles:

1. Physiologic Differences Between Plants

Under this heading comes actual differences in the sensitivity of the protoplasm of different plants to a particular chemical toxicity. The classic example is the resistance of carrots to certain oils which kill most other plants. Carrots absorb the oil but are not seriously damaged by it.

2. Morphologic Differences Between Plants

Differences in the structure of plants such as leaf type and covering (whether narrow, erect, waxy leaves or broad, easily wetted leaves) and location of the growing point (whether basal and protected as in grasses or vulnerable and unprotected as in most broad-leaved plants) determine the effect of many chemicals on plants.

It must be recognized that selective action of many of the herbicides is a relative matter depending on several factors. At times we are trying to draw a fine line in the selective work and disregard of the factors involved can bring about injury to the crop plants or a poor kill of the weeds, or both. The most important factors affecting selective action include the following:

1. Kind of Weeds Present

The actual weed species present often determine where an herbicide can or cannot be successfully used. We can take mustard out of barley rather easily, fiddleneck with greater difficulty, and wild oats not at all. Likewise in carrots, we cannot successfully remove oil-resistant weeds.

2. Size and Age of the Weeds

Frequently selectivity is not possible if the weeds are large or mature. Thus timing of the treatment may be an important consideration.

3. Growth History of the Weeds

Succulent weeds growing under favorable conditions are more easily killed than those stunted or toughened by adverse conditions even though they may be the same age.

4. Weather Conditions at Time of and Immediately After Spraying

Many chemicals lose selectivity in very hot weather. Others will cause greater damage to crops in damp weather when evaporation is very slow.

5. Concentration and Volume of Spray

With certain chemicals selectivity depends to some extent on the concentration as well as the total amount per acre. This may be concerned in rapidity of action of the chemical.

We can group the selective contact herbicides into five groups.

1. Inorganic Salts and Acid

(a) Iron sulphate ($FeSO_4$) and sulphuric acid (H_2SO_4)

Some of the earliest selective work on grain was carried out with iron sulphate. Later sulphuric acid was used. Both of these materials had limited selectivity, required humid conditions and special spray machinery because of the corrosiveness of the chemicals. Neither is used in California at present although some areas in the Mid-west and East still use sulphuric acid on onions.

(b) Copper salts ($CuCl_2$ and $Cu(NO_3)_2$)

These chemicals are not widely used in this country. In England they still are common.

(c) Potassium cyanate ($KOCN$)

Used more commonly to control weeds in onions, and crabgrass in lawns.

2. Fertilizer Salts

These chemicals have a small degree of selectivity but may be useful mainly because of the nutrients supplied to the crop. The commonest are:

(a) Sodium nitrate ($NaNO_3$)
(b) Ammonium sulphate ($(NH_4)_2SO_4$)
(c) Potassium chloride (KCl)

3. Fertilizer Salts Applied Dry

The use of certain of the fertilizer materials as dusts or dry treatments has been common in more humid regions.

(a) Calcium cyanamid ($CaCN_2$)

This chemical has been used for controlling growing weeds in asparagus and in certain other crops.

(b) Kainite ($MgSO_4KCl$)

A double salt frequently used in Europe where potash is a required fertilizer.

4. Organic Salts

(a) Sodium dinitro-o-cresylate ($NaDNOC$)

An old stand-by as a selective in grain, now largely replaced by 2,4-D.

(b) Ammonium dinitro-o-secondary butyl phenol (NH_4 DNOSBP)

(c) Ammonium dinitro-o-secondary amyl phenol (NH_4 DNOSAP)

Both of these are available in various commercial preparations. Other preparations containing one or the other of these chemicals will doubtless be on the market. Both are used as selectives in *grain, flax, peas, alfalfa, onions,* etc. They show a higher degree of selectivity than (a) and are widely used.

(d) Sodium pentachlorophenate ($NaPCP$)

Of limited use. Disagreeable to handle but reported as selective on both flax and onions in the Mid-west.

5. Oils

Selective oils are widely used in weeding carrots and the newer ones on celery and flax. See California Agr. Ext. Service Circ. 136.

(a) Stove oil

The commonest material on carrots. Due to differences in different lots of stove oil, results not always satisfactory. Gravity should be 37.5° A. P. I. or higher. It is not recommended on celery or flax.

(b) Commercial selective contact oils

Most of the major oil companies are now supplying oils of this type.

C. TRANSLOCATED HERBICIDES

This group includes those chemicals which can move within the plant. They are thus adapted for controlling deep-rooted perennial weeds as well as annuals. There is selectivity with several of them. All the factors in translocation or movement of these herbicides are not well understood. Some move in the xylem of the plant; some in the phloem. Several are relatively new to the workers in the field and our knowledge of their use is incomplete.

1. Acid Arsenical (Na₂AsO₃ + H₂SO₄)

This was a common spray for morning-glory control ten or fifteen years ago, but has now been almost completely replaced by newer chemicals. Conditions of atmosphere and soil conducive to good results with the chemical were so limited that results with the method were not generally good.

2. Sodium Chlorate (NaClO₃)

When used to as 10 percent to 12 percent solution, this chemical translocates into the roots of many weeds. It has been widely used in the Midwest but the fire hazard resulting from its application has limited its use in California. Some weeds such as white top or hoary cress are resistant.

3. Growth Regulator Type Herbicides ("Hormones")

With the advent of this group of complex organic chemicals, new vistas were opened in the field of herbicides. Most have some selectivity and several are highly effective for many weed problems. New compounds of this type will likely appear.

(a) 2,4-D (2,4-Dichlorophenoxyacetic acid)
Discussed in Circ. 133.

(b) 2,4,5-T (2,4,5-Trichlorophenoxyacetic acid)
Similar to 2,4-D, more effective on certain woody species, and possibly less selective.

(c) IPC (Isopropyl-N-phenyl carbamate)
Toxicity somewhat the reverse of 2,4-D. More toxic to grasses and less to broad-leaved plants. However, there are exceptions. Not water soluble.

(d) TCA (Trichloroacetate)
Used as the sodium salt which is water soluble. It appears more promising than IPC for many of the weedy grasses.

(e) PMAS (Phenyl mercuric acetate)
Promising for removal of crab grass from lawns. Other uses not yet known. (This chemical may not belong under the heading of translocated herbicides but is placed here provisionally.)

D. SOIL STERILANTS

This group of chemicals are applied to the soil and render it unfit for plant growth. We usually divide soil sterilants into two groups on the basis of how long they persist in soils. It should be recognized that such persistence in the soil depends upon the amount of chemical applied, soil type, rainfall, and temperature.

1. Temporary Soil Sterilants

Those which last less than one year in the soil following normal application. These are all liquids applied with injection equipment.

(a) Carbon disulphide (CS_2)

See California Agr. Expt. Sta. Bulletin 693.

(b) Chloropicrin (CCl_3NO_3)

Not as widely used as CS_2, more expensive, but will kill seeds in soil. Used for potting soil, greenhouse beds, etc.

(c) D.D. (Dichloropropene—dichloropropane mixture)

Herbicidal use not well established but possibly some weed killing where high dosages are used for wire worms and nematodes.

2. Permanent Soil Sterilants

Those which last longer than one year in the soil following normal applications.

(a) Sodium chlorate ($NaClO_3$)

Applied dry, usually at rates of 3 to 8 lbs. per square rod. Leaches readily, high toxicity, decomposes rather rapidly. Less effective on soils high in nitrate. Some species resistane. Fire hazard.

(b) Boron compounds (Borax, $Na_2B_4O_7 \cdot 10H_2O$)

All boron compounds toxic in proportion to borate ion. Fixed in clay soils, leaches slowly, soil fertility of little importance. Slow acting. Many species relatively resistant. Usually 10 to 20 lbs. per square rod applied dry. Cheap.

(c) White arsenic (As_2O_3)

Highly toxic, insoluble, slow acting, little leaching fixed in clay soils and red soils. 4 to 10 lbs. applied dry. Poisonous.

(d) Sodium arsenite $Na_3H_2O_3$)

Similar to (c) except soluble, leaches more readily and may be applied dry or as a concentrated solution.

(e) Combinations of sterilants

(1) Chlorate plus borax

Good, high initial toxicity of chlorate and persistence of borax lessens fire hazard. 2 lbs. $NaClO_3$ + 8 lbs. borax per square rod.

(2) Chlorate plus either arsenical

Dangerous, both explosive and poisonous.

(3) White arsenic plus sodium arsenite

Good except poisonous. Has both immediate toxicity and persistence.

KEY TO THE FAMILIES

I. Non-flowering plants
    Reproduction by seeds_____YEWS (**Taxaceae**), p. 36

    Reproduction by spores
      Non-vascular plants (no stems, leaves, roots)
                         FUNGI (mushrooms ergot, etc.) p. 33

      Vascular plants (stems, leaves, roots)
        Stems jointed, hollow_____HORSETAILS (**Equisetaceae**), p. 35
        Stems not jointed, not hollow
          Land plants_____FERNS (**Polypodiaceae**), p. 33

        Aquatic or subaquatic plants____CLOVER FERNS (**Marsileaceae**), p. 35

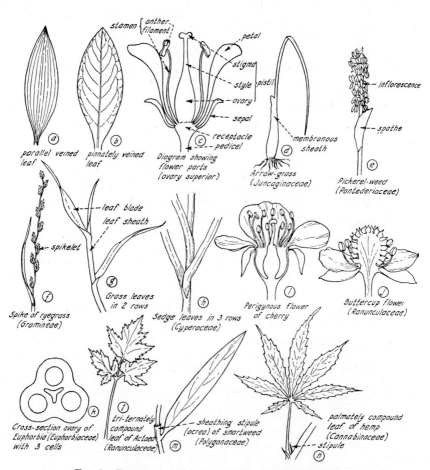

FIG. 1. Botanical characters to illustrate key to families.

II. Flowering plants
  A. Leaves with parallel venation (Fig. 1a) ; parts of flowers usually in 3's, never in 5's
    Flowers without distinct perianth segments or calyx-like (Fig. 1c)
      Immersed aquatics_____PONDWEED FAMILY (Naiadaceae), p. 37

      Plants of marshes or rising out of the water or growing on land
        Flowers arranged in spikes and spikelets composed of a number of chaffy scales (Fig. 1f)
          Stems usually cylindrical and hollow ; leaves in two rows (Fig. 1g)
                GRASSES (Gramineae), p. 44

          Stems usually triangular and solid ; leaves in three rows (Fig. 1h)
                SEDGES (Cyperaceae), p. 113

      Flowers not in the axils of chaffy scales or bracts
        Flowers perfect (both stamens and pistils)
              ARROWGRASS (Juncaginaceae), p. 39

        Flowers imperfect (stamens and pistils in separate flowers)
          Inflorescence a dense cylindrical spike
              CAT-TAILS (Typhaceae), p. 36
          Inflorescence a dense globular head
              BUR-REEDS (Sparganiaceae), p. 37
      Flowers with distinct perianth segments
        Inflorescence with a spathe (Fig. 1e) ; pistil 1
          Ovary inferior ; leaves opposite or whorled
              FROG'S BIT (Hydrocharitaceae), p. 43
           Ovary superior ; leaves ribbon-like
              PICKEREL WEEDS (Pontederiaceae), p. 119
        Inflorescence without a spathe
          Pistils several, distinct_____WATER PLANTAIN (Alismaceae), p. 41

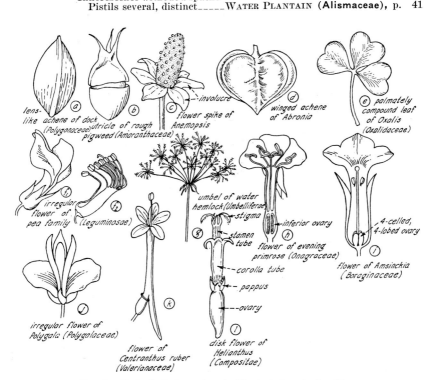

FIG. 2. Botanical characters to illustrate key to families.

Pistil 1
Rush-like plants ; perianth segments green or brown
RUSHES (**Juncaceae**), p. 120

Plants not rush-like ; perianth segments, at least the inner, showy
LILY FAMILY (**Liliaceae**), p. 122
B. Leaves with netted venation (Fig. 1b) ; parts of flowers in 4's or 5's
  1. Corolla none ; calyx present or absent (see alternatives 2 and 3)
a. Flowers with stamens attached to receptacle ; ovary superior (Fig. 1c)
  Calyx present, often petal-like ; corolla none
    Pistils more than 1 and distinct (Fig. 1j)
CROWFOOT FAMILY (**Ranunculaceae**), p. 187
    Pistil 1
      Ovary 5- to 12-celled, fruit a berry__*Phytolacca* in **Phytolaccaceae**, p. 165
      Ovary 2- to 5-celled, fruit not a berry (Fig. 1k)
        Flowers with both stamens and pistils (Fig. 1c) ; herbs
CARPET-WEED FAMILY (**Aizoaceae**), p. 167

        Flowers with stamens only or pistils only, or in some cases both
          perfect and imperfect flowers on the same plant
Ricinus in SPURGE FAMILY (**Euphorbiaceae**), p. 287
      Ovary 1-celled
        Fruit a capsule, splitting at maturity ; leaves opposite
          Calyx 5-lobed_____*Cypselea* in **Aizoaceae**, p. 167
          Calyx of 5 distinct or nearly distinct sepals
PINK FAMILY (**Caryophyllaceae**), p. 174

        Fruit a berry ; leaves bi- or tri-ternately compound (Fig. 1*l*)
Actaea in **Ranunculaceae**, p. 187
        Fruit dry, not splitting at maturity
          Stigma and style 1

            Herbage with stinging hairs_NETTLE FAMILY (**Urticaceae**), p. 127
            Herbage without stinging hairs
FOUR-O'CLOCK FAMILY (**Nyctaginaceae**), p. 166

          Stigmas and styles 2 or several
            Leaves with sheathing stipules (Fig. 1m)
BUCKWHEAT FAMILY (**Polygonaceae**), p. 130

            Leaves without stipules, or if present not sheathing
              Stipules conspicuous, leafy ; leaves palmately compound
                (Fig. 1m)
Cannabis in HEMP FAMILY (**Cannabinaceae**), p. 126

              Stipules papery, or none ; leaves simple, pinnately veined
                Plants usually scurfy ; of alkaline or maritime habitat
GOOSEFOOT FAMILY (**Chenopodiaceae**), p. 142

                Plants not scurfy
                  Fruit a triangular or lens-like achene (Fig. 2a) ;
                    stamens 4 to 9
BUCKWHEAT FAMILY (**Polygonaceae**), p. 130

                  Fruit a utricle (Fig. 2b) ; stamens 3 to 5
AMARANTH FAMILY (**Amarantheaceae**), p. 159
  Calyx and corolla both wanting ; pistil 1
    Flowers perfect, borne in a spike subtended by colored involucre (Fig.
      2c) ; herbs of saline soils_____*Anemopsis* in **Saururaceae**, p. 130

    Flowers imperfect, staminate and pistillate flowers on same plant ;
      borne in clusters ; juice often milky
Euphorbia in **Euphorbiaceae**, p. 279
b. Flowers with stamens borne on the calyx or on a disk ; ovary half-supe-
    rior (Fig. 1i)
  Fruit a capsule_____*Sesuvium* in **Aizoaceae**, p. 169

  Fruit an achene, enclosed by persistent winged calyx (Fig. 2d)
Abronia in **Nyctaginaceae**, p. 166

c. Flowers with ovary inferior (Fig. 2h), that is, more or less adherent to the calyx

Succulent herbs, with entire leaves_____*Tetragonia* in **Aizoaceae,** p. 170

Stout herbs, with divided leaves_____DATISCA FAMILY **(Datiscaceae),** p. 306

2. Corolla and calyx present; petals distinct or nearly so

Ovary superior, that is, free from the calyx (Fig. 1c)
Stamens attached to receptacle, more than 10
Pistils 2 to many_____CROWFOOT FAMILY **(Ranunculaceae),** p. 187

Pistil 1
Leaves opposite_____ST. JOHNSWORT FAMILY **(Hypericaceae),** p. 301

Leaves alternate or basal
Ovary 1-celled; styles or stigmas often more than one
Sepals falling off early; petals 4 or 6
POPPY FAMILY **(Papaveraceae),** p. 197
Sepals persistent
Petals 5; leaves simple_____*Calandrinia* in **Portulacaceae,** p. 171

Petals 1 or 2; leaves compound_____*Actaea* in **Ranunculaceae,** p. 187

Ovary 5- to 30-celled; stamens numerous, united in a tube around the pistil_____MALLOW FAMILY **(Malvaceae),** p. 294

Stamens attached to receptacle, 10 or fewer
Pistils more than 1
Pistils distinct_____CROWFOOT FAMILY **(Ranunculaceae),** p. 187

Pistils more or less united around a central axis
GERANIUM FAMILY **(Geraniaceae),** p. 273
Pistil 1; styles or stigmas 1 or more
Flowers irregular (Fig. 2f1)
Leaves simple_____MIGNONETTE FAMILY **(Resedaceae),** p. 305

Leaves compound
Stamens 10, united in 1 or 2 sets (Fig. 2f2)
PEA FAMILY **(Leguminosae),** p. 251

Stamens 6_____FUMITORY FAMILY **(Fumariaceae),** p. 198

Flowers regular
Flowers cruciferous, that is, 4 sepals, 4 petals, 6 stamens (4 long, 2 short)_____MUSTARD FAMILY **(Cruciferae),** p. 204

Flowers not cruciferous
Ovary 1-celled
Calyx of 2 distinct sepals__PURSLANE FAMILY **(Portulacaceae),** p. 171

Calyx not of 2 distinct sepals PINK FAMILY **(Caryophyllaceae),** p. 174

Placenta basal, capsule 2-4 valved; stamens 4-7
FRANKENIA FAMILY **(Frankeniaceae),** p. 304

Placenta central, capsule 3-10 valved or toothed; stamens 5 (or 10)_____PINK FAMILY **(Caryophyllaceae),** p. 174

Ovary more than 1-celled
Leaves simple_____WATERWORT FAMILY **(Elatinaceae),** p. 304

Leaves compound
Leaves pinnately compound (Fig. 174)
CALTROP FAMILY **(Zygophyllaceae),** p. 287

Leaves palmately compound (Fig. 2e)
Sepals 5, petals 5, stamens 10, ovary 5-celled
SORREL FAMILY **(Oxalidaceae),** p. 271

Sepals 4, petals 4, stamens 6, ovary 2-celled
CAPER FAMILY **(Capparidaceae),** p. 202

Stamens attached to calyx or on a disk
  Herbaceous plants
    Leaves simple_____LOOSESTRIFE FAMILY (**Lythraceae**), p. 311

    Leaves compound
        Sanguisorba and *Alchemilla* in ROSE FAMILY (**Rosaceae**), p. 247, 249

  Trees or shrubs
    Pistils more than 1_____*Rubus* in ROSE FAMILY (**Rosaceae**), p. 249
    Pistil 1

      Style 1
        Fruit a drupe_____*Prunus* in ROSE FAMILY (**Rosaceae**), p. 248

        Fruit a samara_____QUASSIA FAMILY (**Simarubaceae**), p. 291

      Styles 3 to 5
        Leaves broad_____SUMAC FAMILY (**Anacardiaceae**), p. 292

        Leaves minute_____TAMARISK FAMILY (**Tamaricaceae**), p. 305
Ovary inferior, that is more or less attached to the calyx (Fig. 2h)
  Flowers in umbels (Fig. 2g)_____CARROT FAMILY (**Umbelliferae**), p. 317

  Flowers not in umbels_____EVENING PRIMROSE FAMILY (**Onagraceae**), p. 312

      3. Corolla and calyx both present, the corolla with petals united,
                    at least below
Stamens more than 5
  Corolla irregular (Fig. 2j)
    Leaves simple_____POLYGALA FAMILY (**Polygalaceae**), p. 279

    Leaves compound
      Petals 5; flowers of pea type (Fig. 2f)___PEA FAMILY (**Leguminosae**), p. 251

      Petals 4 in two dissimilar pairs; sepals 2
                    FUMITORY FAMILY (**Fumariaceae**), p. 198
  Corolla regular
    Leaves compound, 3-foliate (Fig. 2e)____OXALIS FAMILY (**Oxalidaceae**), p. 271

    Leaves simple_____MALLOW FAMILY (**Malvaceae**), p. 294
Stamens 5 or less, inserted on the corolla
  Ovary superior, that is, free from the calyx (Fig. 2i)
    Corolla regular
      Pistil 1
        Stamens as many as lobes of corolla and opposite them
                  PRIMROSE FAMILY (**Primulaceae**), p. 332

        Stamens as many as or fewer than lobes of corolla and alternate
          with them
          Corolla dry and papery____PLANTAIN FAMILY (**Plantaginaceae**), p. 406

          Corolla colored, not dry and papery
            Ovary 4-celled, commonly 4-lobed (Fig. 2i)
                    BORAGE FAMILY (**Boraginaceae**), p. 354
           Ovary 1-, 2-, or 3-celled
             Style 3-cleft; ovary 3-celled__GILIA FAMILY (**Polemoniaceae**), p. 352

             Style not 3-cleft; ovary 1- or 2-celled
                Calyx of 5 distinct sepals
                  Plants climbing or trailing
                    MORNING-GLORY FAMILY (**Convolvulaceae**), p. 339

                  Plants erect or diffused
                    PHACELIA FAMILY (**Hydrophyllaceae**), p. 352
                Calyx 4- or 5-toothed or cleft__POTATO FAMILY (**Solanaceae**), p. 379
      Pistils 2
        Stamens and stigmas united __ MILKWEED FAMILY (**Asclepiadaceae**), p. 335
        Stamens and stigmas not united__DOGBANE FAMILY (**Apocynaceae**), p. 333

Corolla irregular or strongly 2-lipped
   Fruit a capsule
      Ovary 2-celled_____Figwort Family (**Scrophulariaceae**), p. 394

      Ovary 1-celled_____Martynia Family (**Martyniaceae**) p. 405

   Fruit of 2 to 4 nutlets
      Ovary 4-lobed ; stamens 4 or 2 ; stems square
                              Mint Family (**Labiatae**), p. 365

      Ovary not lobed ; stamens 4_____Vervain Family (**Verbenaceae**), p. 361

Ovary inferior, that is, adherent to calyx tube (Fig. 2h, k, *l*)
   Stamens distinct
      Stamens 1 to 3 ; flowers irregular (Fig. 2k)
                     Valerian Family (**Valerianaceae**), p. 416
      Stamens 4 or 5, rarely 2
        Ovary 1-celled_____Teasel Family (**Dipsaceae**), p. 414

        Ovary more than 1-celled
           Herbs ; ovary 2-celled_____Madder Family (**Rubiaceae**), p. 409

           Shrubs ; ovary 2- to 5-celled
               Honeysuckle Family (**Caprifoliaceae**), p. 412

   Stamens united into a tube around the style (Fig. 2*l*)
      Flowers not in heads ; tendril bearing plants
                Cucurbit Family (**Cucurbitaceae**), p. 307

      Flowers in heads ; not tendril bearing
               Sunflower Family (**Compositae**), p. 416

KEY TO SPECIES OF FLOWERING PLANTS WITH WOODY STEMS

1. Densely spiny shrubs with almost leafless branches
         Furze or Gorse (*Ulex europaeus*), p. 268

2. Densely branched shrub with minute appressed leaves
         Tamarisk (*Tamarix gallica*), p. 305

3. Trees or shrubs with broad leaves
    Leaves compound
       Leaves opposite
         Flowers small, white_____Elderberry (*Sambucus glauca*), p. 412

         Flowers copper or yellow color
           Syrian bean caper (*Zygophyllum Fabago* var. *brachycarpa*), p. 289

       Leaves alternate
         Leaves 1½ to 2 feet long_____Tree-of-Heaven (*Ailanthus altissima*), p. 291

         Leaves much smaller
           Flowers bright yellow_____Scotch broom (*Cytisus scoparius*), p. 257

           Flowers red or white_____*Rubus* species, p. 249

           Flowers greenish_____ ___Poison oak (*Rhus diversiloba*), p. 292

           Flowers pink_____Wild-rose *Rosa* species, p. 248

    Leaves simple
       Flowers in heads
         Leaves ¾ to 1¾ inches long, 3-toothed at apex
           Sagebrush (*Artemisia tridentata*), p. 427
         Leaves not 3-toothed at apex
           Leaves usually less than ½ inch long_____*Tetradymia glabrata*, p. 503
           Leaves usually ½ to 1 inch long (or more)
             Leaves linear to lance-shaped___Arrow-weed (*Pluchea sericea*), p. 491
             Leaves broadly oval
               Leaves ½ to 1 inch long ; achenes 10-nerved
               Coyote brush (*Baccharis pilularis*), p. 429

               Leaves 1 to 3 inches long ; achenes 5-nerved
               Mule fat (*Baccharis viminea*), p. 431
       Flowers not in heads
         Leaves opposite_____Honeysuckle (*Lonicera japonica*), p. 412

       Leaves alternate
         Flowers lavendar or lavender red
           Trailing shrub_____Matrimony vine (*Lycium halimifolium*), p. 482

           Erect, spiny shrub_____Camel thorn (*Alhagi camelorum*), p. 252

           Flowers yellow_____Tree tobacco (*Nicotiana glauca*), p. 385
         Flowers red or white
           Flowers in racemes___Western choke-cherry (*Prunus demissa*), p. 248

           Flowers in corymbs_____*Rubus* species, p. 249

POISONOUS MUSHROOMS

Both humans and livestock are poisoned by certain mushrooms ("toadstools"). The most toxic of the many kinds of fleshy fungi belong to the genus *Amanita*, and the three most common species of this genus are *Amanita muscaria* (fly agaric), *A. phalloides* (death cup), and *A. verna* (vernal amanita). All species of *Amanita* are gill fungi, that is, the spore-bearing tissues are gills on the under side of the cap. Although the cap may be of different colors in the different species, all Amanitas shed white spores. Moreover, they have a "ring" on the stem, and a "cup" at the base of the stem. The fly agaric has a small, yellow, orange or scarlet cap, flecked with white; death cup has a satiny cap, three to five inches broad, and is usually white or yellowish white; and vernal amanita resembles the former, but the cap is white with no tinge of yellow.

ERGOT

This is a fungus, belonging to the genus *Claviceps,* which is parasitic on grasses, including certain cereals. A dormant fungal growth which replaces the mature grain contains a very potent drug known as ergot. It constricts the blood vessels, particularly those of the extremities of the body. Ergot is a valued drug, used to control hemorrhage, particularly during childbirth, but it is known to poison all kinds of animals, including man. In animals it is a well known cause of abortion.

The conspicuous stage of the fungus is a hard, purplish-black horn-like structure about one-quarter to one-half inch long which replaces the kernel of grass or grain.

FERN FAMILY *(Polypodiaceae)*

BRACKEN FERN (*Pteris aquilina* L. var. *lanuginosa* (Bory) Hook.) Fig. 3
Other common names : Common brake, hog brake, adderspit, eagle fern.

This plant is common throughout California in the cooler regions, occurring in the Coast Range and in the Sierra foothills up to the yellow pine belt. It is a troublesome weed in pastures, meadows, recent clearings, cultivated fields, and foothill orchards. It has covered thousands of acres of grazing lands in the coastal range of mountains.

Bracken fern is a perennial, with slender, branching and widely spreading dark cord-like rootstocks. It spreads rapidly by means of these underground stems. The plants often stand 1 to 4 feet high. The leaves (fronds) are of the fern type; they have long, slender, straw-colored stalks, with leaf blades more or less triangular in outline and once to thrice divided. The leaflets are deeply lobed below the apex, the lobes all blunt and more or less hairy on the lower surface. Ferns do not bear seeds, but reproduce by means of spores which are developed in small brown spore cases, and densely clustered along the edges of the leaflets on the under side.

Bracken fern has been known to poison livestock, being equally toxic in the green and dry states at all times of the year.

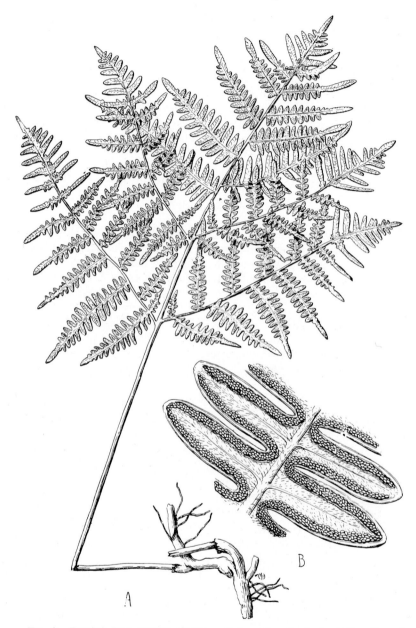

FIG. 3. Bracken fern (*Pteris aquilina* var. *lanuginosa*). **A,** leaf (frond) of the bracken fern showing the long stalk and compound blade formed of many leaflets; **B,** underside of a section of a leaflet showing the densely clustered spore-cases (sporangia) at the margins of the lobes.

MARSILEA FAMILY *(Marsileaceae)*

CLOVER FERN *(Marsilea vestita* H. & G.)

This is an aquatic perennial, with creeping rootstocks rooted in the mud. The 4-parted clover-like leaves are borne on long stems; leaves blunt, hairy. Spore-bearing case solitary on a short peduncle which arises from the rhizome.

HORSETAIL FAMILY
(Equisetaceae)

This family possesses but one genus, *Equisetum*, of which there are 6 species in California, resembling each other in their general appearance. The characteristics of the family are as described in the following account of common horsetail.

COMMON HORSETAIL *(Equisetum arvense* L.) Fig. 4

This is widely distributed in California, occurring in sandy, wet soils or in swamps.

Common horsetail is not a flowering plant. It reproduces by means of spores. It is a perennial from rootstocks. From these arise two kinds of stalks: Those that branch (appearing "leafy"), and those that are unbranched (Fig. 4). All stems are jointed, the sections being hollow. The branched stems are sterile, 1 to 3 feet high, with 4-angled branches in whorls at the joints; the branches are 4 to 6 inches long, and numerous.

FIG. 4. Common horsetail (*Equisetum arvense*). Left, sterile, leafy stalk; right, spore-bearing, unbranched stalk.

The unbranched stems terminate in a spore-bearing cone, which may be 1 to 4 inches long. The leaves are reduced to mere scales united by their margins and sheathing the stem joints.

In places it is a weed, but of chief importance is the fact that it, as well as other species of *Equisetum*, is poisonous to livestock, particularly horses and sheep; cattle are immune.

COMMON SCOURING-RUSH *(Equisetum hiemale* L. var. *californicum Milde)*

Scattered throughout California by streams or in wet places, usually in colonies. Perennial, reproducing by spores and rootstocks. Stems simple, or rarely somewhat branched, 2 to 4 feet high, many-ridged; ridges with 2 indistinct lines of tubercles. Leaves reduced, united to form sheaths at the nodes, their tips thinner and prolonged into teeth. Sheaths cylindric, appressed, marked with an ashy band, bordered at the base and top with black.

Var. *robustum* (A. Br.) A. A. Eat. Similar to preceding, but ridges with one row of tubercles; sheath whitish with a broad black band below and a narrow black band above, at the base of the deciduous teeth.

YEW FAMILY *(Taxaceae)*

WESTERN YEW *(Taxus brevifolia* Nutt.)

This representative of the Yew Family occurs in the Santa Cruz Mountains, here and there in the Coast Range, Marin to Mendocino County and northward to Mount Shasta, thence south in the Sierra Nevada.

It is a small, evergreen tree, 10 to 30 feet high. The leaves are needle-like, 2-ranked by a twist in their petioles, dark green above, and yellow-green below. The fruit has the appearance of a red berry. There is one seed in each fruit, borne in a cup-shaped, fleshy, red, berry-like structure.

There are scattered reports that illness and death among cattle have been caused by eating large quantities of the twigs and foliage.

CAT-TAIL FAMILY *(Typhaceae)*

There is but one genus, *Typha,* in this family, and about 10 species. They are widely distributed and common marsh plants with rootstocks.

Cat-tails are often associated with and confused with "tule" (*Scirpus* species). Cat-tails are chiefly a nuisance as weeds in over-irrigated lands, in rice fields, and in irrigation ditches. In the latter situation they may retard the flow of water, making necessary periodic dredging. When once established they are difficult to eradicate unless the area is drained.

Cat-tails are regarded with suspicion as poisonous to livestock.

NARROW-LEAF CAT-TAIL *(Typha angustifolia* L.)

Abundant along irrigating canals in Imperial Valley; also occurs elsewhere in southern and central California. Similar to the following but leaves mostly narrower, 4-10 mm.; and the staminate and pistillate flowers usually separated by a short naked interval of the stem.

COMMON CAT-TAIL *(Typha latifolia* L.)

Common cat-tail is the more widespread of the two species within our borders. It is a perennial marsh herb, with erect, unjointed, stout and pithy stems, 4 to 7 feet high, rising from creeping, scaly rootstocks and bearing long, alternate grass-like leaves 6-25 mm. broad with sheathing bases, and terminated by dense flower clusters. The flowers are of two sorts, the staminate and pistillate portions commonly contiguous. Staminate flowers are grouped in a light yellow spike at the top of the stem, and pistillate flowers are grouped below. The two clusters form a spike ("cat-tail") $\frac{1}{2}$ to 1 foot or more in length. The fruit is very small and is enveloped in the "cotton" of the cat-tail.

BUR-REED FAMILY *(Sparganiaceae)*

These marsh or aquatic plants are perennials from creeping rootstocks, with fibrous roots and long and ribbon-like leaves. The genus *Sparganium*, is represented in California by three species, *S. eurycarpum* Engelm., *S. simplex* Huds. and *S. angustifolium* Michx. The two latter species occur only at fairly high altitudes.

Sparganium species have the flowers in spherical heads, the lower pistillate, the upper staminate. The fruit is a nutlet partly surrounded by scale-like sepals. Each nutlet contains 1 to 2 seeds.

COMMON BUR-REED *(Sparganium eurycarpum* Engelm.)

This species occurs from the Los Angeles River to the San Joaquin Valley, north to B. C.

Common bur-reed is a more or less erect plant from 3 to 8 feet tall. The leaves are thin, flat, and somewhat keeled beneath. The inflorescence is branching, the pistillate heads from two to four on a branch, the staminate ones 5 to 13. The flowering heads are from $\frac{3}{4}$ to $1\frac{1}{4}$ inches in diameter. The nutlets are several-angled, cut off squarely at the top, and tipped with a short style.

Var. *Greenei* Graebner, has a more erect, narrow flowering head. The nutlets are rounded at the top. It occurs over about the same range as the species.

PONDWEED FAMILY *(Naiadaceae)*

Perennial fresh-water plants with floating or submerged leaves or both. Leaves alternate, petioled or sessile, capillary or expanded into a blade, or rarely reduced. Fowers sessile in small clusters in the leaf axils, or on peduncled spikes which rise above the water for wind pollination. The numerous erect spikes are conspicuous—sticking up out of the water in early summer. They usually are below the surface as the fruit matures. Calyx and corolla absent, but the flowers sometimes enclosed in a membranous sheath. Stamens 1-4, pistils of 1-4 distinct carpels, fruits small, sessile or on short stems, the seeds without endosperm. There are several genera in California, the principal ones being keyed and described below.

KEY TO GENERA OF PONDWEED FAMILY

Flowers perfect
    Calyx of 4 distinct sepals_____*Potamogeton*
    Calyx none _____*Ruppia*
Flowers unisexual
    Leaves entire; pistils about 4_____*Zannichellia*
    Leaves with spiny-toothed margins; pistil 1_____*Naias*

BUSHY PONDWEED *(Naias marima* L.)

Stems slender and freely branched; leaves narrow and ribbon-like, enlarged at the base; fruits with membranous walls, solitary in the leaf axils; fruits bear one seed, 4-5 mm. long, round in cross section, pointed at each end.

PONDWEED. POTAMOGETON

These perennial herbs occur in streams and in fresh or brackish ponds. They are becoming a menace in irrigation ditches and drainage canals. There are many species of *Potamogeton* in California, which are extremely difficult to distinguish. The stems arise from rootstocks. The leaves are alternate, some (of which) are floating and broad, others submerged and narrow. Flowers are in heads or spikes. The flowers have 4 sepals, 4 stamens, and 4 ovaries, each 1-seeded. Fruits are nutlet-like.

COMMON FLOATING PONDWEED (*Potamogeton natans* L.)

This pondweed has leaves of two kinds, floating and submerged, the former 1 to 3 inches long, and 1 to 2 inches wide, and leathery in texture. The submerged leaves are reduced to bladeless stems, commonly perishing before the fruiting season. Fruiting stems 2 to 4 inches long, spikes cylindric, about 2 inches long, dense; fruit 4-5 mm. long, narrowly obovoid, turgid, scarcely keeled, nutlet hard, more or less pitted or impressed on the sides, 2-grooved on the back. The embryo forms an incomplete circle, the apex pointing toward the base.

SAGO PONDWEED (*Potamogeton pectinatus* L.) Fig. 5

This pondweed is the most widely distributed and abundant species on the Pacific Coast. It has the leaves all submerged and similar, much branched, very narrowly linear, tapering to the apex, one-nerved, with a few transverse veins. Stipules attached to leaf one-half their length, $\frac{3}{4}$ to 1 inch long. Fruiting stems threadlike, $\frac{1}{4}$ to 1 inch long, the flowers in two to six whorls; nutlets obliquely egg-shaped, rounded on the back, $\frac{3}{4}$ mm. long with 2 obscure keels; embryo complete or incomplete spiral, the embryo pointing toward the base.

Pea-sized tubers are frequently borne by the rootstocks.

WIDGEON GRASS, DITCH GRASS (*Ruppia maritima* L.)

This species is an immersed aquatic of alkaline or blackish waters. The stems are thread-like often very long, widely branched; leaves all submerged, very slender, one nerved, tapering to apex and with membranous sheaths at base. Flowers consisting of 2 sessile anthers attached to back of peduncle, several pistillate flowers with sessile peltate stigmas in 2 sets on opposite sides of the rachis. At first the flower is enclosed in the sheathing base of the leaf but as the flower stem develops it is extended upward and fertilization takes place at the surface, after which the peduncle coils up. Fruit ovoid, about 2 mm. long, equilateral or bulged on one side and oblique, with short stipe at the base and with the style at the apex short and stout or tapering.

HORNED PONDWEED (*Zannichellia palustris* L.)

This is a cosmopolitan species. The stems are thread-like from a creeping rhizome; leaves all submerged, thread-like but flat, opposite, 1-nerved. The fruits are borne in bunches of 2-5, scarcely stalked; the fruits are flattish and usually toothed down one side.

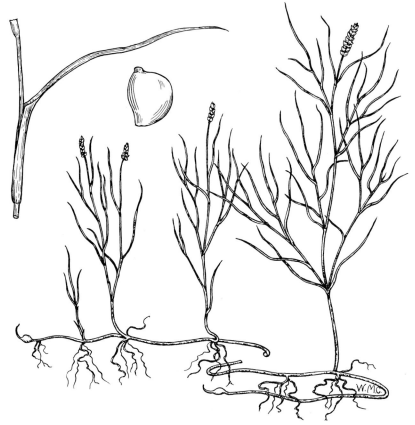

FIG. 5. Sago pondweed *Potamogeton pectinatus.*

ARROW-GRASS FAMILY *(Juncaginaceae)*

These are marsh herbs of wide distribution. They are rush-like in appearance. The best known genus is *Triglochin*, of which there are several species.

ARROW-GRASS *(Triglochin maritima* L.) (Fig. 6)

Common arrow-grass occurs along the coast from the San Francisco Bay region south, and also over a considerable area in northeastern California, and less abundantly in other parts of the interior. It is a plant of marshy areas.

Arrow-grass is a grass-like perennial from short rootstocks, and usually grows in scattered clumps about a foot wide or in patches up to 20 feet across. The leaves are grass-like in appearance, but differ from grass leaves in being thick, spongy, and semicircular in cross section rather than flat. The leaves are all basal. The flowering stalks may attain a height of 1 to $2\frac{1}{2}$ feet, terminating in a raceme of flowers 10 to 15 inches long. The flowers are small and greenish. Each flower consists of 6

FIG 6.   Arrow-grass (*Triglochin maritima*). Habit, fruiting branch, and fruit.

greenish sepals, 3-6 stamens, and a 3-sided ovary which matures into a 3-sided slender fruit about ¼ inch long.

Arrow-grass is suspected of causing losses among cattle and sheep although is not known to have caused serious trouble.

WATER PLANTAIN FAMILY *(Alismaceae)*

This is a family of marsh or aquatic herbs. The leaves are basal, and flower stalks are scape-like.

KEY TO GENERA OF WATER PLANTAIN FAMILY

Stamens 6; achenes in a single ring, forming a disk
    Petals entire; achenes with minute beak; style lateral_____*Alisma*
    Petals toothed; achenes with long beak; style terminal_____*Damasonium*
Stamens 9 to many; achenes numerous, forming a head
    Leaves entire; all flowers perfect_____*Echinodorus*
    Leaves sagittate; some of the flowers imperfect
        Achenes flattened _____*Sagittaria*
        Achenes swollen _____*Lophotocarpus*

WATER PLANTAIN *(Alisma Plantago* L.) (Fig. 7)

This widely distributed species, occurring along the margins of wet shores, ponds and rivers, is an erect perennial, 2 to 6 feet tall, arising from rootstocks. The leaves have a long petiole, sheathing at the base, with oval to oblong leaf-blades, which are often somewhat heart-shaped at the base; the blades are 2 to 6 inches long. The flower-branches are in whorls, and the whole inflorescence is a pyramid-shaped panicle. The flowers are white, small and on pedicels about 1 inch long. The flower has 3 sepals, 3 petals, 6 stamens, and numerous ovaries on a disk-like receptacle. The fruit is a flattened achene; the achenes occur in a single whorl.

FRINGED WATER-PLANTAIN *(Damasonium californicum* Torr.)

Occurs in shallow water and mud from Modoc County through the Sacramento Valley, also in the coastal region, and Sonoma County.

This is a perennial herb with erect and slender stems 8-16 inches tall from tuberous rootstocks; leaves ovate to linear-oblong, obtuse at the apex and obtuse to subcordate at the base, 3 to 5 nerved, the petioles or some of them much longer than the blades. Flowering stems several together, the flowers in a terminal umbel or several umbels. Sepals 3, broad ribbed, about 4-5 mm long, petals about twice as large, almost orbicular, more or less irregularly toothed, withering persistent. Achenes 6 to 10, horizontally-radiating, bayonet-shaped, ribbed on the back.

BUR-HEAD *(Echinodorus cordifolius* (L.) Griseb.) (Fig. 7)

This weed occurs mostly at the borders of pools along roadsides and at the edges of streams: Sacramento Valley; San Joaquin County and west of the Sierras south to Southern California; Palo Verde Valley.

Bur-head is an annual herb, 1 to 2 feet tall, with long-stalked, entire leaves, the blades of which are oval, 5- to 9-nerved, blunt at the tip, somewhat heart-shaped at the base, 1½ to 8 inches long. The flowers are in umbel-like whorls, the umbels distinct. There are 3 sepals, 3 petals, 12

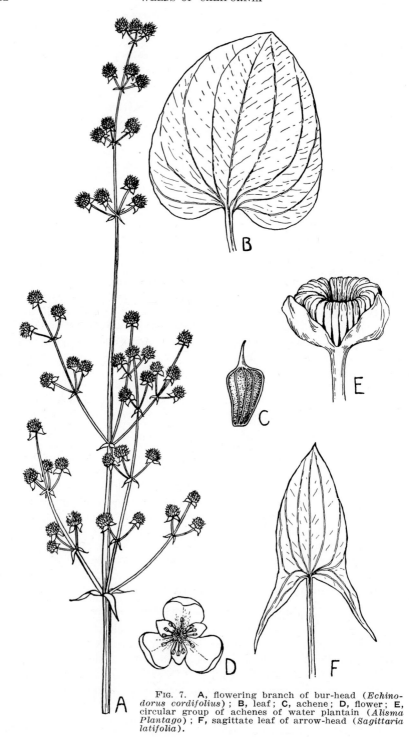

Fig. 7.   **A,** flowering branch of bur-head (*Echino-dorus cordifolius*); **B,** leaf; **C,** achene; **D,** flower; **E,** circular group of achenes of water plantain (*Alisma Plantago*); **F,** sagittate leaf of arrow-head (*Sagittaria latifolia*).

stamens, and numerous ovaries crowded on a rounded receptacle. There are numerous achenes, each about 1/12 inch long, strongly ribbed, and with a conspicious, erect, straight beak.

CALIFORNIA LOPHOTOCARPUS (*Lophotocarpus calycinus* (Englem) J. G. Sm.)

Annual aquatic or bog plant with basal long-petioled sagittate or cordate leaves. Simple flower-bearing stems about as long as the leaves with three to five whorls at the summit. Plants emersed or submerged; fruiting pedicels short and thick, ½ to 1 inch long; numerous stamens inserted at the base of the receptacle; sepals broadly ovate, 6-9 mm. long; fruiting heads 10-12 mm. in diameter, achenes 2-5 mm. long; the beak minute, the wing on the back broad and thick. Occurs from Oregon to Sacramento Valley and to Southern California.

ARROW-HEAD. SAGITTARIA

There are several species of *Sagittaria* in California, all marsh or aquatic perennials, some of which are troublesome in rice fields. The plants arise from tuberous or thickened rootstocks. The leaves are sheathing at the base, variable in width. The flowers occur in whorls of 3 on the upper part of the stem. There are two types of flowers, stamen-bearing and pistil-bearing, the former above. There are 3 sepals, 3 petals, numerous stamens inserted above the receptacle, and numerous ovaries crowded on a rounded receptacle. The fruit is a flat achene, beaked, and either winged or margined.

BROAD LEAVED ARROWHEAD (*Sagittaria latifolia* Willd.) (Fig. 7)

Perennial with tuber-bearing rootstocks. Plants partially or wholly emersed, approximately ¾ to 4½ feet tall, leaves variable, usually arrow-shaped, the terminal lobe deltoid to ovate or even very slender. Flowering stem erect, angled, either thick or slender, flower bracts 6, usually less than ½ inch long. Fruiting head ½ to 1¼ inch in diameter, achenes about 3 mm. long, broadly winged especially at the top, the beak horizontal or nearly so.

FROGBIT FAMILY *(Hydrocharitaceae)*

Representatives of this family are aquatic herbs, the following being most important from the weed standpoint.

WATERWEED (*Anacharis (Elodea) canadensis* Michx)

This species is of general distribution almost throughout North America, occasionally a pest in the northern part of California.

Waterweed is a perennial. The stems are slender, ¼ to 2 feet long. Leaves are in whorls, rarely opposite, lance-shaped, oval or linear, 1.2 to 4 mm. wide. Flowers are solitary in a leaf-like spathe; stamen-bearing flowers are minute, with 3 sepals, 3 white or pinkish petals, and 9 short stamens; pistillate flowers with 3 calyx-lobes, 3 petals, and a simple ovary with 3-lobed stigma. The calyx tube of pistillate flowers elongates bringing the stigmas to the water surface; and at maturity staminate flowers break loose, rise to the surface, and shed their pollen. The fruit which matures under water is indehiscent, and produces 1 to 5 spindle-shaped seeds about 4 mm. long.

GRASS FAMILY (Gramineae)

This is a family of some 4,500 species. Members of the family are widely distributed over the surface of the earth, from tropical to polar regions, and from low to very high altitudes. No family of plants is of greater economic importance. It includes the cereals, such as wheat, oats, barley, rye, corn, and rice, and many meadow, pasture, and range plants. Most grasses are herbs. A few, such as the bamboos, are shrubs or trees. The stems of grasses are cylindrical (rarely flattened) and divided into sections which are usually hollow. Some grasses, such as common timothy, are bulbous at the base; others, such as Johnson grass and quackgrass,

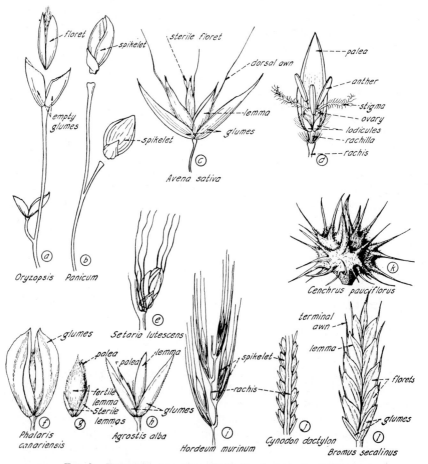

FIG. 8.   Botanical characters illustrating key to grass family.

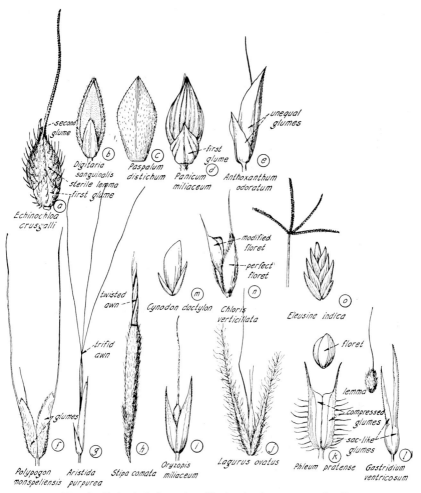

FIG. 9. Botanical characters illustrating key to grass family.

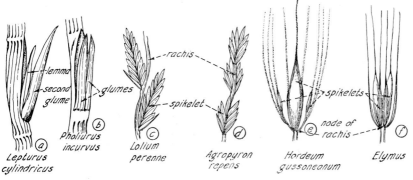

FIG. 10. Botanical characters illustrating key to grass family.

possess rootstocks; and others, such as Bermuda grass, develop stolons. The leaves are disposed in a 2-ranked fashion on the stem (Fig. 1g). Each leaf has two distinct parts, the sheath and the blade. The sheath forms a tube around the stem, and the more or less flattened part of the leaf which spreads away from the stem is the blade. The blades are parallel-veined. At the junction of the sheath and blade is a membranous or cartilaginous fringe or ring, the ligule; and also at the juncture of the sheath and blade is often a more or less pointed, thin, ear-like projection, the auricle.

The flower cluster consists of a number of groups of flowers, each group being called a spikelet (Fig. 1f). The spikelets are attached to a main axis, the rachis (Fig. 8d, i, j). In grasses the flower groups may be a spike, as in wheat, barley, rye, and many other grasses, or a raceme, as in sheep's fescue, or a panicle, as in oats and brome grasses. A typical spikelet consists of a short axis, bearing a number of chaff-like, 2-ranked, overlapping bracts. Each spikelet is subtended by two empty bracts (glumes) (Fig. 8c), that is they do not subtend flowers. Above the two glumes on the axis of the spikelet are one or more bracts, each known as a lemma. Normally, there is a single flower in the axil of each lemma. Opposite each lemma is a more fragile bract, the palet, and within the palet or palea and enveloped by it are usually 3 stamens and a single pistil (Fig. 8d). The ovary of the pistil becomes the grain. The awns or beards of grasses are on lemmas or glumes, usually on the former.

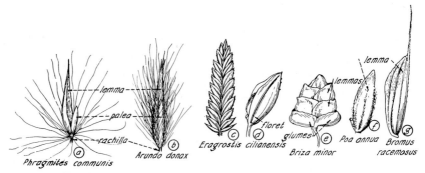

Fig. 11.   Botanical characters illustrating key to grass family.

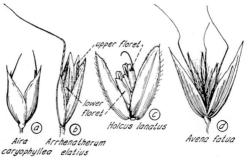

Fig. 12.   Botanical characters illustrating key to grass family.

KEY TO THE TRIBES AND GENERA OF GRASSES

Spikelets round, or more or less flattened dorsally, usually jointed below the empty glumes, so that the spikelet falls as a whole (Fig. 8b) _____**Tribe Paniceae**

Spikelets more or less flattened laterally, jointed above the empty glumes, which persist after the rest of the spikelet falls (Fig. 8a)

Spikelets with one floret, or with one or more sterile lemmas below the fertile floret; inflorescence a panicle, or a raceme

Spikelets 1-flowered, strongly flattened, glumes reduced or none_____*Oryzeae*

Spikelet with two sterile lemmas below fertile floret (Fig. 8g) __**Tribe Phalarideae**

Spikelet without sterile lemmas below the fertile floret_____**Tribe Agrostideae**

Spikelets with one to several florets, usually more than one; spikelets usually form a spike

Spikelets in two rows on opposite sides of the rachis, thus forming a symmetrical spike (Fig. 8i) _____**Tribe Hordeae**

Spikelets in two rows on same side of the rachis, thus forming a one-sided spike (Fig. 8j) _____**Tribe Chlorideae**

Spikelets with two to several florets

Empty glumes usually shorter than the lemmas, and shorter than spikelet as a whole; lemmas awnless, or with a straight terminal awn____**Tribe Festuceae**

Empty glumes longer than the lemmas, usually enclosing the whole spikelet; lemma awnless or with a bent, dorsal awn (Fig. 8c) _____**Tribe Aveneae**

Tribe Paniceae. Spikelets with one perfect terminal floret and below this a sterile floret and two glumes; spikelets jointed below the empty glumes, so that the spikelet falls as a whole

Spikelets subtended or surrounded by 1 to many bristles, which form an involucre

Bristles persistent, the spikelets deciduous (Fig. 8e) _____*Setaria*

Bristles falling with the spikelets at maturity

Bristles not united at base_____*Pennisetum*

Bristles united into a bur-like involucre (Fig. 8k) _____*Cenchrus*

Spikelets not subtended by bristles

Glumes or sterile lemma awned (Fig. 9a) _____*Echinochloa*

Glumes and sterile lemma awnless

Fruit hard and elastic, like cartilage (Fig. 9b) _____*Digitaria*

Fruit hard, papery, and rigid

First glume wanting (Fig. 9c) _____*Paspalum*

First glume present (Fig. 9d) _____*Panicum*

Tribe Oryzeae. Spikelets 1-flowered strongly compressed

Glumes minute _____*Oryza*

Glumes wanting _____*Leersia*

Tribe Phalarideae. Spikelets with one perfect terminal floret, and below this one or two imperfect ones

Spikelets much compressed (Fig. 8f) _____*Phalaris*

Spikelets almost cylindrical (Fig. 9e) _____*Anthoxanthum*

Tribe Agrostideae. Spikelets 1-flowered, in open, contracted or spike-like panicles, but not in true spikes nor in one-sided racemes

Articulation below the glumes, the spikelets falling entire_____*Polypogon*

Articulation above the glumes, the spikelets not falling entire

Fruit hard, awned; callus well developed

Awn trifid (Fig. 9g) _____*Aristida*

Awn not trifid

Awn persistent, twisted and bent, several to many times longer than the fruit (Fig. 9h) _____*Stipa*

Awn deciduous, not twisted, sometimes bent, rarely more than 3 or 4 times as long as the fruit (Fig. 9i) _____*Oryzopsis*

Fruit thin or firm, but scarcely indurate; callus not well developed

Panicle feathery; spikelets woolly_____*Lagurus*

Panicle not feathery, spikelets not woolly

Glumes compressed and keeled_____*Phleum*

Glumes not compressed and keeled

Glumes sac-like at base; lemma with long awn_____*Gastridium*

Glumes not sac-like at base; lemma awned or awnless_____*Agrostis*

Tribe Hordeae. Spikelets 1- to several-flowered, sessile on opposite sides of a jointed or continuous axis; inflorescence a spike (not one-sided)

Spikelets solitary at each node of the rachis

  Spikelets one-flowered

    First glume wanting (Fig. 10a) _____*Lepturus*

    First glume present (Fig. 10b) _____*Pholiurus*

  Spikelets 2- to several-flowered

    Spikelets placed edgewise to the rachis (Fig. 10c) _____*Lolium*

    Spikelets placed flatwise to the rachis (Fig. 10d)

      Plants perennial _____ *Agropyron*

      Plants annual _____*Aegilops*

Spikelets more than 1 at each node of the rachis

  Spikelets 3 at each node of the rachis, each 1-flowered (Fig. 10e) _____ *Hordeum*

  Spikelets 2 at each node of the rachis, 2- to 6-flowered (Fig. 10f) _____ *Elymus*

Tribe Chlorideae. Spikelets 1- to several-flowered, in two rows on one side of a continuous rachis, forming 1-sided spikes and spike-like racemes, which are solitary, digitate or racemose along the main axis

Spikelets with more than one perfect floret

  Spikes few, digitate or nearly so (Fig. 9o) _____*Eleusine*

  Spikes numerous, not digitate_____*Leptochloa*

Spikelets with only 1 perfect floret, often with additional imperfect florets above or below

  Spikelets without additional modified florets (Fig. 9m) _____*Cynodon*

  Spikelets with 1 or more modified florets above the perfect one (Fig. 9n) *Chloris*

Tribe Festuceae. Spikelets more than 1-flowered; lemmas awnless or awned from the tip or from a bifid apex; glumes shorter than the first floret

Tall stout reeds with plume-like panicles

  Lemmas naked; rachilla hairy (Fig. 11a) _____*Phragmites*

    Lemmas hairy; rachilla naked (Fig. 11b) _____*Arundo*

Low or rather tall grasses, rarely more than 4 feet tall

  Perennial dioecious plants of salt or alkaline soils_____*Distichlis*

  Plants not dioecious (except in few species)

    Spikelets of two forms, sterile and fertile intermixed; panicle dense, somewhat one-sided

      Panicle dense, spike-like_____*Cynosurus*

      Panicle branches nodding_____*Lamarckia*

    Spikelets all alike in the same inflorescence

      Lemmas 3-nerved, the nerves prominent, often hairy (Fig. 11c, d) *Eragrostis*

      Lemmas 5- to many-nerved, the nerves sometimes obscure

        Lemmas as broad as long (Fig. 11e) _____*Briza*

        Lemmas longer than broad

          Lemmas keeled on the back

            Lemmas awnless, spikelets small (Fig. 11f) _____*Poa*

            Lemmas awned (except in *Bromus catharticus* and *B. brizaeformis*); spikelets large (Fig. 7l, 11g) _____*Bromus*

          Lemmas rounded on the back

            Lemmas awned or awn-tipped from a minutely bifid apex (Fig. 11g) (awnless in *B. brizaeformis*) _____*Bromus*

            Lemmas entire, pointed, awnless or awned from the tip

              Spikelets awned; lemmas pointed_____*Festuca*

              Spikelets awnless _____*Poa*

Tribe Aveneae. Spikelets 2- to several-flowered in open or contracted panicles; glumes usually as long as or longer than the first lemma; lemmas usually awned from the back or from between the teeth of a bifid apex, the awn usually bent and twisted (Fig. 8c)

Florets 2, one perfect, the other staminate

  Lower floret staminate, the awn twisted, exserted (Fig. 12b) ____*Arrhenatherum*

  Lower floret perfect, awnless; upper floret awned (Fig. 12c) _____*Holcus*

Florets 2 or more; all alike except the reduced upper ones

  Spikelets several flowered_____*Schismus*

  Spikelets 2-flowered, sometimes a rudimentary third

    Spikelets large, the glumes more than 1 cm. long (Fig. 12d) _____*Avena*

    Spikelets less than 1 cm. long (Fig. 12a) _____ *Aira*

FIG. 13. Barb goatgrass (*Aegilops triuncialis*). Spikes showing strongly-
veined awned glumes.

JOINTED GOATGRASS (*Aegilops cylindrica* Host.)

This is established to a limited extent in Siskiyou County. The flowering spike is very slender and cylindric. The glume bears but one awn.

OVATE GOATGRASS (*Aegilops ovata* L.)

This species has been reported from the vicinity of Willits, Mendocino County. It differs from barb goatgrass in that its culms are shorter (6 to 10 inches tall), the spike has from 2 to 4 spikelets, and the glumes have 4 stiff spreading awns. The grain is shorter and broader than that of *A. triuncialis*.

BARB GOATGRASS (*Aegilops triuncialis* L.) (Fig. 13)

This European introduction has become a troublesome, mechanically injurious weed on range lands. Specimens were collected in 1917 near Clarksville in the Sierra foothills where "it was noticed for the first time about 3 years ago where some cattle from Mexico had been pastured. This season it is said to have practically destroyed a crop of wheat." In 1929 its distribution as given by Jacobsen was "from the upper reaches of Deer Creek, where this stream is crossed by the state highway to Placerville, westward to Clarksville in El Dorado County, thence spottedly south along Deer Creek and across the hills to Sloughhouse on the Cosumnes River. There appears to be more or less of a gap between this group of infestations until Calaveras County is reached, where it is found abundantly in spots throughout its southwestern portion, extending over into eastern San Joaquin County and northwestern Stanislaus County."

Barb goatgrass is an annual plant from 8 to 20 inches tall and with few to many culms. The leaf sheaths and blades have scattered white hairs when young, but become more or less smooth at maturity. The blades are rather rigid, sharp-pointed and spreading. The flowers are in a spike about 3 inches long, including the awns, and consist of 4 to 7 spikelets; the lower spikelets are broad and fertile, the upper rudimentary. The glumes are stout, thick, strongly veined, and terminate in 3 awns about 1 inch long, the central one usually the shortest. The lemmas terminate in 2 or 3 very short unequal points. In the terminal spikelet the awns may branch so as to appear like 7 awns to each glume. The caryopsis or grain is about one-fourth inch long, resembling a slender wheat kernel.

Cattle avoid this plant on range lands, although it has been found that they can eat the plant with no ill effects, and that if they are held on an infested area they will greatly reduce the infestation.

RUSH-LIKE WHEATGRASS (*Agropyron junceum* (L.) Beauv.)

This native of the Mediterranean Coast which is rare in California has been found thus far near San Francisco. Like quackgrass, it has creeping rootstocks. The leaf-blades are rolled and the spike is stout, readily breaking apart at the joints when mature.

QUACKGRASS (*Agropyron repens* (L.) Beauv.) (Fig. 14)
Other common names: Couchgrass, witchgrass, quitchgrass, quickgrass, wiregrass.

Quackgrass is a very important common weed in that section of the United States north of the Ohio River and east of the Missouri River. It is increasing in certain parts of California, chiefly in the Bay region and the northwest counties. Small infestations occur in the potato fields of the Delta. This weed first attracted serious attention in America about 1837 and its spread has been fairly rapid, particularly in the northern states. Apparently it does not flourish at southern latitudes, but attains its most luxuriant growth in cool, moist climates; hence we may expect its spread chiefly in the coastal areas of California. Quackgrass grows in a variety of soils—sand, clay, or gravel; it also occurs in peat soils, and is somewhat tolerant of alkali. Seed may occur as an impurity in commercial seed; it is carried in hay, in the hair of animals, in feed stuffs and bedding, and also by water. The plant does have some value as a forage plant, and to a limited extent it is used as a soil binder.

Quackgrass is a perennial. A prominent characteristic is the pale yellow or straw-colored, cord-like rootstocks, about ⅛ inch in diameter, which run just beneath the surface of the ground, usually at a depth of about 4 inches, but occasionally reaching 6 to 8 inches. The deepest and most vigorous rootstocks occur in cultivated fields, whereas in undisturbed soil, in meadow lands, and pasture lands, the rootstocks are more shallow. At each joint of the rootstock there is a tough, brownish sheath, giving a scaly appearance, while branches are produced at nearly every joint. Rootstocks may extend laterally 3 to 5 feet, and may become so numerous as to form a tough, tangled mass or matted bed; in fact, this habit makes the grass an excellent soil binder. The ends of rootstocks are often very sharp-pointed, so sharp that they are known to push their way through potatoes; it has been reported that in certain potato fields from 15 to 20 percent of the tubers had holes in them caused by penetration of the sharp-pointed rootstocks; this explains the ability of quackgrass to penetrate hard soils. If broken into a number of pieces by the hoe or cultivating implements, each rootstock piece is capable of propagation. It is this habit which makes quackgrass such a pernicious weed. The rootstocks are storage organs and are well supplied with reserve food. They are not absorbing organs, but from them arise masses of small, fibrous, absorbing roots.

Quackgrass grows from 1 to 3 feet tall. The leaves often are covered with a whitish bloom, especially in the drier sections of the country; in the more humid sections they are dark-green. At the base of each is a small pair of claws (auricles) and a ragged, membrane-like fringe. The flower groups (spikes) resemble somewhat those of a slender head of wheat and vary in length from a few inches to 10 inches. The spikelets are usually about five-flowered. The glumes are 3- to 7-nerved and usually awn-pointed; the lemmas bear an awn which varies in length from a mere bristle to a structure as long as the lemma itself; the palet is obtuse and about as long as the lemma. The seed, with investing glumes, is elongated toward the slender, short-awned tip, broadest below the middle and tapered to the obliquely blunt base. The grain is slender, brownish, pointed at the base, and topped by a ring of hairs. It seems that when rootstocks are free to develop rapidly, fewer seeds are produced than when they are retarded. The maximum vitality of the seed is approximately four years when stored under dry conditions. In the soil, those seeds within the upper 3 to 4 inches either germinate or die within two years. Very immature seeds, even those in the dough stage, will germinate. Hence, quackgrass cut before the seed hardens may be a source of danger.

REDTOP (*Agrostis alba* L.) (Fig. 8)

Redtop is a perennial, spreading by strong underground rhizomes. The stems are erect, or somewhat decumbent at the base, 1 to $3\frac{1}{2}$ feet tall; leaf blades flat, 5 to 10 mm. wide. The delicate often reddish-tinged, pyramidal flowering tops are 2 to 12 inches long, somewhat spreading, the lower branches in whorls. This native of Eurasia is cultivated in pastures and lawns and widely escaped in many parts of California.

HAIRY-FLOWERED BENTGRASS (*Agrostis retrofracta* Willd.)

This is a tufted perennial 8 inches to 2 feet tall. The branches of the flowering spike are in distant whorls, very fine and hair-like. The leaves are flat, 1-2 mm. wide, somewhat roughish. This is an Australian species common in the Hawaiian Islands; introduced near Stockton, San Joaquin County.

WATER BENTGRASS (*Agrostis semiverticellata* (Forsk.) C. Christ)

This is a species, naturalized from Europe, which occurs in moist ground especially along irrigation ditches and near the coast, Mendocino, Mariposa, and Inyo Counties, south to southern California.

Water bent grass is a perennial, sometimes with long, creeping and rooting stolons. The culms are usually decumbent at the base, and the leaf blades usually short and broad. The panicle is contracted, densely flowered, whorled, 4 to 10 cm. long, and light-green or, rarely, purplish in color. Each spikelet is 1-flowered, 2 mm. long, with 2 equal glumes, the lemma awnless and toothed at the apex. The grain is amber-colored, pointed toward apex and rounded at base, a distinct groove along one side.

Agrostis palustris Huds., seaside bent, *A. tenuis* Sibth., colonial bent, and *A. stolonifera* L. C., carpet or creeping bent, also have escaped and

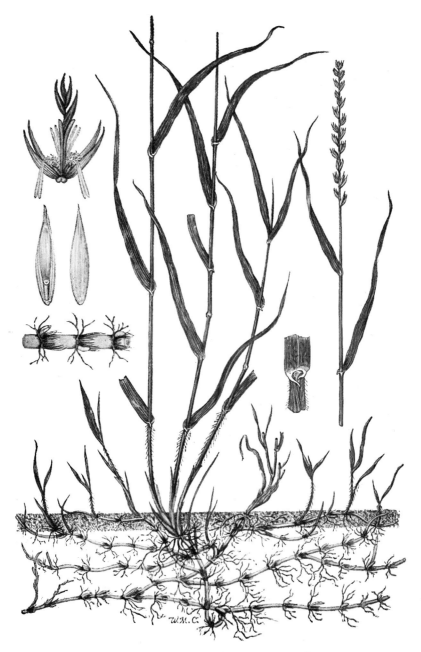

FIG. 14. Quackgrass (*Agroypron repens*).

become established where soil and moisture conditions are favorable. The last named is known only in the vegetative form.

FINE HAIRGRASS (*Aira capillaris* Host.)

Closely related to silver hairgrass is fine hairgrass, introduced from Europe and occurring in the coast region of northern California. The spikelets are smaller than those of silver hairgrass and are disposed singly at the ends of the panicle branches. Moreover, only one lemma, the upper one, bears an awn.

SILVER HAIRGRASS (*Aira caryophyllea* L.) (Figs. 12 and 15)

This species, naturalized from Europe, is fairly common on old cattle ranges in the coast counties. It has no forage value. It is a small, delicate, annual grass, with tufted erect stems 6 to 12 inches tall. The leaves are fine and hair-like, 2 inches or less in length, and inrolled above. The spikelets are silvery-shining and usually clustered at the ends of the spreading branches of the panicle. The spikelets are 2-flowered, about 3 mm. long, the glumes boat-shaped, the lemmas tapering into 2 slender teeth and bearing on the back a slender, abruptly bent, twisted awn.

SPIKE HAIRGRASS (*Aira praecox* L.)

A tufted annual, stems 4 to 8 inches tall, the flower panicle, narrow and dense, 1-2 inches long. The spikelets yellowish and shiny. A native of Europe, established in Del Norte and Humboldt Counties.

BUSHY BEARDGRASS (*Andropogon glomeratus* Watt)

A tufted coarse perennial often forming dense clumps 2 to 6 feet tall. Flowering stems compressed, freely branching toward the summit, appearing feathery. The branches of the inflorescence are partly enclosed by and about equal to the spathe. The lower sheaths are broad, keeled and overlapping, the elongate blades 3 to 8 mm. wide. In late summer the whole plant turns a characteristic tawny reddish color. Southern California north to Butte County.

SILVER BEARDGRASS (*Andropogon saccharoides* Swartz)

A tufted perennial resembling the preceding species, but the flowering panicle silvery white, silky, oblong, dense, about 2½ to 6 inches long. Southern California; Topango Canyon.

BROOMSEDGE (*Andropogon virginicus* L.)

A perennial very similar to *A. glomeratus,* growing in small tufts, stems about 18 inches to 3½ feet tall, freely branching above, the lower sheaths compressed, keeled and enfolding each other as in Iris. Blades flat or folded, 2 to 5 mm. wide. The inflorescence is elongate and narrow, the 2 to 4 branches partly included and shorter than the inflated tawny or reddish-brown spathes. Widely established in Butte County, also in El Dorado and Nevada Counties.

ANNUAL VERNALGRASS (*Anthoxanthum aristatum* Boiss.)

Similar to the following but annual, lower growing, more bushy in habit, the spikelets smaller. Introduced from Europe and now established near Ingot, Shasta County, also in Del Norte, Sonoma and Marin Counties.

SWEET VERNALGRASS (*Anthoxanthum odoratum* L.)
(Fig. 9e)

This is a sweet-scented perennial grass introduced from Eurasia. In California it occurs in meadows and waste grounds in Humboldt and Del Norte Counties. It is sometimes used in meadow mixtures to give fragrance to the hay but it has little forage value.

Sweet vernalgrass has tufted, slender, erect culms 1 to 2 feet tall, flat leaf-blades and spike-like, brownish-green panicles 1½ to 5 inches long. Each spikelet has 1 terminal perfect flower and 2 sterile lemmas. The glumes are unequal, the sterile lemmas shorter than the glumes, awned on the back and golden-hairy, the fertile lemma shorter than the sterile one, brown, smooth, shining and awnless. The first sterile lemma is short-awned below the tip, whereas the second sterile lemma has a twisted awn which arises from near the base. The seed with inner glumes is oval, 3 mm. long, gradually sharp-pointed at the apex, rounded at the base and wider at one side than the other. The color is shiny reddish-brown, the foldings of the glumes apparent. The kernel is shaped like the seed, the color light-brown with darker reddish-brown dots.

FIG. 15. Silver hairgrass (*Aira caryophyllea*).

PRAIRIE THREE-AWN (*Aristida oligantha* Michx.)

Annual, gray-green, much branched and spreading from below, 6 inches to 1 foot tall, the blades flat or involute, commonly not more than 1 mm. wide. Inflorescence open, the lower spikelets often in pairs; glumes about equal, tapering to an awn; lemma about ¾ inch long, tipped by the 3 divergent awns about 1½ to 3 inches long. Open dry ground often showing up as the only green vegetation on overgrazed areas.

Poverty grass is another name by which this worthless weed is known, due to the fact that it is unpalatable to all classes of livestock.

NEEDLEGRASS (*Aristida purpurea* Nutt.) (Fig. 16)
Other common names: Triple-awned grass, purple three-awn grass.

There are 10 species of *Aristida* in California, characterized by the occurrence of a 3-branched awn which terminates the lemma. *A. pur-*

purea is one of the widely distributed needle-grasses, a native at lower altitudes throughout the State and the southwest.

This species is perennial, often in large tufts, with stout stems 1 to 2 feet high. The leaf blades are usually inrolled above, 2 to 6 inches long, the leaf sheaths being short. The inflorescence is a loose purplish panicle, 4 to 6 inches long, its branches and longer pedicels thread-like and more or less drooping. The spikelet is narrow, 1-flowered, the glumes being very unequal in size, the second about twice as long as the first. The lemma is purplish, about $\frac{1}{2}$ inch long, tipped with a 3-pronged awn, each prong about $\frac{1}{2}$ inch long. The grain is very slender elongate.

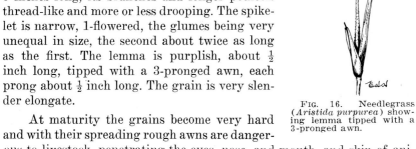

FIG. 16. Needlegrass (*Aristida purpurea*) showing lemma tipped with a 3-pronged awn.

At maturity the grains become very hard and with their spreading rough awns are dangerous to livestock, penetrating the eyes, nose, and mouth, and skin of animals, particularly sheep, causing ulcerations. In the wool of sheep the value of the fleece is reduced.

TALL OATGRASS (*Arrhenatherum elatius* (L.) Mert. & Koch.) (Fig. 17)

This introduction from Europe is rare in California. It is recorded by Jepson as an adventive near Berkeley and at Jackson in Amador County. It is cultivated as a meadow grass in the northern humid regions. It is a perennial, 3 to 5 feet tall, with flat leaf blades; the flowering group is 5 to 12 inches long, shining, pale or purplish, the short branches in whorls. The spikelets are 2-flowered, the lower stamen-bearing, the upper perfect; the glumes are broad and papery; the lemma of the lower spikelet bears near its base a twisted, bent awn about twice as long as the lemma itself. The seed is about 8 mm. long, broadest at the center and tapering toward both ends, short hairy above, the hairs markedly longer at the base. The color is light yellowish-brown. The grain is the same shape and color, with hairy surface.

REED GRASS (*Arundo Donax* L.) (Fig. 11b)

This species, a native of the warm regions of the Old World, is distributed from Texas to California. It occurs along irrigation ditches in central and southern California, and it may become so well established in waterways as to constitute a serious pest by reducing the carrying capacity of the ditch. The plant is frequently planted as an ornamental because of its large, plume-like inflorescences, and in certain parts of the southwest the culms are used in the building of adobe huts, also for mats, screens, and lattices. Parish says "An aged Mexican informed Mr. Lyon that as early as 1820 it was so plentiful along the Los

Angeles River that it was gathered for roofing material, for which it was preferred to the tules commonly used for the purpose.''

The species is a perennial, attaining a height of 6 to 18 feet. The culms may be as much as an inch in diameter at the base, and arise from thick, knotty rhizomes. There are numerous leaves in two distinct ranks; the leaf blades are flat and broad, the leaves of the main culm being $1\frac{1}{2}$ to 3 inches wide, those of the branches being narrower; the leaf-base is heart-shaped and more or less hairy. The flowers are in plume-like terminal panicles, 1 to 2 feet long. Each spikelet has several flowers, successively smaller. The glumes are somewhat unequal, m e m b r a n o u s, 3-nerved, slender, and taper to a point. The densely soft-hairy lemma investing the slender grain is 3-nerved, the 2 lateral nerves ending in slender teeth, the middle one in a straight awn.

SLENDER OAT (*Avena barbata* Brot.) (Fig. 18a)

Slender oat is similar to *A. fatua*, with spikelets somewhat smaller, usually 2-flowered, the lemma clothed with stiff reddish hairs. This species was introduced from Europe, and now is a common weed from Washington to Arizona. It was first reported in California in 1885. On range

FIG. 17. Tall oatgrass (*Arrhenatherum elatius*) showing flowering branch and 2-flowered spikelet, the lemma of lower flower with twisted, bent awn.

lands it is often associated with wild oats and, like the latter, has considerable forage value. It differs from *A. fatua* in having two fine awns, about $\frac{1}{16}$ inch long, terminating the teeth of the lemma.

WILD OAT (*Avena fatua* L.) (Figs. 12 and 18b)
Other common names: Wheat oats, oat-grass, flax-grass.

This is one of the most widely distributed of our common weeds, occurring from one end of the State to the other. It is introduced from Europe, but in California and other northwest and Pacific Coast states behaves like a native, apparently thriving not only in cultivated and waste areas but dominating much of the grazing lands. On grazing lands it has great value as a forage plant; also in certain parts of the State it yields a considerable amount of wild hay. However, the plant is often especially troublesome as a weed in grain fields; also in cultivated grounds and waste places. Wild oat grows on many different types of soil, such as clay loam, sandy loam, and stiff adobe.

Wild oat is an annual, with erect, stout culms 1 to 3½ feet tall. The leaf blades are long and broad, and rough; the leaf sheaths smooth or slightly hairy. The inflorescence resembles that

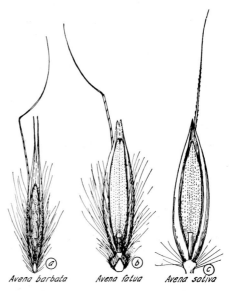

Avena barbata   *Avena fatua*   *Avena sativa*

FIG. 18.   Florets of three species of *Avena*.

of cultivated oats. The spikelets are 2- or 3-flowered, and about 1 inch long, not including the awns. The base of the lemma and its short stalk are clothed with stiff, long brown hairs; the lemma is 2-toothed at the apex, and arising from its back is a twisted awn about 1¼ to 1½ inch long. The short stalk (rachilla) against the front face of the seed is hairy and terminates in a pointed oval depression. The grain is silky hairy, hairs longer above, very pale yellow.

Ordinary cultivated oat varieties may be readily distinguished from wild oats by the absence of hairs on the lemma, and the awn which, if present, is straight. (Fig. 18c)

ANIMATED OATS (*Avena sterilis* L.)

Animated oats, an introduction from Europe, is established to a limited extent in California. It is an annual resembling *A. fatua* from which it is distinguished by its longer awns (sometimes more than 2 inches long). The awns are hygroscopic, twisting and untwisting as they lose or absorb moisture.

BRACHYPODIUM (*Brachypodium distachyon* (L.) Beauv.)

This is an annual, 4 to 8 inches tall, with short flat blades and an erect stiff raceme of 1 to few appressed almost sessile awned spikelets. The general appearance suggests darnel or chess. This *Brachypodium* is a native of Europe, locally established in eastern Sacramento County and in Marin County, having been noted earlier as a ballast weed near Portland, Oregon, and also on the Atlantic seaboard.

SMALL QUAKING GRASS (*Briza minor* L.) (Fig. 19)

This species, an adventive from Europe, occurs in scattered localities in the Eastern States, and on the Pacific Coast. It is becoming quite widely distributed in California. Occasionally it forms a part of the spring forage in central and northern California, but usually it acts as a weed. It is a low annual with smooth, erect culms, 4 to 16 inches high. The leaves have flat blades 1 to 4 inches long and about $\frac{1}{3}$ inch wide; the leaf sheaths are sometimes roughened, and are shorter than the internodes. The inflorescence is an open, spreading panicle, its branches very slender or thread-like, permitting the spikelets to vibrate with the slightest breeze. This latter characteristic has suggested the common name of the plant. The spikelet is about 3 mm. long, broad, flattened, heart-shaped, and several-flowered. The glumes and lemmas are broad, with papery margins. The broad-oval grain is much flattened and light-brownish in color.

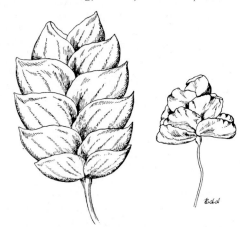

LARGE QUAKING GRASS (*Briza maxima* L.) (Fig. 19)

This is cultivated as an ornamental garden plant and has sparingly escaped. The spikelets are about 12 mm. long and 10 mm. broad. The grain is very broad, and a distinctive bluish-green color.

FIG. 19. Left, spikelet of large quaking grass (*Briza maxima*); right, spikelet of small quaking grass (*Briza minor*).

BROMEGRASS. BROMUS

The genus *Bromus* is a large one, possessing many species, both perennial and annual, of considerable forage value. The most important cultivated species is *B. inermis*, a native of Europe, known as smooth brome grass. Several species of brome grasses, chiefly annuals, have become weeds in certain situations. The following key will serve to distinguish these species:

KEY TO WEEDY SPECIES OF BROMUS

Spikelets strongly flattened, the lemmas compressed
 Lemmas awnless _____*B. catharticus*
 Lemmas awned _____*B. carinatus*
Spikelets more or less cylindrical, the lemmas not compressed
 Lemmas broad, rounded above, the teeth mostly less than 1 mm. long
  Plants perennial _____*B. inermis*
  Plants annual
   Inflorescence rather dense, contracted, the branches erect or ascending
    Lemmas glabrous _____*B. racemosus*
    Lemmas pubescent
     Spikelets compressed_____*B. scoparius*
     Spikelets turgid_____*B. mollis*

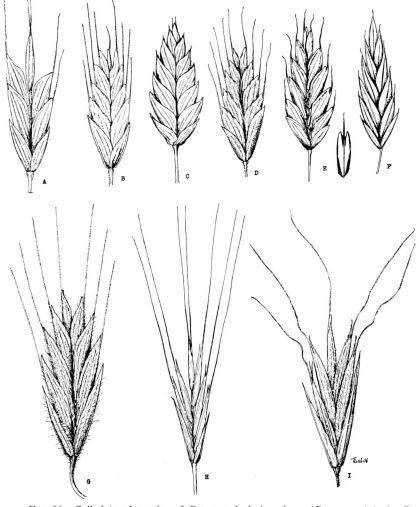

FIG. 20. Spikelets of species of *Bromus*. **A**, hairy chess (*B. commutatus*); **B**, upright chess (*B. racemosus*); **C**, rattlesnake chess (*B. brizaeformis*); **D**, soft chess (*B. mollis*); **E**, chess (*B. secalinus*); **F**, rescue grass (*B. catharticus*); **G**, Australian chess (*B. arenarius*); **H**, compact chess (*B. madritensis*); **I**, Chilean chess (*B. Trinii*).

Inflorescence open, the branches spreading
    Awn short or wanting_____*B. brizaeformis*
    Awn well-developed
        Sheaths smooth _____*B. secalinus*
        Sheaths pubescent
            Branches of inflorescence stiffly spreading, not flexuous
                                                B. commutatus
            Branches of inflorescence slender, lax or flexuous
                Panicle 3 to 4½ inches long ; lemmas pubescent_____*B. arenarius*
                Panicle 6 to 10 inches long ; lemmas smooth or slightly rough
                                              B. japonicus
Lemmas narrow, gradually tapering, 2-toothed, the teeth ⅛ to ¼ inch long ;
    awns usually more than ½ inch long
    Inflorescence dense, erect ; awns ½ to ¾ inch long
        Culms pubescent below panicle_____*B. rubens*
        Culms glabrous below panicle_____*B. madritensis*
    Inflorescence open, branches spreading
        Second glume usually less than ½ inch long ; pedicels very slender,
            even hair-like_____*B. tectorum*
        Second glume more than ½ inch long ; pedicels not hair-like
            Awns twisted_____*B. trinii*
            Awns straight
                Awns about ¾ inch long_____*B. sterilis*
                Awns 1¼ to 2 inches long_____*B. rigidus*

AUSTRALIAN CHESS *(Bromus arenarius* Labill.) (Fig. 20g)

    This is an annual quite common on sandy roadsides and dry hills from San Francisco Bay south. It is naturalized from Australia. The plant is erect, 6 to 18 inches tall. The leaf sheaths and blades are soft-hairy. The inflorescence is open, drooping, the pedicels sinuously curved. The spikelets are 5- to 11-flowered with densely hairy glumes and lemmas, and straight awns from ⅜ to ⅝ inch long.

RATTLESNAKE CHESS *(Bromus brizaeformis* Fisch. and Mey.) (Fig. 20c)

    This is an annual, introduced from Europe. It is distributed across the United States. Occasionally it is found in California, as a weed in sandy fields and waste ground. Sometimes it is cultivated as an ornamental. The lemmas are broad, inflated, smooth, and awnless, with a broad, papery margin. The stems are from 1 to 2 feet tall, the leaves short-hairy, the inflorescence very lax, somewhat one-sided and drooping. The spikelets are usually few in number, about ⅝ to 1 inch long, and ⅜ inch wide, and when mature suggest in their appearance the rattles of the rattlesnake.

CALIFORNIA BROME *(Bromus carinatus* Hook. and Arn.)

    This native bromegrass is common in open ground and waste places around habitations at low and middle altitudes.

    It is annual or perennial, 2 to 4 feet tall, blades flat, sparsely hairy to almost smooth, about ¼ inch wide. The panicle as long as 10 inches, with spreading or sometimes drooping branches; in small plants quite narrow. Spikelets 1 to 1½ inches long (excluding awns), glumes about ½ inch long, lemmas more or less appressed-hairy (rarely smooth), awns ¾ to 1½ inches long.

RESCUE GRASS (*Bromus catharticus* Vahl.) (Fig. 20f)

This plant is grown in the Southern States as a winter forage plant and has escaped from cultivation. It is a native of South America. Thus far it is not widely distributed in California. This is an annual or biennial, attaining a height of 3 feet. Unlike other common bromes, the spikelets and lemmas are strongly compressed. The inflorescence is open and as much as 8 inches long. The seed, with lemmas sharply folded, is about 2 mm. wide, 10 mm. or more long, flat-hairy to smooth.

HAIRY CHESS (*Bromus commutatus* Schrad.) (Fig. 20a)

This species occurs in fields and waste places at lower altitudes throughout the State, but is of minor importance as a weed. It is introduced from Europe, and is sparingly found on our ranges. It resembles *B. secalinus*, from which it is distinguished by its hairy leaf sheaths, and longer awns. This is an annual or biennial attaining a height of 1 to 2 feet. The leaf sheaths are hairy, the inflorescence drooping, about 6 inches long, and the spikelets smooth.

SMOOTH BROME (*Bromus inermis* Leyss.)

This is a native of the plains of Hungary and Russian Steppes, which was introduced about 1880 into California and planted extensively as a pasturage and hay crop. It has rarely escaped from cultivation, and grows in a volunteer fashion on ranges. It scarcely can be regarded as a weed, although it sometimes grows in waste places. It is an erect perennial, 20 to 50 inches tall, from creeping rhizomes. The leaf blades are short, usually smooth beneath, and somewhat hairy above. The panicle is 4 to 8 inches long, narrow, erect, the branches short. The spikelets are 7- to 11-flowered, the lemmas hairy along the margin and across the back at the base. The seed is flat, as compared to the folded seed of *B. catharticus*. The thin edges of investing glumes are open spreading; the apex varies from a more or less blunt point to a short, sharp awn.

JAPANESE CHESS (*Bromus japonicus* Thunb.)

This is a weed widely distributed in the Old World, and rather generally distributed across the United States. It occurs in waste places at lower elevations in California. Japanese chess is an annual, 14 to 30 inches tall. The leaf blades and sheaths are soft pubescent. The inflorescence is $4\frac{1}{2}$ to 8 inches long, rather diffuse, the lower branches 3 to 5, all branches being flexuous. The glumes and lemmas are broad; the awns are about $\frac{3}{8}$ inch long, somewhat twisted and widely divergent at maturity.

COMPACT CHESS (*Bromus madritensis* L.) (Fig. 20b)

This naturalized species from Europe occurs sparingly in California on open ground and in waste places. The plant resembles *B. rubens*, from which it differs in having less dense panicles, and culms smooth below.

SOFT CHESS (*Bromus mollis* L.) (Fig. 20d)

This species is also introduced from Europe, and is rather common as a weed on the Pacific Coast in waste places and cultivated soil. It is also one of the prevalent grasses of the ranges of northwestern California, where in some localities it has taken possession of depleted range lands.

This is annual or biennial and is characteristically soft-hairy throughout. The stems are 8 to 32 inches tall, the leaves flat, the inflorescence contracted, 8- to 12-flowered, from 2 to 4 inches long, and both the glumes and lemmas are broad and hairy. The species resembles *B. racemosus* from which it is distinguished by its pubescent, papery lemmas.

UPRIGHT CHESS (*Bromus racemosus* L.) (Fig. 20f)

This plant, naturalized from Europe, has become a weed in waste places throughout California, especially the northern half. It occurs chiefly west of the Rocky Mountains, although it is reported in the middlewest and eastern parts of the United States. The species is an annual, growing to a height of 8 to 32 inches. The inflorescence is contracted, 2 to 4 inches long; the glumes are broad, coarsely soft-hairy; the lemmas are also broad, soft, and usually smooth, the inner definitely shorter than the outer, which is awned.

RIPGUT GRASS (*Bromus rigidus* Roth. and *B. rigidus* var. *Gussonei* (Parl.) Coss. & Dur.)

This species and variety are fairly common in the Pacific Coast States and those bordering them on the east. It occurs sparingly in Maryland, Virginia, and Texas. In California the species is relatively abundant in the southern half of the State, the variety more common than the species in the central and northern half. The variety is one of the dominant plants of the ranges in northwestern California. They are naturalized from southern Europe.

The plant is 16 to 28 inches tall. The leaf sheaths and blades are soft-hairy. The inflorescence is open, nodding, few-flowered, $2\frac{3}{4}$ to 6 inches long, the lower branches $\frac{3}{8}$ to $\frac{3}{4}$ inch long. The spikelets are usually 5- to 6-flowered, $1\frac{1}{4}$ to $1\frac{5}{8}$ inches long, the glumes smooth, the lemmas rough or minutely pubescent, the awn stout and $1\frac{1}{4}$ to 2 inches long.

The mature seeds of ripgut grass are mechanically injurious to livestock.

The variety, *B. rigidus Gussonei*, differs from the species in having a more open panicle, and longer flexuous branches and pedicels, the lower branches being as much as 4 to $4\frac{3}{4}$ inches long.

RED BROME (*Bromus rubens* L.) (Fig. 21)

This species is a common weedy grass throughout California. It spreads rapidly from seed, and the sharp awns of the mature grass make it a troublesome weed. It is widely distributed in the interior valleys of the State and much of the first cutting of alfalfa grown in these valleys is infested with this weed. It is regarded as one of the most obnoxious weeds in southern California. It has come to replace much of the native vegetation of plains and hills. It is worthless as forage, and when dry becomes a serious fire hazard. The species is naturalized from Europe.

Red brome is an annual species, with erect, hairy stems, 4 to 16 inches tall. The leaves have hairy sheaths and blades. The inflorescence is erect, compact, about $1\frac{1}{4}$ to $2\frac{3}{4}$ inches long, and usually reddish-purple.

FIG. 21. Red brome (*Bromus rubens*). **A,** clump of spikelet-bearing culms; **B,** single spikelets, x 4, showing glumes below and florets above; **C,** single floret, x 4, with lemma and palea separated.

The spikelets are about 1 inch long, and 7- to 11-flowered. The glumes are narrow, pointed, either smooth or hairy; the lemma is $\frac{1}{2}$ to $\frac{5}{8}$ inch long, lance-shaped, keeled, with an awn about $\frac{3}{4}$ inch long.

BROOM BROMEGRASS (*Bromus scoparius* L.)

This species, naturalized from Europe, is relatively rare in California, thus far occurring at Santa Barbara and Mariposa. It is an annual, 8 to 12 inches tall, with more or less long hairy leaf sheaths and blades, short-stalked, 5- to 11-flowered spikelets, smooth glumes, and 2-toothed lemmas, with a spreading awn.

CHESS (*Bromus secalinus* L.) (Fig. 20e)
Other common names: Cheat-grass, wheat-thief, rye-brome.

This is a weed of considerable importance in grain fields throughout Europe, northern Africa, northern Asia, and North America. It has been introduced into this country as an impurity in seed. As yet it is not common in grain fields of California. There is a common impression that wheat turns to cheat, for it is often observed that the weed comes in where perfectly clean seed has been sown. This is due to the fact that chess seed retains its vitality in the soil for a long period. The soil may have been infested with chess seed several years previous to its first appearance in the field, the conditions at the time being unfavorable to its germination. Its presence in a field is evidence that at some time chess-infested grain seed was sown.

Chess is an annual, having a height of 1 to 3 feet. The leaf sheaths are smooth, usually shorter than the nodes. The inflorescence is rather open, the branches each bearing 2 to 3 spikelets, the whole inflorescence being 2 to 8 inches long, and drooping at maturity. The spikelets are $\frac{1}{2}$ to $\frac{3}{4}$ inches long and 6- to 10-flowered. The lemmas, narrow at the tip, bear an awn $\frac{1}{8}$ to $\frac{1}{4}$ inch long, sometimes very short or wanting. When the grains are mature, the swollen florets are spread apart sufficiently to permit light to pass through the spikelet. The seeds of chess are from $\frac{5}{16}$ to $\frac{3}{8}$ inch long, somewhat trough-shape in cross-section and are smaller and lighter than those of either wheat or rye. A sample of grain suspected of containing chess can be tested by stirring into a pail of water; the seeds of chess float, whereas those of wheat and rye sink.

BARREN BROME (*Bromus sterilis* L.)

This species is widespread in the eastern United States and on the Pacific Coast. It is naturalized from southern Europe. It occurs in waste places, along roadsides and stream banks, and in fields. The plant ranges in height from 20 to 40 inches. The stems are often somewhat bent at the base. The leaf sheaths and blades are somewhat hairy. The inflorescence is open, drooping, the branches long and slender, each usually bearing a single spikelet. The spikelets are 4- to 10-flowered, 1 to $1\frac{1}{4}$ inches long, the glumes, broad at the base and tapering from the base to a sharp point, the lemmas rounded, rough, and with an awn $\frac{3}{4}$ to $1\frac{1}{4}$ inch long.

Not infrequently grazing animals are injured by the sharp-pointed "seeds" which may penetrate the eyes, nose, and mouth parts.

DOWNY CHESS (*Bromus tectorum* L.)

This brome is widespread throughout North America, and is especially abundant on the Pacific Coast. It occurs along roadsides and in waste places, also in fields and pastures, usually on dry or gravelly soils. It is introduced from the Mediterranean region. It is a tufted annual, with slender stems 1 to 2 feet high. Both the leaf sheaths and blades are very hairy. The inflorescence is dense, soft, drooping, often purple, 1-sided, 2 to 6 inches long, with slender branches. The spikelets are nodding, ⅜ to ¾ inch long, with soft hairy glumes, lance-shaped, pubescent lemmas, each with an awn ⅜ to ⅝ inch long. A very common form in California is *B. tectorum nudus,* which has smooth spikelets.

CHILEAN CHESS (*Bromus Trinii* Desv.) (Fig. 20)

This introduction from Chile occurs from Siskiyou southward, especially in the desert regions. The stems are 1 to 3 feet tall, erect, sometimes branched below, and hairy at the nodes. The leaf sheaths and blades are pubescent with long, soft hairs or sometimes nearly smooth. The inflorescence is 3 to 12 inches long, narrow, rather dense. The spikelets are narrow, ½ to ¾ inch long, and 5- to 7-flowered. The awn of the lemma is about ¾ inch long, twisted below, bent below the middle and strongly spreading when old.

In the Panamint Mountains of California there occurs the variety *B. Trinii excelsus* Shear, the awns of which are scarcely twisted or bent.

BUR-GRASS (*Cenchrus echinatus* L.)

An annual similar to sandbur. The bur is broad, or broader than long, the lobes erect or incurved; spikelets usually 4 in each bur.

A native of Tropical America, this sandbur was collected at La Mesa in San Diego County.

SANDBUR (*Cenchrus pauciflorus* Benth.) (Fig. 8k and Fig. 22)
Other common names: Burgrass, hedgehog grass, sandspur, bear grass.

The sandbur is a native of North America, and occurs in practically every state across the continent, especially in the warmer areas. The weed is spreading rather rapidly in the San Joaquin Valley and southern California, being found in orchards, vineyards, cultivated fields, alfalfa fields, waste grounds, along ditch banks and railroads. It is especially troublesome in orchards and vineyards. It prefers a light, well-drained, sandy or gravelly soil. Before the burs are formed it has considerable forage value.

The plant is a spreading or trailing annual, sometimes erect, sometimes forming large mats. The roots are fibrous and shallow; hence the plants readily succumb to cultivation. The stems are flattened, much branched, and often mat-forming. The leaf blades are smooth, narrow, and either flat or rolled; the leaf sheaths are hairy along the margins and at the throat. The upper leaves often partly enclose the burs. The spikelets sometimes are solitary, but more frequently several occur together; they are subtended by a spiny involucre, which hardens and encloses the seeds when they mature, thus forming a characteristic straw-colored bur about

½ inch long, often densely hairy, and with strong, downwardly-barbed spines. The grain is light reddish-brown, flattened oval in shape with a conspicuous large scar at base and acute point at apex. The spines on the mature burs are sometimes so rigid that they are capable of penetrating shoe leather. The seeds germinate within the bur. It has been determined that a single sandbur plant will produce close to one thousand seeds.

In fields where sheep are pastured sandbur is particularly obnoxious and may severely injure wool and even the skin of animals. The burs have been known to cause swelling and ulcers in the mouths of grazing animals. They fall off readily at maturity, and the seeds are spread by the burs clinging to clothing, hair, or wool of animals.

Fig. 22.   Sandbur *Cenchrus pauciflorus*

FINGER GRASS. *CHLORIS*

KEY TO WEEDY SPECIES OF CHLORIS

Lemmas awnless _____ *C. distichophylla*

Lemmas distinctly awned
    Plants with long, stout stolons_____*C. Gayana*
    Plants without stolons
        Spikes feathery _____ *C. virgata*
        Spikes not feathery_____ *C. verticillata*

FINGER GRASS (*Chloris distichophylla* Lag.)

Perennial, to 3 feet tall, spikes numerous, drooping, feathery. An introduction from South America, escaped from cultivation in southern California and at Berkeley. In general appearance similar to following, but lemmas awnless.

RHODES GRASS (*Chloris Gayana* Kunth)

Rhodes grass is an introduction from Europe. Occasionally found as an escape in California. It is perennial, with long stout leafy stolons, the internodes somewhat flattened. The spikes are several to many, 5 to 10 cm. long, the spikelets with lemmas about 3 mm. long, lemmas hairy on the margins near the tip and more or less so below. The awn on the fertile lemma is about 1 to 5 mm. long, shorter on the sterile.

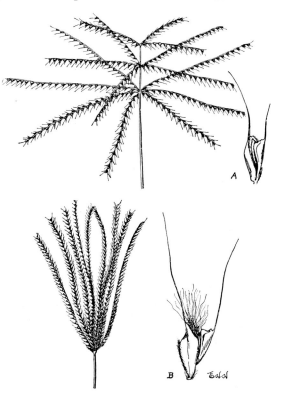

WINDMILL GRASS (*Chloris verticillata* Nutt.) (Fig. 23A)

Windmill grass, a low perennial, is a native of Texas, now occurring sparingly at Berkeley. It is similar in general habit to the following species. Windmill grass has long, stiff, divergent slender spikes, and the entire inflorescence may break away at maturity and be blown along as a tumbleweed. The spikes are not feathery as they are in *C. virgata*.

FIG. 23. **A,** inflorescence and floret of windmill grass (*Chloris verticillata*); **B,** inflorescence and floret of feather fingergrass (*Chloris virgata*).

FEATHER FINGER GRASS (*Chloris virgata* Swartz) (Fig. 23B)

This is a tropical American species distributed from Nebraska to Texas and southern California, and introduced in a few eastern localities. In California it occurs in fields and waste places from Riverside to the Colorado Desert.

Feather finger grass is annual, with culms 1 to 3 feet high. The sheaths of the leaves, especially the lowermost, are compressed, whereas those of the upper leaves are inflated around the base of the inflorescence. There are from 2 to several spikes arranged finger-like; they are 2 to 8 cm. long, erect, whitish or tawny, and feathery or silky. The spikelets are arranged in two rows along one side of a continuous rachis, and each consists of one perfect flower, and from 1 to several sterile ones.

The lemma is about 3 mm. long, distinctly hairy and with slender awn from 5 to 10 mm. long. The back or keel of the lemma has a definite hump about two-thirds of the way up, with a tuft of spreading long hairs at apex.

BERMUDA GRASS (*Cynodon Dactylon* (L.) Pers.) (Fig. 24)
Other common names: Devil grass, scutch grass, dog's tooth grass, wire grass.

This plant, named after the Bermuda Islands, is a native of the warmer parts of the Old World. It is now widely distributed throughout subtropical and semi-arid regions where the winters are not severe

FIG. 24.   Bermuda grass (*Cynodon Dactylon*).

enough to kill the roots and rootstocks. It has become well established in the southern part of the United States and the warmer parts of California, where it has become one of the most troublesome of our weeds. It is spread widely throughout the Sacramento, San Joaquin, and Imperial valleys, and other warmer sections of the State. It does not occur in upland valleys or other regions where there are freezing temperatures during the winter.

Bermuda grass is a perennial, producing stems, some of which, the rootstocks, are underground, and some of which, the runners or stolons, trail along the soil surface. The rootstocks may be superficial or deep-seated. Both rootstocks and runners are many-jointed structures which grow rapidly and root readily at the nodes. They may run out several feet from the parent-crown. The stems are flat, wiry, and smooth. The leaves on the rootstocks and runners are short, broad, thick, and scale-like; those of the erect stems are longer, the sheaths being short, the blades 1 to 4 inches long, smooth on the lower surface and rough above. At the juncture of leaf blade and leaf sheath there is a characteristic and conspicuous ring of white hairs. The erect flower-bearing stems or culms are 4 to 18 inches high. The groups of flowers are in threes or fives. The individual spikelets of each group are arranged in two alternate rows on spikes that are characteristically one-sided. Each spikelet is about 2 mm. long, flattened, closely attached to the axis of the spike, and slightly overlapping its neighbor spikelet. There is one flower in each spikelet, the lemma flattened and boat-shaped. The seeds are very small, pale straw color when mature.

It is very drought resistant and also tolerant of alkali. It is on record that "patches of Bermuda grass near Mecca, California, although submerged in the Salton Sea for over two years, were still alive and making new growth from the stems when that body of water finally evaporated to a lower level." Bermuda grass does not flourish in the dense shade, which suggests the utilization of smother crops as a method of control. The roots, turned to the sun, are easily killed.

Bermuda grass is introduced into new areas in many ways; the seeds are a common impurity in commercial seeds; plants bearing seeds are carried in hay, in packing, in bedding for livestock, in feed stuffs, in shipments of all sorts; the seeds are readily carried by wind and irrigation water. Locally, the plants spread in any of the above ways, and in addition are dragged from place to place by cultivating machinery.

In the Southern States it is an important pasture crop, and a lawn grass. In California also it is employed in a limited way as a pasture crop for livestock, as a lawn grass, and in some instances as a soil binder on ditch and canal banks.

CRESTED DOGTAIL (*Cynosurus cristatus* L.)

Crested dogtail is an introduction from Europe and has been reported from one locality (Los Angeles) in California. It is a perennial, with narrow, spike-like panicles, and otherwise differs from *C. echinatus* in having definitely shorter awns, about 1 mm. long. The lemma is reddish-brown in color, rough, hairy on the back and the gradually elongated apex twists slightly to one side. The seed occurs as an impurity in commercial seed.

DOGTAIL GRASS (*Cynosurus echinatus* L.) (Fig. 25)

This grass is introduced from Europe, and occurs in scattered locations from British Columbia to central and southern California. It is a low weedy annual with culms 8 to 16 inches tall. The leaf blades are short and flat. The panicles are dense, 1-sided, spike-like, bristly, and from 1 to 4 cm. long. There are two kinds of spikelets, sterile and fertile. The fertile one is sessile and almost covered by the sterile one. The fertile spikelets are 2- to 3-flowered, the glumes narrow, the lemmas broader, rounded on the back

FIG. 25. Dogtail grass (*Cynosurus echinatus*). Left, fertile sessile spikelet almost covered by sterile spikelet.

and awns 5 to 10 mm. long; the sterile spikelets have 2 glumes and several narrow 1-nerved lemmas on a continuous rachilla.

ORCHARD GRASS (*Dactylis glomerata* L.)

This cultivated pasture grass, a native of Europe has escaped and established itself in many parts of the State. The large bunches of coarse flat blades are exceeded by the flowering culms 2 to 4 ft. tall. Panicles with few stiff solitary branches, the lowermost standing out like a thumb, or the spur on a cock's foot. Called cocksfoot in England.

SMOOTH CRABGRASS (*Digitaria Ischaemum* (Schreb.) Muhl.) (Fig. 26)

This species, a native of Europe, is reported from Pasadena, and San Diego County, and is particularly troublesome in lawns in the vicinity of Petaluma. It differs from the common species, *D. sanguinalis*, in having smooth leaf sheaths. The sterile lemma is nerved and soft hairy; the fertile lemma investing the lightish grain is conspicuously very dark-brown to almost black in color.

HAIRY CRABGRASS (*Digitaria sanguinalis* (L.) Scop.) (Fig. 26)

This plant, naturalized from Europe, occurs throughout the United States. Here it is a common weed in waste and cultivated areas. It is found along irrigation ditches, in pastures, poorly drained alfalfa fields, and is very common in lawns. Parish states that this is "a common and long-established weed in cultivated grounds, as abundant thirty-five years ago as now." Parish also makes the note that in the southern counties, crabgrass "is abundant in cultivated districts, as it has become in most of the warmer regions of the world. It is especially prevalent in orchards, cornfields, and gardens.'' On account of its abundant growth in late summer under favorable conditions, it is often utilized for forage and sometimes cut for hay.

Crabgrass is an annual of pale green color, usually much branched at the base. The stems have a tendency to spread by rooting at the lower-

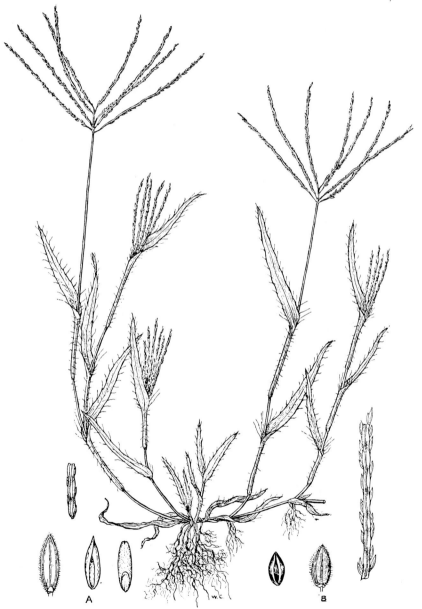

F1G. 26. Hairy crabgrass (*Digitaria sanguinalis*). A, winged rachis, spikelet, floret and grain of same ; B, smooth crabgrass (*D. Ischaemum*) showing rachis, spikelet, and fertile floret.

most swollen joints. The leaf blades are 2 to 5 inches long, ¼ to ⅓ in wide, rather lax and flat, and the sheaths are rough-hairy, with long, stiff, white hairs. The spikelets are usually in pairs on one side of an axis, forming slender racemes which are distributed at the end of the culm, resembling the long claws of a bird. The spikelet is about ¼ inch long, the first glume very small, the second about one half as long as the spikelet. The sterile lemma is strongly nerved and soft hairy on the lateral internerves; the fertile lemma investing the somewhat opaque grain is cartilaginous and pale yellowish-green in color.

SALTGRASS (*Distichlis spicata* (L.) Greene) (Fig. 27)

Other common names: Seashore salt grass, marsh spike grass.

This species of saltgrass occurs along both coasts of the United States from Nova Scotia to Florida and Texas, and from British Columbia to Mexico; it is also found along the Pacific slope of South America; and it is quite common in the interior valleys and deserts of California. It is cited by Hilgard (1891) as the most widely troublesome native grass. The plant is one of salt marshes and alkaline soils. Because of its ability to spread by means of rootstocks, saltgrass has become a weed in certain places. It possesses some value as a forage plant, and also as a sand binder.

This species is a low perennial with extensively creeping, scaly rootstocks, which root at the joints and bear numerous erect stems from the axils of the scale leaves. The stems are 4 to 12 inches high. There are numerous leaves in two rather distinct ranks; the leaves are narrow, flat, or rolled, and from ½ to 4 inches long; the ligule forms a ring of white, crinkly hairs. Saltgrass is one of the few grasses which have the sexes in different individuals; that is, some plants bear stamens only and other plants bear pistils (and seeds) only. The flower groups are similar in appearance, and only by close examination of the spikelets can one determine whether they are staminate or pistillate. As a rule, the pistillate spikelets are more leathery in texture than are the staminate. The spikelets are clustered at the tops of the culms or one or two smaller spikelets may occur below; the spikelets are somewhat flattened, ⅓ to ¾ inch long, mostly 5- and 9-flowered. The glumes are unequal in length, broad, and acute; the lemmas are closely imbricate, those of pistillate spikelets being somewhat leathery; the paleae are as long as the lemma or shorter, those of the pistillate spikelets being leathery and enclosing the grain. They narrow somewhat abruptly over the apex of the grain, extending beyond it in a collapsed point. The seed as found in commercial seed often suggests a small bulblet. As the grain matures, the scales change from a pale green to a purplish color.

JUNGLE-RICE (*Echinochloa colona* (L.) Link.)

This species is closely related to watergrass. It is an introduction into the United States from the tropical regions of both hemispheres. It is occasionally found in moist places in southern California. Unlike *E. Crusgalli*, the awn of the sterile lemma is reduced to a short point, and the spikelets are crowded in about 4 rows.

FIG. 27. Saltgrass (*Distichlis spicata*) showing habit, and pistillate spikelet.

WATERGRASS (*Echinochloa Crusgalli* (L.) Beauv.) (Fig. 28)

Common names: Barnyard grass, cockspur grass, cocksfoot panicum.

This plant is fairly well distributed throughout the Eastern Hemisphere. It was probably introduced into this country from Europe, and is now generally distributed throughout the entire United States. It is found in all agricultural sections of California, occurring in moist pastures, in irrigated fields and orchards, and along streams and ditches.

Watergrass is a stout annual. The culms are stout, 2 to 4 feet tall, and often branch from the base. The leaf sheaths are smooth and more

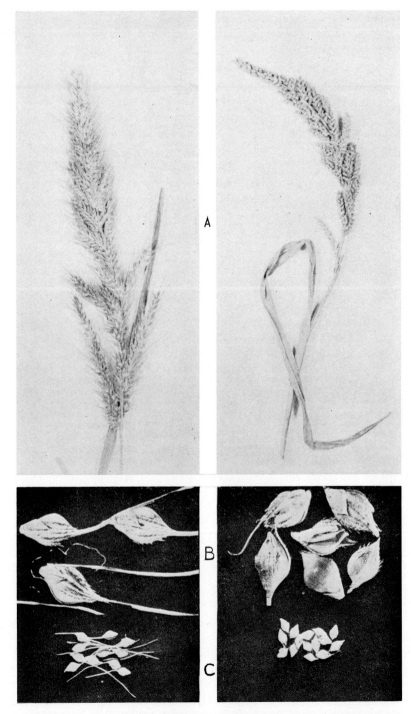

Fig. 28. Watergrass (*Echinochloa Crusgalli*). A, panicle, x ½ ; B, seeds, x 4 ; C, seeds, natural size.

or less flattened; the leaf blades are usually smooth, sometimes roughened toward the end, 4 to 20 inches long, $\frac{1}{4}$ to $\frac{3}{4}$ inch wide, and with a prominent midrib. The flower-group is a panicle, either erect or drooping, purple-tinged, and from 4 to 8 inches long; the lower branches of the panicle are often remote from each other, whereas the upper ones are more or less aggregated into a terminal clump. The spikelets are densely crowded in 2 to 4 rows on each side of the stem. Each spikelet is about $\frac{1}{4}$ inch long, excluding the awn; the spikelets are green or purple, oval in shape, the glumes unequal, pointed and bristly on the back; in each spikelet there is one perfect floret, and one sterile floret; the lemma of the fertile floret is smooth, shining, and hard, the margins inrolled below, partly enclosing the palet, which in turn surrounds the ovary; the sterile floret is represented by a lemma only, which is pointed, sometimes long-awned, and enclosing a membranous palet and stamens. The seed is strongly convex on one side, flat on other face, broad below and narrowed toward apex. It is hard and shiny, varies in color from pale straw to dark-gray. The naked grain is somewhat chalky. Watergrass is a prolific seeder, it having been estimated that single plant may produce as many as 40,000 seeds.

Watergrass is one of the most troublesome weeds in California rice fields. This grass was present in California when the rice industry first started, and it has spread from year to year in rice fields. The old method of rice culture, which consisted of irrigating and draining the land at frequent intervals until 30 days after the rice had emerged, after which the land was submerged about six inches until the fields were drained for harvest gave conditions ideal for the growth and distribution of barnyard grass. The cultural practices employed in growing cotton and beans are favorable for the spread of watergrass, and in such crops the losses have been heavy because of its presence.

There are three varieties of *E. Crusgalli* known to occur in California: *E. Crusgalli* var. *mitis* (Pursh) Peterm., *E. Crusgalli* var. *zelayensis* (H. B. K.) Hitch., and *E. Crusgalli* var. *frumentacea* (Roxb.) Wight. In the var. *mitis* the spikelets are awnless or nearly so; in the var. *zelayensis* the awns are short, the plant erect with short ascending racemes; in the var. *frumentacea* the racemes are thick, appressed, incurved, and the spikelets are awnless and mostly purple. The last named variety is commonly known as barnyard millet, certain Japanese strains of which have been introduced into the United States and exploited under the name of "billion dollar grass."

There are several different field varieties of the grass in the rice fields, namely (a) an early form which is short and matures and drops its seed early, before the rice is headed out; (b) a mid-summer form, which heads out about the same time as the rice, but drops most of its seed before the rice is harvested; and (c) a late form which is in full seed at the time the rice is harvested.

GOOSEGRASS (*Eleusine indica* (L.) Gaertn.) (Fig. 29)

Goosegrass, a native of the Old World and a common weed in the warmer regions of both hemispheres, has been found sparingly established in lawns from Yolo County to southern California. It probably was introduced in clover seed of lawngrass mixtures. Goosegrass is a spreading annual, smooth with compressed culms, 15 to 36 inches high. The leaf blades are flat or folded, and 3 to 8 mm. wide. There

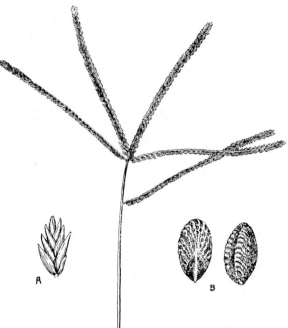

FIG. 29.   Goosegrass (*Eleusine indica*). A, spikelet; B, seeds.

are from 2 to several stout spikes arranged finger-like at the ends of the culms (Fig. 29), sometimes with one or two a short distance below the summit, or rarely just one spike. The spikelets are few- to several-flowered, compressed, closely overlapping, and distributed in two rows along one side of a rather broad rachis. The glumes are unequal and

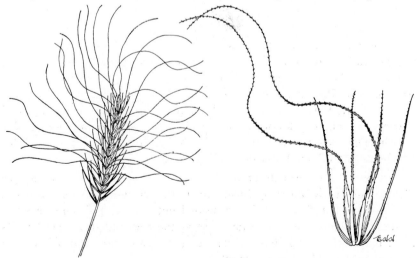

FIG. 30.   Medusa-head (*Elymus Caput-Medusae*). Flowering spike and spikelet.

1-nerved, the lemmas have 3 strong green nerves close together, forming a keel. The grain is about 2 mm. long, in form similar to a wheat kernel, with two prominent cheeks and a deep groove. The color is a dark reddish-amber, the surface sharply ridged with fine transverse lines.

MEDUSA HEAD (*Elymus Caput-Medusae* L.) (Fig. 30)

This introduction from Europe is established on range lands in certain northern counties, where it is said to be spreading.

Medusa-head is an annual, branching at the base, with slender stems 8 to 24 inches tall. The leaf blades are narrow and short. The flowers are in a very bristly spike, from about 1 to 2½ inches long (excluding the long, spreading awns). The glumes are awl-shaped, smooth, hard below, and tapering into a slender awn which may approach 1 inch in length. The lemmas bear a flat spreading awn 2½ to 4 inches long (Fig. 30). The grain with its closely investing bracts is like a small, very slender barley.

Stockmen report that animals will not eat this grass at any stage of its growth. Potentially, it threatens to become a range weed of major importance.

BEARDLESS WILD-RYE (*Elymus triticoides* Buckl.)

This weedy native grass has become gregarious along roadsides throughout the State, particularly in bottom lands and alkaline situations.

Beardless wild-rye is a perennial, 2 to 4 feet high, usually growing in large masses. The stems arise from an extensive creeping rhizome system. Leaves with flat or rolled blades, 2 to 6 mm. wide. The flowering head is erect, slender, rarely branched, 4 to 8 inches long. Spikelets about ½ inch long, the glumes narrow, awl-shaped, and awn-tipped; lemmas somewhat shorter than glumes, brownish, tawny or purplish and awn-tipped.

Beardless wild-rye is frequently mistaken for quackgrass (*Agropyron repens*). In the wild-rye there are two spikelets at each joint of the rachis, whereas in quackgrass there is one spikelet at each joint; rarely in pairs, at the lower joints.

LOVEGRASS. *ERAGROSTIS*

KEY TO WEEDY SPECIES OF ERAGROSTIS

Lemmas glandular on the keel
  Panicle usually rather dense_____*E. cilianensis*
  Panicle open_____*E. poaeoides*

Lemmas not glandular
  Spikelets about 1 mm. wide, linear, slender
    Plants delicate _____*E. pilosa*
    Plants stout _____*E. Orcuttiana*

  Spikelets 1½ mm. wide or wider, ovate
    Panicle narrow _____*E. Barrelieri*

    Panicle open, diffuse
      Plants 1 to 2 feet tall_____*E. diffusa*
      Plants often 3 feet tall_____*E. mexicana*

STINKGRASS (*Eragrostis cilianensis* (All.) Link.) (Fig. 31)
Other common name: Snakegrass.

This is an Old World species that is widely distributed throughout the United States, and south into Mexico, the West Indies, and South America. It occurs in fields, waste places and along roadsides throughout California, at lower altitudes.

This is an ill-scented annual weed with smooth branching stems ½ to 2 feet high. There is a ring of glands below each node (Fig. 31). The leaf blades are 3 to 8 inches long, rough on the upper side, but smooth on the lower side, their sheaths smooth. The leaf surface is sparsely covered with glandular depressions. The inflorescence is a panicle 2 to 8 inches long and of a greenish lead-color. The spikelets are oblong, flattened, and each contains from 10 to 40 flowers. The lemma is glandular dotted. The grain is very small, about 1 mm. long, oval in shape and pointed at both ends, maroon to wine-red in color and translucent. The surface is marked by a squarish network of fine lines.

It is reported that horses may be made sick by eating large quantities of stinkgrass when fresh, or eating large quantities of it over a long period of time.

DIFFUSE LOVEGRASS (*Eragrostis diffusa* Buckl.)

This is a native species and a common weed in fields and open ground in southern California. It is a robust annual plant with large panicles, the primary branches of which bear appressed secondary branches with several to many spikelets, the whole thus appearing densely flowered.

MEXICAN ERAGROSTIS (*Eragrostis mexicana* (Lag.) Link.)

Mexican Eragrostis occurs on wet ground in fields and waste places in southern California. It is a stout annual with stems up to 3 feet tall, flat leaf blades, sheaths hairy at the throat. The panicles are 8 to 16 inches long, and spikelets dark grayish-green, 8- to 12-flowered. The pedicels are slender, mostly longer than the spikelets. The lemmas are smooth, with the lateral nerves not prominent.

ORCUTT'S ERAGROSTIS (*Eragrostis Orcuttiana* Vasey.)

This species is a rather stout annual occurring in southern California on sandy river banks and in fields and waste places. It closely resembles *E. mexicana*. The stems are 2 to 3 feet tall, with flat leaf blades, an open panicle 6 to 12 inches long, and with spikelets 6- to 10-flowered.

INDIA LOVEGRASS (*Eragrostis pilosa* (L.) Beauv.)

India lovegrass is a weedy annual, also introduced from Europe, which is found in waste places and moist open ground. It occurs in rice-growing sections, where it impedes the flow of water in laterals. The stems are 4 inches to almost 2 feet tall, ascending from a decumbent base. The blades are flat, the panicle open and delicate, about 2 to 8 inches long. The branches are very fine and flexuous, ascending or spreading, sparsely long-hairy in the axils.

LOW ERAGROSTIS (*Eragrostis poaeoides* (L.) Beauv.)

This species, closely resembling *E. cilianensis*, is sparingly established in California. It is an introduction from Europe, and an annual.

E. Barrelieri Daveau. is another annual species of lovegrass introduced from southern Europe. It is similar to the more common *E. pilosa* and *E. Orcuttiana*, but differs particularly in its broader spikelets.

FESCUE. *FESTUCA*
KEY TO WEEDY SPECIES OF FESTUCA

Plants perennial, lemmas awnless_____*F. elatior*
Plants annual, lemmas awned
  Lemmas minutely hairy along the margins toward the apex_____*F. megalura*
  Lemmas not hairy along the margins
    First glume about 4 mm. long, the second 6 to 7 mm. long_____*F. dertonensis*
    First glume about 1 to 1½ mm. long, the second 4 to 4½ mm. long_____*F. Myuros*

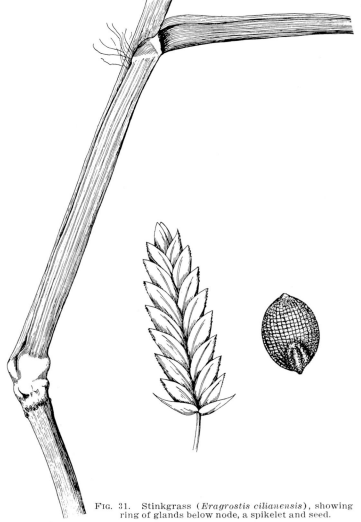

FIG. 31. Stinkgrass (*Eragrostis cilianensis*), showing ring of glands below node, a spikelet and seed.

Festuca dertonensis (All.) Aschers and Graebn. (Fig. 32c)

This fescue grass is introduced from Europe and now is distributed from British Columbia to southern California, occurring on dry hills and in meadows, and also not infrequent in cultivated grounds. It resembles *F. megalura* and *F. Myuros*, but differs from them in having the lower glume about 4 mm. long. The second 6 to 7 mm. long.

MEADOW FESCUE (*Festuca elatior* L.) (Fig. 32a)

Meadow fescue, a native of Eurasia, is cultivated for meadow and pasture, and sometimes escapes and becomes a weed in fields and waste places. It is a perennial grass, with culms 20 to 50 inches tall, flat, soft leaf-blades, erect panicles, 4 to 8 inches long, and 6- to 8-flowered spikelets, in which the lemmas are awnless and hardened.

FOXTAIL FESCUE (*Festuca megalura* Nutt.) (Fig. 32b)

Foxtail fescue is a native of the Western States and the Pacific slope of South America. It occasionally occurs in cultivated ground and

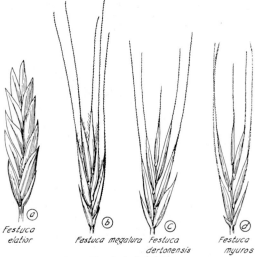

FIG. 32. Spikelets of *Festuca*.

in waste places. This native fescue is very similar in general appearance to the following introduced species. The seed is slender, rounded on the back and elongated into a fine awn about twice the length of the body of the seed. In foxtail fescue the margins of the lemma are ciliate, which readily distinguishes that species from rat's-tail fescue.

RAT'S-TAIL FESCUE (*Festuca Myuros* L.) (Fig. 32d)

This fescue grass is a native of Europe, which as early as 1838-42 was collected by John Torrey at San Francisco, and in 1861 was found at Monterey by Brewer. It now occurs in southern California, and is one of the prevalent grasses of the ranges of northwestern California. It is a slender, annual grass with culms 8 to 24 inches tall. The spikelets are loosely 1- to 5-flowered, in narrow erect panicles. The lower glume of each spikelet is about one-half as long as the upper, and the lemmas are smooth on the margin, thus differing from *F. megalura*.

NITGRASS (*Gastridium ventricosum* (Gouan) Schinz and Thell.) (Fig. 33)

This is a European species which is found in waste places from Oregon to California, in Texas, and Massachusetts. In California nitgrass has become quite common in the coast counties, occurring along roadsides, and on dry slopes. The grass appears late in the spring, and has slight forage value. The species is annual, with many smooth stems and about 1 foot tall. The leaves have flat, light green blades, 2 to 6 inches long, and leaf sheaths shorter than the internodes. The inflorescence is a dense, bristly, spike-like panicle, 2 to 6 inches long, pale green and shining. Each spikelet is 1-flowered, the glumes tapering into a long point, the lemma very small, globular, plump, finely hairy, terminating in a delicate, abruptly bent awn. The rachilla segment or small appendage on the face at the base is bairy or white bristly. The free grain is the shape of a wheat kernel, about 1 mm. long, pointed at the base. It is amber in color, darker toward the tip, with obscure longitudinal lines.

MARSHGRASS (*Heleochloa schoenoides* (L.) Host.)

This European species, which occurs in waste places from Massachusetts to Illinois, has been found in Yolo and Sonoma Counties.

FIG. 33. Nit-grass (*Gastridium ventricosum*), showing spikelet and awned lemma.

Marshgrass is a low spreading annual with dense spike-like panicles. The leaves subtending the panicles have inflated sheaths and very small blades. Spikelets 1-flowered; glumes of equal size, narrow and sharp-pointed; lemma broader than glumes, 1-nerved; palea about as long as lemma.

VELVET GRASS (*Holcus lanatus* L.) (Fig. 12)

This species is introduced from Europe and used somewhat as a meadow grass on light or sandy soils. It has escaped from cultivation, and in the Coast Ranges of California has become, in some areas, a weed of minor importance. Velvet grass is a perennial, grayish velvety grass. The stems are erect, 1 to 3 feet tall. The leaves have soft, flat blades, 6 inches or less in length, and inflated sheaths. The inflorescence is a soft, plume-like purplish panicle, 2 to 5 inches long. Each spikelet is 2-flowered, about $\frac{1}{6}$ inch long, the upper lemma bearing a short, hooked awn. The seed with inner glumes is about $2\frac{1}{2}$ mm. long, widest below the middle, pointed toward both ends. In cross section it is somewhat heart-shaped. The surface is smooth and very shiny, and light straw-colored. The free grain is darker.

CREEPING VELVET GRASS (*Holcus mollis* L.)

This species, also introduced from Europe and resembling *H. lanatus*, has been found at Santa Rosa, Sacramento, Eureka, and Mendocino Pine Barrens. It differs from *H. lanatus* in having vigorous, slender rhizomes, is bright-green in color, with glumes unequal in length and more elongate pointed. It is occasionally persistent and unsightly in lawns.

HORDEUM

The name "wild barley" is applied to several species of grasses belonging to the genus *Hordeum*. Other common names are squirrel-tail grass, tickle grass, flicker-tail, and skunk-tail. To this same genus belong also the cultivated barleys. In all species of *Hordeum* the spikelets form a spike or "head" similar to that with which we are familiar in wheat and cultivated barleys. At each joint of the axis of the spike there are three spikelets, each one-flowered. Each spikelet is subtended by two narrow glumes, and hence at each joint of the axis will occur three pairs of glumes which, due to their narrowness, appear as short awns, while the true awn of the lemma is very long and much stiffer. The seeds, which resemble a barley grain but are narrower and flatter, are scattered by water, by wind, and carried by animals, to which they cling by reason of the barbed awns.

As a group, the wild barleys are mechanically injurious grasses; the mature beards may bore into the skin, or the mucous membrane of the mouth, causing ulcers.

KEY TO WEEDY SPECIES OF HORDEUM

Perennials, with slender awns
    Awns 1 to 2 inches long_____*H. jubatum*
    Awns not over ½ inch long_____*H. nodosum*
Annuals, with stout awns
    Sheaths and blades more or less pubescent; head ¾ to 1¼ inches long _*H. Gussoneanum*
    Sheaths and blades smooth; head 2 to 3 inches long
        Glumes or some of them ciliate_____*H. murinum*
        Glumes not ciliate, dilated above middle_____. _____*H. pusillum*

MEDITERRANEAN BARLEY (*Hordeum Gussoneanum* Parl.) (Fig. 34)

This species, naturalized from Europe, occurs in the states west of the Rocky Mountains and in Massachusetts and New Jersey. It is fairly common in central and northern California, but rare in southern California. This is an annual, varying in height from 6 to 20 inches. The sheaths and blades of the leaf are more or less pubescent. The head is erect, ¾ to 1¼ inch long, and from ⅜ to ⅝ inch wide. The glumes are bristle-like, and about ½ inch long; the lemma of the central spikelet is ¼ inch long, and the flower of lateral spikelets is reduced in size and short-awned.

FOXTAIL BARLEY (*Hordeum jubatum* L.) (Fig. 34)
Other common names: Squirrel-tail barley, tickle grass, flicker-tail, skunk-tail.

This is an introduced species, now widespread in all states, except those of the southeast. In California it is generally distributed, although not such a common weed as is *H. murinum*. It occurs along roadsides and in waste places, in gardens and cultivated fields, in alfalfa and pasture land. It is tolerant of alkali. This is a tufted perennial with stems 1 to 2 feet tall. The plant stools freely, as many as 40 stalks coming from a single seed. The leaf sheaths are smooth, the blades somewhat harsh to the touch, and 1 to 6 inches long. The head is nodding, 2 to 4 inches long and about 1 inch broad; when mature it resembles a squirrel's tail. The awns on the seed-bearing and sterile flowers are long (1 to 1½ inches) and the flowers are surrounded by long, beard-like glumes so that the entire head is covered with long bristles that are rough and upwardly barbed. The head breaks up at maturity and the separate parts are scattered broadcast.

COMMON FOXTAIL (*Hordeum murinum* L.) (Fig. 34)

Other common names : Farmer's foxtail, mouse barley, wild barley.

This species is naturalized from Europe, and is now distributed throughout the eastern states and south to Oklahoma, Arizona, Idaho, and the states westward. In California it is the most abundant of the wild barleys, occurring in cultivated fields, meadows, alfalfa fields, orchards, along roadsides and irrigation canals, and in waste places. It is one of the commonest weeds in alfalfa, causing a decrease in the quality of the first cutting particularly. It is one of the most widely distributed grasses in over-grazed range and pasture lands. As early as 1890, Hilgard described this plant as ''a fearful nuisance'' in central California.

This species is a bushy-branched, spreading annual. The sheaths and blades of the leaves are smooth. The head is erect, 2 to $2\frac{3}{4}$ inches long, and is often partially enclosed by the uppermost inflated leaf-sheath. The glumes of the central spikelet are about 1 inch long, narrowly spindle-form, and bear bristles on the margin; the glumes of the lateral spikelets are unlike, the inner being similar to the central ones, the outer bristle-like and smooth on the margin; the lemmas are broad, the awns exceeding somewhat those of the glumes. The seed with lemmas has the general shape of a barley grain, but narrower and flatter.

MEADOW BARLEY (*Hordeum nodosum* L.) (Fig. 34)

This species is widely distributed in the Old World. It is very common in the Rocky Mountain states and westward, and occurs sparingly in a few eastern states. It occurs throughout California, but is by no means as abundant as *H. murinum*. It is found in meadows and open ground. This is a tufted perennial with stems 4 to 20 inches tall. The leaf growth is scant. The heads are slender and from $\frac{3}{4}$ to 3 inches long; all the glumes are bristle-like and $\frac{3}{8}$ to $\frac{5}{8}$ inch long; the lemma of perfect spikelets is about $\frac{1}{4}$ to $\frac{3}{8}$ inch long, the awn exceeding the glumes. The seed with lemmas is like a slender, flattened barley grain. The lateral florets generally remain attached and are set up on relatively long pedicels or stems on either side of the grain-bearing spikelet.

LITTLE BARLEY (*Hordeum pusillum* Nutt.)

This is a native species which extends from Maine to Florida and westward. It occurs on plains and open ground, especially in alkaline areas, and is more common in the west, particularly in southern California.

Little barley is an annual, about 4 to 10 inches tall, with an erect spike about 1 to 3 inches long and about 1 inch wide. Both glumes of the central fertile spikelet and the first glume of the lateral spikelet are dilated just above the base and elongated into a slender awn about $\frac{1}{2}$ inch long. The lemma of the central spikelet is definitely awned, while those of the lateral spikelets are merely awn pointed.

ANNUAL KOELERIA (*Koeleria phleoides* (Vill.) Pers.)

This introduction from Europe has been collected at several points in California. It is an annual, smooth throughout, with stems 6 to 12 inches tall. The leaves are sparsely hairy. Panicle dense, ¾ to 3 inches long; spikelets 2- to 4-flowered; glumes of about equal length, but unlike in shape; lemmas short awned from a bifid apex, and shining.

HARE'S-TAIL (*Lagurus ovatus* L.) (Fig. 35)

This Mediterranean species, sometimes cultivated for ornament, is an occasional escape along the coast at San Francisco, Berkeley and Monterey. It is an annual with slender, hairy stems 4 to 12 inches tall, hairy leaves, and a flowering head about one inch long and about as wide as long, pale and downy and bristling with dark beards. The spikelets are 1-flowered, the lemmas bearing on the back above the middle a

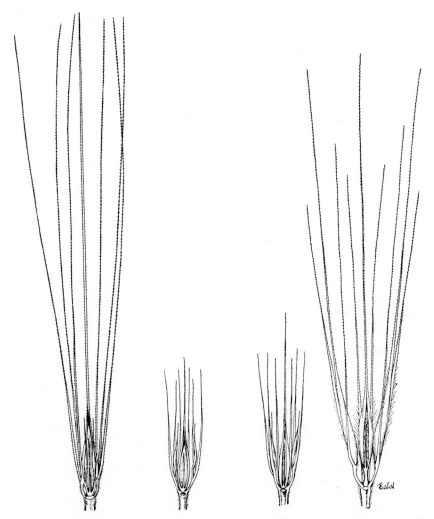

FIG. 34. Groups of spikelets in species of *Hordeum*. Left to right: Foxtail barley (*H. jubatum*), meadow barley (*H. nodosum*), Mediterranean barley (*H. gussoneanum*), common foxtail (*H. murinum*).

slender, bent awn, and terminating in two very fine elongated tips.

GOLDEN-TOP (*Lamarckia aurea* (L.) Moench.)

This plant, sometimes cultivated for ornament, is an introduction from the Mediterranean region, and now occurs in cultivated and waste ground from Texas to California. It is less common in the northern part of the State than in the southern part, where it was in great abundance as early as 1881.

Golden-top is an erect annual, 4 to 16 inches tall. The leaf-blades are soft and smooth; there is a prominent ligule decurrent as a broad scarious margin. The panicle is 1 to 5 inches long, and ½ to 1 inch wide, shining, and golden-yellow or purplish. The spikelets are of two kinds in bundles, the terminal one of each bundle fertile, the others sterile. The fertile spikelet has one perfect flower on a slender stalk and a rudimentary flower on a long joint of the rachilla, both having awned lemmas. The fertile spikelet is about 2 mm. long, its awn about twice as long as the spikelet, whereas the sterile spikelet is 6 to 8 mm. long. The free grain is spindle-shaped, about 2 mm. long, pearly gray and somewhat translucent.

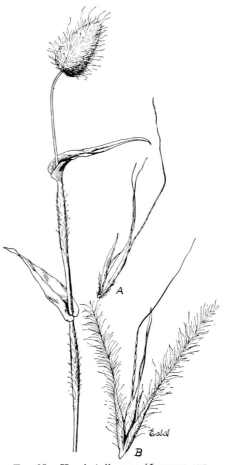

FIG. 35. Hare's-tail grass (*Lagurus ovatus*). A, floret; B, spikelet.

RICE CUT-GRASS (*Leersia oryzoides* (L.) Swartz)

This is a European species occurring in eastern and southern United States, and at several points in California: Woodland, Biggs, and in the southeastern area. It is a plant of wet places, often troublesome when bordering ditches.

Rice cut-grass is a perennial from creeping rootstalks. The stems are slender, weak, 3 to 4 feet long. Leaf blades are flat, and rough. The panicles are open with thin, spreading branches; spikelets 1-flowered, glumes wanting, and the lemma hard-papery.

SCALE GRASS (*Leptochloa fascicularis* (Lam.) A. Gray)

Other common names: Sprangletop, spreading millet, ray grass.

Scale grass occurs across the United States, and south through tropical America to Argentina. It occurs in brackish waters along the coast and in alkali flats, ditches, and marshes. In California it is a common weed in wet places throughout the interior valleys, and is usually associated with alkaline soils. It is becoming fairly abundant in rice fields, although it has not thus far seriously interfered with the rice crop.

The species is a somewhat succulent annual, with erect to spreading or prostrate, freely branching stems, 1 to 3 feet tall. The stems terminate in a succession of erect, slender spikes 3 to 5 inches long. The spikelets are 7- to 11-flowered. The lemma investing the seed is $\frac{1}{8}$ to $\frac{1}{4}$ inch long, toothed at apex and bears a short awn. It is hairy below on the prominent nerves and margins, tapering toward the apex, the margins lighter colored.

The seeds are readily spread by irrigation water, but they are much smaller than rice grains and easily separated from them.

RED SPRANGLETOP (*Leptochloa filiformis* (Lam.) Beauv.) is another species which occurs to a limited extent in southern California.

SPRANGLETOP (*Leptochloa uninervia* (Presl.) Hitchc. and Chase), closely related to and resembling scale grass, occurs in similar habitats. It is particularly troublesome in the Imperial Valley. This species is distinguished from scale grass by the absence of awns on the lemma.

THINTAIL (*Lepturus cylindricus* (Willd.) Trin.) (Fig. 36)

This is an introduction from the Old World which borders mudflats and salt marshes from the San Francisco Bay area south to San Diego. Thintail is a bushy-branched, spreading or prostrate annual, 4 to 12 inches tall. The spikes are hard, cylindric and curved. The spikelets are 1-flowered and embedded in the hard, jointed cylindric rachis. The spikelets fall attached to the joints of the rachis. The first glume is wanting except on the terminal spikelet; the second glume closes the cavity of the rachis and is flush with the surface. The mature seed looks like a short length of straw about $\frac{1}{4}$ inch long, the grain and investing lemmas embedded in the hard rachis or joint of stem.

FIG. 36. Thintail (*Lepturus cylindricus*), showing thickened rachis and indurated glume.

RYEGRASS. LOLIUM
KEY TO WEEDY SPECIES OF LOLIUM

Annuals; glume as long as or longer than the spikelet
Spike flat; spikelets much wider than rachis
                                        L. temulentum
Spike almost cylindric; spikelets but slightly wider
    than rachis _____*L. subulatum*
Perennials; glume shorter than spikelet
    Lemmas nearly or quite awnless_____*L. perenne*
    Lemmas, at least the upper, awned_____*L. multiflorum*

ITALIAN RYEGRASS (*Lolium multiflorum* Lam.) (Fig. 37B)
Other common name: Australian ryegrass.

This plant, introduced from Europe, has about the same range as *L. perenne*. It is very common in California, especially in the Coast Ranges, occurring in waste places and along roadsides. It is sometimes cultivated as a meadow or pasture grass, and as a lawn grass. The plant is a short-lived perennial, resembling *L. perenne*. It differs from the latter in its more robust habit, larger spikelets and awned lemmas. The spikes are nodding, often as long as 12 inches, the spikelets up to an inch long, and from 10- to 12-flowered. Seed is similar to perennial ryegrass, but awned.

PERENNIAL RYEGRASS (*Lolium perenne* L.) (Fig. 37C)
Other common name: English ryegrass.

Perennial ryegrass, an introduced plant from Europe, occurs throughout the northern part of the United States and southern Canada, and as far west as California. It is sometimes used in grass mixtures for tame pastures. In this State it is rare. It is found in waste places and along roadsides. This species is a short-lived perennial with stems erect or decumbent at the base, and 1 to 2 feet tall. The leaf blades are glossy and slender. The spike is 6 to 10 inches long, the spikelets 6- to 10-flowered, the lemmas awnless or nearly so. Lemmas investing the grain are almost as long as in Italian ryegrass, but definitely narrower and flatter. The palet is not wrinkled.

Lolium strictum Presl.

This annual ryegrass, introduced from Europe, occurs sparingly in California, as at Berkeley. It resembles *L. subulatum* except that the spikelets are not sunken in the depressions on the rachis.

NARROW-SPIKED RYEGRASS (*Lolium subulatum* Vis.)

This is a European species naturalized sparingly in ballast and waste areas. The spikelets are partly sunken in the depressions on the rachis, and partly covered by the conspicuously nerved glumes.

DARNEL (*Lolium temulentum* L.) (Fig. 37A)
Other common names: Cheat, poison ryegrass, ivray.

This species, introduced from Europe, is widespread in the United States and Canada. It is common in California and other Pacific Coast states. It is a weed in grain fields, pastures, and waste lands.

Darnel is an annual, with stout, erect, smooth stems, 1 to 3 feet high, bearing 5 to 7 leaves. The leaf sheaths are overlapping, the blades 3 to 8 inches long and about $\frac{1}{3}$ inch wide, smooth on the under surface but somewhat roughened above. The inflorescence is a spike, 4 to 8 inches long, the spikelets arranged on alternate sides of the axis. Each spikelet is several-flowered, solitary on the axis, much flattened, and placed edgewise in alternate notches of the axis. The first glume is wanting, the second is about 1 inch long, firm and pointed; the lemma, about $\frac{1}{4}$ inch long, is strongly convex, broadest above the middle, smooth, 2-toothed

FIG. 37.   Spikes and seeds of *Lolium*. **A,** darnel (*L. temulentum*) ; **B,** Italian ryegrass (*L. multiflorum*) ; **C,** perennial ryegrass (*L. perenne*).

at the apex, and usually tipped with an awn about $\frac{1}{4}$ inch long. The palet is usually somewhat transversely wrinkled. The free grain is oval, plump and brownish with a tuft of hairs at the apex. It is a common impurity in cereals and imparts a bitter taste and gray color to flour if ground with wheat.

The grains of darnel are thought to be poisonous. It is believed that the poisonous properties of the grains are caused by the presence within them of a fungus (*Stromatinia temulenta* Prill. & Del.), which possesses a poisonous narcotic alkaloid, *temulin*. Horses, cattle, sheep, and man are poisoned.

ORCUTT GRASS (*Orcuttia californica* Vasey)

Extensive stands of this native annual were found on the site of the abandoned airfield on Southwestern Avenue, Los Angeles, where its denseness excluded almost all other vegetation. It also occurs in Riverside County. The mats are formed by the spreading stems which turn up at the ends. The foliage is thin, sheaths loose, blades 1 to 2 inches long. The flower-spike is open and sparse below, compact at the summit. The lemmas are about $\frac{1}{4}$ inch long, deeply cleft into 5 awn-tipped teeth.

RED RICE (*Oryza sativa* L.) (Fig. 38)

Red rice closely resembles commercial rice in the field, and is differentiated with difficulty in the hull. The free grain, however, is dark red and somewhat translucent. If allowed to mature, red rice either shatters its seed or is harvested with the rice. Its presence is detected in a test by a "rubout" which removes the investing bracts and thereby discloses the red grains. It is believed that red rice was introduced into California with seed rice from other states. About 30 years ago it was almost unknown here but a survey over the ten-year period, 1922-32, indicated that 23 percent of the lots of seed rice tested in California carried red rice.

SMILO GRASS, SAN DIEGO GRASS (*Oryzopsis miliacea* (L.) Benth. and Hook.) (Fig. 39)

This species is naturalized from the Mediterranean region and occurs sparingly in waste places where there is adequate moisture as at Los Angeles, Ventura, Santa Barbara, and Calito in Mendocino County. It is sometimes cultivated for forage. This grass is a stout perennial, 2 to 5 feet tall, with flat-leaf shiny light-green blades, 5 to 10 mm. wide, and loose panicles 4 to 12 inches long. The spikelets are 1-flowered, the glumes of about equal size, the lemma hard, usually about as long as the glumes, and with a straight awn about 4 mm. long. The seed, including palet and lemma from which the awn usually has been broken, is about 2 mm. long, smooth and shiny grayish-brown, largest above the middle and narrow toward the base. There is a single light-colored line on the back, two on the front face. The free grain is brown with light-colored, short point at apex, and a crease about one-third length of seed extending upward from

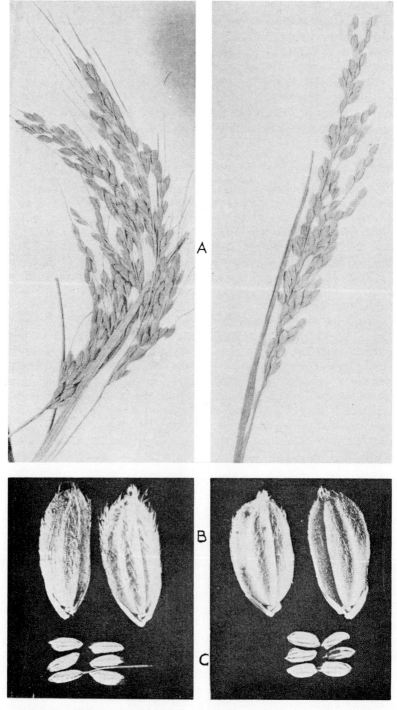

Fig. 38.   Red rice (*Oryza sativa*), showing long and short-seeded forms.
A, panicle x ½ ; B, seeds x 4 ; C, seeds, natural size.

base. The surface is marked by a network of very fine lines.

PANICUM

There are 160 species of *Panicum* described in Hitchcock's Manual of Grasses of the United States. Jepson records 13 species as occurring in California. Among these are annual and perennial grasses of various habits, three of which are here considered as weeds.

The following species are annuals, with the spikelets arranged in panicles. The lowermost glume is broad, and about one-half the length' of the spikelet; the second glume is the length of the spikelet. Within the second (longer) glume is the lemma of a sterile flower; this lemma is slightly shorter than the glume surrounding it, and encloses a very small palet. Above this sterile flower is a perfect one. The lemma of this is parchment-like; it encloses a palet. The seed is firmly surrounded by the indurated, shining lemma and palet, very convex on the back and more or less flattened on the face. The gen-eral shape is oval, roundly narrowed at the base and more pointedly so at the apex.

FIG. 39.   Smilo grass (*Oryzopsis miliacea*), showing panicle and detail of spikelet.

KEY TO WEEDY SPECIES OF PANICUM

First glume not over ¼ length of spikelet, sheaths smooth_____*P. dichotomiflorum*
First glume about ½ length of spikelet, sheaths hispid
    Panicle erect _____*P. capillare*
    Panicle drooping _____*P. miliaceum*

WITCHGRASS (*Panicum capillare* L.) (Fig. 40)

This is a common weed in the eastern United States, but is rare with us, having been reported from but a few localities: Pine Grove, Amador County, San Francisco, Upland, Santa Ana River and Davis.

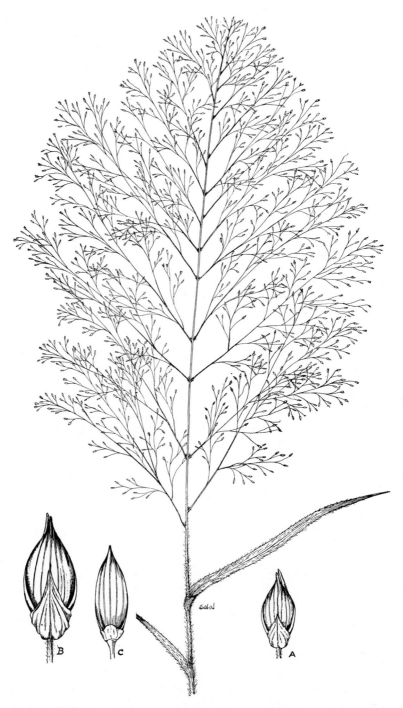

FIG. 40. Panicle of witchgrass (*Panicum capillare*). **A**, spikelet of same; **B**, spikelet of hog millet (*P. miliaceum*); **C**, spikelet of fall panicum (*P. dichotomiflorum*).

FALL PANICUM (*Panicum dichotomiflorum* Michx.) (Fig. 40)

This is known also as smooth witchgrass. It is a native of the eastern United States and is found in moist ground, along streams, as a weed in waste places and in cultivated soil. It occurs occasionally in California; is reported from around Fresno and southward.

HOG MILLET (*Panicum miliaceum* L.) (Fig. 40)

This is known also as broomcorn millet and proso. It is cultivated in the cooler parts of the United States to a limited extent for forage and seed. In California it has escaped here and there from cultivation. In hog millet the panicle is drooping which differentiates it from the two preceding species.

VINE MESQUITE (*Panicum obtusum* H.B.K.)

This grass which occurs from western Missouri to Texas and Arizona has been reported from southern California; Palo Verde Valley. It prefers sandy soil, as along river banks and irrigation ditches.

Vine mesquite is a perennial, from a tufted knotted crown, with stolons six feet long or longer. The internodes are long, and the joints or nodes angled, enlarged and conspicuously hairy. The blades are compressed, 10 inches to 3 feet long, 2 to 7 mm. wide; smooth or almost so. The flowering panicle is about 2 to 6 inches long and about $\frac{1}{2}$ inch wide. The first glume is nearly as long as the brownish, obtuse spikelets.

DALLIS GRASS (*Paspalum dilatatum* Poir.) (Fig. 41b)

Resembling knotgrass is the South American species commonly known as Dallis grass, now grown occasionally as a pasture grass. As an escape from cultivation, it has promise of becoming a weed, especially in waterways.

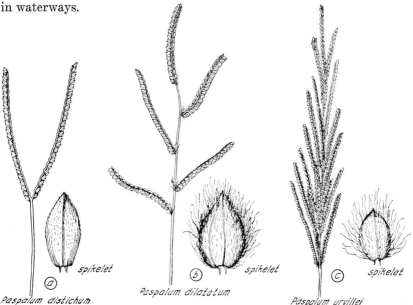

FIG. 41. Inflorescences and spikelets of *Paspalum*. **A,** knotgrass; **B,** Dallis grass; **C,** Vasey grass.

Dallis grass is a tall perennial, distinguishable from knotgrass by the presence of a number of racemes scattered along the axis. The spikelets are rounded in outline, elongated at apex, definitely flattened and long hairy, particularly at the outer edge. The lemma is slightly convex on the back and rolled over the flat palet on the front face. It is smooth, shiny and light straw color.

KNOTGRASS (*Paspalum distichum* L.) (Figs. 41a and 42)
Other common names: Jointgrass, ditchgrass.

Knotgrass is found throughout the warmer parts of both hemispheres, especially near the coasts. It is quite common throughout California at lower altitudes, occurring in wet pasture lands and along irrigation ditches, in some cases tending to fill up the water channels.

The species is a perennial, developing numerous creeping rhizomes. The culms are from $\frac{1}{2}$ to 2 feet high. It often has a bulbous stem development due to a gall. The leaves are crowded on the stem, usually smooth and flat, the blades 2 to 6 inches long. The spikelets are in characteristic

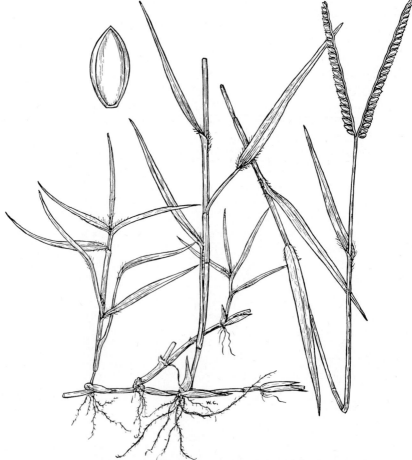

FIG. 42. Knotgrass (*Paspalum distichum*), showing habit, 2-branched spike and seed.

one-sided slender groups (racemes) and as a rule there are but two of these, although sometimes there is a third raceme below the pair. The spikelets are elliptic, broadest just above the middle, about 3 mm. long, and pale green in color. Sometimes the first glume in the spikelet is undeveloped, but as a rule, in this species it is developed and resembles the second glume, which is nerved and pubescent. The lemma is convex, smooth and somewhat shiny, the palet flattened to somewhat concave.

VASEY GRASS (*Paspalum Urvillei* Steud.) (Fig. 41c)

This species, a native of South America, has been found along irrigation ditches at Berry Creek, Butte County, and at Palm Springs. This species, like *P. dilatatum,* has a number of racemes along the axis. In *P. dilatatum* the racemes usually number from 3 to 5 whereas in *P. Urvillei* they number 12 to 18.

KIKUYU GRASS (*Pennisetum clandestinum* Hochst.) (Fig. 43)

Kikuyu grass, although not new to California, became prominent as a weed pest the past few years. An inspection was made of this plant growing in avocado and orange groves in San Diego County, where it had been planted to prevent soil erosion. It was found that the extremely favorable conditions for its growth made excessive competition for the trees, the result being death or definite disorder in the grove. Following this inspection, a State survey was made. It was learned that Kikuyu grass was imported about 15 years ago from Africa, propagated, and distributed to several coastal counties. Other than in San Diego County, it was found in Orange, Ventura, Santa Barbara and San Luis Obispo, and

FIG. 43.   Kikuyu grass (*Pennisetum clandestinum*), showing habit, and spikelet with long, exserted stigmas.

reported to be in Los Angeles and Monterey Counties. It is used both for lawns and to prevent soil erosion. Its use for the latter purpose so far has been confined to controlled test plantings. Kikuyu has been observed to set seed in Orange County and seedling growth has been recorded from that area. The free seed or grain is about 3 mm. long, with a relatively large scar at the rounded base and an acute point at the apex. The color is a rather shiny dark brown.

FOUNTAIN GRASS (*Pennisetum Ruppelii* Steud.) and FEATHERTOP (*P. villosum* R. Br.) are both African introductions and ornamentals which rarely escape from cultivation. Both are perennials with dense, thick flower clusters, the former species 1 to 2 feet high, with one spike, 2 to 4 inches long, broad and with feathery bristles; the latter species 3 to 4 feet high, with one curved or nodding spike, 6 to 10 inches long, the bristles prominent and 1 inch or more long.

SHORT-SPIKED CANARY GRASS (*Phalaris brachystachys* Link) (Fig. 44e, f)

This is introduced from the Mediterranean region, and has been found in waste ground at Nelson, Butte County, in Yolo County, and elsewhere. It is a rice field weed of some importance. The seed is only slightly smaller than canary grass, but the sterile lemmas are minute, less than 1 mm. long, as contrasted with *P. canariensis* which are half the length of the seed.

CANARY GRASS (*Phalaris canariensis* L.) (Fig. 44g)

This native of the Mediterranean region, which furnishes the canary seed of commerce, is an occasional escape from cultivation. It is now

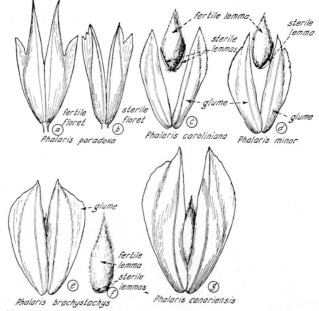

FIG. 44. Botanical characters of *Phalaris*. (a) (b) gnawed canary grass; (c) Carolina canary grass; (d) Mediterranean canary grass; (e) (f) short-spiked canary grass; (g) canary grass.

established in widely scattered localities in California. It is an annual 1 to 2 feet tall with conspicuously striped glumes. The seed, including fertile lemmas, is the same general shape as the two preceding species, but larger, being about 5 to 6 mm. long. It is commonly shiny-straw color, appressed hairy on the surface, the two sterile lemmas about half the length of the seed. The free grain is flattened—oblong and slightly translucent.

MEDITERRANEAN CANARY GRASS (*Phalaris minor* Retz) (Figs. 44d and 45)

This grass occurs throughout central and southern California and behaves as a weed in waste land and along roadsides, especially in heavy soils. It is a native of the Mediterranean region. It is an annual in which the glumes of the spikelets are broad, strongly winged on the keel above, with a green stripe on each side of the keel at the base of the wing. The seed, including the fertile lemmas, is smooth and shiny, commonly grayish-brown with lighter veins or nerves, sometimes straw colored. It is about 3 mm. long, rounded at base and gradually narrowed above to a slender tip, sparsely hairy, especially along the sides and toward the apex. The sterile lemma remaining attached at the base is about 1 mm. long. The free grain is oblong and flattened, grayish-green and slightly translucent.

GNAWED CANARY GRASS (*Phalaris paradoxa* L.) (Fig. 44a, b)

This species is introduced from the Mediterranean region, and is widely distributed in California, especially in grain fields, including rice. It is an annual with tufted, erect stems 1 to 2.5 feet high. The leaves are flat, 3 to 8 inches long, rough on both sides and somewhat whitened with a bloom, their sheaths more or less inflated. The inflorescence is a dense, spike-like panicle, oblong in shape, narrowed at base, 1 to 2 inches long, often enclosed at the base in the uppermost enlarged sheath. The spikelets fall from the axis in groups of 6 or 7 (usually 7), the central one of the group being fertile, the others sterile. The glumes of the fertile spikelets have a prominent tooth-like wing near the middle of the keel; the glumes of the sterile spikelets are smaller and with toothed-winged keels. The seed with the fertile lemma investing the oblong flattened grayish grain, is about 3 mm. long and sparsely hairy near the apex. The sterile lemmas are wanting, but there are two divergent short, plump, yellowish scales appressed to the seed at the base.

HARDING GRASS (*Phalaris tuberosa* L. var. *stenoptera* (Hack) Hitchc.)

This grass, introduced into California by the Agricultural Experiment Station for forage, has become sparingly naturalized on the coast, as along roadsides, Marin County.

It is a perennial, with rhizomatous base, forming large very leafy bunches. The flowering stems are tall, to 4 feet or more. The panicle, 2½ to 5 inches long, is typical of the canary grasses. Glumes 5 to 6 mm long, keel narrowly winged on upper two-thirds, fertile lemma 4 mm. long, sterile lemma usually solitary, about one-third as long as the fertile lemma.

FIG. 45. Mediterranean canary grass (*Phalaris minor*), showing habit.

FIG. 46. Timothy (*Phleum pratense*) showing flowering heads, bulbous enlargements at crown, glumes, floret and grain.

CAROLINA CANARY GRASS (*Phalaris caroliniana* Walt.) (Fig. 44c) is a Mediterranean introduction which has been collected at Palms in Los Angeles County, at San Diego and Ojai.

In addition to the preceding six species of *Phalaris* which may sometimes behave as weeds, there are three other native species which are of some forage value. These are *P. angusta*, Nees., *P. Lemmoni* Vasey, and *P. californica* H. & A.

TIMOTHY (*Phleum pratense* L.) (Fig. 46)

Timothy, a common cultivated plant of meadows and pastures, has become naturalized to a limited extent in California. It is sometimes troublesome in lawns, where it develops a prostrate habit, forming large mats with coarse, bulbous enlargements at the crown. Timothy is a perennial, 8 to 12 inches tall. The inflorescence is cylindric, 2 to 4 inches long, and about ¼ inch in diameter. The glumes are about equal, membranous, keeled, terminated by short awns; the keels are ciliate. The seed is ovate, with an abrupt point at both the base and apex.

SICKLE GRASS (*Pholiurus incurvus* (L.) Schinz and Thell.) (Fig. 47)

This European introduced species occurs in mud flats and salt marshes from Marin County to San Diego; also Colusa County. It is a low, tufted, prostrate annual 4 to 8 inches high. The spikes are cylindric, long and flexuous, with spikelets sunken in hollows in the rachis. The spikelets are 1- or 2-flowered, and fall attached to joints of the rachis. Each spikelet has two glumes (unlike *Lepturus*), placed in front of the spikelet and enclosing it; they appear like halves of a single split glume. As in the case of *Lepturus,* the seed embedded in a section of the rachis appears to be a short stem section. Upon close scrutiny the two glumes

FIG. 47. Sickle grass (*Pholiurus incurvus*), showing habit, and a single spikelet attached to joint of rachis.

flattened against the rachis may be detected, and under these a transparent lemma and palea investing the grain or free seed.

COMMON REED (*Phragmites communis* Trin.) (Fig. 11a)

This is a cosmopolitan aquatic grass occurring in Europe, Asia, Africa, Australia, and throughout the United States, Mexico, Central America, and parts of South America. In California it is found in fresh water swamps, along irrigation ditches, and streams, particularly in the Delta, and southern counties. It occurs sparingly in northern counties. In the Southwest the weed has been used for lattices in the construction of adobe huts; also for mats and screens, for thatching and carrying nets.

The species is perennial, the stout, leafy culums, 6 to 12 feet tall, arising from long, creeping jointed rootstocks or runners; the latter, along the surface of the ground, may attain a length of 20 feet or more. The leaves are from 6 inches to 1 foot long, about one inch wide, flat, and smooth, with loose, overlapping leaf-sheaths. The inflorescence is a feathery panicle, usually a foot or more in length, dense and soft, usually purplish and sometimes nodding. Each spikelet is several-flowered, about $\frac{1}{2}$ inch long, the axis of which has long silky hairs at the joints. The glumes are 3-nerved, the lemmas narrow, smooth, 3-nerved, about 3 mm. long and the palea much shorter than the lemma. The long silky white hairs remain attached to the seed on the short stem-like projection at the base. The slender grain is dark brown in color. The lemmas are thin, 3-nerved, densely and softly hairy, the nerves ending in slender teeth, the middle one extending into a straight awn.

ANNUAL BLUEGRASS (*Poa annua* L.) (Fig. 48)
Other common name : Walkgrass.

This Old World introduction is quite generally distributed throughout the United States, and at high altitudes in tropical America. It occurs in open ground, lawns, pastures, open woods, and waste places. It usually enters lawns as an impurity in the "lawn mixture." In the lawn it may grow luxuriantly in the spring, later giving rise to unsightly dry spots when it has completed its short period of growth.

This is an annual tufted grass, with light-green, flattened stems a foot or less tall, which are usually bent at the base and often root at the lower nodes. The leaf blades are soft and weak, about 3 inches long, smooth on both sides, and the leaf sheaths loosely invest the stems. The inflorescence is a terminal panicle, 1 to 4 inches long, which is sometimes more or less one-sided. Each spikelet is 3- to 6-flowered ; the lemma is distinctly 5-nerved bulging broad below the folded tip, dull brownish when mature. Unlike many species of *Poa*, the lemma is not cobwebby at the base ; however, the lower half of all nerves on the lemma bear long hairs. The naked grain is plump and bright amber, pointed at both ends.

CANADA BLUEGRASS (*Poa compressa* L.)

This is also an Old World species which is widely distributed in California, and often troublesome as a weed. It is a sod-forming perennial, with flattened, wiry, bluish-green stems, 6 to 20 inches tall. The conspicuously flattened stems distinguish it from *P. annua,* as do the lemmas which

FIG. 48.   Annual bluegrass (*Poa annua*), showing habit. **A**, florets, and **B**, spikelet.

are not conspicuously nerved. The lemma is light colored at the base and flared at the apex.

ROUGH BLUEGRASS (*Poa trivialis* L.)

This is a European introduction which has been found in Humboldt County. It is a perennial, differing from the preceding species in having no creeping rhizomes. The seed is very slender boat-shaped and the lemma sharply 1-nerved about half way between the keel and front edge.

POLYPOGON

The *Polypogons* are grasses with flat leaf blades and dense, bristly, spike-like panicles. The spikelets are 1-flowered, the glumes of equal size, entire, or 2-lobed, and awned, the lemma much shorter than the glumes and also awned.

KEY TO WEEDY SPECIES OF POLYPOGON

Leaf sheaths rough to the touch___*P. lutosus*

Leaf sheaths smooth
  Glumes prominently lobed, the lobes ciliate-fringed; awn twice as long as the glumes _____*P. maritimus*
  Glumes slightly lobed, the lobes ciliate; awns slightly exceeding body of glumes
                P. monspeliensis

DITCH POLYPOGON (*Polypogon lutosus* (Poir.) Hitchc.)

This species, which is an introduction from Europe, is fairly abundant in waste ground throughout the State, especially along irrigation ditches and in low ground.

It is a perennial, 1-2 feet or more in height, with scabrous sheaths. The panicle is about 2-6 inches long, somewhat interrupted or spreading. The glumes are equal, about 2-3 mm. long, tipped by an awn of about the same length as the glumes. The smooth shining lemma, investing the seed, is about 1 mm. long, blunt and toothed at the apex, terminating in an awn about 2-3 mm. long.

FIG. 49. Rabbitfoot grass (*Polypogon monspeliensis*) showing soft, dense, spike-like panicle.

MARITIME BEARDGRASS (*Polypogon maritimus* Willd.)

This is an annual, very similar in general aspect to *P. monspeliensis.* It may be distinguished from that species by the glumes which are prominently lobed with the lobes ciliate fringed. It has been collected on waste ground in Marin and Lake Counties.

RABBITFOOT GRASS (*Polypogon monspeliensis* (L.) Desf.) (Fig. 49)
Other common names: Annual beardgrass, beardgrass, tawny beardgrass.

This species, introduced from Europe, occurs in a majority of the states and is especially common along the east coast and in the western states. It is widespread in California along irrigation ditches and in over-irrigated, tilled land, and in waste places where it is moist. Due to its preference for moist soils, it often becomes an impurity in hay, reducing its sale value.

The plant is an annual with smooth, erect, or decumbent stems at the base, 6 to 24 inches tall. The leaf blades are flat, $\frac{1}{4}$ inch wide or narrower, 2 to 6 inches long, and the sheaths fit loosely about the stem. The inflorescence is a soft, dense spike-like panicle, tawny or yellowish in color, and 1 to 6 inches long. Each spikelet is 1-flowered; the glumes, which are slightly lobed and not ciliate, bear straight, slender awns which give the bristly appearance characteristic of the flower cluster; the lemma is much shorter than the glumes, papery, and usually bears a slender straight awn which is shorter than the awns of the glume. The free grain, or with investing lemma and palea, occurs as an impurity in bent grass seed. The grain is about 1 mm. long, much the shape of a kernel of wheat, amber colored and translucent, minutely roughened by horizontal lines.

Schismus barbatus (L.) Chase (Fig. 50)

This Old World species has been reported from Marin, Kern, Santa Barbara, Los Angeles, San Bernardino and Imperial Counties. It occurs in yards, along roadsides and in dry river beds, and is of value as a winter forage where locally abundant.

S. barbatus is a low tufted annual, two inches to about one foot tall. The blades very narrow, inflorescence $\frac{1}{2}$ to $1\frac{1}{2}$ inches long, oval to linear and usually rather dense. The color is pale or purple tinged. The lemmas are broad, about 2 mm. long, nine-nerved, the summit membranous, two-toothed, the margin appressed hairy on the lower half. The palet is concave, about the same size as the lemma.

S. arabicus, similar in appearance to *S. barbatus,* is reported from Fresno and Kings Counties. It has a deeply bifid lemma.

HARDGRASS *Scleropoa rigida* (L.) Griseb.

This European grass is sparingly introduced in waste places and fields, as a sidewalk weed: Massachusetts, Florida, South Dakota, Washington to California. It is an annual, the flowering stems erect or spreading, 5 to 10 inches tall. Panicles narrow, to 5 inches long, sparsely

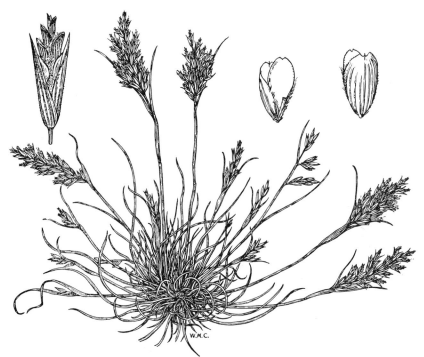

Fig. 50. *Schismus barbatus,* with enlarged spikelet and floret.

branched, one-sided. Spikelets 4 to 10-flowered, 5 to 8 mm. long, glumes about 2 mm. long, lemmas 2.5 mm.

BRISTLEGRASS. *SETARIA*

The Setarias are troublesome in alfalfa fields, especially along borders and in thin stands, and their presence lowers the grade. The seeds are a common impurity in alfalfa seed, and the species are usually spread in the alfalfa growing section by planting alfalfa containing the seeds of the Setarias as impurities.

KEY TO WEEDY SPECIES OF SETARIA
Plants annual
Bristles backwardly barbed_____*C. verticillata*
Bristles forwardly barbed
    Bristles below each spikelet 5 or more_____*C. lutescens*
    Bristles below each spikelet 1-3_____*C. viridis*
Plants perennial by short knotty rhizomes_____*C. geniculata*

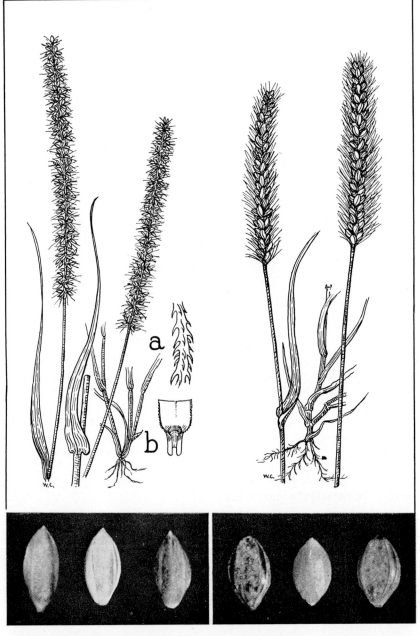

FIG. 51. (Left) bur bristlegrass (*Setaria verticillata*), showing annual root system, divergent slender spikelets; (a) retrorse barbs on bristles, (b) scabrous leaf margins. (Right) green bristlegrass (*Setaria viridis*) showing annual root system, ascending small spikelets much exceeded by the bristles.

KNOTROOT BRISTLEGRASS (*Setaria geniculata* (Lam.) Beauv.) (Fig. 52)
Other common names : Perennial foxtail, perennial pigeon grass.

Knotroot bristlegrass is found in scattered localities from Riverside northward to Glenn County; known also in tropical America, Argentina and Chile. It occurs on moist or dry sites, in open ground and pastures and to a lesser extent in cultivated areas. Ditch banks and laterals are often covered so densely as to exclude all other vegetation and through the seed the weed is disseminated along the waterways.

Knotroot bristlegrass may be recognized readily by the typical foxtail spikes or heads which extend well above the rather wiry basal leafage. The knotty perennial rootstocks are short branching rhizomes which give the clumps of grass a bunched rather than creeping or spreading appearance. The plants remain green into the fall, the tops browning during the winter and new green shoots appearing from the knotty roots early in the spring.

The stems are branched at the crown with geniculate or knee-like joints, flowering heads about 3 to 4 inches long on erect stems $2\frac{1}{2}$ to 3 feet tall or more. A group of 5 to 7 bristles subtends each spikelet (seed and investing bracts). The bristles, about twice as long as the spikelet, are antrorsely or upwardly barbed and may be either pale or tawny. The mature seed is slender, more than twice as long as wide, markedly transversely and wavily ridged, and of dull appearance with a short but definite cusp or point at the apex.

YELLOW BRISTLEGRASS (*Setaria lutescens* (Weigel) F. T. Hubb) (Fig. 52)
Other common names : Bristly foxtail, foxtail millet, yellow foxtail, pigeon grass, summergrass, golden foxtail, wild millet.

This species is widely distributed in the North Temperate Zone. It occurs throughout the United States, but as yet is not widespread or abundant in California. It is introduced from Europe. The species is a weed in waste places, in stubble fields, in bare places in pastures and meadows. It finds its way into fields as an impurity in seed.

Yellow bristlegrass is an annual with erect, leafy stems, 1 to 2 feet high, which branch at the base. The stems are somewhat compressed. The leaf blades are flat, 4 to 12 inches long, and often have a spiral twist; the leaf sheaths loosely surround the stem, and the lower ones are often tinged with red. The inflorescence is a dense, bristly spike, 1 to 4 inches long, the tawny yellow bristles $\frac{1}{3}$ inch long or less, rising from the stalks of the spikelets; the axis of the spike is densely hairy. The spikelets are usually 1-flowered, and each is subtended by 5 or more tawny upwardly-barbed bristles (sterile branchlets), the longer bristles being two to three times as long as the spikelet. The seed is about 2 mm. long, broadly oval, plane on one side and strongly convex on the opposite. The transverse wavy ridges are quite definite, the color yellowish to dark mummy-brown, and comparatively dull. The free grain is grayish-green in color, pointed at the tip, and very slightly translucent.

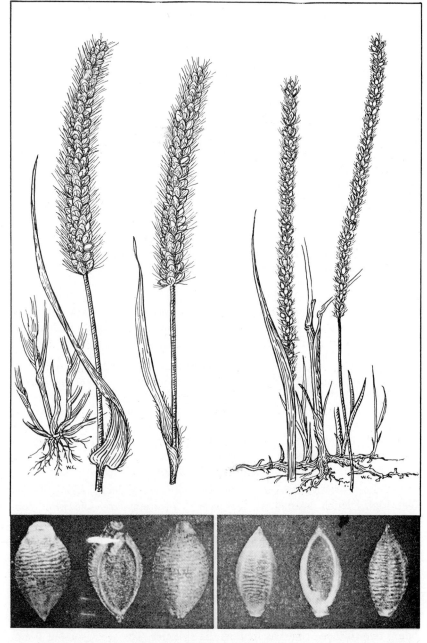

Fig. 52. (Left) yellow bristlegrass (*Setaria lutescens*), showing annual root system, broad spike and spikelets and hairs at base of more or less twisting leaf blades. (Right) knotroot bristlegrass (*Setaria geniculata*), showing perennial root system, slender spike and spikelets, and straight, relatively stiff leaf blades.

BUR BRISTLEGRASS (*Setaria verticillata* (L.) Beauv.) (Fig. 51)
Other common names: Bristly foxtail, pigeon grass.

This has been found as a weed sparingly distributed in southern California. A few infestations are also reported in San Joaquin and Sacramento counties. It is introduced from Europe, and occurs in the Eastern States and certain sections of the Middle West. It is a weed in cultivated soil and waste places.

The species is annual and resembles *S. lutescens*. However, as compared with the latter, it has a more spreading and branching habit, rougher stems and leaves, downwardly-barbed bristles, and usually only 1 bristle below each spikelet, rarely 2 or 3. The slender seeds are faintly and finely transversely ridged on the back, somewhat smooth and shiny on the three veins, about twice as long as wide. Commonly the seed is straw colored, rarely obscurely mottled with brown.

GREEN BRISTLEGRASS (*Setaria viridis* (L.) Beauv.) (Fig. 51)
Other common names: Green foxtail, bottlegrass, pigeon grass, wild millet.

This species is common throughout the cooler sections of the United States and southern Canada. It occurs sparingly in the Southern States, and in California. Introduced from Europe, it has become a weed in grain stubble, cultivated ground, and waste places. It is frequent in the rice fields of northern California, and is established in the Sacramento and San Joaquin valleys.

This species, an annual, also resembles *S. lutescens*. The plant branches at the base, sometimes the lower joints of the stem being bent abruptly. The leaf blades are flat, and not twisted, as they often are in *S. lutescens*. The flowering head is erect or somewhat nodding, densely flowered, with green or purple upwardly barbed bristles; 1 to 3 bristles occur below each spikelet, and they are 3 to 4 times the length of the spikelet. The seeds are slightly over 1 mm. long, wide in relation to length, and very faintly wrinkled. They are light straw colored to very dark brown, most frequently mottled with small darker spots.

JOHNSON GRASS (*Sorghum halepense* (L.) Pers.) (Fig. 53)
Other common names: Means grass, Aleppo grass, evergreen millet, maiden cane, Egyptian millet, false Guinea grass, Cuba grass, Syria grass, St. Mary's grass.

Johnson grass is a native of the Mediterranean region, found in the tropical and warmer regions of both hemispheres. It is one of the major noxious weeds of California, and is now well established throughout the warmer sections of the State.

Johnson grass is a stout persistent perennial plant with creeping rootstocks. These have prominent sheaths at the nodes. Three classes of rootstocks of Johnson grass have been described.

(1) Primary rootstocks, or those that are alive in the ground at the beginning of the growing season in the spring; (2) secondary rootstocks, or those that arise more or less vertically from the primaries come to the surface, and produce crowns, thus forming new plants; (3) tertiary rootstocks, or those that the plant begins to send out from the base of its crown about flowering time; these are large and deeply penetrating.

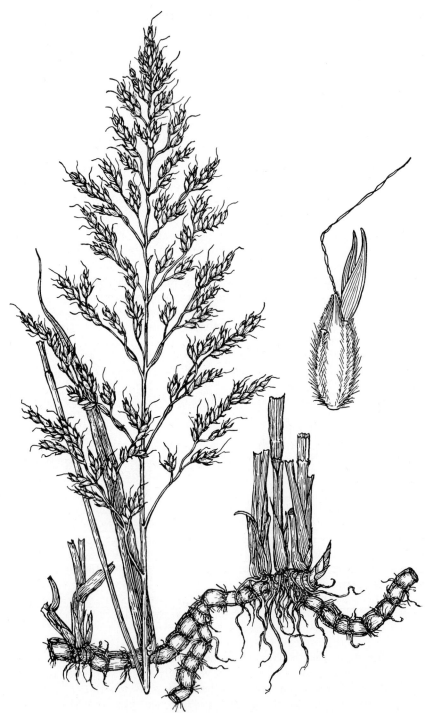

FIG. 53.   Johnson grass *Sorghum halepense.*

The primary rootstocks decay each year, whereas secondary and tertiary ones live over winter and produce new plants the following year. Tertiary rootstocks make practically all of their growth after flowering; consequently the longer the plants stand after blooming, the larger and deeper these tertiary rootstocks become. Although Johnson grass develops tertiary rootstocks usually after the flowering heads appear, a few will form late in the season even if heads are allowed to develop.

The culms or stems are from 3 to 6 feet high, smooth, erect, and very leafy. The leaves have a blade up to 2 feet long, $\frac{1}{4}$ to $\frac{3}{4}$ inch wide, pointed at the tip, smooth or rough on the edges, many-nerved, and with a conspicuous midrib; the ligule is short, papery, ciliate on the margin, and somewhat hairy on the back where the leaf blade joins the leaf sheath. The inflorescence (flowering head) is an open, loose panicle, 6 to 24 inches long; branches 2 or 3 at a node and more or less drooping; the branches are devoid of flowers along their lower portions, the 3-5 flowered racemes being clustered toward the extremities.

The spikelets usually occur in pairs, although toward the tip of the inflorescence they may occur in threes. When in pairs, usually the lower is sessile, broad, thick and perfect, the upper being pedicelled, narrow, long, and stamen-bearing. Whenever three spikelets are in a group, one (usually the middle one) is sessile and perfect, whereas the other two are pedicelled and staminate.

The fertile or perfect spikelet is sessile, broadly lanceolate, acute, about $\frac{1}{4}$ inch long, pale green or violet, becoming dark maroon or nearly black at maturity; the glumes are thick, leathery, and of about equal length; the outer one partially wraps about the inner; the outer glume is sparingly pubescent on the back, 5- to 7-nerved; the inner glume is similar in texture to the first, convex below, somewhat keeled above, acute at the apex, the margin being hyaline, ciliate, and somewhat turned inward. Within the two glumes of the fertile spikelet are two flowers, the lower sterile, the upper with both stamens and pistil. The so-called "third glume" is the lemma of the lower sterile flower; moreover, it is the only remnant of this flower; it encloses the parts of the fertile flower. The lemma of the fertile flower, sometimes called the "fourth glume," is a broad, hairy, and two-cleft at the tip, and there arises in the cleft, as a rule, a long awn which projects from the spikelet. The palet is frequently absent; when present it is small and thin. Three stamens are present. The ovary is smooth and is unlike that of wheat, oats, and rye, in that it does not bear a tuft of hairs at the tip.

The staminate spikelet is stalked and is narrower and more pointed than the fertile one. The pedicel or stalk is clothed with hairs. The spikelet is two-flowered, and subtended by two leathery glumes. Immediately within the two glumes is the lemma of the sterile flower of the spikelet, and within this is the lemma of the fertile flower. The stamens resemble those of the fertile spikelet, but there is no ovary. Staminate spikelets are short-lived; they soon fall, leaving the slender hairy stalks.

The unhulled seed of Johnson grass is 0.15 to 0.22 inch long, smooth, rounded, and usually with a light-colored, smooth, and callous-like scar at the base. Sometimes there are a few seeds which bear a stem at the base, a feature characteristic of the unhulled seed of Sudan grass. The appendages are mostly entire, expanded, cup-shaped, and smooth at apices. The hulls are normally brownish-black, sometimes reddish or lighter in color. Hulled seed is 0.08 to 0.12 inch long, mostly oval and widest above the middle, dark reddish-brown in color with almost microscopic longitudinal striations. The hulled grains of Sudan grass are somewhat larger, light reddish-brown, and more elliptical in outline, widest below the middle.

Johnson grass as a weed is scattered in a number of ways: (1) as an impurity in commercial seed, (2) in manure, as it is known to pass unharmed through the digestive tract of an animal, (3) in irrigation water, and (4) by means of cultivating implements, which drag the broken rootstocks from one part of a field to another, or from field to field.

In many sections Johnson grass has taken over large agricultural areas to such an extent that their abandonment became necessary. It has led to the pulling of orchards in order to carry out eradication programs, and added greatly to the costs of maintaining irrigation districts. In one potato-growing section Johnson grass grew so dense that root competition caused the formation of irregular-shaped tubers, resulting in a crop of unmarketable potatoes.

Under certain conditions Johnson grass is poisonous to livestock. The toxic substance is hydrocyanic acid, which may be present in all parts of the plant. Young plants are more toxic than mature ones. Interruption of growth, as by frost and drought, tends to increase the poisonous properties of the plant.

SMUTGRASS (*Sporobolus poiretii* (Roem. and Schult.) Hitchc.)

This is an introduction from tropical Asia which occurs in the warmer parts of America to Argentina. It has been found in the Eason district of Fresno County, where the report states "in a pasture very undesirable, as cattle will not go anywhere near it."

Smutgrass is an erect perennial, the culms 1 to 3½ feet tall. The leaf blades are flat or somewhat rolled, elongated, tapering to a fine point. The flowering head is spikelike, 4 to 16 inches long. The spikelets are 1-flowered, glumes blunt, about ½ as long as spikelet; lemma papery, acute, awnless. When the seeds are mature, they are reddish in color and for a time remain attached to the panicle by the mucilaginous outer coat. They are often affected with a black fungus, hence the common name, "smutgrass."

ST. AUGUSTINE GRASS (*Stenotaphrum secundatum* Kuntze)

This species, a native along the Gulf Coast of Mexico, has been used in Elysian Park, Los Angeles County, and elsewhere in lawn plantings for a number of years. Howell has found it as a sidewalk weed at Fairfax, Marin County, and locally naturalized west of Mill Valley.

It is a coarse creeping stoloniferous perennial with flat stems, spreading leaves, and spikelets much like those in *Panicum*. The flowering shoots are 4 to 12 inches tall. Spikelets are embedded in one side of the flat, corky rachis. At maturity the rachis near the tip breaks apart, the spikelets remaining attached to the joints. The lower glume is short, the upper about equal in length to the sterile lemma.

NEEDLEGRASS. *STIPA*

There are some 15 species of *Stipa* in California, known variously as porcupine grass, bear grass, spear grass, feather grass, and sleepy grass, most of which are of considerable forage value. They are tufted perennials with inrolled leaf blades. Some of the species, when mature, have grains with hard sharp points which penetrate the membranes and skin of animals.

NEEDLE-AND-THREAD (*Stipa comata* Trin.) (Fig. 9)

This species occurs on plains and dry hills from Indiana to Alaska south to California and Texas.

The flowering stems are from about 1 to 3 feet tall, blades 5 to 15 inches long, very narrow, flat or with the margins rolled inward. The narrow flowering spike is 5 to 10 inches long, usually enclosed at the base. The lemma is about $\frac{1}{2}$ inch long, pale or becoming brownish, the callus about 3 mm. long, sparsely hairy or becoming smooth above. The awn is very slender and loosely twisted below, indistinctly twice bent or angled, often deciduous.

The forage is of only fair quality and the needles are sometimes troublesome to livestock.

SLEEPY GRASS (*Stipa robusta* Scribn.)

A characteristic feature is the awn of the lemma, which is twisted below, abruptly bent, usually persistent on the grain, and quite long. The spikelets are 1-flowered; when the grain, which is commonly long and slender, is mature it has a bearded sharp-pointed callus at the base. The glumes are membranelike, usually long and narrow.

Sleepy grass is said to act as a narcotic on animals, especially horses, that graze upon it.

Stipa brachychaeta Godr., from Argentina, is reported by Tofsrud as adventive near Fresno. It has been recorded as an impurity in Argentine alfalfa seed.

SEDGE FAMILY *(Cyperaceae)*

This is a large family widely distributed over the world. Sedges are grass-like or rush-like herbs, usually with solid stems, and 3-ranked leaves. The fruit is an achene or nutlet, thus differing from that of its close relatives, the grasses, which is a grain. The horticultural species include papyrus (*Cyperus papyrus*), umbrella-plant (*C. alternifolius*), and chufa (*C. esculentus*). The principal genera are *Cyperus* (Fig. 54c), *Dulichium* (Fig. 54d), *Scirpus* (bullrushes) (Fig. 54a, b), *Eleocharis* (spike-rushes) (Fig. 54e), *Eriophorum* (cotton-grass), and *Carex* (sedges).

SEDGE. CAREX

Jepson describes 126 different species of *Carex* as occurring in California. All are grass-like perennial plants, from rootstocks. The stems are triangular, thus differing from those of grasses which are cylindrical. The leaves of sedges are 3-ranked, (Fig. 1h) whereas those of grasses are 2-ranked. The flowers are of two kinds, staminate and pistillate, arranged in spikes. The fruit is a 3-angled, plano-convex or lens-shaped achene, completely enclosed by a sac-like membrane. Sedges are widespread in the State, forming a large part of native mountain meadows, and many of them constitute an important element in native hay and forage.

GALINGALE. CYPERUS

In California there are over a dozen species of the genus *Cyperus*. The plants in this group closely resemble the grasses, but may be distinguished from true grasses by their triangular ꜱstem and closed leaf sheath. The flowering spikes are borne in terminal clusters subtended by several unequal linear leaves which spread out after the manner of the ribs of an umbrella.

Two species treated hereafter bear tubers or nutlets on the rootstocks. These underground nutlets, which explain the common name, nutgrass, are food storage reservoirs which make the weeds extraordinarily persistent. They are made up of thickened and greatly shortened internodes and are borne on thread-like scaly rhizomes. Each nutlet is capable of giving rise to a number of sprouts, and the nutlets in general are possessed of a remarkable vitality. A small portion of one dried nutlet, given the proper conditions to promote growth, will shortly exhibit a well developed root system, a strong above-ground shoot, as well as the beginnings of underground rhizomes.

Nutgrasses can well be classed with our most serious weed pests. With the ability to live over in soil under drought periods due to the abundance of stored food in the nutlets, they are exceedingly difficult to control.

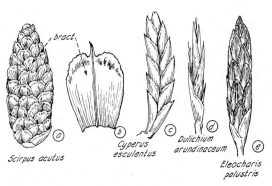

FIG. 54. Distinguishing characters of genera in sedge family.

UMBRELLA-PLANT (*Cyperus alternifolius* L.)

This species, the papyrus of literature, was introduced from Madagascar and has escaped from cultivation to a limited extent, becoming established locally in moist situations from Marin County southward.

Umbrella-plant is a perennial, similar in appearance to the following species, but distinguished by the showy, more numerous and longer leaves subtending the umbrella-like inflorescence.

SMALL FLOWERED UMBRELLA-PLANT (*Cyperus difformis* L.)

This is a native of tropical and subtropical regions of the Old World, and a pest in the rice fields of Japan and Russia. It has become abundant in the Biggs-Colusa area since 1926, and with us a rice weed of major importance.

The species is annual, the flowering stems not bulbous-thickened at the base. The inflorescence, reddish at maturity, often appears lateral, the longest bract of the involucre being more or less erect; scales less than 1 mm. long, round-obovate, rounded at the apex; stamens 1 or 2; achene triangular, nearly as long as the scale.

TALL UMBRELLA-PLANT (*Cyperus Eragrostis* Lane.)

This species has become well established throughout California. It is a perennial with sharply 3-edged stems. The inflorescence is subtended by 3 to 6 leaves; spikelets 2-4 mm. wide, yellowish-green or whitish blotched with brown; achenes abovoid, the short stipe broadened at the base.

This species is confused with the closely related and infrequent *C. virens* Michx. in which the achenes are more slender and the base is not prominently flanged.

YELLOW NUTGRASS (*Cyperus esculentus* L.) (Fig. 56)
Other common names: Chufa, ground almond, rush nut.

Yellow nutgrass is widely scattered throughout California, north to Alaska, and east to the Atlantic. It is known on all continents, preferring moist or even wet locations, and is at its best in the tropics and subtropics. It is becoming widespread and particularly troublesome in some of the potato, bean, and fruit growing areas, where frequent irrigations are needed for crop growth, thus furnishing sufficient moisture for the nutgrass.

The flowering stem or culm is sheathed at the base by smooth, bright green, grass-like leaves with prominent midvein. The leaves are commonly about ¼ inch wide, usually longer than the culm. They are rather stiff at first, but become lax and ribbon-like with age. The inflorescence consists of yellowish-brown to straw-colored flattened spikelets placed in two ranks. These are borne in heads at the end of rays of unequal length, with one head or spike sessile, or nearly so. The umbrella-like leaves which subtend the inflorescence are unequal, varying from 2 to 10 inches or more in length. The achene is encased in a straw-colored "flower" scale, and in the immature stages bears a three-cleft style. The seeds, which are

FIG. 55. Left—Yellow nutgrass (*Cyperus esculentus*). Right—Purple nutgrass (*Cyperus rotundus*).

less than ⅛ inch long, are three-angled, and narrow gradually from a square shouldered apex toward the base. The color is brownish-gray to brown.

The underground tubers or nutlets are unevenly globose or slightly flattened transversely. As the nutlets mature, the leaf scales which are present on the young tubers disappear, so that the surface of a fully developed nutlet is fairly smooth. The taste is not unlike that of an almond, somewhat sweeter and with an earthy flavor. The common name "earth-almond" is properly descriptive. Under the name "chufa," the nutlets are occasionally to be found in the markets of the Southern States. *C. esculentus* is cultivated to a limited extent in the Gulf States for hogs, the nutlets affording a palatable and nutritious forage.

PURPLE NUTGRASS (*Cyperus rotundus* L.)
Other common names: Coco-sedge, coco-grass.

This species has become naturalized in California more recently than yellow nutgrass. At first considered local in southern California, it is now known in scattered localities northward. It is frequently reported as being particularly obnoxious in lawns and gardens. *C. rotundus* has a wide distribution in the Eastern States, and is considered a troublesome weed in the South.

In general appearance it is very similar to yellow nutgrass. The flowering stem is usually longer than the basal leaves. The leaves which subtend the inflorescence are not as long as those of yellow nutgrass; even the longest are seldom more than twice as long as the flower-bearing rays. The scales, and hence the color of the inflorescences, are a dark purple-brown. Sometimes the individual scales appear green on the margin and mid-vein. The achene narrows toward the base and apex and is widest at about the center. It is commonly blackish-brown, darker than the more wedge-shaped achene of yellow nutgrass. The underground nutlets are somewhat oblong and covered with a persistent reddish-brown coarse, fibrous coat.

COMMON SPIKERUSH (*Eleocharis palustris* R. & S.) (Fig. 54e)
Other common name: Wiregrass.

Closely related to bulrush, this spikerush or wiregrass is sometimes a weed of rice fields. It is a stout perennial ½ to 2 feet high, with cylindrical, wiry, leafless stems arising from creeping stolons. The flowers are in spikelets which are from ½ to 1 inch long. The fruit is a 3-angled achene, with a persistent tubercle at apex.

KYLLINGA (*Kyllinga brevifolia* Rottb.)

This native of the American tropics occurs in southern California where it behaves as a weed. It is a perennial, 10 to 30 inches tall, with solitary, globe-shaped or oval, greenish spikes from 5 to 10 mm. long. The spikelets are 1-flowered, thus differing from those of *Cyperus*.

BULRUSH. *SCIRPUS*

There are some 16 species of *Scirpus* growing in California, all rush-like herbs, most of which inhabit moist, marshy ground. One of the most common species in California is *S. acutus,* known as ''common tule'' which occurs in salt and fresh water marshes and along borders of lakes and streams. There were originally many thousands of acres of tule lands in California, many of which have been reclaimed to cultivation. Tules are frequently a great nuisance along irrigation ditches. Here they may grow so dense as to seriously retard the flow of water, necessitating periodic dredging of the ditches. Tule stems, used by native tribes to build their balsas or small boats and to weave mats, are now used for packing nursery stock and as a source of potash.

COMMON TULE (*Scirpus acutus* Muhl.) (Fig. 54)

The common tule is a perennial from creeping rootstocks, with erect, leafless stems 3 to 9 feet high, round in cross section or very obtusely angled above, spongy-cellular. The flowering head is 1 to 5 inches long, the perianth bristles downwardly barbed. The fruit is a dull obovate lens-shaped achene about 2 mm. wide.

CALIFORNIA BULRUSH (*Scirpus californicus* Britt.)

This is a perennial from creeping rootstocks, with the general habit of growth, appearance, and distribution of *S. acutus*. The erect, leafless stems are 3 to 9 feet high. The spikelets are dark reddish-brown, cylindric or narrow-oval, in long-rayed umbels. The perianth bristles are somewhat short-plumose, ribbon-shaped and dark red. Achenes nearly white, plano-convex, the surface obscurely netted.

BULL TULE *(Scirpus campestris* Britt.)

This species occurs throughout California in wet alkaline soils, and salt marshes. It is a perennial, 1 to 3 feet tall, with stout, triangular stems. Often where the stem joins the root stock it is enlarged, forming a woody tuber. The leaves equal or exceed the stem in length, flat or channeled and keeled. Bracts of the involucre are leaf-like, 3 to 13 inches long, one being much longer than the rest. The inflorescence is terminal, the spikelets in clusters of 1 to 3. Spikelets oval, sharp-pointed, ½ to ¾ inches long; scales papery, usually bifid at the apex, with a short awn between the teeth; bristles 2 to 6; style 2-cleft; achene shiny, dark brown.

RIVER BULRUSH (*Scirpus fluviatilis* (Torr.) A. Gray)

River bulrush which occurs in the San Joaquin and Sacramento Valleys and eastward, resembles the bull tule. Whereas in the bull tule, the awn of the scale is smooth, that of the river bulrush is rough to the touch.

ROUGH-SEED BULRUSH (*Scirpus mucronatus* L.) (Fig. 56)

This weed is a native of the Old World and is of wide distribution in Europe. In 1948 it occurred over an estimated 10,000 acres in the rice growing section of northern California, and in some fields constituted up to 75 percent of the stand. It is difficult to differentiate between the rice and the bulrush in the early stages of growth.

The smooth leaf-like flowering stem of rough-seed bulrush attains a height of from two to three feet and is sharply three-angled with the sides concave and the angles extended to knife-edge thinness. The solitary bract extends beyond the flower cluster as an oblique bayonet-like continuation of the stem. The small overlapping fracts of the flower clusters are edged with very dark brown. At maturity these flower bracts conceal numerous shiny black, horizontally ridged, trigonous seeds. The seeds bear weak downwardly barbed bristles which are sometimes persistent. Handling or recleaning the rice tends to remove these bristles. The rootstocks in cross-section appear distinctly two-colored: a corky indistinctly rayed outer rim surrounds a starchy inner portion often with a vaguely defined darker line between.

TUBEROUS-ROOTED BULRUSH *(Scirpus tuberosus* (L.) Desf.)

This bulrush, which is troublesome locally in rice fields near Willows, Glenn County, is similar in appearance to the preceding, somewhat taller and coarser, with heavy fibrous-coated creeping rhizomes. These are

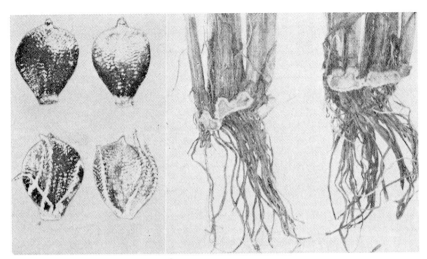

FIG. 56. Rough-seed bulrush (*Scirpus mucronatus*). Left, detail of seed enlarged to show horizontal ridges, mucronate tip, and barbed bristles. (x12) Right, base plant with cross-section through tuber-like rootstock.

enlarged at intervals to form tubers ¾ to 1½ inches in diameter. The tubers, spread by cultivation enable this bulrush to persistently resist control measures.

PICKEREL WEED FAMILY *(Pontederiaceae)*

This is a small family of fresh-water herbs, which float on the surface or are attached to the bottom of bogs or shores. The genera with us are *Heteranthera* and *Eichhornia*, the latter represented by one species.

WATER HYACINTH *(Eichhornia crassipes* Solms.) (Fig. 57)

This native of tropical America has become established as a weed in a few California localities, especially in the lower Sacramento and San Joaquin Valleys. It is of importance because of its clogging of streams, thus impeding navigation and water flow. It is the famous "million-dollar weed" that obstructs navigation in the St. John's River, Florida. The history of its establishment is not known but it was certainly introduced as an ornamental aquatic and is said to have been planted in a pond near Palatka, Florida, where it soon became so abundant as to necessitate control measures and was taken up and thrown into the St. John's River.

Water hyacinth is a floating perennial, the aerial leaves forming rosettes usually 1 to 2 feet in height from the water surface. There are two kinds of leaves: Those under water, which are long and narrow, and those above the water line, which are usually broad to nearly circular. The leaf stalks are enlarged into oval bulbs filled with air-cells. The flower stalk is about 1 foot long, and has a single leaf and several sheaths at and above the middle. Each flower stalk bears about eight flowers in a loose, terminal spike. The flowers are funnel-shaped, bluish-purple in color, with six lobes. Inserted on the inside of the funnel-shaped

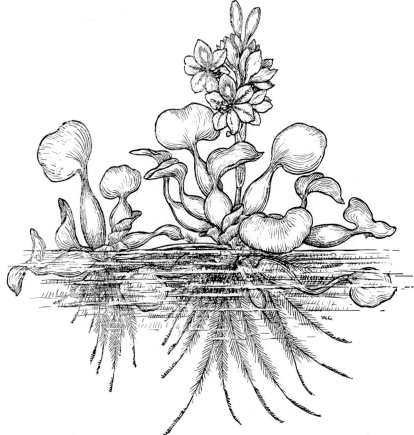

FIG. 57. Water hyacinth (*Eichhornia crassipes*), showing rosettes of leaves with inflated leafstalks, flowers, and root system.

corolla are six stamens—three long, three short. The mature fruit is a 3-celled egg-shaped capsule.

The plant produces only a few seeds, but it spreads rapidly vegetatively, that is, by means of runners which send out roots from the nodes. There are two kinds of roots: thick, fleshy, horizontal ones, and slender, vertical ones with numerous, small fibrous branches. In shallow water the plants may become attached to the soil, but they grow equally well freely floating in deeper water.

RUSH FAMILY *(Juncaceae)*

Members of this family are tufted, wiry or grass-like herbs of both wet and dry situations. Most of them are perennials from stolons or rootstocks. They are widespread geographically. The principal genera are *Juncus* and *Luzula*.

RUSH. *JUNCUS*

Jepson describes 31 species of *Juncus* in California. All are natives, and several behave as weeds.

The rushes are grass-like plants with spongy, sometimes hollow, stems. The leaves are stiff. The flowers are greenish or brownish, and each has 6 similar glume-like segments (corresponding to sepals and petals), 3 or 6 stamens, and a single 3-celled ovary with 3 stigmas. The fruit is a 3-celled capsule.

FIG. 58. Toad rush (*Juncus bufonius*).

BALTIC RUSH (*Juncus balticus* Willd.)

This is widespread in moist situations from Alaska to southern California. It is a perennial, 10 to 30 inches tall, arising from creeping rootstocks, stems round, flowers many in a cluster. The seeds are .8 to 1 mm., oblong and somewhat oblique, finely striate and covered with whitish scurfiness. Seed occurs in commercial lots of lawn grass seed and in seed rice.

TOAD RUSH (*Juncus bufonius* L.) (Fig. 58)

This is very common in clay soils. It is a low, dwarf annual with fibrous roots. The seed is approximately .5 mm. long, amber in color, darker around scar, oblong, minutely longitudinally netted in 30-40 rows. It occurs as an impurity in lawn grass seed.

SOFT RUSH (*Juncus effusus* L.)

This species grows in swampy places. It is a perennial with the flower group apparently lateral, the stems slender and rigid, the flowers small, usually less than $\frac{1}{12}$ inch long and the stamens 3 in number.

YARD RUSH (*Juncus tenuis* Willd.)

This is common in moist or dry soil, especially along paths and roadsides, or in fields and gardens, and is quite difficult to eradicate. It is a tall perennial from underground rootstocks, and often forms dense tufts. The leaves are mostly basal, the stems round and slender and nearly naked above, the flowers small, pale greenish and with 6 stamens. The seeds are .2-.3 mm. long, pointed at both ends, winged at the tips or along one side, brick red and translucent, netted with transverse lines; the seeds often adhere in small groups. This also is carried in lawn grass seed.

LILY FAMILY *(Liliaceae)*

Representatives of the lily family are found all over the world. A number of them are cultivated as vegetables, the principal ones being onions and asparagus. Chief among those cultivated as ornamentals are *Yucca,* lily *(Lilium),* hyacinth, and tulip. Some of the well known natives are camass *(Camassia),* numerous species of wild onion *(Allium), Brodiaea,* Mariposa lilies *(Calachortus), Fritillarias,* many species of lily *(Lilium),* fairy bells and fairy lantern *(Disporum),* trillium or wake robin *(Trillium),* false hellebore *(Veratrum),* and death camas *(Zygadenus).*

SOAP PLANT (*Chlorogalum pomeridianum* (Ker.) Kunth)

This conspicuous plant is widespread on dry open hills and plains of the Sierra Nevada foothills, Great Valley and Coast Ranges, north to Oregon and in southern California west of the mountains. It is perennial from a tunicated bulb which is 3 to 4 inches long and thickly covered with coarse dark fibers. The basal tuft of lily-like linear leaves are about 1 inch wide, bluish green, and more or less wavy-margined. The flowering stem is from 2 to 10 feet tall, with a large sparsely flowered spreading panicle; petals linear, about ¾-inch long, white with purple veins, in age twisted over the capsule. The capsule is about ¼-inch long, 3-lobed, 1 to 2 seeds in each cell. The seeds are similar to onion seed; glistening-black, wrinkled, with a white remnant at the scar.

FALSE HELLEBORE (*Veratrum californicum* Durand) (Fig. 59)
Other common names: corn lily, cow cabbage, wild Indian corn, Indian poke, devil's bit, and skunk cabbage.

This species occurs in wet meadows, around springs, in marshy flats, bogs and swamps. It is distributed throughout the Sierra Nevada at elevations between 4,500 and 9,000 feet, and also in the North Coast Range and high mountains of southern California. *Veratrum californicum* is a tall, stout leafy plant from a short, thick rootstock. It may attain a height of 8 feet. The leaves are broad, sessile, sheathing at the base, oval, coarsely-veined, and 6 to 12 inches long. The flowers are in a panicle, 1 to 1⅓ feet long. The flowers are dull white in color, and the perfect ones have 3 sepals, 3 petals, 6 stamens, and a 3-celled ovary.

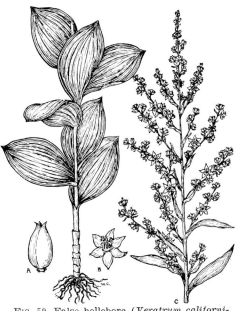

FIG. 59. False hellebore (*Veratrum californicum*) A, capsule; B, flower; C, inflorescence.

The fruit is a thick-walled capsule of three compartments, each containing many flat seeds with broadly winged margins.

The plant is poisonous to livestock, all parts of the plant being more or less toxic.

DEATH-CAMAS. ZYGADENUS

Species of *Zygadenus* are perennial, from a bulb. The stems are simple and scape-like, and bear long, grass-like leaves. Flowers are greenish white or yellowish, and occur in terminal racemes or panicles. There are six similar perianth segments, each of which bears one or two glands at the base. Stamens 6; styles 3, distinct; fruit a 3-lobed, 3-celled capsule.

The three most common species in California, and of particular interest as poisonous plants are described below.

CHAPARRAL DEATH CAMAS (*Zygadenus Fremontii* Wats.) (Fig. 60)

This species is most common in the lower foothills of the Coast Range, and southward. The plants are 1¼ to 2¼ feet high, from a globular bulb ½ to 1¼ inches broad. Basal leaves are 8 to 16 inches long, and from ½ to 1 inch broad. Flowers greenish-white, in racemes, and usually all perfect; the six perianth segments are from $\frac{1}{4}$ to $\frac{1}{2}$ inch long, only the outer clawed, and at the base of each segment is a greenish-yellow gland. Stamens six, with white anthers; styles 3, distinct; fruit, a capsule with 3 distinct lobes.

While no experimental data are available on the controlled feeding of chaparral death camas, sheep owners fear to graze where this species occurs in the absence of adequate suitable forage.

FOOTHILL DEATH CAMAS (*Zygadenus paniculatus* (Nutt.) Wats.)

This species occurs from Nevada County to Siskiyou County. The plants are 8 to 16 inches high, with sheathing leaves, and a rather broad more or less compound raceme. Leaves are narrow, from $\frac{1}{4}$ to $\frac{1}{2}$ inch broad. Lower flowers of the inflorescence are often staminate. The perianth segments are thickened on the back at the base, and usually the claws of the segments are very short. The stamens are longer than, or equal the segments, and bear yellow anthers. The capsule is $\frac{1}{2}$ to 1 inch long.

Foothill death camas is not generally considered as toxic as meadow death camas, however, it is responsible for cattle and sheep losses in the northeastern part of the State.

MEADOW DEATH CAMAS (*Zygadenus venenosus* Wats.)

This is a native species widely distributed in California in moist meadows. It is most abundant from Monterey and Mariposa counties northward, extending altitudinally from sea level in the Coast Range to 9,500 feet in the Sierra Nevada.

Death camas is an herbaceous plant with grass-like foliage and simple, erect, solid stems 1 to 2 feet high, growing from an oblong bulb which is covered with brown, outer scales. The leaves are smooth, long-linear, mainly basal on the stems, generally curving and some-what folded along the prominent midrib; the leaf margins are rough-ened with minute teeth. The flowers are greenish-white, arranged in a raceme at the top of the stem. The raceme is 5 to 10 inches long. The flower is composed of a perianth of 6 segments, each contracted to a short claw at the base upon which is a green gland; there are 6 stamens and a single pistil with 3 distinct, persistent styles. The ovary matures into a deeply 3-lobed, 3-celled capsule containing 18 to 24 seeds. Seeds are about 5 mm. long, broadest about middle and tapering in width and thickness toward the ends, light brown in color and with surface wrinkled.

Meadow death camas is reported to be the most poisonous of all the species and annually is responsible for heavy sheep losses.

FIG. 60.   Chaparral death camas (*Zygadenus Fremontii*).

HEMP FAMILY *(Cannabinaceae)*

The hemp family is a small one containing two genera, *Humulus* (hop) and *Cannabis* (hemp).

COMMON HEMP *(Cannabis sativa* L.) (Fig. 61)
Other common name: Marihuana.

The native home of common hemp is central and western Asia. It has spread, as a result of cultivation, throughout Europe, Asia and America. Although relatively rare as an escape in California, in many other states it has become a rather troublesome weed. However, in California, the so-called Indian hemp, or marihuana has been grown

FIG. 61.   Common hemp *(Cannabis sativa)*, showing habit, a single pistillate flower subtended by a bract, and a seed. Upper right, staminate inflorescence.

for its narcotic properties. By recent legislative action it is unlawful to plant, cultivate, possess, sell or give away marihuana.

The common hemp is a stout, erect, branching annual, 3 to 16 feet high. The green plant has a peculiar narcotic odor, is sticky to the touch, and covered with fine hair. The main stem has four ridges running lengthwise, is hollow and produces a few branches near the top. The leaves are alternate above and opposite below. They are compound, digitate, with 5 to 11 linear-lanceolate, pointed and serrate leaflets; they are of deep green color on the upper side and of lighter green on the lower side. Hemp is dioecious. The staminate inflorescences are in axillary, narrow, and loose panicles, the pistillate in erect, leafy spikes, also axillary. The staminate flower is borne on a slender pedicel subtended by a bracteole; it has 5 distinct sepals and 5 short stamens. Each pistillate flower is subtended by a leafy bract and possesses a single, thin, entire calix segment, wrapped about the ovary. The ovary has 2 thread-like feathery stigmas. Hemp is wind-pollinated. The ovary matures into an ovoid, hard achene about $\frac{1}{8}$ inch long, gray-green to clay color, often with a distinct venation apparent. The curved embryo is imbedded in a fleshy endosperm. The fruits of hemp are much larger and heavier when grown in a moist habitat than when grown in a dry one.

In hemp there is a resinous substance known as cannabin. Cannabinol, with intoxicating properties, is obtained from cannabin. Pammel says, ''The form of hemp commonly reached by commerce is called Bhang or Hashish and consists of dried leaves and small stalks frequently mixed with fruits. This is smoked in India with or without tobacco. Ganjah is obtained from the flowering shoots of the female plant or stalk, a stiff woody stem several inches long which is pruned to produce flowering branches. The tops of these are collected, then pressed by being trodden by the feet. From this comes the drug known as ganjah. * * * The other forms of the plant consumed in India are Bhang and Charras. Subjce or Bhang is used for smoking. The narcotic ingredient found in *majun* and *charras* is undried resin which is obtained by the natives who, when passing among plants, wear rubber aprons to which the resin adheres, after which the product is scraped together. The principal constituents of hemp are resin and a volatile oil.''

NETTLE FAMILY *(Urticaceae)*

Trees, shrubs, and herbs belong to this widely distributed family in which there are about 550 species. Three genera are represented in our flora: *Urtica, Hesperocnide,* and *Parietaria. Parietaria* species have alternate leaves whereas those of *Urtica* are opposite.

JUDEAN PELLITORY *(Parietaria judaica* L.)

This weed, which has been collected from San Francisco south to Santa Cruz County, is an introduction from the Old World. It is a low

annual, with stinging hairs; the leaves alternate, entire, 3-nerved, petioled, and without stipules. Both perfect and pistillate small greenish
flowers occur in axillary clusters. The perianth of perfect flowers becomes
greatly enlarged as the fruit matures.

Parietaria floridana Nutt. is a native species, similar to the Judean
pellitory. While in the introduced species the perianth becomes greatly
enlarged as the fruit matures, that of the native species remains relatively
small.

NETTLE. URTICA

The nettles are annual or perennial herbs with stinging hairs. Leaves
are opposite, petioled, rather strongly 3 to 7-nerved, and have stipules.
Flowers are greenish, and either staminate or pistillate; staminate flowers
have 4 sepals, 4 stamens, and a rudimentary pistil; pistillate flowers have
4 unequal sepals, a one-celled ovary bearing one seed. The fruit is an
achene, enclosed by the persistent calyx.

KEY TO WEEDY SPECIES OF URTICA

Herbage gray _____U. gracilis
Herbage dark-green
    Leaves broadly ovate, deeply cordate, 3 to 4 inches long, and nearly as broad
                                                  U. californica
    Leaves elliptic to ovate, not cordate, $\frac{1}{2}$ to $1\frac{1}{2}$ inches long_____U. urens

COAST NETTLE (*Urtica californica* Greene)

This species is limited in its distribution to the coastal lowlands,
chiefly in the San Francisco Bay region. The plants are 2 to 3 feet tall,
and stolon-bearing. The leaves are broadly oval, heart-shaped at the base,
coarsely toothed, 3 to 4 inches long, and about as broad; the petioles are
1 to 3 inches long.

CREEK NETTLE (*Urtica gracilis* Ait. var. *holosericea* Jepson)

Creek nettle is common throughout California, except in the desert
regions, often forming a thick growth along streams and in moist soil.

This is a perennial herb, 4 to 10 feet high, with staminate and pistillate flowers in separate, spike-like inflorescences. Leaves are opposite,
petioled, 3 to 5 inches long, coarsely toothed, oval or lance-shaped, somewhat bristly above, and gray-pubescent below.

SMALL NETTLE (*Urtica urens* L.) (Fig. 62)

This species is introduced from Europe, and now occurs in the
south Coast Ranges and along the coast of southern California. The
small nettle is an erect annual, a few inches to 2 feet high. The stems
are 4-angled, tough, and slightly hairy (with stinging hairs). The leaves
are opposite, petioled, 3- to 5-nerved, coarsely toothed, $\frac{1}{2}$ to $1\frac{1}{2}$ inches
long, and have 2 short stipules. The leaves bear scattered stinging hairs.
The flower clusters are in the leaf axils. Flowers are of two sorts, staminate and pistillate, on the same plant and mixed in the same cluster.
Staminate flowers have 4 sepals and 4 stamens. Pistillate flowers have a
bell-shaped calyx of 2 to 4 segments, and a single pistil. The fruit is an
achene enclosed by the persistent calyx.

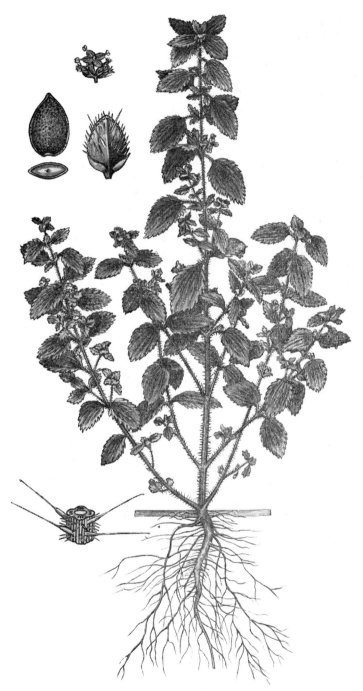

FIG. 62. Small nettle (*Urtica urens*).

Small nettle is particularly troublesome as a weed in truck farming, especially in the Salinas Valley.

LIZARD'S TAIL FAMILY *(Saururaceae)*

These are perennial herbs, the known species being but four. With us, the best known representative is Yerba Mansa.

YERBA MANSA (*Anemopsis californica* (Nutt.) Hook.) (Fig 2c)

This species is common throughout the San Joaquin and lower Sacramento Valleys, also in the south Coast Ranges, Inyo County and southern California, usually occurring in saline and wet lowlands. It has a spicy herbage, and an aromatic rootstock. The stems are hollow and ½ to 2 feet high. The basal leaves are elliptic-oblong, rounded above, heart-shaped at the base, the blade 2 to 8 inches long, the petioles 1 to 8 inches long; on the upper portion of the flowering stem there is a broadly oval clasping leaf, with from 1 to 3 small, stalked leaves in the axil. The flowers are in conical spikes, ½ to 1¼ inches long, surrounded at the base by a persistent showy involucre of 5 to 8 bracts; each flower in the spike is subtended by a small white bract. Calyx and corolla are lacking in the flowers; there are 5 to 8 stamens, a one-celled ovary and 2 to 3 stigmas. The fruit is a capsule which splits open at the apex.

BUCKWHEAT FAMILY *(Polygonaceae)*

There are about 30 genera and 800 species in this family. Rhubarb and buckwheat are the principal cultivated members, while a number of species of *Rumex* (dock) and *Polygonum* (knotweed, etc.) are bad weeds. The stems are conspicuously jointed and usually swollen at the joints. The leaf stipules, with some exceptions, are membranous, sheathing, and united to form a very characteristic structure, the *ocrea*. The fruit is commonly a 3-angled achene.

EMEX (*Emex spinosa* Campd.) (Fig. 63)

This is an Old World species which has been collected near Fillmore, Ventura County. It is an annual herb with entire, oblong, petioled leaves, staminate and pistillate flowers on the same plant, and a characteristic 3-angled fruit, almost enclosed by a tubular, 3-pointed perianth, which measures about ¼ inch in length.

FIG. 63.   Emex (*Emex spinosa*), showing a cluster of 3-angled fruits.

Emex australis, a South African species, has been collected at San Francisco, near Vallejo and at Benicia.

KNOTWEED. POLYGONUM

This genus includes plants commonly known as knotweeds, smartweeds, and black bindweed. In California there are 6 weedy species. In this genus the flowers have 5 sepals, whereas in *Rumex* there are 6. Moreover, the sepals in *Polygonum* are equal in size, while those of *Rumex* species are unequal, there being 3 small outer reflexed sepals and 3 inner larger sepals. A conspicuous feature of the group is the swollen nodes. The fruit (achene) is dry and 1-seeded, and usually triangular in shape.

Several species of *Polygonum* contain an acrid substance which may cause dermatitis in livestock or, if eaten in considerable amounts, result in gastric disturbances.

KEY TO WEEDY SPECIES OF POLYGONUM

Plants twining or trailing ; leaves heart-shaped at base_____*P. Convolvulus*
Plants not twining nor trailing ; leaves tapering at base
  Flowers in axillary clusters ; stems usually forming prostrate mats_____*P. aviculare*
  Flowers in dense spikes ; stems erect
    Spikes often nodding or drooping_____*P. lapathifolium*
    Spikes erect
      Perennials
        Spikes 1 or 2 ; flowers red ; stamens 5, exserted_____*P. coccineum*
        Spikes several to many ; stamens 6 or 8, included_____*P. acre*
      Annuals
        Leaves 4 to 5 inches long_____ *P. Persicaria*
        Leaves ⅜ to 2⅝ inches long_____*P. argyrocoleon*

DOTTED SMARTWEED (*Polygonum acre* H. B. K.)

This species occurs throughout the United States. It is fairly common in low, marshy land, and in mountain meadows. It is sometimes regarded as a pest in hay meadows of northern California where it competes with forage plants. It is a perennial plant, the stems 2 to 5 feet tall, often bending over and rooting at the base. The leaves, 2 to 3 inches long, are oval lance-shaped to narrowly lance-shaped, narrowing to a short petiole. The spikes are erect, loose, slender, and 1 to 3 inches long. The calyx is greenish and conspicuously glandular dotted. The fruit (achene) is lens-shaped or triangular, smooth and shining.

SILVER-SHEATHED KNOTWEED (*Polygonum argyrocoleon* Steud.) (Fig. 64)

In localities where this annual knotweed has become established, it ranks well to the fore as a pest in alfalfa fields. In age the plant is tough and wiry, and consequently most undesirable in hay. It has the added disadvantage of producing abundant seed at such a height and at such time as to be harvested along with the alfalfa seed crop. The seed was brought into California some twenty years ago as an impurity in imported Turkestan alfalfa. The conditions about the Imperial Valley were conducive to its establishment and its invasion of alfalfa fields followed as a natural sequence.

Silver-sheathed knotweed maintains itself and spreads by means of seed alone, having a relatively shallow, sparsely branched taproot. If not allowed to mature and drop seed, it can be controlled, but if unchecked it is a persistent aggressor as are many of our weedy immigrants. Allowed

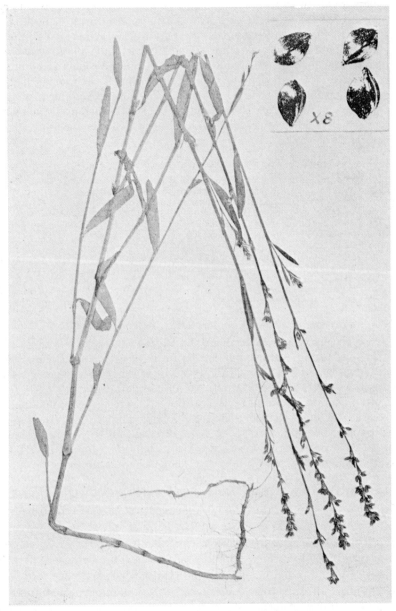

FIG. 64. Silver-sheathed knotweed (*Polygonum argyrocoleon*), showing erect habit of growth and leafless flower spikes. Inset shows the glossy seed surface.

unhampered seeding ground along the highway rights of way, the encroachment and spread of this pest in the alfalfa stands is inevitable.

Silver-sheathed knotweed is annual, 12 to 20 inches high, glabrous, erect. Leaves elliptical to lanceolate, ⅔ to 2⅗ inches long. Leaf bracts form conspicuous silvery sheaths on young parts. Flowers are 2 to 5 in a cluster on pedicels equalling or exceeding the perianth. The inflorescence is a long, slender, interrupted leafless spike. The perianth is pinkish, closely investing the achene. The achene is small, glossy, minutely dotted. This knotweed is commonly mistaken for an upright form of the well known knotgrass or wireweed, *P. aviculare*, which is common everywhere. Silver-sheathed knotweed may readily be distinguished by its erect, long, leafless, rose-colored flower spikes, and the shiny, three-angled seed or achene. Although the achene is minutely dotted, to the naked eye it appears quite glossy and highly polished. The dots or shallow pits are scarcely discernible without considerable magnification. The color is an even mahogany. Common knotgrass, *P. aviculare*, differs in being leafy out to the very end of the stem. It is commonly prostrate or at least procumbent. The three-angled achene is larger, darker, and does not have a high shine although the angles often appear lighter colored and more glossy than the body of the seed.

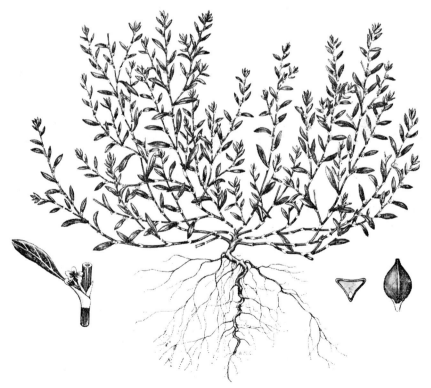

FIG. 65.   Common knotweed (*Polygonum aviculare*).

COMMON KNOTWEED (*Polygonum aviculare* L.) (Fig. 65)

Other common names: Wiregrass, yardgrass, knotgrass, doorweed, prostrate knot-weed, matgrass, pink-weed, birdgrass, stonegrass, waygrass, goosegrass.

This weed is common throughout northern United States and south-ern Canada, and also well known in Europe and Asia. It is usually found in hard, beaten soils in yards and paths, along roadsides, and in waste places, and not infrequently is a bad weed in cultivated fields. Knotweed is an annual, with slender wiry stems, which are highly branched to form, especially in hard ground, prostrate mats. However, in cultivated fields the stem, although prostrate at the base, may stand 4 to 8 inches high. There is a single, central, deeply penetrating root which may give rise to numerous yellowish, fibrous roots. The leaves are a bluish-green or bottle-green color, the blades being narrowly oval in outline, $\frac{1}{2}$ to 1.5 inches long, and about $\frac{3}{8}$ inch wide, and the leaf-stalk short and closely encircled by the papery stipules (ocrea). The flowers are small, rather inconspicuous, on short stalks, and borne in axillary clusters. The 3-angled fruit (achene) is about 3 mm. long, with the faces dull and somewhat roughish, the angles smooth and shiny. The color is dark mahogany brown to almost black; often part of the calyx is persistent.

SWAMP KNOTWEED (*Polygonum coccineum* Muhl.) (Fig. 66)

Other common names: "Kelp," marsh smartweed, swamp persicaria, devil's shoe-string, tanweed.

"Kelp" is the name by which this pest has long been known in the San Joaquin-Sacramento Valley delta section where it is very abundant and troublesome. So far as we have been able to ascertain, the name "kelp" is confined to local usage. While the origin of the term is obscure, the following explanation seems reasonable. Much of the low land on which *P. coccineum* makes its most rank growth is subject to overflow, and during periods of inundation the leaves and stems float on the sur-face of the water. This sprawling aquatic habit strongly suggests the true kelp of our Pacific seacoast.

Usually the stems are from 1 to 3 feet long, somewhat prostrate to erect and little or not at all branched. In the moist peat soil of the delta a height of 6 feet is not unusual. The root system is strong and highly developed, with long horizontal rootstocks. These interlacing rootstocks, many of which are half an inch in diameter, are tough enough seriously to interfere with cultivation operations.

The stem, which has swellings at the joints, is commonly roughish with short flattened down hairs, sometimes smooth and slightly grooved. *P. coccineum* is exceedingly variable, both as to hairiness and leaf form. In swampy sites the plants are usually glabrous or smooth, with the base of the leaves somewhat heart-shaped. In drier situations they are appressed, hairy, with quite narrow or lance-like leaves tapered at the base. The leaf length varies from about 3 to 7 inches. The entire margins are often scabrous or roughish on the edges. The characteristic sheathing

FIG. 66. Swamp Knotweed (*Polygonum coccineum*).

stipules embrace the leaf stems and are of about the same length. They are quite conspicuous and vary in hairiness. The dense terminal flower spikes are a bright rose pink, from 1 to 4 inches long. They are borne singly or in pairs on rough, hairy, and often glandular peduncles or stems. The seeds are lens-shaped, quite convex on both sides, with a short point at the apex. The color is almost black and the surface very shiny. We have no record of seed of this weed having been found in commercial seed.

In addition to the troublesome infestations of "kelp" in the delta lands, the weed extends into irrigated lands north and east of Sacramento, along the borders of sluggish streams and in the vicinity of lakes west to the coast, in the meadows of the northern counties, and south to below Los Angeles. The range for the country as a whole is from British Columbia to Ontario, south to Virginia, Louisiana and Texas. Outside of California *P. coccineum* is most commonly known as swamp persicaria or swamp smartweed. Although the weed seems to thrive best in moist situations, it will grow almost anywhere and varies its growth form to suit the environment.

This polygonum is extremely serious on any land that receives a heavy application of water or along ditches which carry a steady volume of water. Due to the nature of its growth it extends out onto the water, cutting down the carrying capacity of the canal and increasing maintenance costs. Where cultivation is feasible along these ditches the plant can be kept in check, but due to high soil moisture content it is practically impossible to eradicate.

BLACK BINDWEED (*Polygonum Convolvulus* L.)
Other common names: Wild buckwheat, knot bindweed, bear-bind, ivy bindweed, climbing bindweed, corn-bind.

Black bindweed, a plant naturalized from Europe, occurs sparingly in California. However, it is common throughout the northern United States and Canada. It occurs in waste places, grain fields, cultivated fields and gardens. The plant has the general habit of growth of the wild morning-glory (*Convolvulus*) for which it is sometimes mistaken; that is, the stems are twining or creeping. Moreover, the leaves of the two groups are somewhat similar in shape.

Black bindweed is an annual, with small flowers usually disposed in axillary clusters or short racemes; wild morning-glory or common bindweed is perennial and has large funnel-shaped "morning-glory" flowers. The roots of black bindweed are fibrous. The stems may attain a length of several feet. The leaves are simple, smooth, heart-shaped or somewhat halberd-shaped, and taper-pointed. The calyx is 5-parted, and closely invests the mature fruit. The fruit is an achene about 3 mm. long, triangular, the three sides equal and more or less concave, dull black, and minutely scurfy. Part of the reddish-brown calyx is often persistent at the base.

PALE SMARTWEED (*Polygonum lapathifolium* L.)
Other common names: Common knotweed, willow-weed, pale persicaria.

This species, now found throughout northern United States and along the Pacific Coast, is introduced from Europe. It generally grows along streams and in low, wet swales. The species is annual, usually stout, the stems a height of 1 to 4 feet. The stems branch, and often root at the lower nodes. There may be a very scanty glandular pubescence on the flower stalks and rough pubescence on the leaf margins. The leaves are broadly lance-shaped, long pointed at the apex, and wedge-shaped at the base, and 4 to 5 inches long. The whitish or flesh-colored flowers are in drooping or nodding, dense spikes 1 inch or more long. The fruit (achene) is about 2 mm. long, broadly ovate with tip elongated to a point, flattened, dark-brown, the surface being glossy or finely granular.

LADY'S THUMB (*Polygonum Periscaria* L.)
Other common names: Persicary, spotted smartweed, heart-weed, spotted knotweed, red shanks, willow-weed, lover's pride.

This is a widely distributed species throughout the northern United States and southern Canada. It is naturalized from Europe. It occurs in waste places, along roadsides, and not infrequently in cultivated fields. The species is annual, usually stout, the stems 1 to 4 feet high. The leaves usually have a triangular dark spot near the middle. The spikes are usually less than 1 inch long, and erect. The calyx is red or white, and not glandular. The fruit (achene) is about 1.5 mm. long, broadly oval and tapering to a point, flattened, or sometimes three-angled, glossy, and purplish-black.

DOCK. RUMEX

This genus contains the docks and sheep sorrel. In California there are 12 species of *Rumex*, 5 of which are introduced from Europe and weedy in character; in addition 2 native species of the genus are weeds with us. In all representatives of *Rumex* the leaves have a characteristic sheathing structure at the base known as the ocrea. The flowers are usually numerous, small and greenish, sometimes yellowish or reddish, and in clusters along the branches of the inflorescence. The flowers have no corolla, but 6 nearly distinct sepals, the 3 outer ones being reflexed, the 3 inner somewhat larger and continuing to grow after flowering. These latter three may closely surround the fruit at maturity and are thus spoken of as the "fruiting sepals"; these are often veiny and bear on the back a more or less prominent tubercle or wart. There are 6 stamens, and a single ovary with 3 short styles; the fruit is a triangular achene (1-seeded dry fruit).

Of the 7 species of *Rumex* which are weeds in California, all are perennial except one, golden dock, *R. persicarioides*, which is an annual. In all species discussed here, except *R. acetosella*, the individual plants bear perfect flowers, that is, flowers with both stamens and pistils.

Many species of the buckwheat family, including *Rumex* species, and *Polygonum* species also, contain acrid substances which may cause dermatitis or gastric disturbances when eaten by livestock.

FIG 67.   Sheep sorrel (*Rumex Acetosella*), showing habit, fruiting branch
and achene.

KEY TO WEEDY SPECIES OF RUMEX

Individual plants one-sexed, i.e. with flowers either pollen-bearing or seed-bearing,
 roots red, scentless; some of the leaves are halberd-shaped_____*R. Acetosella*
Individual plants with perfect flowers, i.e., flowers having both stamens and pistils;
 roots yellow, bitter, scented; no leaves halberd-shaped (The Docks)
  Inner fruiting sepals with conspicuous slender teeth or bristles
   Annual; flowering branches short_____*R. persicarioides*
   Perennial; flowering branches long
    Flowering branches spreading at wide angles_____*R. pulcher*
    Flowering branches more or less erect_____*R. obtusifolius*
  Inner fruiting sepals without conspicuous slender teeth or bristles
   Leaf surface flat, not crinkly; foliage very light green or whitish____*R. salicifolius*
   Leaf surface crinkly; foliage deep green or bluish-green
    Tubercle or callous grain on fruiting sepals small and surrounded by the
     surface of the sepals as a broad wing_____*R. crispus*
    Tubercle or callous grain on fruiting sepals large, nearly covering its sepal
     and so almost wingless_____*R. conglomeratus*

SHEEP SORREL (*Rumex Acetosella* L.) (Fig. 67.)
Other common names: Field sorrel, horse sorrel, sour-weed, sour-grass, red-top sorrel, cow sorrel, red-weed, mountain sorrel.

This species is common throughout Europe and Asia from whence it was introduced into the United States. It is widely distributed in California, very abundant in places. It is frequently considered an indicator of acid soil, but it will grow in soils neutral or slightly alkaline in reaction, especially if they are deficient in nitrate nitrogen.

Sheep sorrel is a perennial from slender running rootstocks. The roots are red in color. The stems are numerous, wiry, and as a rule, do not branch; they rise to a height of 6 inches to 2 feet. The leaves vary in size and shape from the base to the top of the plant; the lowermost leaves are halberd-shaped, with one or two basal lobes, whereas the upper leaves may be linear in outline; the lobed leaves have slender leaf-stalks as long or longer than the blades, and at the base of the stalk is a pair of sheathing silvery scales (ocrea). The green leaves are sour in taste, and more or less dotted. The inflorescences terminate the stems. The male (staminate) inflorescences are greenish-yellow; the female (pistillate) reddish. The fruit is an achene covered with three inner, persistent fruiting sepals. The achene is 1 mm. long and almost as broad, three-angled, the edges blunt and sides more or less convex. The color is mahogany-red, the surface smooth and shiny.

GREEN DOCK (*Rumex conglomeratus* Murr.) (Fig. 68)

This species is introduced from Europe, and occurs in California in low, moist lands in the valleys and to middle elevations in the mountains. It is a perennial from a vertical rootstock which often gives rise to several spindle-shaped roots. The stems are slender, rising to a height of 3 to 5 feet. The leaf-blades are mostly oblong in shape, only slightly wavy on the margins, and 2 to 4 inches long. The inflorescence is $\frac{1}{3}$ to $1\frac{1}{2}$ feet long, slender and erect. The inner fruiting sepals are oblong, smooth, and usually there are 3 callous grains.

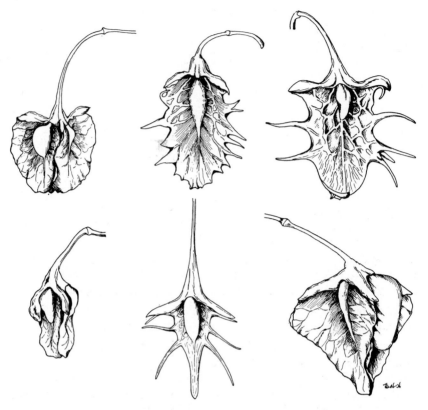

FIG. 68. Achenes with surrounding sepals of *Rumex* species. Note the callous grains on sepals. Top, left to right: curly dock (*R. crispus*), fiddle dock (*R. pulcher*), bitter dock (*R. obtusifolius*). Bottom, left to right: green dock (*R. conglomeratus*), golden dock (*R. persicarioides*), willow dock (*R. salicifolius*).

CURLY DOCK (*Rumex crispus* L.) (Fig. 68)

Other common names: Sour dock, yellow dock, narrow-leaved dock.

This species is introduced from Europe and Asia and is widely distributed throughout the United States. It is one of the most common of the docks in California, occurring in low and neglected lands in the valleys and in the mountains up to middle elevations. Curly dock is a perennial from a stout stem which attains a height of 1½ to 4 feet. During the first year the plant forms a dense rosette of leaves on a stout tap root. The leaves are bluish-green in color and are prominently curly and wavy along the margins; the blades are 3 to 10 inches long, and the petiole 1 to 2 inches long. The inflorescence is rather dense, 1 to 2 feet long, usually leafless, and rose-colored in the fruiting stage. The inner sepals are heart-shaped and either with or without a tubercle or callous grain. The fruit is about 2 mm. long, triangular with sharply crisped angles, the faces somewhat concave just below the abruptly acute point at apex. The color is glossy, reddish-brown.

BITTER DOCK (*Rumex obtusifolius* L.) (Fig. 68)

This weed, introduced from Europe, is common in the lowlands about San Francisco Bay. It is a perennial with tall, slender stems, 3 feet or more high. The leaf blades are oval-oblong or oblong-lance-shaped, somewhat wavy along the margin, more or less heart-shaped at the base, and not more than 6 inches long; the petioles are long. The inflorescence is rather dense. The inner fruiting sepals are up to ¼ inch long and bear 3 to 5 thin triangular or awl-shaped teeth on each side. There is usually but one tubercle, but sometimes two other small ones. The achene is three-angled, somewhat gradually elongated at base and apex, shiny and light brown in color.

GOLDEN DOCK (*Rumex persicarioides* L.) (Fig. 68)

This species is distributed throughout the United States, growing in marshy lands or in wet places by streams, lakes, and irrigation canals. In this State it is very common in Los Angeles County. Golden dock is an annual weed with soft, hollow steams, seldom more than 1 foot tall. The stems and leaves are minutely hairy, and yellowish-green in color. The leaves are 2 to 4 inches long, with oblong or lance-shaped blades which are somewhat wavy along the margin, and short leaf-stalks. The inner sepals bear 2 to 3 awn-like teeth on each side of the pointed tip; there are 3 tubercles or callous grains. The achene is three-angled, about 1.5 mm. long, slender, smooth and somewhat shiny light brown.

FIDDLE DOCK (*Rumex pulcher* L.) (Fig. 68)

This is a very common weed, naturalized from Europe, which is found in meadows and moist lands, and in waste places throughout California. The plant is perennial with a slender rigid stem which has zigzag branches. The leaf blades have a characteristic fiddle-shape and are 3 to 5½ inches long. The inflorescence is spreading, sparsely leafy, and red-brown in fruit. The inner fruiting sepals have 5 to 10 awn-like teeth on each side; callous grains vary from 1 to 3. The achene is three-angled, obtuse at base and somewhat elongated at apex, shiny mahogany-red in color.

WILLOW DOCK (*Rumex salicifolius* Weinm.) (Fig. 68)

This native occurs in wet places almost throughout California. It is a low-spreading or erect perennial, about 1 to 3 feet tall. The leaves are linear-oblong, pointed at both ends, and about 1½ inches long. The flowering branches are about 2 inches long, widely spreading. The fruiting whorls are dense and crowded together, leafless or slightly leafy. The pedicels are shorter than the fruit, and jointed near the base. The fruiting sepals are triangular, commonly with one callous grain, or sometimes with 2 or 3.

GOOSEFOOT FAMILY *(Chenopodiaceae)*

Members of this family are widely distributed geographically, occurring for the most part in saline soils near the ocean or in deserts and steppes. They are characteristic plants of alkaline swamps and meadows of the western states. From an economic standpoint the family is of great importance, the principal cultivated forms being the beet and spinach. The family includes a number of troublesome weeds such as the pigweeds, lambs'-quarters, and Russian thistle.

KEY TO GENERA IN GOOSEFOOT FAMILY CONTAINING WEED SPECIES

Leaves flattened, not fleshy nor scaly
  Flowers monoecious or dioecious, the pistillate enclosed in 2 bracts which enlarge
    after flowering _____*Atriplex*
  Flowers perfect, all with calyx, not enclosed in a pair of bracts
    Calyx in fruit transversely winged_____ *Cycloloma*
    Calyx in fruit not transversely winged_____*Chenopodium*
Leaves not flattened, but fleshy and cylindric, or scaly, or spiny
  Rather large spiny shrubs_____*Sarcobatus*
  Annual herbs, sometimes somewhat woody at base
    Plants smooth
      Tuft of whitish hairs in the leaf axils_____*Halogeton*
      No tuft of hairs in leaf axils_____*Salsola*
    Plants very hairy_____*Bassia*

SALTBUSH. *ATRIPLEX*

Jepson describes 29 species of Atriplex as occurring in California. Several species are weeds in cultivated or broken ground. Some species are herbs, others shrubby. They are usually mealy or scurfy with bran-like scales. There are staminate and pistillate flowers, either occurring on the same individual plant, or on different individuals. Pistillate flowers have a naked pistil enclosed between a pair of appressed leaf-like bracts which enlarge in fruit and may be partly united, more or less expanded and variously thickened and appendaged.

Seeds of *Atriplex* are common impurities in lots of barley, oats and wheat. The saltbushes are hosts for the sugar beet leafhopper.

KEY TO WEEDY SPECIES OF ATRIPLEX

Plants somewhat succulent and mealy ; annuals
  Leaves triangular hastate or deltoid_____*A. hastata*
  Leaves lance-shaped or ovate
    Lower leaves opposite_____*A. patula*
    All leaves alternate_____*A. rosea*
Plants not succulent ; perennial_____*A. semibaccata*

FAT-HEN *(Atriplex hastata* L.) (Fig. 69b)
Other common name : Halberd-leaved orache.

This is a native species distributed from the Atlantic seacoast westward to the Pacific Coast. It is common in salt marshes, and in alkaline soils. Not infrequently it is a weed in waste places and neglected fields. It is a somewhat succulent annual, mealy throughout, 1 to 2½ feet tall. The lower leaves are opposite, the upper alternate. The lower leaves are triangular halberd-shaped, or deltoid, entire or wavy-margined, 1 to 2 inches long, often as broad as long. The flowers resemble those of *A.*

patula. The bracts in fruit are almost circular or triangular-ovate, united at the base, the sides being toothed-crested. They are much smaller than those of *A. patula,* seldom longer than ⅛ of an inch. The seed is brownish and often somewhat wrinkled.

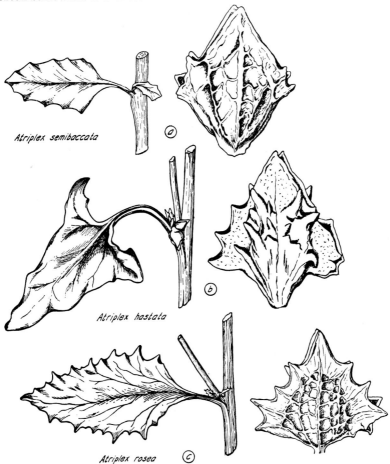

Atriplex semibaccata (a)

Atriplex hastata (b)

Atriplex rosea (c)

FIG. 69.   Leaves and fruiting bracts of *Atriplex* species; (a) Australian saltbush; (b) fat-hen; (c) redscale.

SPEAR ORACHE (*Atriplex patula* L.)
Other common names: Fat-hen, saltbush.

This species is distributed throughout the Northern Hemisphere, occurring chiefly in salt marshes along the seacoast, and in alkaline soil inland. It may be found in waste places and to a limited extent in cultivated fields and gardens. It is an annual herb, rather stout and succulent, 10 to 18 inches tall. The stems are branched and spreading, ridged, somewhat mealy when young but smooth when older. The lower leaves are opposite, the upper alternate; all leaves are simple, either entire or remotely toothed, lance-shaped or halberd-shaped, except the uppermost which are often linear. There are both staminate and pistillate flowers,

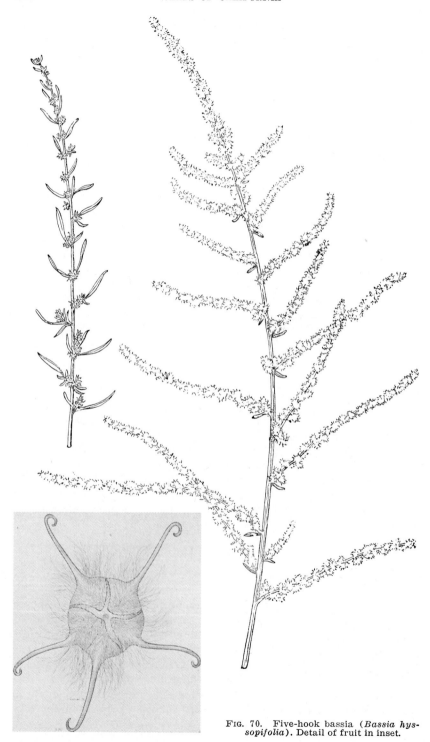

FIG. 70. Five-hook bassia (*Bassia hyssopifolia*). Detail of fruit in inset.

occurring on the same plant. either together or in separate spikes. The staminate flowers have 3 to 5 sepals and 5 stamens; the pistillate has a single pistil surrounded by a pair of bracts. These bracts, triangular in shape, become enlarged and surround the fruit (utricle). The seed is lens-shaped, black and glossy.

REDSCALE (*Atriplex rosea* L.) (Fig. 69c)
Other common names: Red orache, tumbling atriplex.

This species, introduced from Europe, is now found from the northern Rocky Mountains west to California, and sparingly in the Eastern States. It is a low annual, with much branched and spreading stems which are coated with a silvery scurf. The leaves are alternate, also densely scurfy, and often turning red; they are ovate, coarsely-toothed or wavy-margined. The flowers are similar to those of *A. patula*. The bracts of pistillate flowers in fruit are coarsely toothed and warty on the sides. The seeds are flattened with convex sides, yellowish-brown, and unevenly wrinkled.

AUSTRALIAN SALTBUSH (*Atriplex semibaccata* R. Br.) (Fig. 69a)

This species is a native of Australia. The plant has escaped from cultivation and has become a weed in waste places, especially in alkaline soils, and in nonirrigated areas such as grain fields.

It is a diffusely branching perennial half-shrub, 2 to 3 feet tall; the plant is woody below, but the tops of the branches are herbaceous. The slender branches are glistening white. The leaves are $\frac{1}{2}$ to 2 inches long, entire or shallowly toothed or wavy along the margin, light-green on the upper surfaces, silvery beneath. There are staminate and pistillate flowers both on the same plant; the staminate are grouped in short spikes at the tips of branches, and each flower has a 4- to 5-parted calyx, no petals, and 4 to 5 stamens; the pistillate flowers are solitary or in 2's or 3's in the leaf axils, and each has a single pistil, surrounded by two fleshy bracts which become reddish at maturity.

Australian saltbush is cultivated to some extent as a forage plant. It has drought-resistant characteristics and is adapted to alkaline soils.

FIVE-HOOK BASSIA (*Bassia hyssopifolia* .(Prall.) Kuntze) (Fig. 70)

This is a native of the Caspian Sea region which has been introduced into a few localities of the Western States. In the spiny saltbush association in the San Joaquin Valley on such lands as have been cleared and cultivated and then abandoned, a number of invaders, among them *Bassia*, have become fairly common. It is also now fairly abundant from Bishop to Lancaster in the Owens Valley, in the Santa Ana Valley, the Imperial Valley, and the Palo Verde Valley, and northward through the Sacramento Valley. The general habit of the plant is like that of lambs'-quarters (*Chenopodium album* L.), with narrow leaves and flowers borne in rounded clusters along long or short spikelike branches. The flattened short-oval seed, about 1 mm. long, is drab with raised dark spot near center and is enclosed in a five-hooked hairy calyx. Dense clusters of these give the slender elongate branches a woolly appearance.

WILD BEET (*Beta maritima* L.)

This is an important weed in certain sugar beet growing areas. Infestations occur in Imperial County, Oxnard, Chino, Gardena, Compton, Willowbrook, Watts, Santa Ana and Huntington Beach, also near Milpitas and Pleasanton. These wild beets are apparently descendants of crosses between the ancestral wild beets and sugar beets. Possibly shipments of sugar beet seed from Europe contained seed of wild beets or of wild beet hybrids.

LAMBS'-QUARTERS AND GOOSEFOOT. CHENOPODIUM

This genus includes plants commonly known as pigweed and goosefoot. Other representatives are Jerusalem oak, Mexican tea, wormseed, and strawberry blite. In California there are about a dozen species of *Chenopodium*. Many species have white, mealy or glandular leaves, and small, inconspicuous, greenish, sessile flowers which are usually in dense clusters. The calyx consists of 5 (sometimes 3 or 4) parts, and it is usually persistent, enclosing the dry, seed-like fruit (achene). The seed when mature is also closely surrounded by a membranous fruit wall.

KEY TO WEEDY SPECIES OF CHENOPODIUM

Fruiting calyx dry
    Plants not pubescent or glandular, more or less mealy
        Annual, calyx lobes united above middle, seed vertical_____*C. multifidum*
        Annuals, calyx deeply cleft into lobes or segments, seeds horizontal
            Leaves lanceolate to ovate, or rhombic, mealy throughout, seed margin obtuse
                Inflorescence open, interrupted, lax_____*C. Berlandieri*
                Inflorescence dense_____*C. album*
            Leaves broad, only young parts mealy, seed margin sharp_____*C. murale*
            Leaves linear or lance-linear, seed margin obtuse_____*C. leptophyllum*
            Perennial from very large carrot-like root, calyx lobes shallow_____*C. californicum*
    Plants glandular-pubescent and aromatic, not mealy
        Flower clusters all axillary_____*C. carinatum*
        Flower clusters spike-like or in panicles
            Leaves with slender petioles, pericarp not gland-dotted, inflorescence loosely branching _____ *C. Botrys*
            Leaves with very short petioles, pericarp gland-dotted, inflorescence spike-like or paniculate
                Stems puberulent or glabrate_____*C. ambrosioides*
                Stems white villous_____var. *vagans*
Fruiting calyx fleshy, and often reddish
    Calyx deciduous ; leaves lance-oblong to broad-ovate_____*C. rubrum*
    Calyx persistent, the clusters red and berry-like, leaves hastate-triangular
                                    C. capitatum

LAMBS'-QUARTERS (*Chenopodium album* L.) (Fig. 71)
Other common names: White pigweed, white goosefoot, fat-hen, mealweed, frost-blite, bacon-weed, wild spinach.

This weed is a native of the Old World, and is common throughout North America, in gardens, grain fields, cultivated fields, along roadsides, and waste places. It is one of the important host plants of the beet leafhopper. Lambs'-quarters is an annual weed with a slender tap root. The stems are erect, pale green in color, 1 to 4 feet tall, and branching somewhat above. The leaves are often white mealy below, the blade ½ to 4 inches

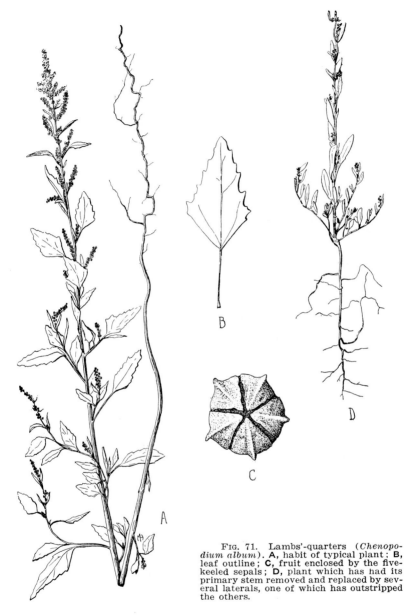

FIG. 71. Lambs'-quarters (*Chenopodium album*). **A,** habit of typical plant; **B,** leaf outline; **C,** fruit enclosed by the five-keeled sepals; **D,** plant which has had its primary stem removed and replaced by several laterals, one of which has outstripped the others.

long, the petiole ½ to 1 inch long; the leaves are somewhat variable in shape but usually more or less wedge-shaped, bluntly pointed, prominently 3-nerved from the leaf base, the blade margins being wavy, toothed or lobed, or the upper leaves entire. The flowers, small and greenish, are in slender spikes which are clustered in panicles. Each flower is usually composed of 5 sepals, 5 (or 6) stamens, and a flattened ovary. The ovary develops into a bladdery fruit (achene) containing a single, glossy black, lens-shaped seed, about 1.4 mm. wide, with a characteristic marginal notch, and definite groove inward from notch to center of each face.

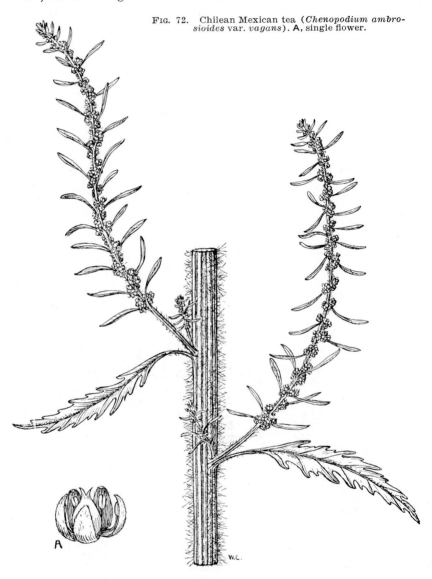

FIG. 72.   Chilean Mexican tea (*Chenopodium ambrosioides* var. *vagans*). A, single flower.

MEXICAN TEA (*Chenopodium ambrosioides* L.)

Other common names: Wormseed, Jerusalem tea, Spanish tea, strong-scented pigweed.

This species is introduced from tropical America. It has become a common weed in the Middle Atlantic and Southern States, and in California it is quite generally distributed, occurring along streams near salt marshes, in fields and waste places. Mexican tea is an annual, or perennial, erect herb, 2 to 3½ feet tall, with ridged, branched and spreading minutely hairy to almost smooth stems. The leaves are often glandular, hairy, and strongly aromatic, with short petioles, blades 2 to 5 inches long, more or less toothed or wavy along the margins. The flowers are small, greenish, in dense axillary clusters upon the branches. Each flower has 3 to 5 sepals, which completely enclose the fruit. The very small seed is glossy, reddish-brown to black, and lens-shaped.

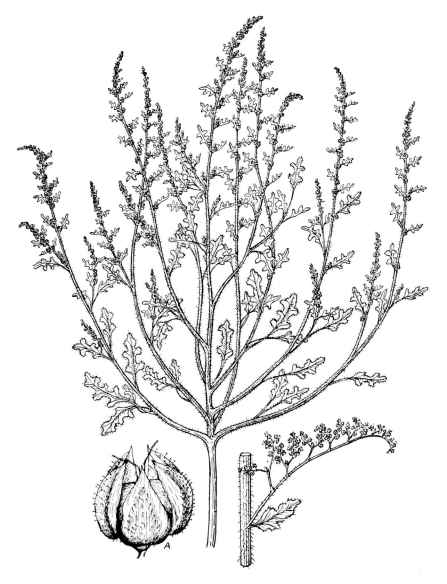

FIG. 73. Jerusalem oak (*Chenopodium Botrys*). **A**, achene surrounded by calyx.

CHILEAN MEXICAN TEA (*Chenopodium ambrosioides* var. *vagans* (Standl) J. T. Howell) (Fig. 72)

Introduced from South America and now scattered throughout the San Joaquin and Sacramento Valleys, this variety has stems which are conspicuously woolly hairy.

PITSEED GOOSEFOOT (*Chenopodium Berlandieri* Moq.)

This native of the southern United States and Mexico is now sparingly established in the northern part of the State. The weed is an ill-smelling annual, closely related to *C. album*. It is slender, the leaves dentate but never lobed and the seed is definitely smaller than that of *C. album*, .8 to 1 mm. broad, conspicuously pitted to almost smooth.

JERUSALEM OAK (*Chenopodium Botrys* L.) (Fig. 73)
Other common names: Feather geranium, turn-pike geranium.

This species, introduced from Europe, is rather widely distributed throughout the United States, but is not very comon in California. Here it occurs in waste places along roadsides, in flood stream beds, and occasionally in cultivated fields. Jerusalem oak is an annual with erect, branching or forked stems ½ to 2 feet tall. The plant is glandular and sticky throughout and has a strong aromatic scent. The leaf blades are ½ to 1½ inches long, pinnately lobed, the lobes usually toothed. The flowers are sessile,

FIG. 74. Soap plant (*Chenopodium californicum*), showing habit and carrot-like root; A, achene, and B, achene surrounded by calyx.

hairy, in open cymes which are grouped into loose clusters. There are 3 to 5 sepals, which are pointed, hairy, and which do not completely enclose the achene. The seed is purplish-black, about .6 mm. wide, subglobose, dull, minutely roughened. A thin whitish pericarp is usually persistent over most of the seed.

SOAP PLANT *(Chenopodium californicum* Wats.) (Fig. 74)

Soap plant is a native perennial, with stem 1½ to 2½ feet tall, erect or decumbent from a large carrot-like root. The herbage is smooth, very slightly mealy, the leaves broadly triangular and coarsely toothed, 1½ to 3½ inches long. The flowers are small, borne in a dense terminal spike, which is leafless or nearly so. The achene is almost globose, but somewhat flattened, about 1/12 inch broad, invested in a persistent pericarp or covering.

STRAWBERRY BLITE *(Chenopodium capitatum* (L.) Asch.)
Other common names: Strawberry spinach, strawberry pigweed, blite mulberry.

This species is a native of North America and Europe. It is quite abundant in the Northeastern States and Rocky Mountain States, but is infrequent in California. It occurs in waste places, in cultivated fields to some extent, and in the Rocky Mountains is particularly known as a weed of new timber clearings. Strawberry blite is an annual, branching at the base, the stems 5 to 15 inches tall. The leaves are mealy, triangular or halberd-shaped, the margin almost entire or irregularly toothed, and ¾ to 2 inches long. The flowers are small, greenish, in rather large clusters which take on a characteristic fleshy, red, berry-like appearance when mature. The sepals, 2 to 5 in number, become fleshy and a red color when mature. The seeds are lens-shaped and of a dull black color.

AUSTRALIAN GOOSEFOOT *(Chenopodium carinatum* R. Br.)

This is an adventive species introduced from Australia and relatively unimportant as a weed in California. It is now recorded from Humboldt County, east Shasta County, Oroville and West Branch in Butte County, Ione, Jackson, Upland and Ontario. Australian pigweed is an annual with stout prostrate or decumbent branches 5 to 18 inches high, glandular hairy throughout and often reddish. The flowers are sessile in dense axillary clusters or in short axillary leafy spikes about ½ inch long or less. The calyx partially encloses the mature fruit which is a dark reddish-brown achene about .5 mm. broad, with thin, slightly adhering pericarp.

NARROW-LEAVED GOOSEFOOT *(Chenopodium leptophyllum* Wats.)

This native goosefoot extends from Manitoba to Lower California. It is infrequent as a weed in California but occasionally the seed is found as an impurity in commercial seed. The plant is erect and slender, with narrowly lance-shaped to linear leaves. The seeds are about 1 mm. broad, lens-shaped with obtuse margins, the surface smooth and shining black.

CUT-LEAVED GOOSEFOOT (*Chenopodium multifidum* L.) (Fig. 75)

This native of South America is fairly rare in California, occurring in the San Francisco sandhills and in waste places east to the Sacramento and San Joaquin valleys, and southward to southern California, where it occurs as a wayside weed. It is a heavy-scented perennial, pubescent herb with prostrate branches, 1 to 2 feet long. The leaves are alternate, pinnatifid, ½ to 1¼ inches long. The flowers are very small,

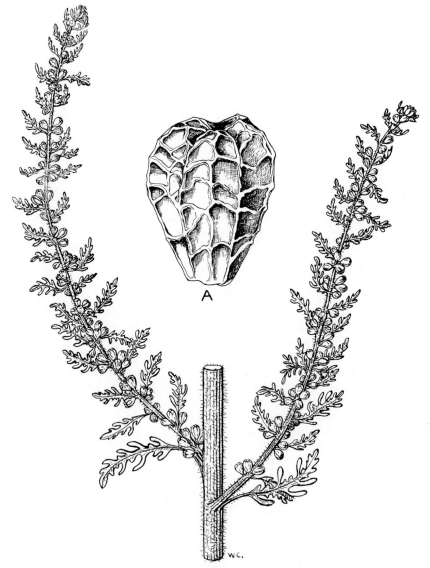

FIG. 75. Cut-leaved goosefoot (*Chenopodium multifidum*). **A,** achene enclosed by net-veined calyx.

perfect or pistillate, singly or 2 or 3 together in the axils.. There are no petals; the sepals are bowl-shaped, 3 to 5 toothed, and later elongate to enclose the mature fruit. There are 5 stamens, 3 styles, and an ovary glandular at the top. When the fruit is mature the surrounding calyx lobes are conspicuously net-veined. The outer wall of the fruit (achene) is membranous, glandular, dotted, thin, and soon falls off. Seed lens-shaped, 1 mm. across, black and shining.

NETTLE-LEAF GOOSEFOOT (*Chenopodium murale* L.)
Other common names: Sow-bane, swine-bane.

This species is an introduced one from Europe, now widespread throughout the United States and Southern Canada. In California it is fairly common as a weed in cultivated fields, gardens, and waste places. With us, it flowers through the winter. The plant is a stout, succulent annual, the stems erect or decumbent, smooth, much branched, and 1 to 3 feet high. The herbage is dark green, the younger parts finely mealy. The leaves have slender petioles, the blades 1 to 1¾ inches long, coarsely toothed or with wavy margins. The flowers are small, greenish, in dense axillary or terminal spike-like panicles. The calyx has 5 sepals, which do not completely cover the fruit, and 6 stamens. The seed is lens-shaped, about 1.5 mm. wide, finely granular, and dull black. A definite pie-plate margin or rim readily differentiates the seed of this species.

RED GOOSEFOOT (*Chenopodium rubrum* L.)

Red goosefoot occurs in low, wet ground, and is reported from the lower Sacramento River, Alvarado, Nigger Slough and Ballona, Los Angeles County. It is an annual, stems erect, 1 to 2 feet high, glabrous throughout and often reddish. The leaf blades are ovate, coarsely sinuate dentate with obtuse teeth, the leaf stems usually shorter than, or equaling, the blades which are sometimes shallowly hastate. The leaves in the inflorescence are smaller, lance-like to linear-oblong, hastate to entire. The flowers are sessile in dense glomerules borne on long or short dense leafy spikes. The fruit equals or exceeds the calyx, which is divided to the base or only half way; the pericarp is green. The seed is lens-shaped, .8 to 1 mm. broad, dark brown and shining, with obtuse margin.

WINGED PIGWEED (*Cycloloma atriplicifolium* (Spreng.) Coult.) (Fig. 76)
Other common name: Tumbleweed.

This species is a native of the Great Plains region, from whence it has spread eastward and westward. In California it has become abundant in several localities, chiefly about Rialto and Ontario. It is found, for the most part, in low-lying ground where there is alkali. Winged pigweed is a much-branched annual, ½ to 2 feet high, with rigid, spreading, angular or grooved stems; the stems are gray-green when young, becoming purplish with age. The plant may break off at the ground

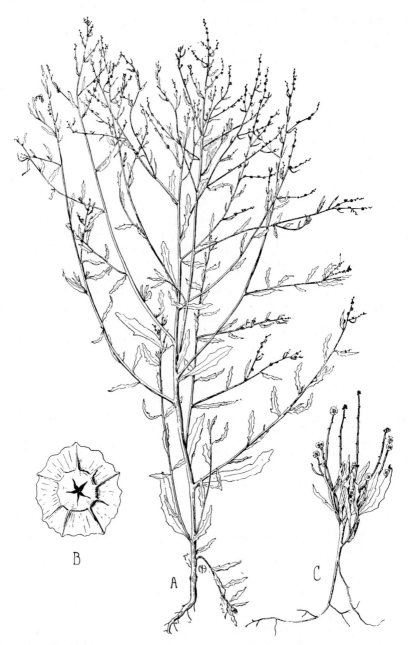

Fig. 76. Winged pigweed (*Cycloloma atriplicifolium*); **A**, habit of good-sized plant bearing flowers and immature fruit; **B**, fruiting calyx viewed from above, showing the five-rayed slit, beneath which is the ovary, and the broad, membranous wing; **C**, plant dwarfed by local conditions but nevertheless bearing developed fruit and viable seed.

line when mature to form a "tumbleweed." The leaves are simple and narrow, 1 to 3 inches long, the margins wavy-toothed, the teeth sharply pointed. The flowers are of two kinds—perfect and pistillate. They are grouped at the ends of slender branches. The calyx has 5 sepals which almost cover the fruit. The perfect flowers have 5 stamens and 2 to 3 styles; the pistillate flowers, styles only. In both kinds of flowers there are no petals. The fruit (achene) is dry, surrounded by a broad-circular, wing-like outgrowth from the base of each sepal. The seed with calyx and wing removed is lens-shaped, 1 to 1.5 mm. across, finely granular, and dull black.

Halogeton glomeratus C. A. May (Fig. 77)

This species is a native of Eurasia. It was first reported in Elko County, Nevada, in 1935. As early as 1946, it was reported in the southeast corner of Lassen County, adjacent to Nevada. It occurs along trails, railroads, and roadsides; it has also invaded thousands of acres of brush and white sage sheep range lands, and areas where the soil has been disturbed.

Halogeton glomeratus is an annual, the lower stems divergent from the crown, then becoming erect and branching. The general growth habit is like that of the tumbleweeds. The size of the individual plants is extremely variable. Under optimum conditions robust specimens measure as much as three feet across and are about a foot tall. On poor soil, with inadequate moisture, the plants may reach full development and mature seed, yet measure only about one inch in height. The leaves are alternate, sessile, about one-fourth to three-fourths inch long. They are fleshy, cylindrical to somewhat angled, blunt at the apex and tipped with a conspicuous bristle-like hair. In the leaf axils there is a tuft of whitish hairs, copious to sparse. The inconspicuous yellowish-green flowers are borne in glomerules (two to several in a cluster) in the leaf axils. There are five sepals, five stamens inserted on the receptacle, and two stigmas. Halogeton has two types of flowers, both found on the same plant. In the more showy form, the flowers have large membranous sepals spreading fan-like just above a slight constriction at the apex of the seed. A thin seed-coat or pericarp encloses the seed, but the spiral form of the embryo is discernible. This seed form suggests the closely related Russian thistle. In the less conspicuous flower form, the five sepals are more coriaceous, their tips reduced to small tooth-like appendages. The seed is more compressed.

Halogeton is a prolific seeder, producing an abundance of seed over a long season. The seed shatters readily. Large plants break off at the ground in the manner of tumbleweeds and scatter seed as they are blown about by the wind.

California has conducted no feeding tests with Halogeton. From the State Department of Agriculture at Reno, we have reports that in Elko County, Nevada, where heavy losses of sheep were investigated, the

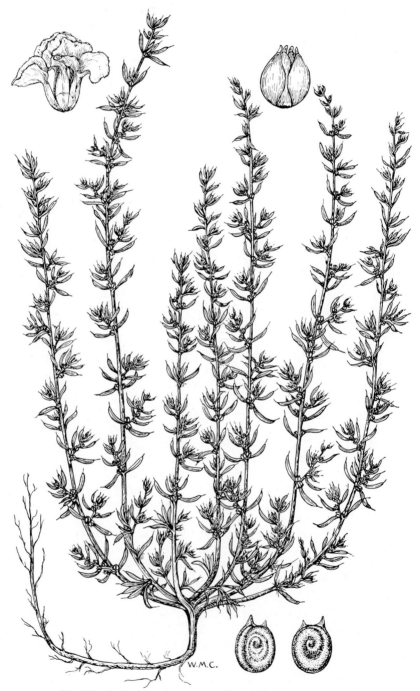

Fig. 77. *Halogeton glomeratus* with detail of flower and seed.

stomach contents of the animals involved were found to be almost 100 percent *Halogeton glomeratus*. While most of the trouble has been with sheep, losses among cattle have also been attributed to Halogeton.

RUSSIAN THISTLE (*Salsola Kali* L. var. *tenuifolia* G. F. W. Mey.) (Fig. 78) Other common names: Tumbling weel, Russian tumbleweed, windwitch.

Russian thistle is a native of the plains of southeastern Russia and western Siberia. Agricultural observers fifty years ago in Russia reported

FIG. 78. Russian thistle (*Salsola Kali* var. *tenuifolia*). **A,** small-sized plant, x 1; **B,** seedling just beginning to develop the spiny bracts characteristic of the mature "thistle," x 1; **C,** flower, x 16; note the surrounding spiny bracts.

that they found there stretches of this thistle for 500 to 600 miles in the most fertile parts of that country, and that it had driven every farmer out of the section.

The plant was introduced into the United States in 1873 or 1874 in flax seed brought from Russia and sown near Scotland, South Dakota. In 1895 Mr. Dewey of the U. S. Department of Agriculture reported that 16 states and 13 Canadian provinces had been infested with Russian thistle and at that time he issued a warning to the Pacific Coast States.

It is not known exactly how long Russian thistle has been in California but today it is distributed here and there throughout the State, from southern California to Lassen County.

Russian thistle is a bushy, annual plant that may break off at the ground line at maturity to form a "tumbleweed." It has numerous slender, ascending stems 10 inches to 3 feet high; these are smooth, striate, often reddish in color; they are tender when young but become rigid and spiny at maturity. The young leaves are an inch or more long, narrow, pointed, and each usually has a short shoot in its axil. These early-forming leaves drop off, those appearing later being very short, awl-shaped, stiff and ending in spines. The flowers are perfect, small, greenish, and axillary. They are borne on the plant from near its base to the tip. The corolla is lacking; the calyx has 5 divisions, and each division bears a veiny wing on its back, and the five wings meet and nearly cover the fruit. There are 5 stamens, a single pistil with 2 styles. The ovary becomes dry at maturity forming a conical fruit horizontally winged at the base by a broad papery border. The seed is gray to yellowish-brown, finely granular, and has a conical, spirally coiled embryo, which suggests a snail or Turk's cap, and no endosperm. A single plant may produce 20,000 to 50,000 seeds. As stated, the mature plant may break off at the ground line, be blown by the wind, and scatter the seeds as it tumbles along.

Russian thistle is a favored host of the sugar beet leafhopper, which is a carrier of the virus causing curly-top of sugar beets and "blight" of spinach, tomatoes, beans, and other plants.

BLACK GREASEWOOD (*Sarcobatus vermiculatus* (Hook.) Torr.)

Black greasewood is a native distributed widely in the Western States, being found in California in alkali soils of Inyo County to Lassen and Modoc counties, and the Mojave and Colorado deserts.

The plant is a shrub, 2 to 6 feet tall, the branches stiff, spiny, and closely interlocking, the bark white, the leaves alternate, simple, narrow, fleshy, $\frac{1}{2}$ to $1\frac{3}{4}$ inches long, flat on the upper surface, rounded beneath. There are staminate and pistillate flowers, both kinds being small, greenish and inconspicuous, and arranged in cone-shaped fruiting spikes about $\frac{1}{2}$ inch long. The ovary is set in a sac-like calyx, which persists, and becomes in the fruit a broad circular, wavy membranous wing.

Black greasewood is known to poison cattle and sheep, the most dangerous period being in early spring.

PAHUTE WEED (*Suaeda depressa* (Pursh) Wats. var. *erecta* Wats.) (Fig. 79)

This native species occurs in coastal southern California, in Modoc and eastward, particularly on alkaline plains. It is an erect annual, $\frac{1}{2}$ to $1\frac{1}{2}$ feet tall, stems simple or branched, with alternate smooth fleshy leaves which are $\frac{3}{4}$ to $1\frac{1}{2}$ inches long. The flowers, consisting of 5 fleshy sepals, are sessile in the axils of the leafy bracts. The calyx lobes are more or less unequal and conspicuously horizontally winged on the back. The seeds are small, with shiny black seed coat and spiral embryo.

ALKALI BLITE (*Suaeda Moquini* Greene.)

Alkali blite, which occurs in the San Joaquin Valley and southern California, is closely related to the preceding species, but is a perennial. It has more or less decumbent stems, irregularly spreading to a length of 2 to 3 feet. The linear leaves are smaller, $\frac{1}{6}$ to $\frac{1}{2}$ inch long.

FIG. 79. Pahute weed (*Suaeda depressa*), showing flowering branch, a single achene surrounded by unequal, winged calyx lobes, and an achene free from calyx.

The calyx lobes are parted almost to the base and unappendaged. The seeds are very similar to those of Pahute weed.

AMARANTH FAMILY *(Amaranthaceae)*

This is a large and widely distributed family, particularly abundant in warm regions. Most of the species are rough or coarse annual and perennial herbs with alternate or opposite simple leaves, and small, dry flowers much like those in the goosefoot family (Chenopodiaceae). The flowers are usually in dense clusters and always subtended by 2 to 3 small, colored, papery bracts or scales. The fruit is a small utricle. The principal genus in California is Amaranthus, a number of species of which are weeds, and the best known ornamental in the family is the cockscomb (*Celosia cristata*).

ACHYRANTHES (*Achyranthes repens* L.)

This species is naturalized from Mexico. It has been found as an adventive at Los Angeles. It is a perennial, pubescent herb with prostrate branched and hairy stems, 8 to 20 inches long. The leaves are opposite, entire, and 2 to 6 inches long. The flowers are in short, axillary spikes.

The flower has 5 distinct and unequal sepals. Petals are absent. There are 3 to 5 two-celled anthers, one lobe of each anther being pollen-bearing and the alternate lobes sterile. The fruit is an utricle. The seed is round-ovate, 1-1.5 mm. long, reddish-brown and shiny.

PIGWEED AND TUMBLEWEED. *AMARANTHUS*

To this genus belong a number of coarse annual herbs known commonly as amaranths or pigweed. In all the different species the leaves are alternate, simple, and entire; the flowers are small, inconspicuous, and usually greenish, perfect or unisexual, and arranged in congested axillary or terminal spikes. The calyx consists of 3 to 5 sepals (rarely 1), which are more or less papery and persistent. The corolla is lacking. There are usually 5 stamens, sometimes fewer. There is a one-celled ovary with 2 or 3 stigmas. The fruit is a small, bladdery one-seeded fruit (utricle), and the seeds are mostly black and shining. At maturity the fruit splits around at the middle (except in one of our species), allowing the single seed to escape.

In California, 9 species of *Amaranthus* are recorded as occurring, 5 of which are weeds. *Amaranthus blitoides, A. graecizans,* and *A. retroflexus* are hosts for the beet leafhopper. In the key following certain distinguishing characteristics of these 5 species are given. In the descriptions of these species characters common to the genus are omitted.

FIG. 80.   Prostrate pigweed (*Amaranthus blitoides*) showing habit, and circumscissile fruit surrounded by sepals.

KEY TO WEEDY SPECIES OF AMARANTHUS

Plants prostrate, spreading along the ground
  Fruit fleshy, not breaking open at maturity_____ *A. deflexus*
  Fruit with dry or papery covering, splitting at maturity_____ *A. blitoides*
Plants erect
  Flowers in small axillary clusters ; plant becoming a "tumbleweed"_____ *A. graecizans*
  Flowers in dense spikes at the tops of the stem ; plants not becoming a "tumble-
    weed"
    Spikes thick, erect ; stems harsh and foliage dull green _____ *A. retroflexus*
    Spikes slender, more or less nodding at the tip ; stems smooth and foliage deep
      green_____ *A. hybridus*

PROSTRATE PIGWEED (*Amaranthus blitoides* Wats.) (Fig. 80)
Other common names : Spreading pigweed, mat amaranth.

  This species is native to western United States. It is not abundant
in California, occurring, however, in many widely scattered localities.

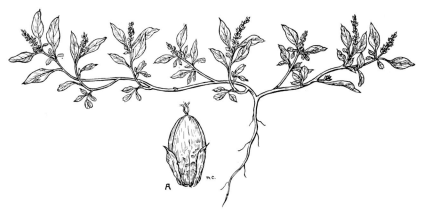

FIG. 81.   Low amaranth (*Amaranthus deflexus*), showing habit. **A**, single fruit.

  It is an annual herb with branching stems which form a mat-like growth
on the soil. The stems are $\frac{1}{2}$ to 2 feet long. The leaves are $\frac{1}{4}$ to $\frac{3}{4}$ inch
long, often white-nerved on the margins and on the under side. The
flowers are in short axillary spikes. The bracts are longer than the
sepals. The utricle is somewhat wrinkled toward the tip, seed lens-shape,
about 2 mm. across, the convex faces meeting in a narrowed rim, bright
shining black.

LOW AMARANTH (*Amaranthus deflexus* L.) (Fig. 81)
  Naturalized from Europe, this is reported from a few scattered
localities in California : Sacramento, Santa Rosa, Berkeley, Santa
Barbara, Los Angeles, and Ontario. It occurs chiefly in gardens and
along streets. It is a prostrate, somewhat succulent annual, with slender
stems 1 to 1$\frac{1}{2}$ feet long. The leaves are ovate or oval, slender petioled,
the petioles often as long as the blades. The flowers are in dense terminal
spikes 1 inch long or more, or in short axillary spikes. There are 2 or
3 oblong sepals which are longer than the bracts. The fruit (utricle) is

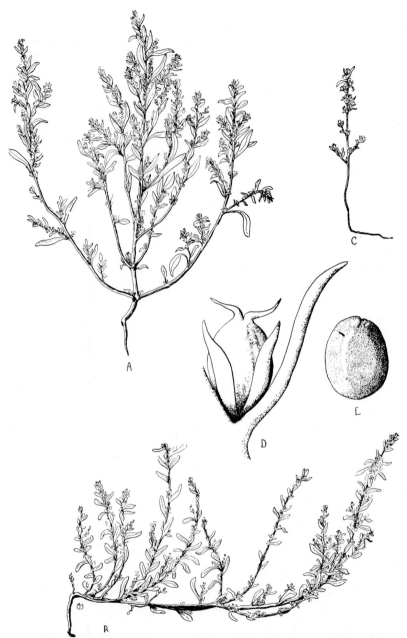

Fig. 82. Tumbling pigweed (*Amaranthus graecizans*). **A**, habit of small plant of semi-erect type, x 1 ; **B**, habit of reclining or spreading type, x ⅔ ; **C**, seed-producing dwarf of dry, hard soil, x 1 ; **D**, single flower consisting of sepals and ovary, only one bract shown, x 40 ; **E**, seed, x 40.

fleshy, 3 to 5 nerved, longer than the sepals and, unlike the other species of *Amaranthus* described here, the fruit does not split open at maturity. The seed is definitely oval, about 1 mm. long, dark reddish-brown, shiny.

TUMBLING PIGWEED (*Amaranthus graecizans* L.) (Fig. 82)
Other common names: Tumbleweed, white pigweed.

This species is introduced from tropical America and has become abundant throughout the United States. It occurs in cultivated fields and in waste places. It is a coarse annual with shallow, spreading roots and stems 1 to 4 feet high. The stems are whitish or light-green and highly branched. When mature the whole plant may become broken from the ground and be carried by the wind, thus scattering its seeds. The leaves are about 1 inch long, thin, light-green above and often reddish beneath. The venation is conspicuous. The flowers are in short, axillary spikes. Each flower has 3 spiny bracts which are longer than the sepals. The fruit (utricle) is dry, wrinkled, and splits open around the middle line. The seed is less than 1 mm. across, rounded in outline, very dark reddish-brown, shiny. The margin or rim is less pronounced than in *A. blitoides.*

GREEN AMARANTH (*Amaranthus hybridus* L.) (Fig. 83b)
Other common names: Spleen amaranth, rough pigweed, amaranth pigweed, red amaranth.

Green amaranth is also introduced from tropical America, and has become widespread throughout the United States. In California it is not as widespread and common as *A. retroflexus,* but may be found associated with it. It is similar to *A. retroflexus,* except that it is a deeper green and less rough, and the spikes are more slender and spreading. Moreover, whereas in *A. retroflexus* the sepals are longer than the utricle, those of *A. hybridus* are shorter than the utricle. The seed of *A. hybridus* is about 1 mm. long, oval lens-shape, dark reddish-brown to black, shiny.

ROUGH PIGWEED (*Amaranthus retroflexus* L.) (Fig. 83)
Other common names: Pigweed, Chinaman's greens, green amaranth, red root, careless weed.

Introduced from tropical America, this plant has become one of the commonest weeds throughout the United States. It is found in all kinds of cultivated crops, in gardens, orchards, along roadsides, and in waste places. Pigweed is an erect annual with a characteristic pink or red tap root. The plant is 1 to 4 feet tall, branched, and has rough, somewhat hairy herbage. The leaves have a stalk about half the length of the blade, which is oval, wavy-margined, and 1 to 3 inches long; the veins are prominent on the under side of the leaves. The dense spikes are 1 to 3 inches long. Each flower is enclosed by stiff, rigid, persistent bracts. The bladder-like fruit is wrinkled and at maturity splits around at the middle, exposing the single, black, shining seed which is very similar to the foregoing.

FIG. 83.   Above, rough pigweed (*Amaranthus retroflexus*). **A**, fruit of rough pigweed; **B**, fruit of green amaranth (*A. hybridus*).

POKEWEED FAMILY *(Phytolaccaceae)*

This relatively small family is best represented by the pokeweed, hereinafter described. It is an escape from cultivation within our borders. *Rivina humilis* is an ornamental grown for its red berries.

POKEWEED *(Phytolacca americana* L.) (Fig. 84)

This is a native of eastern United States. It has been collected in Los Angeles County, Chula Vista, and from Blue Lakes to Ukiah. Pokeweed is a perennial with stout, smooth stems 3 to 10 feet high, and a large, fleshy, white tap root. The leaves are alternate, entire and with long petioles. The flowers are in long, narrow racemes which usually stand opposite the leaves. The flowers are small with 5-petal-like sepals, no petals, 10 stamens, and 1 pistil composed of about 10 united carpels each with 1 seed. The fruit is a dark purple, 10-seeded berry with a crimson juice.

Cases of poisoning of human beings have been reported from eating the roots and berries of pokeweed.

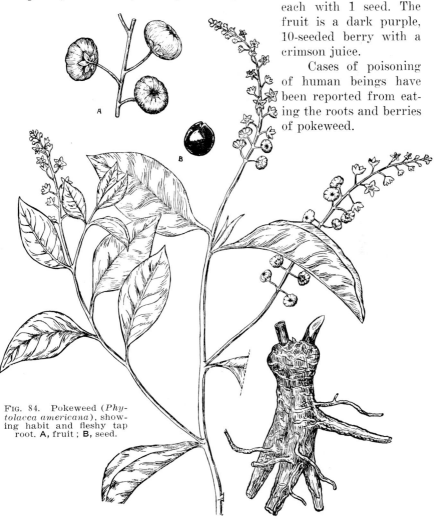

FIG. 84. Pokeweed *(Phytolacca americana)*, showing habit and fleshy tap root. **A**, fruit; **B**, seed.

FOUR O'CLOCK FAMILY *(Nyctaginaceae)*

This widely distributed family has such well known members as *Mirabilis jalapa* of flower gardens, and the ornamental climbers, Bougainvillea. The herbaceous forms have characteristic swollen nodes. The following native is sometimes a weed.

MIRABILIS *(Mirabilis Froebelii* (Behr) Greene) (Fig. 85)

This native is distributed from Kern County to San Diego County and the Imperial Valley. The seed is frequently found in grain screenings. The plant is a perennial, with stout, forking and widely spreading stems forming a circular growth 1 to 3 feet broad. Stems and leaves are glandular hairy. The leaves are broad oval, $1\frac{1}{4}$ to 4 inches long, often broader than long, somewhat heart-shaped at the bases, and either acute or blunt at the tip. The flowers are in groups of 5 or 6 subtended by a calyx-like involucre. The calyx is funnel-form, cleft nearly halfway into acute lobes, bright or pale purple, and from $1\frac{1}{2}$ to $1\frac{3}{4}$ inches long. Corolla is absent. Stamens are usually 5. The fruit is an achene, closely invested by the base of the calyx tube, light-brown in color and marked by 10 vertical lines of a darker color.

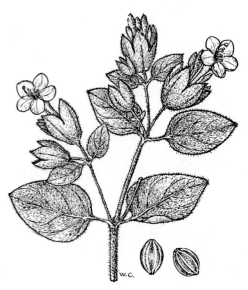

FIG. 85.   Mirabilis *(Mirabilis Froebelii)*, showing habit, and two achenes.

BOERHAAVIA *(Boerhaavia hirsuta* Willd.)

This is a native species, occurring in southern California and reported weedy in Fresno County and southward. It is a slender perennial with branching stem 2 to 3 feet long, stem leaves and internodes sparsely glandular hairy. The blades of the opposite leaves are unequal, $\frac{1}{2}$ to 2 inches long, round ovate, obtuse or acute at the apex and rounded at the base. The very small red flowers, consisting of calyx about $\frac{1}{12}$ inch long, are borne in small clusters at the end of more or less spreading slender stems, grouped together in a loose panicle. The fruit is five-ribbed, once or twice the length of the calyx.

CARPET-WEED FAMILY (Aizoaceae)

The members of this family inhabit chiefly deserts and sandy sea-shores. Many of them are succulent herbs. Well known representatives in California are the fleshy mesembryanthemums, used so extensively by the State Highway Department as soil binders on steep or sandy slopes and embankments.

KEY TO GENERA OF CARPET-WEED FAMILY CONTAINING WEED SPECIES

Petals numerous; leaves 3-sided and very fleshy_____*Mesembryanthemum*
Petals none
  Leaves alternate _____*Tetragonia*
  Leaves opposite
    Calyx of 5 distinct sepals; capsule 3-valved, splitting open longitudinally
      Stamens 3-5; herbage glabrous_____*Mollugo*
      Stamens 5-10; herbage soft-pubescent_____*Glinus*

    Calyx 5-cleft; capsule splitting open by means of circular slit
      Stipules absent _____*Sesuvium*
      Stipules present
        Stamens 1-3 _____*Cypselea*
        Stamens 5 or 6 to 10_____*Trianthema*

CYPSELEA (*Cypselea humifusa* Turp.)

This is a native of the West Indies, which occurs sparingly in California, in the lower San Joaquin Valley, and at Aptos, Santa Cruz County. It is a small, prostrate, annual herb forming mats 1 or 2 inches across. The leaves are opposite, blunt, oval, $\frac{1}{6}$ to $\frac{1}{3}$ inch long, and borne on leaf-stalks about the length of the blade; the members of each pair of leaves are unequal in size. The flowers have no petals, 5 green sepals, united at the base, 1 to 3 stamens, and a 1-celled ovary surmounted by a 2-cleft style. The fruit is a rounded capsule which splits open at maturity about its middle.

GLINUS (*Glinus lotoides* Loefl.)

This weed, which is very closely related to *Mollugo verticillata,* is a native of Europe and is sparingly established in California, at Lathrop, Chico and Lakeport. It is a diffusely branched annual, 4 to 8 inches long, with whorled petioled leaves. The flowers are about $\frac{1}{6}$ inch long, borne in dense glomerules in the upper axils. The seeds are blackish, with a granulated surface.

MESEMBRYANTHEMUM

There are a number of species of *Mesembryanthemum* occurring in California: *Mesembryanthemum nodiflorum* L., ice plant (*M. crystallinum* L.), sea-fig (*M. aequilaterale* Haw.), dew plant (*M. cordifolium* L.), *M. pugioniforme* L., and "Hottentot fig" (*M. edule* L.). *M. cordifolium* is a native of South Africa, which has been cultivated in California for more than 45 years, and in certain localities has escaped from cultivation and become naturalized. It occurs at San Francisco and is also naturalized about La Jolla and San Diego. *M. pugioniforme* is a more recent introduction and is found at only a few localities, namely the Cliff House sand dunes at San Francisco, and at Pacific Grove. *M. edule,* a native of South

Africa, has been planted as a sand-binder, and occasionally has escaped from cultivation along the southern coast. It is probably the most common of the mesembryanthemums. It is a perennial with opposite, 3-sided, curved leaves and large yellow to purple flowers.

The mesembryanthemums are low, very succulent herbs, usually with thick leaves. The flowers are large, the calyx tube grown to the ovary, the petals numerous, narrow, and inserted with the many stamens upon the calyx tube. The ovary is 5- to 12-celled, and the styles are as many as the cells of the ovary. The fruit is a fleshy capsule, with numerous very small seeds.

CARPET-WEED (*Mollugo verticillata* L.) (Fig. 86)
Other common names: Indian chickweed, whorled chickweed, devil's grip.

Carpet-weed is a native of the Old World tropics and also of tropical America. It is locally found throughout the United States, and quite generally distributed in California. It occurs usually in dry, gravelly or sandy soil, chiefly along roadsides, in gardens, lawns, and waste places. It is of little importance as a weed in cultivated fields. Carpet-weed is an annual, with much-branched stems which form mat-like growths on the soil, 4 to 10 inches in diameter. The stems are not fleshy. The leaves are simple, narrow, spatula-shaped, about ½ inch long, and occur in whorls of 5 to 6. The flowers are in groups at each joint of the stem, each flower on a slender thread-like stalk. There are no petals, but 5 thin sepals which are white

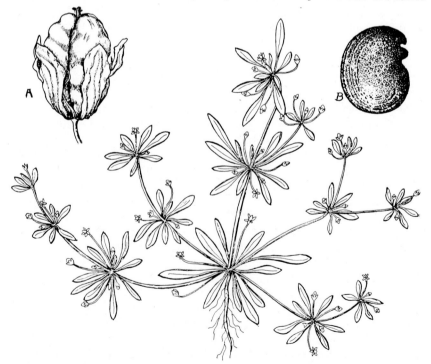

FIG. 86. Carpet-weed (*Mollugo verticillata*), showing habit. A, capsule; B, seed.

inside, and resemble petals when the flower is open. There are 3 stamens, and a solitary pistil with 3 stigmas. The fruit is a dry capsule with 3 compartments, each containing many seeds. The seeds are flattened, kidney-shaped, with a protuberance on the concave side, shining and orange-red.

Mollugo Cerviana (L.) Ser., less common than the above, is naturalized from the Old World, and occurs in southern California; abundant in the southern part of the Mojave Desert. It is an erect plant with narrow leaves.

Fig. 87. Lowland purslane (*Sesuvium sessile*), showing habit. **A**, lid of circumscissile capsule; **B**, seed.

LOWLAND PURSLANE (*Sesuvium sessile* Pers.) (Fig. 87)

This is a plant of alkaline fields and river lowlands, occurring throughout the San Joaquin Valley and south to southern California. It is a fleshy, prostrate herb which branches freely, the stems 1 to 3 feet long. The herbage is finely warty. The leaves are opposite, broadly spatula-shaped, ½ to 2 inches long. The flowers are solitary in the leaf axils, and about ⅓ inch long. The calyx tube is top-shaped, 5-lobed, the lobes pink inside. Petals are absent. Stamens are numerous, and inserted on the calyx. The ovary is 2- to 3-celled, the styles 2 or 3. The fruit is a membranous capsule, the upper part falling off as a lid.

NEW ZEALAND SPINACH (*Tetragonia expansa* Murr.) (Fig. 88)

This is a native of Australia, which is cultivated to some extent in California as summer "greens." It has escaped from cultivation here and there, growing on sea beaches at Alameda, San Francisco, Pacific Grove, and Canada del Refugio, Santa Barbara County. It is a low succulent, prostrate annual, profusely branching and spreading. The numerous upright lateral branches are beset with tender leaves and it is these branch tips which are the edible portion of the plant. The alternate, triangular leaves are rather fleshy, and the surface is covered with crystalline papillae. The flowers are axillary, small, greenish-yellow, and with petals. The fruit is nut-like and has 1 to 9 locules, each containing 1 seed; the fruit is enveloped by the persistent calyx which bears 4 horn-like protuberances.

HORSE PURSLANE (*Trianthema portulacastrum* L.)
Other common name: Desert purslane.

This is a subtropical species which occurs sparingly in southern California, and occasionally is weedy in nature. It is a diffusely branched herb, with succulent, more or less prostrate branches 8 to 24 inches long. The leaves are oval, ½ to ¾ inch long, blunt at the apex, wedge-shaped at the base, with short petioles which are dilated at the base into 2-toothed stipular expansions. The flowers are small,

FIG. 88. New Zealand spinach (*Tetragonia expansa*), showing branch with fruits in leaf axils, and a single fruit enclosed by the 4-horned calyx.

and purplish within; there is a 5-lobed calyx, no petals, and 5 or 6 to 10 stamens. The fruit is a few-seeded capsule. Seed about 2 mm. long, somewhat heartshaped; dark undersurface, heavily overlayed with a light scurfyness suggesting irregular ridges.

Fig. 89. Red maids (*Calandrinia caulescens* var. *Menziesii*), showing habit.
A, seeds.

PURSLANE FAMILY *(Portulacaceae)*

Members of this family are predominantly succulent herbs. It is principally an American family of plants, well known representatives being *Calandrinia* (red maids), *Claytonia* (spring beauty), *Montia perfoliata* (miner's lettuce), and *Portulaca oleracea* (common purslane).

RED MAIDS OR KISSES (*Calandrinia caulescens* var. *Menziesii* Gray)
(Fig. 89)

This is a native plant of western United States, generally distributed at lower altitudes in California, being a conspicuous component of our early spring flora. It has become a rather common weed in orchards and vineyards, and also to some extent in cultivated fields. Red maids is a somewhat fleshy annual herb, ½ to 1 foot high, with alternate, entire, narrow leaves, 1 to 2 inches long. The flowers are rose-red or crimson, with 2 sepals, 5 petals notched at the tip, 7 to 14 stamens, and a single pistil tipped with a 3-branched style. The fruit is a 3-valved capsule, enclosed by the 2 persistent sepals, and bearing numerous seeds. The black, shining seeds are approximately 2 mm. in diameter, lens-shaped and slightly twisted, microscopically pebbly on the surface, particularly at the rim.

MINER'S LETTUCE (*Montia perfoliata* (Donn) Howell) (Fig. 90)

This plant is a native of the western coast. It has become a very common weed in orchards, gardens, and vineyards throughout California.

Miner's lettuce is a smooth, succulent, low annual, with numerous basal leaves, and several erect stems 4 to 12 inches tall. The basal leaves are long and narrow, broadening at the tip; the leaves farther up on

FIG. 90.   Miner's lettuce (*Montia perfoliata*).

the stem are very characteristic in that they are semi-circular in shape, the bases of the pairs being united, forming a circular disk through which the stem appears to project. The flowers are small, each with 2 green sepals, 5 white or flesh-colored petals which are larger than the sepals, 5 stamens, and a single ovary tipped by a 3-branched style. The fruit is a 3-valved capsule, splitting down from the apex when mature. There are numerous black, shining seeds with an obscurely granular surface. Seeds are about $\frac{1}{16}$ inch in diameter, lens-shaped, thickened toward the notched scar which bears a conspicuous white appendage.

Where miner's lettuce is abundant in orchards or vineyards it has some value as a green manure crop. The early pioneers in the miners' camps made some use of the plant as a substitute for lettuce or other salad plants.

Montia spathulata (Dougl.) Howell, somewhat resembling miner's lettuce in general appearance, is a native plant, fairly abundant in California. It also is found as a weed in orchards, vineyards, and other cultivated areas. It is a low, dwarf-like plant, 1 to 6 inches tall, and the stem pair of leaves does not form a disk, as they do in miner's lettuce. The petals are white or light pink, little exceeding the sepals in length. The seed is similar to preceding, but smaller.

PURSLANE (*Portulaca oleracea* L.) (Fig. 91)
Other common names: Pussley, pursley, wild portulaca.

This is a well known weed in Europe, from which country it was introduced into the United States. Throughout California it is widely distributed, being a weed in cultivated fields, orchards, gardens, and waste places. Particularly is purslane a serious pest in lettuce fields in that the cultural practices of lettuce are favorable for the growth of the weed.

FIG. 91.   Purslane (*Portulaca oleracea*). **A**, flower, enlarged; **B**, single flower in leaf axil; **C**, seeds; **D**, three capsules, one with lid off.

Common purslane is a fleshy annual, smooth throughout, forming a mat-like growth. The stems are often reddish in color. The leaves are numerous, alternate, thick, entire, and somewhat wedge-shaped, with rounded tips. The flowers are small, yellow, and open only in the sunshine. There are 2 sepals, fused with the ovary below, 5 small yellow petals, inserted with the stamens on the calyx, 7 to 12 (sometimes more) stamens, and a single pistil with a 5- or 6-lobed style. The fruit is a globular many-seeded capsule, the upper half at maturity breaking around the middle and coming off like a lid. The seeds are flattened, less than 1 mm. in diameter, rounded to somewhat kidney-shape in outline, with a white mark at the scar. The dull to somewhat shiny black surface is given a granular appearance by 3 to 4 concentric rows of minute tubercles.

PINK FAMILY (Caryophyllaceae)

This family has many species of plants which are weeds, such as chickweeds, spurrey, cow-herb, German knotgrass, bouncing Bet, and corn cockle. Representatives of the family are herbs, usually with swollen nodes, simple, entire, opposite leaves, and perfect flowers. The calyx is always persistent. There are 4 or 5 sepals and petals, as many or twice as many stamens, and a single ovary. The fruit is a many-seeded capsule.

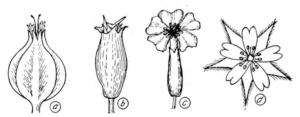

FIG. 92. Botanical characters of certain members of pink family. (a) Five-angled calyx of cow cockle; (b) fruit of bouncing Bet; (c) flower of bouncing Bet; (d) flower of annual mouse-ear chickweed.

KEY TO GENERA OF CARYOPHYLLACEAE CONTAINING WEEDY SPECIES

Sepals united into a tubular calyx (Fig. 92a, b, c)
  Styles 5
    Calyx inflated _____Lychnis
    Calyx not inflated_____Agrostemma
  Styles 3 _____Silene
  Styles 2
    Flowers very small, not showy_____Velezia
    Flowers showy
      Calyx ovate, with 5 prominent angles; petals without scales_____Vaccaria
      Calyx tubular, not angled; petals with scales_____Saponaria
Sepals distinct, or united only at base (Fig. 92d)
  Small prostrate herbs; style 1, 2-cleft or parted or rarely 3-cleft, or styles 2; petals none
    Stipules absent; low annual_____Scleranthus
    Stipules present
      Annual; stipules and flowers minute_____Herniaria
      Perennial; stipules conspicuous_____Paronychia

Low herbs ; styles 3 to 5 and distinct ; petals present
  Stipules absent
    Petals bifid or 2-divided
      Styles usually 5_____*Cerastium*
      Styles usually 3_____*Stellaria*
    Petals entire or merely notched
      Styles fewer than the sepals_____*Arenaria*
      Styles as many as the sepals_____*Sagina*
  Stipules present
    Styles 3 ; leaves opposite_____*Spergularia*
    Styles 5 ; leaves apparently whorled_____*Spergula*
    Style 1, 3-cleft or toothed ; petals minute or none_____*Polycarpon*

CORN COCKLE (*Agrostemma Githago* L.) (Fig. 93)

Other common names: Purple cockle, corn rose, corn campion, corn mullein.

Corn cockle is a weed of European origin which has become troublesome in the principal winter grain districts of the United States, but as yet is not abundant in California. It is established however in the Sacramento and San Joaquin valleys, and in valleys of the Coast Range and south as far as San Bernardino County.

Corn cockle is an annual, 1½ to 3 feet tall, with white-hairy stems. The leaves are 2 to 4 inches long, ¼ inch wide or less, narrow, and without petioles. The flowers are few, solitary, long-stalked, and purplish-red in color. The 5 sepals are united below to form a 10-ribbed tube, the tips being free and somewhat longer than tube. The corolla is dark purplish-red, 1 to 2 inches in diameter, composed of 5 separate petals, which are somewhat b l a c k-d o t t e d. There are 10 stamens and a single pistil with 5 style branches. The fruit is a 1-celled capsule about ½ inch long, containing numerous dark-brown to black wedge-shaped seeds, about 2 to 4 mm. long. The two faces of the seeds are covered by 3 to 5 concentric rows of teeth, which become

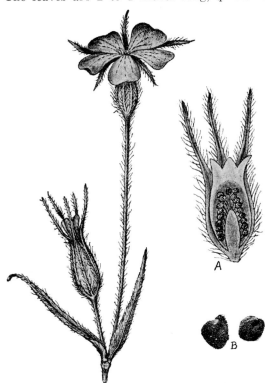

FIG. 93. Corn cockle (*Agrostemma Githago*). A, median lengthwise section of capsule ; B, seeds.

gradually smaller toward the scar, larger and more prominent toward the thickened outer edge.

Corn cockle is listed as a poisonous plant. Feeds which contain a considerable amount of corn cockle seed are injurious to both stock and poultry. Flour made from wheat containing these seeds is unpalatable and produces poorly rising bread.

SANDWORT (*Arenaria serpyllifolia* L.)

This species, naturalized from Europe, is rare in California. It has been reported in lawns at Claremont, Colby's Ranch, San Gabriel Mountains, and in stream beds in Humboldt County. It is a low branching annual, 3 to 9 inches high, with stems that are covered with fine, downward pointing hairs. The leaves are oval, pointed and about $\frac{1}{8}$ inch long. The flowers are white, on short stalks, and with 5 sepals, 5 petals about one-half the length of the sepals, 10 stamens, 3 styles, and a short-oval capsule, the valves of which are 2-cleft. The seeds are about .5 mm. across, dark red-brown, rounded kidney-shaped, with definite cobblestone surface.

KEY TO WEEDY SPECIES OF CERASTIUM

Petals twice the length of sepals_____*C. arvense*
Petals equal to or shorter than sepals
   Flower stalks much longer than flowers_____*C. vulgatum*
   Flower stalks not longer than flowers_____*C. viscosum*

FIELD CHICKWEED (*Cerastium arvense* L.)
Other common name: Meadow chickweed

This species is a native of Europe and North America. It is found in the Coast Ranges and to a limited extent in the Sierras of California. Only rarely is it a weed of any importance. With us it is chiefly in lawns. It is a perennial reproducing by seeds and running rootstocks. The stems usually form mats or tufts, and they may root at the nodes. The leaves are linear to narrowly lance-shaped. The weed may be distinguished from the two following species by its petals, which are twice the length of the sepals. The petals are shorter than, or about equal the sepals in *C. viscosum* and *C. vulgatum*. The seeds are larger than those of the two following, over 1 mm. long, more rounded in outline with notch at scar from which a groove extends inward.

ANNUAL MOUSE-EAR CHICKWEED (*Cerastium viscosum* L.) (Figs. 92d, 94a)

This species is introduced from Europe. It occurs throughout the United States. It is found in fields, gardens, and waste places, in meadows and lawns. It is an annual, sticky-hairy plant, 2 to 12 inches high. The leaves are small, hairy, entire, and oval. The flowers are small and white, on stalks which are not longer than the flowers. The 5 sepals are as long as or somewhat longer than the 5 petals, which are usually 2-toothed at the apex. Usually there are 10 stamens, sometimes only 5 with anthers, the other 5 with scale-like filaments which do not bear anthers. The fruit is a cylindrical capsule, about twice as long as the persistent calyx, containing numerous seeds. The seeds are wedge-shaped, about $\frac{1}{4}$ mm. long, orange or brownish in color and somewhat transparent; minutely roughened with elongate blister-like protuberances.

PERENNIAL MOUSE-EAR CHICKWEED (*Cerastium vulgatum* L.) (Fig. 94)
Other common name : Large mouse-ear chickweed.

This chickweed, which is fairly common throughout California, is an introduction from Europe. It is similar in appearance and closely related to *C. viscosum*. It differs from that species in being a perennial; also in the length of the flower stalks. The flower stalk on *C. vulgatum* is longer than the flower; on *C. viscosum* it is not longer than the flower. The wedge-shaped seed is about ½ mm. long, reddish-brown, with elongated blister-like protuberances which are concentric at the outer margin, but converge to point inward toward the scar.

Fig. 94. Perennial mouse-ear chickweed (*Cerastium vulgatum*), showing habit. A, seed of annual mouse-ear chickweed (*C. viscosum*) ; B, seed of perennial mouse-ear chickweed (*C. vulgatum*).

HERNIARIA (*Herniaria cinerea* DC.)

This is an introduced species from Europe which is found in the foothills on either side of the lower San Joaquin Valley and in a few localities in southern California. It is a very small erect annual plant, 1 to 2½ inches high, or sometimes forming mats 3 to 14 inches wide. The branches bear 2-ranked branchlets. The leaves are opposite with minute papery stipules, the blades oblong and about ⅙ inch long. The flowers are very small, green, and crowded in clusters in all the leaf axils. There are 4 or 5 sepals united at the base, usually no petals, 2 to 5 stamens inserted on the calyx base, and a short 2-cleft or 2-parted style. The fruit is an achene, enclosed by the calyx. The shiny black minute seeds, double-convex lens-shaped, are rimmed by a thin margin.

WHITE COCKLE (*Lychnis alba* Mill.) (Fig. 95)

This is an introduction from Europe which occurs in cultivated fields here and there in California. It is a biennial or perennial herb, with spreading, hairy, jointed stems. The leaves are opposite, simple, hairy, and oval to lance-shaped. There are staminate and pistillate plants. In both types of flowers there is a calyx tube with 5 long tapering teeth, 5 white or pink petals which are much longer than the calyx. There are 10 stamens in the staminate flowers, and no pistil, whereas in pistillate flowers there is a single pistil with 5 styles, and no stamens. The fruit is

an oval-conical, many-seeded capsule. The seeds are rounded kidney-shaped, approximately 1 mm. across, clay-gray in color with irregular lines of black-tipped projections. Projections are reduced in size and compactly raised in ring almost surrounding scar. (Fig. 95A)

WHITLOW-WORT (*Paronychia franciscana* Eastw.)

This is an introduction from Chile, now found from San Francisco to Sonoma County and southward on grassy hilltops near the ocean. It is a prostrate, tufted perennial,

FIG. 95.   White cockle (*Lychnis alba*), showing habit, and (A) seed.

with tough stems, 4 to 12 inches long, and composed of very short internodes, usually less than ⅙ inch long. The leaves are lance-shaped, pointed, tipped with a short hard point from ⅙ to ⅓ inch long, stipulate, and very much crowded on the stems. The flowers are clustered in the leaf axils. The flowers are very small, with 5 bristle-tipped sepals, 5 thread-like petals, or none, 5 stamens inserted at the base of the sepals, and a 2-parted style. The fruit is a utricle enclosed by the persistent calyx.

FOUR-LEAVED ALL-SEED (*Polycarpon tetraphyllum* L.)

This native of Europe has a limited distribution in central and southern California. It grows in beaten gravelly places, and in the crevices of brick walks. It is a low, branching, prostrate annual, the stems 2 to 6 inches long. There are numerous small leaves, seldom over ½ inch long, which are oblong and either opposite or in 4's. There are 5 sepals, greenish or purplish, 5 petals shorter than the sepals, 3 to 5 stamens, and a single pistil. The fruit is a 3-valved capsule, containing several seeds.

DWARF PEARLWORT (*Sagina apetala* Ard.)

This is an introduced European species. It has been found at Pasadena, Jackson, and in Tehama County. It is a very small, erect annual herb, 1 to 2 inches high, and usually minutely glandular-hairy. The leaves are opposite, very narrow and seldom more than ⅛ inch long. The flowers are minute, with a 4-parted calyx, 4 minute petals, or none, 5 to 10 stamens, and a single pistil bearing 4 styles. The fruit is an egg-shaped capsule, about 1½ times as long as the calyx. A variety of the species, *Sagina apetala* var. *barbata* Fenzl., has been reported at Jackson, Ione, Auburn, and Crane Creek, Tehama County. It occurs about ranches and dwellings.

BOUNCING BET (*Saponaria officinalis* L.) (Fig. 96)

Other common names: Soapwort, Fuller's herb, sweet Betty, scourwort, hedge pink.

This is an introduced species from Europe, now abundant throughout eastern North America but as yet common only in northern California. It is an escaped garden ornamental which occurs in waste places, along roadsides and ditch banks. Bouncing Bet is a stout, erect, smooth, perennial, 2 to 3 feet high, from a short rootstock. The leaves are simple, oval or lance-shaped, entire, and 3 to 4 inches long. The flowers are in dense terminal clusters. The sepals are united to form a long tube with 5 very small unequal teeth. There are 5 petals, white, pink or rose-colored, each crested with 2 awl-shaped teeth. (These are absent in *Vaccaria vulgaris*.) There are 10 stamens, and a single pistil with 2 styles. The fruit is a capsule, opening with 4 teeth, and containing numerous seeds. The almost black seeds are rounded kidney-shape, about 2 mm. across, roughened on the faces by about 6 rows of blister-like shiny protuberances.

KNAWEL (*Scleranthus annuus* L.)

Other common name: German knotgrass.

This plant, introduced from Europe, is a troublesome weed along the Atlantic Coast but is not common in California. It has been found at Placerville, El Dorado County, and at Pala, San Diego County. It is a weed of gardens, lawns, fields, and waste places.

Knawel is an annual with long, tough roots, and low, spreading stems 2 to 4 inches long. The leaves are small, $\frac{1}{4}$ to $\frac{1}{3}$ inch long, pointed and awl-shaped, the bases united about the nodes. The very small flowers are in axillary clusters, greenish-white, without petals. The 5 white-margined sepals are united below to form a cup about the fruit. There are 5 to 10 stamens, and a single pistil with 2 styles. The fruit is dry and bladdery, enclosed within the persistent calyx, and contains 1 seed. The investing calyx is about 3 mm. long and half as wide, with 10 ribs and 5 calyx teeth, yellowish brown in color and slightly rough. The seed is oval, pointed at the apex, about 1.5 mm. long, with fine lengthwise lines on surface.

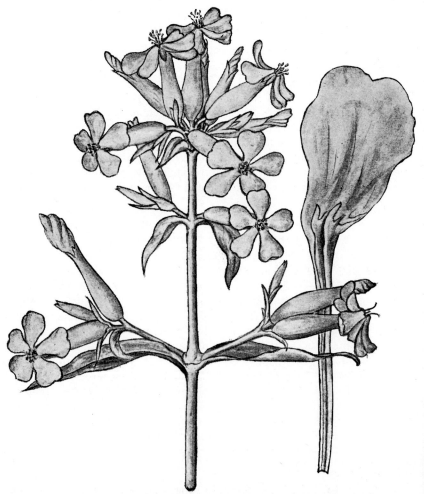

FIG. 96. Bouncing Bet (*Saponaria officinalis*), showing flowering branch and single petal with characteristic awn-shaped teeth.

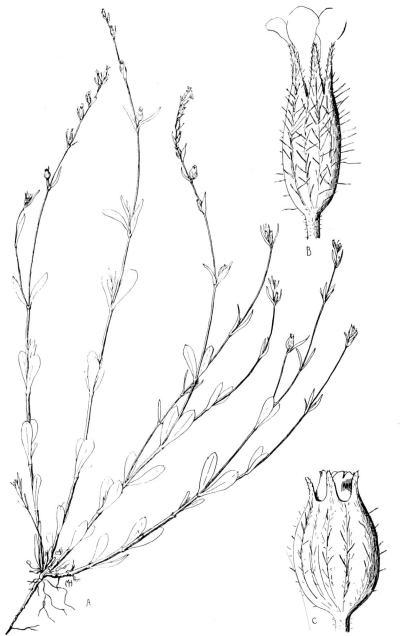

Fɪɢ. 97.   Windmill pink (*Silene gallica*). **A,** habit of windmill pink showing the swollen joints enclosed by the leaf bases of the opposite leaves ; **B,** single flower, x 10 ; **C,** fruiting calyx showing capsule opened at the top, x 10.

CATCHFLY AND CAMPION. *SILENE*

KEY TO WEEDY SPECIES OF SILENE

Calyx much inflated and bladdery, perennial_____*S. latifolia*
Calyx merely expanded by ripening capsule, annual
    Night-blooming _____*S. noctiflora*
    Day-blooming
        Plants sticky-hairy, without glandular bands; flowers in racemes____*S. gallica*
        Plants glabrous to minute hairy, with a portion of each upper internode glandular; flowers in panicles_____*S. antirrhina*

SLEEPY CATCHFLY (*Silene antirrhina* L.)

This native of the Old World is fairly common throughout California, particularly in sandy soil, but is nowhere abundant. It is a slender, sparingly branched annual, 1 to 2½ feet high. The herbage is mostly glabrous above, minutely puberulent below, leaves oblong-lanceolate to linear, 1 to 2 inches long. There is a black glandular band at about the middle of the upper internodes. The flowers are pink or red, emarginate, the blade about 2 mm. long, crests minute. The ovoid one-celled capsule is about ¼ inch long, and contains numerous grayish seeds which are 0.6 mm. long, short kidney-shaped, their surface, roughened by more or less concentric rows of blunt tubercles.

WINDMILL PINK (*Silene gallica* L.) (Fig. 97)
Other common names: English catchfly, small-flowered catchfly.

Windmill pink is an introduction from Europe which has become common throughout northern United States. In California it is widely distributed, being found along roadsides, in gardens and fields, and in neglected places.

This is an annual, 1 to 2 feet high, with erect, slender, more or less hairy and sticky stems. The leaves are opposite, there being 4 or 5 pairs to a stem, the petioles broadened at the base and clasping the stem, the leaf blades 1 to 1½ inches long. The flower groups are mostly 1-sided. The calyx is tubular, formed of 5 united sepals, the tube bulging somewhat; 10-nerved, hairy, and persistent in fruit. The 5 petals are separate, white or pale pink, contracted to narrow claws. The petals are often twisted, and thus they appear as vanes of a windmill. There are 10 stamens, and a single pistil with 3 or 4 styles. The fruit is a dry capsule, opening at the top. The numerous black seeds are kidney-shape, about 1 mm. across, faces roughened by elongated fine protuberances which converge toward the scar, around which on either face is a definite depressed area.

BLADDER CAMPION (*Silene latifolia* (Mill.) Britton and Rendle) (Fig. 98)

This species, naturalized from Europe and fairly common in eastern United States, occurs sparingly in the State. Now in Sacramento, Sonoma and Orange Counties. Bladder campion is a perennial, spreading from a short rootstock. The herbage is glaucous; leaves ovate lanceolate, entire, or denticulate in the rosette. The five petals are white, 2-cleft; stamens 10, styles 3. The one-celled capsule contains numerous short kidney-shaped tuberculate grayish seeds.

Fig. 98. Bladder campion (*Silene latifolia*), showing habit, and three seeds in different views.

NIGHT-BLOOMING CATCHFLY (*Silene noctiflora* L.)

This native of Europe has been found in lawns as far south as Los Angeles County. It has long been common in eastern North America, and recently has spread to the Pacific Northwest, in meadows, clover and alfalfa fields.

Night-blooming catchfly is an annual or winter annual, a foot or more tall, the jointed stems covered with sticky hairs.

The leaves are spatulate to lance-shaped. The flowers are solitary on long stems or in open cymes, white or yellowish, opening at night; calyx tube hairy, 5-10 nerved. The short kidney-shaped seeds are about 1.2 mm. long, roughened by curved rows of minute tubercles, the bases of which are delineated by dark wavy lines.

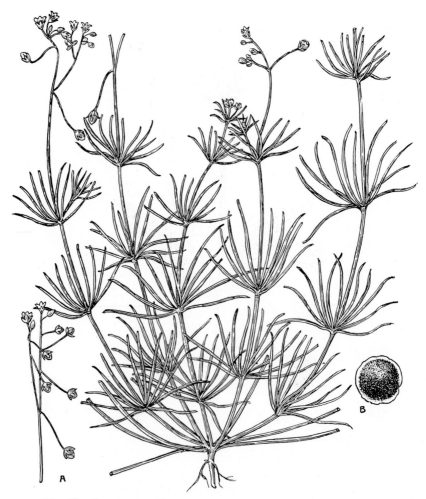

Fig. 99.　Corn spurry (*Spergula arvensis*), showing habit. **A**, fruiting branch; **B**, seed.

CORN SPURRY (*Spergula arvensis* L.) (Fig. 99)
Other common names: Devil's-gut, sandweed, pick-purse, yarr.

This introduction from Europe is widespread throughout the Eastern States and Canada, and the Pacific Northwest. In California it is more often found along the coast than in the interior. It may occur in grain fields, in cultivated fields, orchards, and gardens. Corn spurry is a spreading annual, the stems slender, conspicuously jointed and somewhat sticky. The stems may be 1 to 2 feet long. The leaves are threadlike, $\frac{1}{2}$ to $1\frac{1}{2}$ inches long, and appear to be in whorls. The flowers are small, white, and open only in sunlight. There are 5 sepals, 5 entire petals, usually 10 stamens (sometimes 5), and a single pistil with 5 styles. The fruit is a 5-valved capsule, containing numerous thick lens-shaped, dull black roughened seeds which are about 1.5 mm. in diameter and margined by a narrow light-colored wing.

SAND SPURRY (*Spergularia rubra* (L.) J. & C. Presl. var. *perennans* (Kindb.) Rob.)

In California there are six species of *Spergularia* recorded, but only the one here mentioned is of significance as a weed. This species, introduced from Europe, is gradually spreading in the central and northern parts of the State. It is usually found along roadsides and paths. Sand spurry is a prostrate perennial with fibrous roots and slender, wiry straggling stems, 4 to 9 inches long, from a matted center. The leaves are less than $\frac{1}{2}$ inch long. Flowers are produced along stems from the middle to the end. Each flower has 5 sepals, 5 reddish entire petals, 10 stamens, and a single pistil, usually with 3 styles. The fruit is a 3-valved capsule bearing dull brown wedge-shaped seeds bordered by a thickened margin.

GRASSY STARWORT (*Stellaria graminea* L.) (Fig. 100)

This species introduced from Eurasia has been seen in lawns at Claremont, La Verne, and San Gabriel. It is closely related to the following, common chickweed, and similar in appearance.

Grassy starwort is a perennial reproducing by seeds and creeping stems. The seeds are dull brown, about 1 mm. in diameter, broadly ovate or nearly circular, and narrowed slightly toward the notch at the scar. The seed, which is an impurity in commercial lawn seed, is similar to the following but smaller. The surface protuberances are elongated-wavy, and the margin outline suggests rounded scallops.

COMMON CHICKWEED (*Stellaria media* (L.) Cyr.) (Fig. 100)
Other common names: Starwort, starweed, satin flower.

This chickweed is introduced from Europe. It has become a common weed throughout North America, occurring in gardens, cultivated fields, in vineyards and orchards, in shady lawns, among shrubbery, along fence lines and ditches. It is one of the earliest weeds in California, often coming up in onion fields, asparagus beds, peas, and other crops

FIG. 100. Common chick-weed (*Stellaria media*). Left, seed of *S. media*; right, *S. graminea*.

during rainy springs, and giving trouble before the soil is dry enough to cultivate. The plant thrives best in the shade or during cool, moist weather. With the onset of hot, dry days it soon dries up.

Common chickweed is annual or winter annual, sometimes perennial in California, which may bloom throughout the winter in sheltered places. The stems are slender and weak, with rows of hairs running lengthwise. The stems may strike root at the prominent joints. The leaves are opposite, about ½ inch or less long, entire, oblong in shape, the upper ones without petioles, the lower on hairy petioles. The flowers are small, white, with 5 sepals, 5 deeply cleft petals, 3 to 7 stamens and a single pistil with 3 or 4 styles. The fruit is a many-seeded dry capsule. The seed is circular, slightly elongated toward the notch at scar. It is about 1 mm. across, dark brown, the surface covered with irregular wart-like but not definitely elongated projections which give the margin outline an irregular toothed appearance.

COW COCKLE (*Vaccaria vulgaris* Host.)
Other common names: Spring cockle, pink cockle, cowherb.

Cow cockle is introduced from Europe. It is chiefly a grain field weed, common in the Northwestern States and western Canada, and rather widely distributed but not abundant in California.

The plant is an erect annual, from a narrow tap root. It has smooth, stout stems, forked-branching, 2 to 3 feet high. The leaves are opposite, simple, 3 to 4 inches long, and clasp the stem. The flowers are showy, in clusters, the calyx of 5 united sepals and 5-angled, the corolla of 5 separate red petals. There are 10 stamens and a single pistil with 2 styles. The fruit is a capsule, opening with 4 short teeth (Fig. 92a), and containing many globular seeds about 2 mm. in diameter covered with very minute tubercles, dull black in color except at the hilum, which is whitish.

The seeds, like those of corn cockle, contain a poisonous saponin, which may cause distress to livestock and poultry when eaten.

VELEZIA (*Velezia rigida* L.)

This species is introduced from southern Europe. It occurs on dry foothills at La Grange, Stanislaus County, and Hupa, Humboldt County. It is an annual with tough, slender, trailing stems 4 to 8 inches long, which in age readily break up into joints. The leaves are awl-shaped, glandular-hairy, and from ⅙ to ½ inch long. The flowers are pink, and usually solitary in the leaf axils or in clusters of 2 or 3. The calyx is tubular, narrow, cylindric, 15-ribbed, and sharply 5-toothed, the teeth being much shorter than the tube. The corolla consists of 5 minute petals, each with a scale, and with the blade notched. There are 5 stamens and 2 styles. The fruit is a slender capsule, opening by 4 short teeth.

CROWFOOT FAMILY *(Ranunculaceae)*

This is a widely distributed and well known family of plants. Familiar representatives are the *Paeonia*, marsh marigold (*Caltha*), globe flower (*Trollius*), hellebore (*Helleborus*), columbine (*Aquilegia*), baneberry (*Actaea*), larkspur (*Delphinium*), aconite (*Aconitum*), *Anemone*, *Clematis*, buttercup or crowfoot (*Ranunculus*), and meadow rue (*Thalictrum*).

Some of the members of this family are poisonous to livestock.

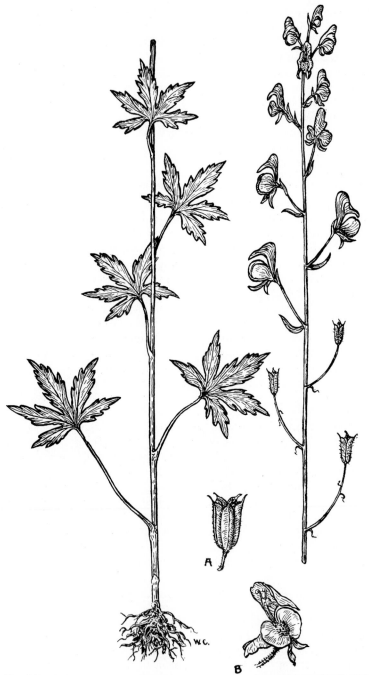

FIG. 101. Western monkshood (*Aconitum columbianum*), showing leaves and flowers with characteristic hood. A, fruit; B, single flower, with part of hood removed.

WESTERN MONKSHOOD (*Aconitum columbianum* Nutt.) (Fig. 101)

This native of the Western States occurs in California in the Sierra Nevada from Modoc County south to Kern County, at elevations from 1,000 to 12,000 feet. It frequents wet mountain meadows, and sometimes grows in small dense patches.

Western monkshood is an erect, stout, single-stemmed plant sometimes attaining a height of 6 feet. The leaves are palmately lobed, resembling those of larkspur. The flowers have a characteristic hood, hence the common name "monkshood." The flowers are showy, blue or purple,

FIG. 102.   Baneberry (*Actaea spicata* var. *arguta*).

sometimes white, irregular in shape, and distributed in loose clusters. There are 5 petal-like sepals, the upper of which is helmet- or hood-shaped. There are usually 5 small petals, the upper 2 of which are concealed inside the sepal hood. Stamens are numerous, and pistils number 3 to 5. The fruit is a follicle (pod-like), 3 to 5 of them being more or less joined at the base. The seed is wedge-shaped, approximately 3 mm. long, dark brown with about five transverse distinctly and sharply raised wavy ridges.

Monkshood is definitely known to be poisonous to livestock but usually it is eaten in such small quantities that it is seldom the cause of losses.

BANEBERRY (*Actaea spicata* L. var. *arguta* Torr.) (Fig. 102)

This species occurs on wooded and brushy north slopes throughout the mountains of California. Baneberry is a perennial herb, 1½ to 3 feet tall, arising from a rootstock. The leaves are bi- or triternately compound, 1½ to 3 feet long, the leaflets broadly or narrowly oval, deeply cut and coarsely toothed, 1 to 2½ inches long. The flowers are in terminal racemes and are small and white. There are usually 4 sepals, their tips often pinkish, and from 1 to 10 small petals, or none. Stamens vary in number from 11 to 35. There is a single pistil, usually bearing 10 seeds in two rows. The fruit is a red or white berry, with a polished surface. There are about 6 reddish-brown seeds about 3 mm. long, straight on the front face, rounded on the back, and laterally flattened.

Baneberry is reported as being poisonous to humans.

LARKSPUR. DELPHINIUM

The native larkspurs are all perennial herbs with palmately divided leaves and flowers in terminal racemes. There are 5 sepals, the upper one being extended into a characteristic spur, which has suggested the common name "larkspur." There are 4 petals, in unequal pairs, the upper pair being developed backwards into the spur of the calyx. Pistils are 3 in number, becoming many-seeded follicles. The seeds are variously squared due to close packing in the follicles, and are often encased in a more or less inflated or collapsed outer coat.

In *Delphinium decorum* and *D. Menziesii* there is a globular tuber or a cluster of fleshy roots. In the other species described the roots are hard, woody and slender.

The larkspurs probably cause more losses among cattle in the State as a whole than any other group of plants. Other domestic livestock are not seriously affected.

Jepson described 16 species of *Delphinium* as occurring in California. It is known definitely that a number of these are poisonous, and all should be regarded with suspicion by stockmen. All of the following described California larkspurs are known to be poisonous:

Tall Larkspurs

COAST LARKSPUR (*Delphinium californicum* T. & G.)

Coast larkspur is widely distributed, occurring on low hills near the coast from Marin County to San Luis Obispo County, and also on

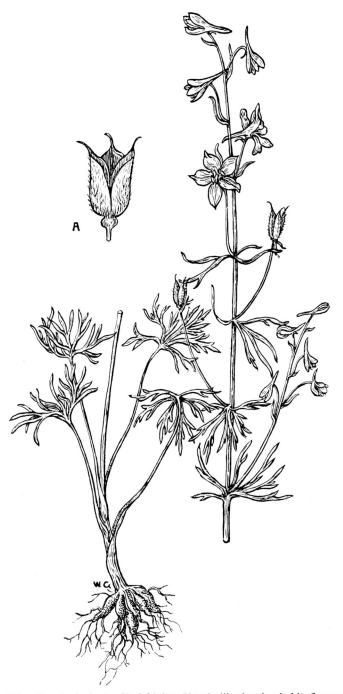

FIG. 103. Menzies larkspur (*Delphinium Menziesii*), showing habit, flowers with characteristic spur. **A,** united follicles.

north slopes of inner Coast Range peaks. Stems stout, 2½ to 7 feet tall; root a cluster of hard woody fibres. Leaves large, 4 to 6 inches broad deeply divided into 3 to 5 segments, the broad terminal segments unequal, lanceolate or acute, herbage pubescent. Flowering racemes ¾ to 1¼ feet long, very dense, the flowers white to whitish or lavendar inside, rather long soft-hairy, never fully opened, sepals about ¼ inch long. Follicle oblong, turgid, about ⅓-½ inch long; seeds black, wrinkled.

MOUNTAIN LARKSPUR (*Delphinium scopulorum* Gray var. *glaucum* Gray)

Mountain larkspur is distributed from 5,000 to 8,000 feet in the Sierra Nevada. Stems 2½ to 6 feet tall, from a cluster of hard woody root fibres; herbage smooth. Leaves 4 to 5 inches broad, 5- to 7-parted; divisions wedge-shaped, the division cleft with the central segment in each division lanceolate and prominent. Flowering racemes 1 to 1½ feet long, pedicels ½ to 1 inch long, flowers blue or purplish, minutely soft-hairy. Sepals and spur about ½ inch long. Follicles smooth, about ½ inch long. Seeds about 1½ mm. long, blackish with a loose light-colored cellular coat which extends from the angles to form transparent wings.

COW POISON (*Delphinium trollifolium* Gray)

Cow poison is along the coast from Humboldt County north. This species grows 4 to 6 feet tall, herbage smooth, leaves thin and narrow, cut into blunt segments, the segments cut or with rounded teeth. The flowering racemes, ¾ to 2 feet long, are very loose below, sometimes more dense above. The widely spreading, smooth or hairy pedicels are 1 to 2 inches long, or the lowest up to 5 inches long. Flowers deep blue, the slender spur about ⅔ inches long. Follicles smooth, ¾ to 1 inch long, slightly spreading to occasionally strongly recurved-spreading.

Low Larkspurs

ANDERSON'S LARKSPUR (*Delphinium Andersonii* Gray)

Anderson's larkspur is found on the east side of the northern Sierra Nevada. It is low growing, 1½ to 2 feet, from a cluster of fibrous roots, herbage smooth or nearly so, leaf blades lightly soft hairy. Leaves thickish, 1 to 2½ inches broad, deeply 2 to 3 parted into oblong or linear segments. Flowering racemes open, 7 to 10 inches long, pedicels ½ to 1½ inches long. Flowers blue, spur short, stout and curved at the blunt tip. Follicles about ½ inch long, smooth.

SMOOTH LARKSPUR (*Delphinium decorum* F. & M var. *patens* Gray)

This variety of the smooth larkspur is a plant of the mountains from Calaveras County to Tulare County. It is 1 to 2 feet tall from tuberous thickened roots; herbage smooth, pedicels smooth or sparsely glandular pubescent. Basal leaves thick, round in outline, 1 to 2½ or more inches broad, 3 to 5-parted into rounded or wedge-shaped segments, these entire or 3-lobed. Stem leaves 3 to 5, or 7-parted into narrow lobes. Flowering racemes several-flowered, not spreading; flowers smaller than in the species, deep blue, magenta, pink or lavender-white, sepals less than ½ inch long, spur as long or longer. Follicles smooth, thickish, about

$\frac{1}{2}$ inch long, spreading from the middle; seeds brownish, invested in a scaly coat; about 3 mm. long.

In the species, which is frequent in the foothills of the Coast Range and Sierra Nevada, Central California to San Diego County, the purple-violet flowers are larger, herbage glabrous or sometimes pubescent, especially the petioles and pedicels.

WESTERN LARKSPUR (*Delphinium hesperium* Gray)

Western larkspur is found in dry, open ground in the Coast Ranges from Humboldt County to Monterey County. The stem is usually simple, $1\frac{1}{2}$ to 3 feet tall, from a cluster of thick fibrous roots or a single woody taproot. The herbage is short pubescent, leaves 2 to 3 times palmately divided. The flowering raceme is dense, slender, 6 to 14 inches long; pedicels erect, the lowermost longest, about 1 inch long. The flowers usually blue, sometimes pink, white or intermediate shapes. Sepals about $\frac{1}{2}$ inch long, densely minutely hairy on the outside, or alternate ones with a hairy band on the outside; petals slightly shorter. Spur equal or longer than the sepals. Follicles $\frac{1}{4}$ to $\frac{1}{2}$ inch long, hairy. Seeds angled, about $1\frac{1}{2}$-2 mm. long with loose light colored and sometimes mottled netlike coat forming wings on the angles.

MENZIES' LARKSPUR (*Delphinium Menziesii* DC.) (Fig. 103)

Menzies' larkspur is distributed at elevations between 1,000 to 6,500 feet from northern Mendocino County to Siskiyou County and north-ward. Stems 6 to 11 inches tall, arising from a cluster of connected rounded or cylindric tubers. Branched from the base, branches often strongly divergent. Herbage quite smooth or sometimes pubescent. Leaves twice palmately divided, cleft into mostly obtuse lobes. Flowering racemes few to several flowered, $2\frac{1}{2}$ to 6 inches long, pedicels short or the lowermost elongated, spreading. Flowers blue, sparsely short-hairy, sepals $\frac{1}{2}$ to $\frac{2}{3}$ inch long, the spur longer. Follicles divergent, about $\frac{3}{4}$ inch long, almost smooth to sparsely short hairy.

Seeds roughly cone-shaped, cellular-rounded wing-margined at the broad end, slightly so at the pointed end and on the sides.

PARRY'S LARKSPUR (*Delphinium Parryi* Gray)

Parry's larkspur is distributed from coastal southern California to the Colorado Desert, and north to Tulare County. The stems, 1 to $2\frac{3}{4}$ feet tall, and usually simple, arise from a cluster of fibrous roots crowned by a short stout caudex.

The herbage is minutely hairy, the leaves twice divided and the segments redivided into narrowly linear lobes, the lobes $\frac{1}{2}$ to $2\frac{1}{2}$ inches long. The upper leaves are often 5-divided, and the division split again into very narrow lobes. Flowering heads cylindric, sometimes loose, 4 inches to a foot long, flowers blue or lavender to rarely white, on pedicels $\frac{1}{3}$ to 1 inch long, or the lowermost longer; pedals about $\frac{1}{4}$ inch long. Sepals and spur about $\frac{1}{2}$-$\frac{2}{3}$ inch long or longer. Follicles minutely hairy, about $\frac{1}{2}$ inch long, seeds with loosely cellular margin at the angles.

Fɪɢ. 104. California buttercup (*Ranunculus californicus*), showing habit, single leaf, and single achene.

CROWFOOT. *RANUNCULUS*

There are several species of buttercup or crowfoot in California which are regarded as weeds in other sections of the United States but which are thus far of little significance as such with us. Small-flowered buttercup, *R. parviflorus* L., an introduction from Europe, is reported a serious pest in white clover seed production in Louisiana. It is tall-growing, with small achenes.

KEY TO WEEDY SPECIES OF RANUNCULUS

Achenes prickly or with stiff hooked hairs
    Leaves deeply divided, 2 or 3 times ; border of achene spiny_____*R. arvensis*
    Leaves 3- to 5-lobed, the lobes toothed ; border of achene not spiny____*R. muricatus*
Achenes not prickly, nor with hooked hairs
    Herbage smooth or nearly_____*R. scleratus*
    Herbage pubescent or hirsute
        Perennials from a bulb-like base_____*R. bulbosus*

Perennials from a cluster of fibrous roots
  Stems trailing, rooting at the nodes _____*R. repens*
  Stems erect, one var. prostrate_____*R. californica*

CORN CROWFOOT or HUNGER-WEED (*Ranunculus arvensis* L.) (Fig. 105B)

This is an introduction from Europe which has been collected in Mariposa County. It is an annual, stems erect, 1 to 1½ feet tall. The lower leaves have 3 rounded lobes; the upper are divided into narrow, acute segments. The achene is spiny on the raised border as well as on the sides.

BULBOUS BUTTERCUP (*Ranunculus bulbosus* L.)

This is a perennial herb from a short, thick, bulbous base, which is a native of Europe and has been found as an escape in Humboldt County. The stem is erect, herbage hairy, leaves three parted, their peduncles furrowed.

CALIFORNIA BUTTERCUP (*Ranunculus californicus* Benth.) (Fig. 104)

This is the most common species in California, occurring abundantly in the Coast Ranges and south to southern California, also in the Sacramento and San Joaquin valleys and bordering foothills. It is an erect perennial from 9 to 12 inches tall, much branched above; the herbage is hairy, especially on the lower parts, sometimes almost smooth above. The leaves are roundish in outline, divided into about 3 lobes, or these again divided into many smaller divisions. The flowers are yellow, about 1 to 1½ inches in diameter. The beak of the achene is very short and recurved.

SPINY-FRUITED CROWFOOT (*R. muricatus* L.) (Fig. 105)

Spiny-fruited crowfoot is a naturalized European weed, scattered widely in northern and central California. Occasionally it becomes a pest in grain fields in the Sacramento Valley. The seed is difficult to clean out of grain. Spiny-fruited crowfoot is a stout annual, 3 to 10 inches high, with somewhat succulent, smooth, yellowish-green herbage. The leaves are roundish or kidney-shaped, coarsely toothed, ¾ to 2 inches broad, and usually 3-cleft. The achene has flat sides, usually prickly, surrounded by a smooth conspicuous raised border.

CREEPING BUTTERCUP (*Ranunculus repens* L.)

This attractive buttercup, a double form of which is frequently seen in gardens, is a native of Europe which has become sparingly naturalized in the marshes along the coast from central California northward. It is a low, hairy, creeping perennial with roots at the nodes. The achene has a beveled margin with short recurved beak which is somewhat hooked at the tip.

CURSED CROWFOOT (*Ranunculus sceleratus* L.) (Fig. 106)
Other common names: Blisterwort, celery-leaved crowfoot, bog buttercup.

This species, a native of Europe and North America, has been found thus far only in Modoc County, occurring in marshy places. With us, it cannot be considered a weed of importance, although in other sections

FIG. 105. Spiny-fruited crowfoot (*Ranunculus muricatus*), showing habit. **A**, achenes. **B**, achenes of corn crowfoot (*R. arvensis*).

of the country it is so regarded. This crowfoot is a stout annual herb, $\frac{1}{2}$ to 2 feet tall. The stems are thick, smooth, pale green, somewhat fleshy and hollow. They arise from a cluster of stout fibrous roots. The basal leaves are thick, with a leaf stalk 2 to 3 inches long, and a blade deeply 3- to 5-lobed; the upper leaves are without stalks, very much smaller than the lower ones, deeply lobed, the lobes being entire or toothed. The flowers are numerous, less than $\frac{1}{2}$ inch across, with 3 to 6 green, reflexed sepals, 5 yellow petals which are shorter than the sepals, numerous stamens, and a cone-shaped receptacle bearing numerous pistils. Each ovary develops a one-seeded

Fig. 106. Cursed crowfoot (*Ranunculus sceleratus*), showing habit and achenes.

dry fruit (achene), more or less oval in shape, broader above and with a short straight beak.

Cursed crowfoot has a bitter and acrid sap which may raise blisters on the skin of many individuals, or may cause sores in the mouth of cattle. However, the plants are seldom eaten by animals.

POPPY FAMILY *(Papaveraceae)*

Members of this family are herbs with milky or colored sap. An important genus is *Papaver*, which includes the opium poppy (*Papaver somniferum*), the oriental poppy (*Papaver orientale*), corn poppy

(*Papaver Rhoeas*), and others. Prickly poppy (*Argemone*) is mainly west American. The California state flower is *Eschscholtzia californica*.

CHICALOTE (*Argemone platyceras* Link & Otto var. *hispida* Prain.)

This is a native annual herb, sometimes perennial, which ranges from Lake County to San Diego. It is frequently a weed in waste places and in cultivated fields. The plant has an acrid, orange-colored juice, and densely stiff bristly hairs throughout, and is armed with stout yellow spines. The stems are 1½ to 2¾ feet tall. The leaves are 2 to 9 inches long, oblong, pinnatifid, the lobes spiny-toothed; the leaf blade tapers to a winged petiole. The flowers have 2 or 3 spiny sepals with a horn-like appendage below the apex, 4 to 6 white petals, 1 to 2 inches long, many stamens, and a 1-celled ovary. The fruit is a prickly capsule an inch or more long, containing many pitted grayish-brown to black seeds, the form almost globose, about 2 mm. in diameter with a slight protuberance at either end of an elongated scar.

CALIFORNIA POPPY (*Eschscholtzia californica* Cham.)

This, the State flower, is widespread throughout lower altitudes in California. It is not uncommon as a weed in grain fields. It is a smooth herb with a bitter juice, finely divided leaves and orange or yellow flowers. The roots may live for a year or two, becoming thick and a foot or more in length. The plants are 1 to 2 feet high. Basal leaves are large, grayish-green, compound, the ultimate segments narrow or oblong; stem leaves are smaller, short-stalked or nearly sessile. The flowers are large, 2 to 4 inches across, composed of 2 sepals united into a single cup-like calyx which is pushed off by the expanding corolla, 4 large, rounded petals, numerous stamens, and a single, slender ovary 1 to 4 inches long. The fruit is an elongated 10-nerved capsule containing many dark-brown or blackish seeds, about 2 mm. in diameter, the surface covered by what appears to be a superimposed irregular netting.

YELLOW SEA POPPY (*Glaucium flavum* Crantz)

This European species is reported as naturalized at Elsinore. It has yellow flowers and sap, alternate lobed or dissected leaves, 4 petals, many stamens, and characteristic lattice-veined seeds.

ROUGH POPPY (*Papaver hybridum* L.)

This native of Europe and western Asia has been found near Modesto and Los Angeles, probably introduced in wheat from Australia where it is widespread.

An erect more or less hairy annual, 1 to 2 feet tall; leaves once or twice divided into narrow lobes. Peduncles usually with appressed hairs; petals about 1 inch long, purplish red; usually with a purple blotch at the base; capsule ovoid with stiff curved bristles.

FUMITORY FAMILY *(Fumariaceae)*

Members of this family are weak herbs with characteristics resembling somewhat those of the poppy and mustard families. The principal genera are *Dicentra, Corydalis,* and *Fumaria.* Well known is *Dicentra spectabilis,* which is the bleeding-heart of gardens.

FITWEED (*Corydalis caseana* Gray) (Fig. 107)

This is a native species distributed at altitudes from 5000 to 7000 feet in the Sierra Nevada from Nevada County to Plumas County. Fitweed is a smooth-stemmed perennial $1\frac{1}{2}$ to 3 feet tall, arising from thickened roots. The leaves are alternate, compound, 2- or 3-pinnate, $\frac{1}{2}$ to $1\frac{1}{4}$ feet long, the leaflets oval, short-pointed, and $\frac{1}{4}$ to $\frac{3}{4}$ inch long. The flowers are in dense racemes, $1\frac{1}{2}$ to 3 inches long, and cream-colored. In the flower there are 2 small, scale-like sepals, 4 petals in 2 dissimilar pairs, one petal spurred, the spur being $1\frac{1}{2}$ to 2 times as long as the petals, 6 stamens in

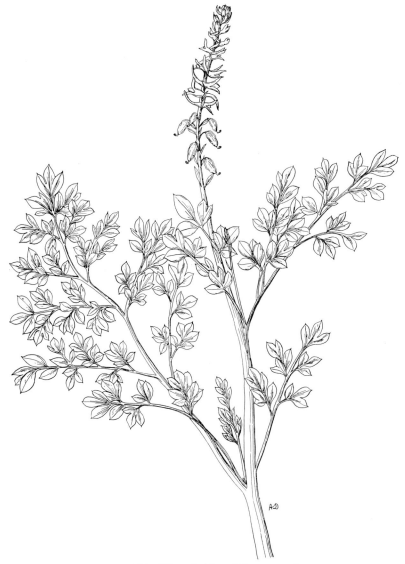

FIG. 107.   Fitweed (*Corydalis caseana*).

2 sets of 3 each, and a single pistil, the ovary of which develops into a 1-celled capsule. The seeds are bordered by a broad wing.

Fitweed is known to be poisonous to cattle and sheep.

GOLDEN EAR-DROPS (*Dicentra chrysantha* (H. & A.) Walp.)

This is a smooth, perennial herb, 2 to 5 feet tall, the coarse, leafy stems arising from stout roots. The leaves are alternate, bipinnate, ½ to 1 foot long. The flowers are sulphur-yellow, erect, and in large clusters. There are 2 small, scale-like sepals, 4 distinct petals, somewhat swollen at the base, in 2 dissimilar pairs, 6 stamens in 2 sets of 3 each, and a single pistil. The fruit is a 1-celled capsule. The seed is about 2 mm. across, circular in outline with a notch at one edge, flattened laterally. The surface is finely and sharply roughened, glistening black.

This widely distributed native species is suspected as a stock-poisoning plant.

FUMITORY (*Fumaria officinalis* L.) (Fig. 108)

This species is locally introduced from Europe, there being records of its occurrence at San Luis Obispo, Ontario, and Upland, and at scattered sites from Yuba to Riverside County. It has been found in orchards, in fields, and in waste places. The plant is an annual, up to 3 feet tall, and freely branching. The leaves are long-stalked, and finely dissected. The flowers are in long racemes. The flowers have 2 sepals, 4 petals, one of which is spurred, 6 sta-mens and a single pistil. The petals are flesh-col-ored, purplish at the tip. The pistil becomes a small globular 1-seeded nutlet. There is a small depression at the apex, and around the base a light smooth rim, the remainder of surface rough, yellowish to green-ish-brown.

SMALL-FLOWERED FUMARIA
(*Fumaria parviflora* Lam.)

This species has been found in a beet field near Woodland, Yolo County, and in San Benito, Mon-terey, and Santa Cruz Counties. The flowers are smaller than those of *F.*

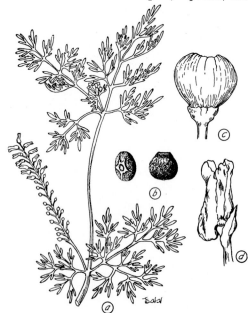

FIG. 108.   Fumitory (*Fumaria officinalis*). (a) leaves and flowering branch; (b) seeds; (c) fruit; (d) flower.

officinalis, and it has characteristic very narrow, sharp and channeled leaf-segments, and apiculate roughish nutlets.

FIG. 109.   Rocky Mountain bee plant (*Cleome serrulata*).

CAPER FAMILY *(Capparidaceae)*

This is a relatively small family, the flowers of which resemble those of mustards *(Cruciferae)*. In both cases there are 4 sepals, 4 petals, and 6 stamens. In capers, however, all six stamens are alike, whereas in mustards there are 4 long stamens and 2 short ones. Furthermore, most capers have palmately compound leaves, whereas the leaves of mustards are simple.

STINK CLOVER *(Cleome platycarpa* Torr.)

This native species, which occurs from Butte to Siskiyou and Modoc, often forms dense stands along roadsides and into adjoining pastureland. It is similar in habit to the following but has golden yellow flowers and capsules $\frac{1}{2}$ to 1 inch long, the stipe a little shorter.

ROCKY MOUNTAIN BEE PLANT *(Cleome serrulata* Pursh) (Fig. 109)

This species, native Arizona to Washington, occurs as an occasional waif in California. It is an erect annual species, from 1 to 3 feet tall. The leaflets are 3, entire, and from 1 to 2 inches long. The flowers are in dense racemes. The flowers are purple, with a 4-cleft calyx, 4 distinct petals, 6 stamens which are longer than the petals, and a single 1-celled ovary. The fruit is cylindrical, but bulging at irregular intervals, and 1 to $2\frac{1}{4}$ inches long. The pedicel and stipe together almost equal the length of the capsule. The seed is 3-4 mm. long, broad oval and somewhat pointed toward notched scar end, grooved through center and roughened by blunt projections which become more prominent at the edges. The color is variable, dull yellowish-brown to black.

STINKWEED *(Cleomella obtusifolia* Torr.) (Fig. 110)

This native of the Colorado and Mojave deserts and northward is 6 inches to 1 foot tall, freely branching from the base. Leaves 3-divided, pale green and more or less pubescent, oblong, $\frac{1}{4}$ to $\frac{3}{4}$ inch long, the petiole about the same length. Stipules fringed, resembling a tuft of wool. Small yellow flowers in leafy racemes; petals about $\frac{1}{4}$ inch long. Capsule about $\frac{3}{8}$ inch broad, its valves conical and produced into a blunt beak. Stipe in fruit about $\frac{1}{4}$ inch long, reflexed on its pedicel.

FIG. 110.   Stinkweed *(Cleomella obtusifolia)* showing capsule and stipe.

SMALL-FLOWERED CLEOMELLA *(Cleomella parviflora* Gray)

This native, similar in general habit to the preceding, is often abundant in alkaline soil from Lassen to Inyo County. The leaflets are linear, $\frac{3}{4}$ to 1 inch long, stipules none. The capsule is about 4 mm. broad, deltoid, inconspicuously horned; pedicel about 1 inch long; stipe scarcely 1 mm. long.

JACKASS CLOVER (*Wislizenia refracta* Engelm.) (Fig. 111)

This member of the caper family is highly valued as a bee plant. It is a native of southeastern California, eastward to New Mexico, but has spread northward and become abundant in the southern San Joaquin

FIG. 111.   Jackass clover (*Wislizenia refracta*), showing flowering branches and (inset) fruit.

Valley. In some sections it has become a weed of importance in pastures and noncultivated areas. Jackass clover is an annual herb with a strong scent. The stems are erect, 1 to 2 or occasionally up to 6 feet tall. The leaves are compound with 3 leaflets, each about $\frac{1}{3}$ to $\frac{2}{3}$ inch long. The flowers are in dense racemes which become considerably elongated at maturity. The flowers are yellow, 4-parted, and have 6 conspicuous, long exserted stamens. There is a single pistil, the ovary of which develops into a 2-celled and 2-seeded fruit, with a bristle-like and persistent style. The fruit stalk at maturity is curved downward, the fruits light straw color, short club-shaped in form with a crest of irregular tooth-like projections around the broad or apical end.

MUSTARD FAMILY (Cruciferae)

The family *Cruciferae* includes many of our important vegetables, such as cabbage, cauliflower, broccoli; cover crops such as the mustards; and numerous weeds, among them noxious species such as the hoary cresses, perennial peppercress and Austrian field cress. The family is of world-wide distribution, and there are in the neighborhood of 2000 species in 200 genera. This group of plants is characterized by alternate leaves, without stipules, and flowers borne in a terminal branching inflorescence. The 4 petals narrow to a claw below the wide or blade part, which spreads in the form of a cross, hence cruciform. There are 4 regular distinct sepals which usually fall very early, and commonly 6 stamens, 4 long and 2 short, occasionally only 4 or 2. The "pod" is usually 2-celled, the valves opening from below upward, or it may be 1-celled and remain attached to the seed or break up into 1-seeded joints. The seeds are in one or two rows in each cell. The herbage has a characteristic pungent or peppery taste peculiar to this family.

KEY TO GENERA IN MUSTARD FAMILY CONTAINING WEED SPECIES

Pods flattened contrary to narrow partition (subglobose in *Hymenophysa*)
    Pods elongated, several times as long as wide (Fig. 147) ; racemes leafy ; flowers
        yellow _____*Tropidocarpum*
    Pods orbicular or obcordate, not more than twice as long as wide ; racemes not leafy
        Pods twin-like (Fig. 127) _____*Coronopus*
        Pods not twin-like
            Pods not bladdery inflated
                Cells of the pod 1-seeded_____*Lepidium*
                Cells of the pod 2- to several-seeded
                    Plants smooth ; leaves not divided_____*Thlaspi*
                    Plants hairy ; leaves incised or divided_____*Capsella*
            Pods somewhat bladdery inflated to subglobose, cells 1-2 seeded_____*Cardaria*
Pods not flattened contrary to narrow partition
    Pods elongated, several times longer than wide
        Pods breaking transversely into 1-seeded joints_____*Raphanus*
        Pods not breaking transversely into 1-seeded joints, dehiscent by valves
            Petals usually with a narrow limb
                Pods with a stipe_____*Thelypodium*
                Pods sessile _____*Streptanthus*
            Petals usually with a broad limb
                Pods with a long distinct beak (Fig. 119) _____*Brassica*

Pods short-beaked or beakless
  Seeds in 2 rows in each cell
    Flowers yellow, 5 mm. long _____*Diplotaxis*
    Flowers white, or, if yellow, not over 2 mm. long
      Pubescence of forked hairs, leaves twice pinnatifid into minute
        segments _____*Descurainia*
      Pubescence simple or none ; leaves once pinnate or pinnatifid__*Rorippa*
  Seeds in 1 row in each cell
    Flowers yellowish or orange
      Leaves lobed to pinnatifid
        Plant glabrous or with simple hairs
          Annuals ; pod terete_____*Sisymbrium*
          Perennials ; pod somewhat 4-angled_____*Barbarea*
        Plant with forked hairs_____*Descurainia*
      Leaves not lobed or pinnatifid : elliptic, clasping_____*Conringia*
    Flowers white, rarely pinkish (Fig. 142) _____*Arabidopsis*
Pods short, not more than 3 or 4 times longer than wide (Fig. 121)
  Pods more or less turgid
    Pods globose to oblong_____*Rorippa*
    Pods pear-shaped (Fig. 121) _____*Camelina*
  Pods not turgid
    Pods indehiscent, 1-seeded
      Pods margined all around with a wing (Fig. 146)
        Pods orbicular _____*Thysanocarpus*
        Pods elliptical _____*Isatis*
      Pods not winged_____*Athysanus*
    Pods dehiscent, 2- to several seeded_____*Draba*
      Pods 1 or 2 seeded_____*Alyssum*
      Pods 2 to many seeded_____*Draba*

SWEET ALYSSUM (*Alyssum maritimum* Lam.)
(Fig. 112)

Sweet alyssum is a garden plant from Europe which is sparingly established in California, especially in the coastal region. It is a perennial, with leaf blades lanceolate to linear, the pubescence of simple hairs. The flowers are white, with petals about twice the length of the early deciduous sepals, which are about 1/12 inch long. The pods are marginless, approximately circular in outline, somewhat pointed and flattened. The seeds are oval, about 1.5 mm. long, greatly flattened, light reddish-brown with a thin whitish translucent margin or wing.

THALE CRESS (*Arabidopsis Thaliana* (L.) Britt.) (Fig. 142)

Other common name : Mouse-ear cress.

Thale cress occurs in old fields and rocky places in Massachusetts, the middle west and southward. It is introduced from Europe. This is a comparatively rare weed in California, occurring in open places in Alameda and Lake Counties, north to Oregon where it is known in flax fields.

FIG. 112. Sweet alyssum
(*Alyssum maritimum*).

Thale cress is a fragile annual or biennial, 6 inches to a
foot tall. The leaves are smooth
on the upper surfaces, pubescent with spreading hairs underneath, the basal leaves with
stellate (star-shaped) hairs.
The minute white flowers are
borne in a branching inflorescence. The pods are ⅓ to ½ inch
long on thin spreading stems
about ¼ inch long or less.

ATHYSANUS (*Athysanus pusillus* (Greene) (Fig. 113)

This was formerly included
with the fringed pods. The
name is taken from the Greek,
a—without, and *thysanus*—
fringe—and explains its sepa-
ration from the fringed pods.
This is a common plant in the
foothills and gravelly plains
west of the Sierra Nevada, almost throughout California.
The plant is an annual, 4 to 12
inches tall, leafy below and
branched into many fine flowering stems above. The leaves are
up to an inch long, entire, or
with a few coarse teeth on each
side. The flowers have minute
petals or none, and the very
small wingless pods borne along

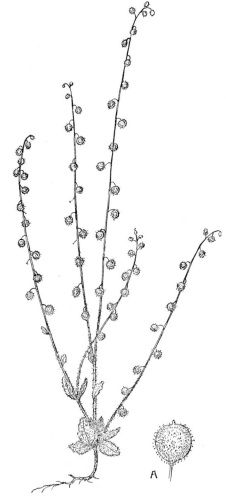

Fig. 113.   Athysanus (*Athysanus pusillus*)
showing habit. **A**, wingless pod.

one side of the stem are strongly flattened and covered with hooked hairs.

WINTER CRESS (*Barbarea vulgaris* (L.) R. Br.) (Fig. 114)
Other common names: Yellow rocket, St. Barbara's cress, bitter cress, yellow weed,
water mustard, pot-herb.

Winter cress is introduced from Europe; also native to northern
North America. It is common in the east and central states and established to a limited extent on the Pacific Coast. It prefers moist rich soil
and may occur in meadows and on cultivated land.

Winter cress is a biennial or perennial, reproducing by seeds and,
under favorable conditions, by shoots from the old crown. The angled
stems are erect, about one foot tall. The leaves are smooth, the basal

ones often numerous, with several pairs of small lateral lobes and a large
terminal one. The stem leaves are similar in form. The bright yellow
flowers are borne in terminal leafless racemes, the pods about one inch
long, ascending on slender short pedicels. The broadly oval to oblong
seeds are 1 to 1.5 mm. long,
notched at the scar end. The
color is dull grayish-brown,
and the surface roughened.

MUSTARD. BRASSICA

The genus *Brassica* com-
prises a number of species to
which the common name
"mustard" is applied. The
plants within this group are
characterized by rather large
lower leaves, variously lobed,
smooth or sparsely coarse-
hairy, usually more or less
deeply cut into irregular
lobes. The flowers are yellow
with four spreading blades
which narrow more or less
abruptly into a claw. The
elongated cylindric pods or
siliques terminate in a beak;
seeds are commonly arranged
in 1 row in each cell. The
mustards all have a pungent
or biting taste. There are
about 80 species, natives of
Europe and Asia, with 8 species established in California.

Fig. 114. Winter cress (*Barbarea vulgaris*).

KEY TO THE WEEDY SPECIES OF BRASSICA
Pods ascending, 1 inch or more long, not closely appressed to stem (Fig. 116)
  Beak much shorter than body of pod
    Upper leaves clasping the stem with ear-like projections (Fig. 116)
                                                            B. campestris

    Upper leaves not as above
      Upper stem leaves smooth (Fig. 119) _____*B. juncea*
      Upper stem leaves pubescent
        Stem leaves diamond-shaped (Fig. 116) _____*B. arvensis*
        Stem leaves oblong or linear (Fig. 120) _____*B. Tournefortii*
    Beak as long or longer than body of pod (Fig. 115) _____*B. alba*
Pods commonly 1 inch long or less, strongly appressed to stem (Fig. 118)
  Stems smooth or nearly so
    Beak weak and short, pods somewhat square (Fig. 119) _____*B. nigra*
    Beak stout, flat, ⅓ length of body (Fig. 117) _____*B. Eruca*
  Stems downwardly hairy, pods roundish, beak almost the length of pod
    (Fig. 118) _____*B. incana*

WHITE MUSTARD (*Brassica alba* Boiss.) (Fig. 115)
Other common names: Charlock, senvre, kedlock.

White mustard is a native of Eurasia and known locally as an escape from cultivation in most sections of the United States. It is cultivated rather extensively in the Lompoc Valley of California. It is very rarely met with as a weed in California.

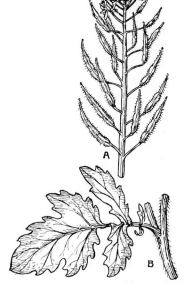

The plant is an annual of erect branching habit, 1 to 2 feet tall, with herbage somewhat sparsely stiff hairy. The leaves are much divided into irregular segments, with a large rounded terminal one. The flowers are pale yellow, about ½ inch in diameter. The bristly hairy pods are divergent from the main stem on pedicels about ½ inch long. The sword-shaped beak is as long or longer than the pod proper. The seeds are pale straw-color, almost smooth to obscurely netted.

WILD MUSTARD (*Brassica arvensis* (L.) B.S.P.) (Fig. 116)
Other common names: Charlock, field mustard, field kale, kedlock.

Wild mustard is a European species now established throughout North America except in the extreme north. It is mentioned as a noxious weed in nineteen states. This species is very common in California on cultivated lands, waste places, and in grain and flax fields, where it occasions heavy losses.

FIG. 115. White mustard (*Brassica alba*).

Wild mustard is an annual, reproducing by seed. The habit is erect, commonly 1 to 2 feet tall, occasionally much taller, branching above. The whole plant is rather dark green, somewhat roughish with scattered stiff hairs. The leaves are very deeply lobed or merely toothed, the terminal lobe often quite large and rounded; the teeth on the margins of the leaves are fine. The upper leaves are stemless and rhombic (diamond-shaped). The rather bright yellow flowers are about ½ inch across, the sepals spreading from the base of the petals. The pods commonly divergent are rarely quite closely appressed to the stem; they are from 1 to 1½ inches long, with the beak somewhat flattened and often containing a seed. The stout beak is ¼ to ½ inch long. The seeds are globular, commonly black, almost smooth to minutely pitted, often with a whitish scurfiness about the scar.

COMMON YELLOW MUSTARD (*Brassica campestris* L.) (Fig. 116)
Other common names: Wild turnip, wild kale, rutabaga.

This widespread weed is introduced from Europe and occurs in the North Central and Eastern States. In California common yellow mustard is of common occurrence in the early spring along roadsides, in fields and in orchards. It succumbs to competition somewhat more readily than our other mustards.

The weed is a winter annual, sometimes biennial. It is of erect habit, commonly 18 inches to 3 feet tall, widely branching from below. It is bluish-green and smooth, the leaves clasping the stem with ear-like

FIG. 116.   Left, common yellow mustard (*Brassica campestris*) ; right, wild mustard (*B. arvensis*).

projections (auricles). The flowers are about $\frac{1}{2}$ inch across, and pale yellow. The pods are essentially divergent from the main stem, and the awl-shaped beak is $\frac{1}{4}$ to $\frac{1}{2}$ inch long. The seeds are quite round, blackish, and appear shiny or glistening due to the reflection of light from the walls of the minute surface pits.

Fig. 117. Garden rocket (*Brassica Eruca*).

GARDEN ROCKET (*Brassica Eruca* L.) (*Eruca sativa* Mill.) (Fig. 117)
Other common name: Rocket salad.

Garden rocket is a native of Eurasia and is a common impurity in commercial seed from that region. The weed is known as an escape in the Eastern and North Central States and has been recorded from scattered localities in California in the past. With the recent rapid growth of the flax industry here much seed flax carrying this impurity has been imported from India and China; thus, garden rocket has assumed a new importance in California. The weed has taken a strong hold in the flax fields in Imperial Valley, and several hundred acres in the Merced region are heavily infested. It can completely crowd out flax. The history of garden rocket in other parts of the United States and Canada has been that the weed disappeared some time after the discontinuance of flax production in the region. That may be its future here.

As would be expected, the general aspect of garden rocket is that of the common mustards: plants from 2 to 4 feet, herbaceous. The leaves are mostly near the base, alternate and commonly lobed. The flowers with four spreading petals are borne on somewhat elongated terminal branches. The seeds are borne in a broad pod tipped by a beak-like extension. In the following characters garden rocket differs from the mustards and radishes, and these points in combination should be sufficient to permit definite determination in the field. The petals are pale yellow, sharply and definitely veined with dark brownish purple, about ¾ inch long. The leaves are very irregular in form, many of the lobes being relatively long and narrow, the segments commonly rounded in outline, and the texture smooth and somewhat thickish. When crushed the leaves emit a strong disagreeable odor. This odor is a reliable differentiating characteristic and permits definite determination at a very early stage of growth. The pod is short and thick, about twice as long as broad, and the flattened tapering beak is about as long as the pod. The seeds are dull yellowish brown, sometimes tinged with green. They are unlike the seeds of the true mustards in that they are flattened laterally, appear larger and have slight grooves along one edge. The flattened seed of garden rocket makes it more difficult than the other mustards to remove from threshed flax, and no doubt is an important factor in perpetuating the weed pest as a companion of flax.

SHORT-PODDED MUSTARD (*Brassica incana* Meigen.) (*B. geniculata* (Desf.) J. Ball) (Fig. 118)

This European weed, established first in coastal southern California, has now become common inland and northward through the Sacramento Valley. It is a frequent weed along the edges of highways and thrives on hard, dry waste areas. Its pale blooms appear about the middle of May, and the plant persists throughout the hot, dry summer, dense stands forming brittle. woody thickets in the late fall.

Short-podded mustard is a biennial or perennial. The plant branches widely above from more or less of a rosette of basal leaves. The stem is

FIG. 118.   Short-podded mustard (*Brassica incana*).

retrorsely hairy; leaves rough hairy on both sides, somewhat felty to the touch. They are much divided, with a large terminal lobe, the upper leaves often with only shallow lobes or a wavy margin. The flowering branches are somewhat flat topped, elongating in fruit, the flowers very small, petals $\frac{1}{6}$ to $\frac{1}{4}$ inch long. The pods, about $\frac{1}{2}$ inch long, are closely appressed to the stem. The beak is one-half the length of the pod or less, with a seed borne beyond the pod proper at the point of constriction. The seeds are tightly compressed in the valves and so are somewhat

FIG. 119. Left, Indian mustard (*Brassica juncea*). **A,** pod; **B,** lower leaf. Right, black mustard (*B. nigra*) **A,** pod; **B,** lower leaf.

irregular in form, which serves to distinguish this from our other mustard seeds. There is a slight protuberance at one side of the scar, opposite the darkened area. The general color is reddish-brown, the network slightly raised but definite.

INDIAN MUSTARD (*Brassica juncea* (L.) Cosson.) (Fig. 119)
Other common names: Leaf mustard, brown mustard, "Trieste" mustard.

A native of Asia, this mustard is rather widespread, chiefly in the grain fields of the North Central States, being listed as noxious in Wisconsin. It is established in limited sections of the north Pacific Coast and is rarely met with as an adventive southward in California.

Indian mustard is an erect annual 2 or 3 feet tall or taller, smooth or almost so throughout, and somewhat blue-green. The lower leaves are deeply lobed, with the large terminal segment commonly tapering at the apex; leaf margins coarsely toothed. The upper leaves are broadly lance-shaped, tapering gradually to a broad base, the leaf blades ascending. The flowers are spreading in elongated racemes, the individual flower stems about $\frac{1}{2}$ inch long. The pods are $1\frac{1}{4}$ to 2 inches long, and the conical beak approximately $\frac{1}{4}$ the length of the pod (Fig. 119A, left). The seeds are rounded and reddish-brown, the surface net-veined. This surface netting differs from the concave walled pits of *B. nigra*.

BLACK MUSTARD (*Brassica nigra* Koch) (Fig. 119)
Other common names: Wild black mustard, "Trieste" mustard.

Black mustard, a native of Eurasia, is a widespread and common weed throughout the United States. It is one of the commonest grain field weeds of California, where its bloom yellows hundreds of acres of grain and causes heavy loss. This mustard was widespread in the State at the time of the Spanish occupation.

Black mustard is an erect annual, branching above, 3 to 6 feet tall, occasionally much taller. The herbage is slightly hairy, often becoming almost smooth in age. The leaves are all petioled, the lower leaves divided, with a large terminal lobe. The marginal teeth are fine. The uppermost leaves narrow to an elongated petiole-like base, the leaf blade often drooping or pendant by this weak base. The flowering racemes are long, the upper branches often widely divergent. The flowers are bright yellow, with the petals abruptly narrowed to a claw at the base. The pods, approximately $\frac{1}{2}$ to $\frac{3}{4}$ inch long, are closely appressed to the stem axis, and the beak is very short and weak (Fig. 119A, right). The seeds are somewhat oval and a dark reddish-brown; their surface is pitted, the pits being thick-walled with concave sides.

WILD TURNIP (*Brassica Tournefortii* Gouan.) (Fig. 120)

This member of the mustard group is a native of Eurasia, now established in South Africa and Australia where it is an aggressive and persistent competitor of crops in all stages of its growth; also troublesome in pasture lands where the large basal rosette displaces more desirable

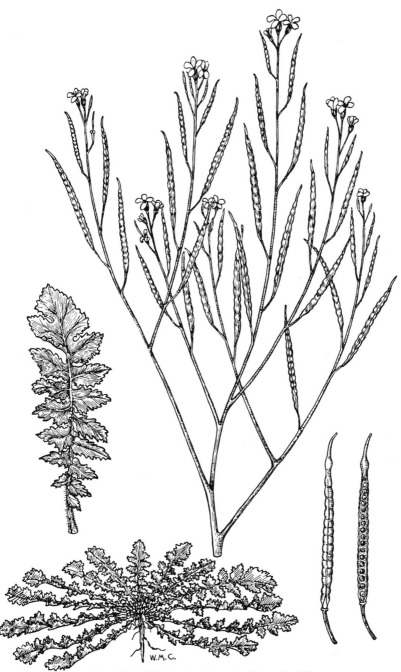

FIG. 120. Wild turnip (*Brassica Tournefortii*).

species. In California it has spread from a few patches in the Coachella Valley in 1938 to Guasti, San Bernardino County, a distance of about 80 miles.

Brassica Tournefortii is an erect bristly-hairy annual from a few inches to six feet high, the basal rosettes being from one to two feet in diameter under favorable conditions. The basal leaves are lyrate-pinnatifid, the terminal lobe being almost obovate-oricular in outline, more or less three-lobed, the margins crenate-toothed. The lateral lobes decrease in size from above to below. The stem leaves are much smaller, with bristly stiff hairs on both sides, oblong or linear, with margins entire or toothed. The pods are one and one-half to two and one-half inches long, erect-spreading to widely spreading. The seeds are the smallest of any Brassica, round, a pale reddish brown with reticulations that appear as a fine network of silvery lines on the surface of the seeds.

When wild turnip matures its heavy crop of seeds and becomes dry, it is easily snapped from its long deep-seated tap root and moves with the wind as a tumbleweed. It appears that natural spread by the wind is the main method of distribution, though unclean seed, hay and chaff may carry seed from infested areas to clean lands. Seed of *Brassica Tournefortii* occurred as an impurity in Hubam sweet clover from Imperial County, harvest of 1947.

SMALL-SEEDED FALSE FLAX (*Camelina microcarpa* Andrz.) (Fig. 121)
Other common names: Small-fruited false flax, false flax, Dutch flax, western flax, Siberian oil seed.

This European weed, widely established in the northwest and occasionally in the Eastern States, occurs in southern California and northward. It is a weed of grain and flax fields and waste places. It is an erect annual, slightly hairy, with sparse branches. The leaves are 1 to 1½ inches long, the lower lance-shaped, the upper arrow-shaped and clasping the stem. The pale yellow flowers are borne on slender branches from ½ to 1 inch long. The seed pods, which are about ¼ inch long, not flattened, split into two valves (Fig. 121A). The oblong reddish-brown seeds are very small, about 1 mm. long, with a granular surface and a groove on each side of the central ridge which is not as prominent as in *C. sativa*.

LARGE-SEEDED FALSE FLAX (*Camelina sativa* Crantz)
Other common names: Wild flax, gold-of-pleasure.

An introduced European species, this is an occasional weed in the State from Yreka to southern California. It is an erect annual, about 1 to 3 feet tall. The lower leaves taper to a petiole, the upper clasp the stem and are more slender. The yellow petals are about ¼ inch long, pods about ⅓ inch long and half as wide. The seeds are about 2 mm. long, usually oval, reddish-yellow and granular, with a groove on each side of a prominent vertical or oblique ridge.

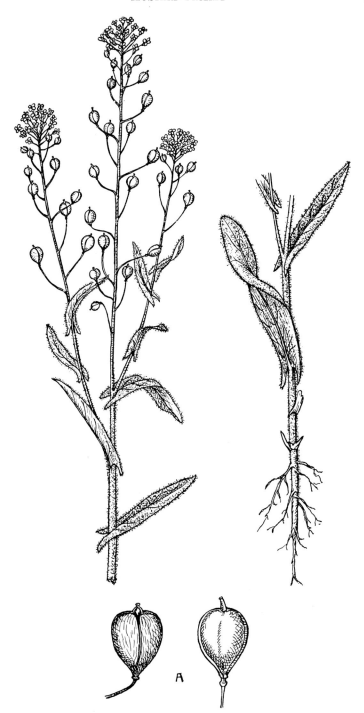

Fig. 121. Small-seeded false flax (*Camelina microcarpa*). A, (left) single pod with valves intact; (right) with valves removed showing partition.

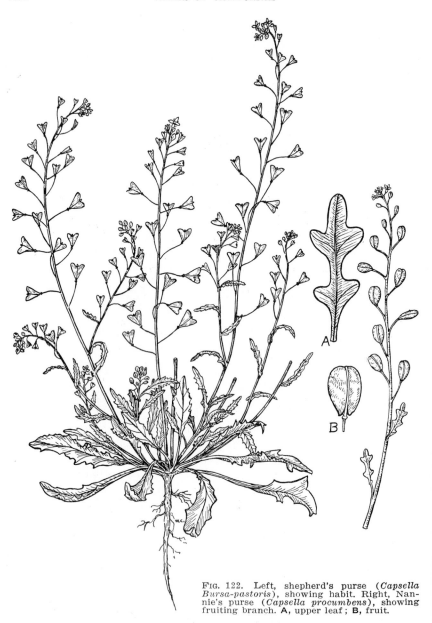

FIG. 122. Left, shepherd's purse (*Capsella Bursa-pastoris*), showing habit. Right, Nannie's purse (*Capsella procumbens*), showing fruiting branch. **A**, upper leaf; **B**, fruit.

SHEPHERD'S PURSE (*Capsella Bursa-pastoris* (L.) Medic.) (Fig. 122)

Other common names: Lady's purse, St. James' weed.

This plant, naturalized from Europe, is a common weed in lawns and waste places throughout California west of the mountains. It is an erect annual, 3 to 18 inches tall, sparsely hairy; the stems simple or branching; the basal leaves, which are commonly deeply cut with a large terminal lobe, spread in the form of a rosette; the blades of the upper

FIG. 123.   Lens-podded hoary cress (*Cardaria Draba* var. *repens*). A, enlarged
lens-shaped pod viewed from side and top.

leaves are toothed and clasp the stem with ear-like lobes. The very small
white flowers are borne on short stems, which elongate as the pods develop.
The pods are heart-shaped, flattened and contain numerous seeds (Fig.
122). Shepherd's purse is exceedingly variable in size, pod and leaf form.
The seeds are about 1 mm. long, oblong and flattened, with two longitudinal grooves separating the seed face into three almost equal parts.
The color is a dark reddish-brown, with elongated microscopic network.

NANNIE'S PURSE (*Capsella procumbens* Fries.) (Fig. 122 A, B)

This is a native weed of alkaline soils occurring in southern California and northward. It is an annual, erect, 3 to 6 inches high. The leaf
blades are broadest toward the tip and more or less divided into segments.
The white flowers are minute, with sepals about the same length as the
petals. The pods are eliptic, oblong, with no notch at the apex.

WHITETOP or HOARY CRESS (*Cardaria Draba* Desv.) (*Lepidium Draba* L.) (Fig. 124. See also Figs. 123 and 125.)

Other common names: Perennial peppergrass, heart-podded hoary cress, whiteweed.

This is a native of Central Europe and Western Asia. At the present time it is common throughout Europe and in the British Isles. Its presence was first noted in 1898 about the seaports of New York, Washington, and elsewhere, indicating introduction in ballast. Almost simultaneously, however, it was found in the alfalfa-growing sections of the southwest, which suggests introduction in imported alfalfa seed. It is now a well established and serious pest on the east coast, in some central states and on the west coast. Scattered almost throughout California, hoary cress is a pest of major importance, particularly in alfalfa, sugar beets, and truck crops. Early blooming makes hoary cress quite conspicuous, often appearing like patches of snow in the early spring.

Hoary cress is an erect perennial 8 to 20 inches high, often becoming procumbent or "lodged" in age. The entire plant has a grayish-green soft-hairy appearance. The leaves are 1½ to 3 inches long, broadly ovate to lance-shaped, irregularly toothed to almost entire. The first leaves on new plants are often much larger, the upper stem leaves are sessile, strongly clasping the stem with ear-like lobes. The basal leaves are more slender, and narrow into a short petiole. The flowering branches bear numerous showy, small, white flowers on very slender stems or pedicels, the pedicels divergent from the main axis. The inflorescence has a flat-top appearance, the individual spikes or racemes elongating in fruit. There are 4 obtuse sepals and 4 petals which are broad at the apex and narrow to a claw at the base. The flower measures about ⅛ inch or more across; the pod or silicle is 2-valved, somewhat heart-shaped, acutely converging to a short persistent style at the apex. It is little inflated and becomes prominently veined at maturity (Fig. 124). The seeds are about 2 mm. long, 1.5 mm. wide, dark reddish-brown, only slightly flattened, rounded at one end and narrowed to a blunt point at the other.

Hoary cress is capable of establishing itself in many soil types and under many environmental conditions, making it one of the most serious agricultural weed pests. The root system consists of well developed large white rootstocks, which penetrate to a depth of several feet and spread horizontally in all directions. During the growing season food is stored in the rootstocks so that the next year the plant is able to produce new plants from shoots sent out from the joints. Due to this fact it competes with all types of crops, and in many sections has completely taken high-producing agricultural lands. The present known methods of eradication often cost more than the land is worth, making it very important to prevent its becoming established.

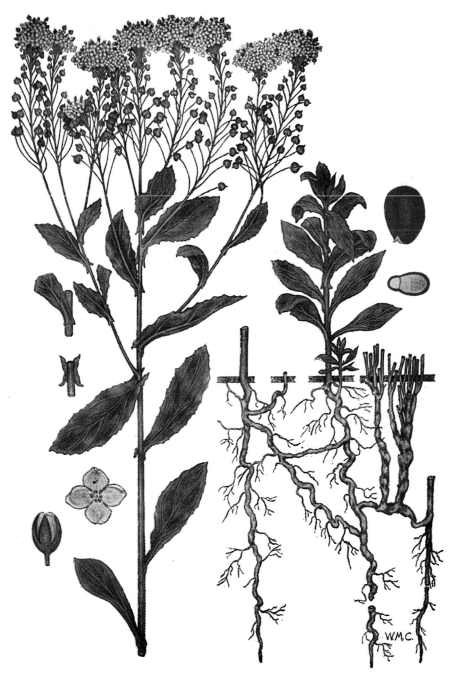

Fig. 124.   Whitetop or hoary cress (*Cardaria draba*).

FIG. 125.   Globe-podded hoary cress (*Cardaria pubescens*). **A**, enlarged globose pod viewed from side and top.

WHITETOP OR HOARY CRESS (*Cardaria Draba* (L.) Desv. var. *repens* (Schrenk) O. E. Schulz (*Lepidium Draba* L. var. *repens* Thell.) (Fig. 123. See also Figs. 124 and 125.)

Other common names: Lens-podded hoary cress, lens peppergrass.

This weed is a native of Asia, and we are unable to venture an opinion at this time as to the mode of introduction. It occurs in a large number of widely scattered sections in California and is known in other parts of the northwest. It is, like *Cardaria Draba*, a serious pest.

Except for the structure of the pistil or pod, var. *repens* is similar in appearance to *C. Draba*. The difference in pod form, however, is constant and affords a ready means of distinction. The pod is lens-shaped, remaining inflated upon drying. The valves frequently contain 2 ovules or seeds, both fully developed in a well matured plant. The circular outline of the pod (Fig. 124) as distinguished from the heart-shaped pod of *C. Draba* is discernible on the lower stems while the tops of the spikes are still in blossom. A line drawn at right angles to the mid-vein across the center of the pod divides it into two approximately equal parts. It is glabrous or smooth and does not develop the pronounced venation upon drying as does *C. Draba*; also the style or appendage at the apex is commonly longer. The flower spikes do not elongate greatly in fruit, giving the whole plant a somewhat flared and comparatively flat-topped appearance. The seed is 2.5 to 3 mm. long, more flattened and commonly larger and more red than *C. Draba*. The lighter and redder color is striking when the seeds are compared in bulk.

HAIRY WHITETOP, HOARY CRESS (*Cardaria pubescens* C. A. Mey.) (*Hymenophysa*) (Fig. 125)
Other common names: Ball cress, globe-podded hoary cress.

This is a native of Central Asia. The first collection for North America was made in Michigan in 1919. It is now established in California in scattered infestations, and recently it was reported from the southwest and Oregon.

The weed is a perennial, similar in general appearance to hoary cress (*Cardaria Draba*), described on page 220, but differs in the following respects: The seed pods are nearly globose, covered with minute pubescence, and remain inflated even after maturity. (See Fig. 125 inset.) The pod stems are not divergent, giving the fruiting spike a strict, roughly cylindrical appearance. Approaching maturity the fruiting spikes commonly take on a purplish hue. The early flower buds also frequently are faintly purple-tinged. This plant is so similar to *C. Draba* in its noxious characteristics that it is often confused with that species in the field. The seeds are oval, narrowing toward the notched basal scar, to which a slender pointed white appendage often remains attached. The color is lighter and redder than that of *C. Draba* and the variety *repens*.

HARE'S EAR MUSTARD (*Conringia orientalis* (L.) Dum.) (Fig. 126)
Other common names: Treacle mustard, klinkweed.

Hare's ear mustard is a European weed common in the grain fields in the Northwestern States. It is sparingly established in southern California, where it occurs in cultivated fields, gardens and waste places. This weed is erect, 2 to 3 feet tall, little branched and becoming stiff and wiry in age. The smooth leaves are elliptic in shape, 1 to 3 inches long, with the base clasping the stem with heart-shaped lobes. The flowers are borne in slender racemes, the pale yellow petals about ¼ inch long. The pods are narrow and erect, about 2 to 4 inches long. The dark mahogany seeds are oblong, about ⅛ inch long, with 2 lengthwise grooves separated by a ridge. They are about circular in cross section, the surface roughened with minute shallow pits. Distinct lip-like projections usually extend beyond the scar at the base.

WART CRESS (*Corono-
pus didymus*
Smith) (Fig. 127)
Other common name : Swine
cress.

Wart cress was in-
troduced from South
America. Frequently
found established about
habitations and trouble-
some in gardens and
nurseries, this weed is
an annual, reproducing
by seeds. The habit is
prostrate or nearly so,
the numerous freely-
branching stems
spreading from 6 inches
to 2 feet. The leaves are
about $\frac{1}{2}$ to 1 inch long,
divided into entire or
toothed segments. The
pods are small, con-
spicuously and finely
wrinkled, about $\frac{1}{12}$ of
an inch broad; a deep
crease both above and
below makes the pod ap-
pear two-lobed.

GREEN TANSY MUSTARD
(*Descurainia incisa*
(Engelm.) Britt.)
(*Sisymbrium*)

Green tansy mus-
tard is known from Ari-
zona to Tennessee and
northward. It is com-
mon, but of rather scat-
tered occurrence, in
northern and southern
California in grain
fields, roadsides and
waste places, especially
in disturbed land. It is
an annual reproducing
by seeds. The plant is

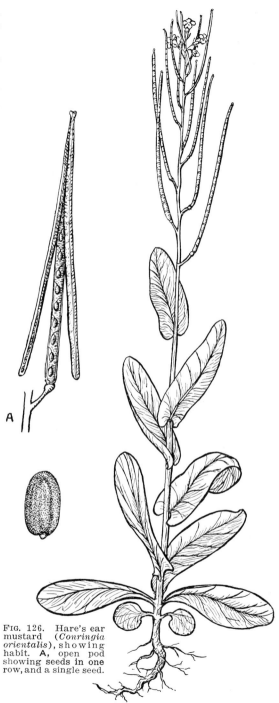

FIG. 126. Hare's ear
mustard (*Conringia
orientalis*), showing
habit. **A,** open pod
showing seeds in one
row, and a single seed.

erect, 1 to 2½ feet tall, with leaves finely divided into very small segments, somewhat hairy with branched hairs. The petals are yellow, about ⅛ inch long, on slender spreading stems about ½ to ¾ inch. The narrow linear pods are between ½ to ¾ inch long, standing erect on slender spreading stems, which about equal the pods in length—sometimes equal, or a little longer or shorter.

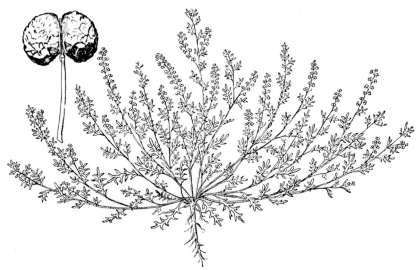

FIG. 127. Wart cress (*Cornopus didymus*), showing habit, and a single 2-lobed pod.

TANSY MUSTARD (*Descurainia pinnata* (Walt.) Britton) (Fig. 142)

This is fairly prevalent in some places in Humboldt, Siskiyou and Modoc counties; also in the upper San Joaquin Valley, south to the deserts and west to coastal southern California. Tansy mustard is an annual erect plant ¾ to 2 feet tall. The leaves are once or twice divided into fine segments, ashy, hairy, with branched hairs to almost smooth. The small yellow flowers with petals about ⅛ inch long are borne on long slender spreading stems which elongate as the pods develop. The pods are about ½ inch long, shorter than the stems on which they are borne. *Sisymbrium* of authors.)

Abrams lists 5 subspecies embracing wide variation.

FLIXWEED (*Descurainia Sophia* (L.) Wats.) (*Sisymbrium*) (Fig. 143)

Flixweed, introduced from Europe, is infrequent about eastern cities, and now locally established in both northern and southern California. It is not yet common, but its occurrence is reported with increasing frequency.

The plant is an erect annual 1¼ to 1¾ feet high. The leaves are 2 or 3 times divided into narrow segments (Fig. 143A), and very finely pubescent with branched hairs. The flowers with cream colored petals, about ⅛ inch long, are borne on somewhat spreading very slender stems ½ to 1 inch long. The pods are very narrow, erect, and about 1 inch long.

SAND ROCKET (*Diplotaxis muralis* (L.) DC.) (Fig. 128)
Other common names: Flixweed, crossweed.

An introduction from Europe, this weed is now locally common in the Northeastern States and is reported from southern California. Sand rocket is an annual reproducing by seeds. Occasionally it acts as a biennial, living over into the second year. This is much like the following species, wall rocket, but is less leafy and the smaller flowers are borne on shorter stems. Seeds are about 1 mm. long, broad oval and almost circular in cross section. The surface is minutely roughened and sometimes an obscure network is superimposed. The color is light yellowish or reddish-brown.

FIG. 128. Left, wall rocket (*Diplotaxis tenuifolia*); right, sand rocket (*D. muralis*).

WALL ROCKET (*Diplotaxis tenuifolia* DC.) (Fig. 128)
Other common name: Large sand rocket.

This weed is introduced from Europe and known from Atlantic seaports and California, where it is restricted mostly to the southern coastal counties. Wall rocket is a perennial; the plants are branching and leafy, erect or sometimes spreading or decumbent, 1 to 4½ feet tall. The herbage is glabrous to slightly hairy; the leaves are alternate, somewhat elongated, and divided into deep lobes or merely toothed. The yellow flowers, about ½ inch across, are borne terminally on leafless branchlets. The pods are 1 to 1¼ inches long, with a short beak, are on spreading stems from ½ to 1 inch long. Yellowish-orange seeds, slightly flattened and grooved, are in two rows in each cell. The surface is roughened, but not conspicuously net-veined.

SHAD-FLOWER (*Draba verna* L.) (Fig. 129)
Other common name: Whitlow grass.

This European introduction, found in poor gravelly soils from Lake County to Siskiyou County, is of little economic importance. It is an annual, rarely biennial. The naked stems, 2 to 6 inches tall, arise from a rosette-like cluster of leaves. The leaves are lanceolate or broader above, toothed near the apex and covered with branched hairs. The white petals are minute and cleft almost to the middle, about twice the length of the sepals. The straight oval pods are smooth, about ¼ inch long, flattened parallel to the partition. The obovate seeds are minute, flattened and notched at the base, the color light reddish-brown.

DYER'S WOAD (*Isatis tinctoria* L.) (Fig. 130)
Other common name: Marlahan mustard.

This European plant is naturalized as a weed in Siskiyou County, where it has given trouble in Scott Valley. It is known locally as

FIG. 129. Shad-flower (*Draba verna*).

Marlahan mustard, from the Marlahan Ranch on which it occurs. It has become abundant in pastures and grain fields. It seems to thrive on a light gravel or sandy soil. The habit is perennial or biennial, reproducing by seeds and from the roots. The weed is erect, 1 to 3 feet tall, somewhat bluish-green and mostly smooth. The oblong to lance-shaped lower leaf blades are 3 to 4 inches long, narrowed to leaf stems of about the same length. The upper leaves clasp the stem with ear-like projections. The

FIG. 130. Dyer's woad (*Isatis tinctoria*), showing habit, and (inset) winged fruit.

yellow flowers are very small and crowded into a rather flat-topped inflorescence, and the pod is about ½ inch long and winged like an ash or maple seed (Fig. 130).

PEPPERGRASS AND CRESS. *LEPIDIUM*
KEY TO WEEDY SPECIES OF LEPIDIUM

Style distinctly developed and persistent (Fig. 131)
  Pods winged and notched at apex
    Pods thin, short winged at apex, upper leaves cordate clasping, entire
    (Fig. 135) _____*L. perfoliatum*
    Pods thick, long winged at apex, upper leaves sagittate clasping, toothed
    (Fig. 131) _____*L. campestre*
Style minute or none (Fig. 132) ; corolla white or none
  Pods neither notched nor winged at apex, perennial_____*L. latifolium*
  Pods notched but not winged, annuals
    Flower stems cylindric or only slightly flattened.
      Plants erect
        Petals present _____*L. virginicum*
        Petals minute or none_____*L. densiflorum*
      Plants prostrate or diffuse_____*L. pubescens*

Flower stem very much flattened
  Pods hairy _____L. lasiocarpum
  Pods smooth _____L. nitidum
  Pods winged at apex with two lobes or teeth, annuals.
  Petals broad spatula-shaped, greenish_____L. latipes
  Petals none or very minute_____L. acutidens

MULE'S-EAR PEPPER CRESS
(*Lepidium acutidens* (A.
Gray) Howell)
Other common name: Mule's ear
peppergrass.

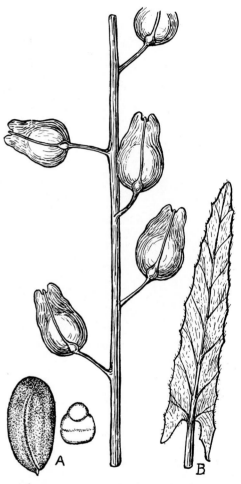

This plant occurs in al-
kaline soil in the south coast
ranges, west side of the San
Joaquin and Sacramento valleys, Lassen and Siskiyou
counties. It is an annual with
branching stem 4 to 12 inches
high. The lower leaves are 1
to 3¾ inches long divided into
a few segments, the stem
leaves mostly entire. The
flowering racemes are rather
dense, the petals minute or
absent. The pods are elliptic,
about ⅛ inch long, glabrous
to slightly pubescent and
lightly veined. The teeth at
the apex are widely spreading and wing-like, half to as
long as the pod. The pod
stems are flattened and somewhat curved, shorter than the
pod.

POOR-MAN'S PEPPER (*Lepidium campestre* R. Br.)
(Fig. 131)
Other common names: Field peppergrass, field cress, cow
cress.

This weed, which is a
native of Europe, is widespread locally, abundant in

FIG. 131.   Poor-man's pepper (*Lepidium campestre*), showing fruiting branch. A, seed; B,
stem leaf.

the northeastern United States, where it occurs in new grain fields, waste
places and new stands of alfalfa and clover. It is rare in California, and
has been reported only from Placer County.

Poor-man's pepper is an annual or biennial reproducing by seeds.
The plant is erect, 9 to 15 inches tall, the stems single or in clusters

Fig. 132.   Perennial peppergrass (*Lepidium latifolium*). Stem leaves taper to point of attachment. Pod has sessile stigma.

with stiffish branches above. The herbage is soft hairy. The alternate and crowded stem leaves, about 1 to 3½ inches long, are oblong in form and' clasp the stem with ear-like projections. The blades of the lower leaves are divided into lobes and taper to a stem-like base. The flowers, in a branched inflorescence, are small, white, and with 4 spreading petals. The thickish pods are broadly egg-shaped and winged all around with a style extending through a narrow notch at the apex. The seeds are about 2 to 2.5 mm. long, obovoid and somewhat flattened on three sides, pointed at base, often with a white appendage in the notch (Fig. 129A). The seed color is dark, dull brown, and, as with most of the Lepidiums, is mucilaginous when wet.

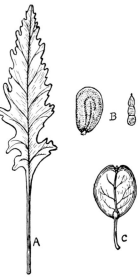

MINER'S PEPPER (*Lepidium densiflorum* Schrad.) (Fig. 133)
Other common names: Wild tonguegrass, green-flowered peppergrass.

This weed, introduced from Europe, is now widespread in the United States. It occurs in the arid region southwest and west of the Sierra Nevada from the Mojave desert to Siskiyou County, but is infrequent on the west slope of the Sierra Nevada. It is very similar in appearance and habit to bird's pepper (*L. virginicum*), but the petals are usually wanting, or 2 and minute. The ovate, flattened seeds are about 1.5 mm. long, rounded on one edge and almost straight on the others. The cotyledon foldings afford a

FIG. 133. Miner's pepper (*Lepidium densiflorum*). A, basal leaf; B, external view of seed and also as seen in cross section showing the cotyledons; C, pod.

ready means of differentiation between this and the very similar *L. virginicum*. In *L. densiflorum* a cross section reveals three almost equal divisions from the thin to the thick edge of the seed (Fig. 132B).

SAND PEPPER CRESS (*Lepidium lasiocarpum* Nutt.)
Other common name: Sand peppergrass.

This weed is common in sandy flats and valleys of coastal southern California; through the Colorado and Mojave deserts into Inyo County east and south. It is an annual with stems several from the base, decumbent or ascending, 3 to 10 inches long; the herbage is hairy; leaf blades broader toward the tip, toothed or more deeply cut into segments. The flower heads are numerous, the sepals commonly purple, edged with white, the petals minute or none. The short pod stems are flattened with the pods thin-margined at the top, commonly hairy on the margin, the faces hairy to almost smooth, the notch at the apex shallow; the seeds have a winged margin.

PERENNIAL PEPPERGRASS (*Lepidium latifolium* L.) (Fig. 132)

Other common name : Slender perennial peppercress.

This species is well established in parts of Mexico, introduced along the New England coast, and was recently reported from Montana. A newly recorded weed for California, it is now known in Stanislaus, San Joaquin, and Solano Counties with dense and extensive infestations on rich delta lands in Yolo County. Possibly introduction was through beet seed.

The plant is an erect perennial, about 1 to 2 feet or more tall with a heavy sometimes woody crown and an extensive vigorous creeping root system, and somewhat leathery foliage. The flowers and pods are definitely smaller than those of hoary cress. The lower leaves taper to a somewhat elongated stem. The upper leaves are sessile, but do not clasp the stem as in the case of hoary cress. The rounded pod is about 2 mm. in diameter and flattened, with a few scattered hairs. There is almost no style, the stigma appearing sessile (Fig. 133).

The seeds are about 1 mm. long, broadly oval and somewhat flattened. On the seed face the cotyledon foldings describe an indistinct groove dividing the central raised part from the thickened outer loop. The surface is minutely roughened, the color light reddish-brown with definite darkening at the scar, to which a dingy white appendage often remains attached. In a laboratory test California seed sprouted 100 percent.

DWARF PEPPERGRASS (*Lepidium latipes* Hook.)

Other name : Dwarf peppercress.

Dwarf peppergrass occurs on alkaline flats of the Coast Ranges and Great Valley, extending well into southern California. It is an annual, reproducing from seed. The stems are short and thick, about 1 to 2 inches long, prostrate or rarely erect, with leaves 3 to 5 inches long, linear or divided. The flowering racemes are dense, 1 to 1½ inches long; the flowers are very small with greenish petals. The broadly oblong pods are about ¼ inch long, strongly veined and from slightly hairy to smooth. The winged apex is notched, the two teeth nearly as long as the body of the pod.

COMMON PEPPERGRASS (*Lepidium nitidum* Nutt.) (Fig. 134)

Other common names : Common peppercress, California tonguegrass.

This is our most common peppergrass and is found everywhere in the region west of the Sierra Nevada but is infrequent in deserts. It is an annual, 1 to 16 inches tall, with stem branching from near the base. The herbage is smooth or very slightly hairy. Leaves are ½ to 4 inches long, divided, with the terminal lobe enlarged. Upper leaves often have entire blades. The minute petals are white, narrowing to a distinct claw.

There are six stamens, but two of these are greatly reduced. The circular pods, about $\frac{1}{6}$ inch long, have a narrow margin notched at the apex (Fig. 134A). They are smooth and shiny, often dark-purple tinted. The upper face is plane, the lower convex. Dense colonies in the pod stage

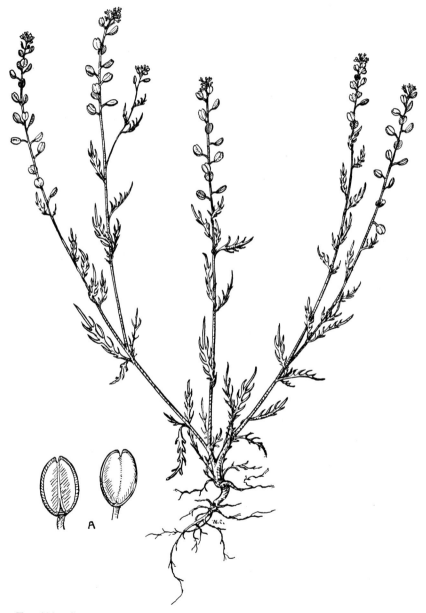

FIG. 134.   Common peppergrass (*Lepidium nitidum*), showing general appearance of plant. A, pods.

often color whole hillsides reddish in the late spring. The seed is about 2 mm. long, elongated oval, flattened and with one groove on the face conspicuous toward the scar fading out above. The color is pale reddish, covered with white scurfiness.

SHIELD CRESS (*Lepidium perfoliatum* L.) (Fig. 135)
Other common name : Clasping-leaved peppercress.

Shield cress which is a comparatively recent introduction from Europe, is abundant in the Great Basin and established locally across the northern United States. It occurs at the edges of fields in waste places and often forms a wide conspicuous border along highway rights-of-way.

The plant is an annual with erect simple stem, or diffusely branching, 6 inches to 2 feet tall. The lower leaves are finely cut, the upper round-ovate, entire and clasping the stem with heart-like lobes. The small yellow flowers are borne on spreading stems, and the pods are rhombic-orbicular, about ¼ inch in diameter and minutely notched. The plant takes on a reddish hue at maturity and because of this color and the collar-like clasping upper leaves presents an interesting appearance. The seed is about 2 mm. long, broad, oval, flattened and bordered all around by a cord-like white rim.

WAYSIDE PEPPERGRASS (*Lepidium pubescens* Desv.)
Other common name : Wayside peppercress.

This peppergrass, introduced from Chile, is a common weed along paths and dooryards in the Coast Ranges from Humboldt to San Luis Obispo, Northern Sacramento Valley and

FIG. 135. Shield cress (*Lepidium perfoliatum*), showing habit and pod.

south to the northern borders of the San Joaquin Valley and Sierra Nevada foothills. It is an annual, branching diffusely from the base, 3 to 6 inches long, sometimes forming a mat. The herbage is light green, somewhat hairy. The leaves are divided, ½ to 2 inches long, the segments linear and entire, or commonly 3-toothed to 3-cleft. The flower heads are many, dense, and narrow, with white petals so minute as to appear lacking. The pods are about 1/10 inch long, elliptic, with short, broad teeth at the apex.

ROADSIDE PEPPERGRASS (*Lepidium ruderale* L.) is naturalized from Europe, and reported from Smetzer, Orange County. It is an annual weed of cultivated land and open pastures, possibly introduced into California as an impurity in Rhodes grass seed from Australia.

BIRD'S PEPPER (*Lepidium virginicum* L.) (Fig. 136)

Other common names : Poor man's pepper, tonguegrass, tall peppergrass.

Bird's pepper is a native weed, widespread from the Atlantic Coast westward. It occurs in grain fields, cultivated ground and waste places throughout California, mostly in moist valleys and stream bottoms. It is an erect plant about 1 to 2 feet tall, herbage almost smooth to sparsely pubescent. The lower leaves are deeply cut to shortly toothed, 1 to 3 inches long, narrowing toward the stem to a petiole 1 to 3 inches long. The stem leaves are sessile, or almost so, linear or widened toward the apex, toothed or smooth on the margins or, more rarely, cleft. The very small flowers are white, and the smooth pods are about ½ inch or more long, slightly enlarged at the apex, which is narrowly winged. The pod stems, about $\frac{1}{16}$ inch long, spread horizontally from the main axis. The seeds are about 1 to 1.5 mm. long, with groove on each side, the length of the seed often bordered by a narrow translucent margin (Fig. 136B). The color is dull reddish-yellow. The cotyledon foldings in cross section show a small oval section at narrow edge, with two long, thin sections perpendicular to it.

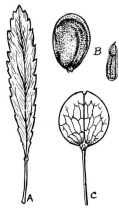

FIG. 136. Bird's pepper '(*Lepidium virginicum*). **A**, lower leaf; **B**, external view of seed and also as seen in cross section showing the cotyledons ; **C**, pod.

JOINTED WILD RADISH (*Raphanus Raphanistrum* L.)

Other common names : Jointed charlock, white charlock.

This native of Europe is common in the Northeastern States, Canada, and the Pacific Northwest. In California it occurs sparingly in grain fields in scattered locations from San Diego to Sacramento County. Jointed charlock is an annual similar in appearance to wild radish, but the flowers are yellow and conspicuously veined, fading to purplish or white. The pods, 1 to 2 inches long, are somewhat longitudinally ribbed, abruptly pointed and bead-like. Seeds are slightly smaller than, but similar to the following.

WILD RADISH (*Raphanus sativus* L.) (Fig. 137)

Wild radish is naturalized from Europe and now widely established in the Northeastern States. It is also a common and widespread weed in fields and around habitations in California. Some years it is very prevalent and causes serious losses, especially in the grain fields of the Great Central Valley. The yields of grains in some areas have been reduced more than 50 percent due to radish. It is especially serious in flax, and in a few cases has brought about complete loss of the crop. It is sometimes used with mustard as a cover crop in the fruit growing areas.

Radish is an erect annual, branching above, 2 to 5 feet tall, herbage hispid to almost glabrous, lower leaves pinnately divided, with a large rounded terminal segment. The upper leaves are mostly undivided or with a few small segments. Flowers are about ¾ inch across, purple to white,

Fig. 137. Wild radish (*Raphonus sativus*), showing at left a single basal leaf, also mature pods, and upper portion of flowering stem.

variously veined with purple to pink, sometimes tinged with yellow. The pods are pithy or spongy, about $1\frac{1}{2}$ to 3 inches long and $\frac{1}{4}$ inch in diameter, sometimes slightly constricted between the 2 to 8 indehiscent seeds, narrowed to a stout beak above. The seeds are about $\frac{1}{8}$ inch long, broadly oval, with a fine surface network and often covered with a white scurfiness. Their color is yellowish to reddish-brown.

AUSTRIAN FIELD CRESS (*Rorippa austriaca* (Crantz) Besser) (*Radicula austriaca* (Crantz) Small) (Fig. 138)

Austrian field cress is of European origin and relatively recently has become established in Minnesota, Wisconsin, and South Dakota. The only known infestation of Austrian field cress in California is located on the Corporation Ranch near Likely, Modoc County. In the last few years some of the hay fields where this weed is growing have been mowed and stacked at a season when the seed was mature; feeding the hay in the winter months accounts in part for the acreage now infested, although high water and irrigation also contributed to the spread. Before its identity was established, Austrian field cress was confused with the relatively innocent mustards which, upon casual observation, it may be said to resemble. The very noxious habit of Austrian field cress, however, would not permit it to remain long among the unnoticed and unknown.

Under our conditions, Austrian field cress grows to a height of about 18 inches to 2 feet, with few side branches except toward the summit, where numerous very bright yellow flowers are borne on thread-like stems about ½ inch long. The floral arrangement is after the manner of our common weedy mustards, with the usual flat, four-petaled flowers. The leaves are a bright, deep-green with smooth surfaces. They vary in length from about 2 to 3 inches and clasp the stem at the point of juncture with small ear-like projections. The margins are sharply serrate or saw-toothed, sometimes not so below the middle. The entire plant presents a slender appearance. Relatively few pods develop fully and mature seed. The seed is about 1 mm. in diameter, flattened, pale amber, with definite pitted surface and notch at edge near scar. The roots, which branch profusely, penetrate to a considerable depth. The root system is such that new plants form readily from root sections occurring at or brought near the surface of the ground. If exposed for its entire length, a piece of root will dry out and succumb, but if any part remains buried and moisture is available, a new plant results. In Minnesota it has been found to compete with hay crops, and has come back strongly on plowed and cultivated lands.

This weed is very difficult to eradicate under the conditions in which it is growing. It grows best under wet soil conditions and is confined to a meadow that is wet for six to eight months each year, making both chemical and cultural control difficult. Its vegetative spread is quite rapid and it crowds out all forage plants, completely taking over the area.

Austrian field cress has some forage value and cattle will eat the plant. It is not known how a steady diet would affect animals. Most members of this family are not considered important as forage plants.

MARSH CRESS (*Rorippa palustris* Bess.)

This is native to North America, Europe and Asia. While it is widely distributed in California, it is not common. In Iowa marsh cress is considered a pest, and reported occasionally so in Ontario, Canada. So far it has not proved serious in California.

Marsh cress is described in the literature as annual, biennial, and perennial in habit. The stem is erect, simple to somewhat branched above, commonly around 18 inches to 2 feet in height or taller. The leaves are smooth, narrowly oblong, toothed on the margins or deeply cut on the lower part of the blade. The yellow flowers are small, petals and sepals about the same length. The oblong pods are about $\frac{1}{4}$ to $\frac{1}{2}$ inch long on pedicels about the same length. The minute seeds are flattened, circular in outline, microscopically pitted and pale amber in color.

SAND CRESS (*Rorippa sinuata* Hitch.)

This is a native species of little importance as a weed, occurring particularly in sandy situations at higher altitudes. It has prostrate to decumbent stems, arising from deep and extensively creeping rootstocks. The pale green, puberulent leaves are narrowly oblong in outline, pinnately divided into more or less toothed segments. The small yellow flowers, fading white, are followed by very turgid pods about $\frac{1}{4}$ inch long, on pedicels of about the same length or slightly shorter.

HEDGEMUSTARD. *SISYMBRIUM*

The sisymbriums are erect plants with finely divided leaves, their bases not clasping the stem. The very small yellow or white flowers are grouped in small head-like clusters on the ends of the elongating pod-bearing branches. The almost cylindrical pods are from $\frac{1}{2}$ inch to several inches long, their valves more or less distinctly 3-nerved. There are about 30 species, with 9 known to be established in California.

KEY TO WEEDY SPECIES OF SISYMBRIUM

Pods appressed to stem (Fig. 141) _____*S. officinale*
Pods divergent
    Pods elongated 2-4 inches long, seeds in 1 row, leaves divided
        Upper leaves almost entire to hastately lobed_____*S. orientale*
        Upper leaves with very fine divisions (Fig. 139) _____*S. altissimum*
    Pods $\frac{3}{4}$ to $1\frac{1}{4}$ inches long, all the leaves of one plant more or less similar
        Leaves with a few divisions, large terminal lobe and 1 or 2 prominent lobes
        below (Fig. 140) _____*S. Irio*

TUMBLING MUSTARD (*Sisymbrium altissimum* L.) (Fig. 139)
Other common names: Jim Hill mustard, tall hedge mustard.

Tumbling mustard is introduced from Europe, now widespread in the middle and northwestern United States. It is a common weed, especially in southern California, and is rapidly becoming established throughout the State at levels below 5,000 feet. The weed has become abundant and a serious pest in the Tule Lake area of the northern part of the State, which is a newly developed agricultural area. Under these soil and climatic conditions this plant grows very rapidly, competing with grain especially, but also troublesome in row crops and thin stands of alfalfa. It is a prolific seeder, which adds to its seriousness. It has some little value as forage when young. Due to its ability to readily establish itself, it serves as a soil binder on light soils.

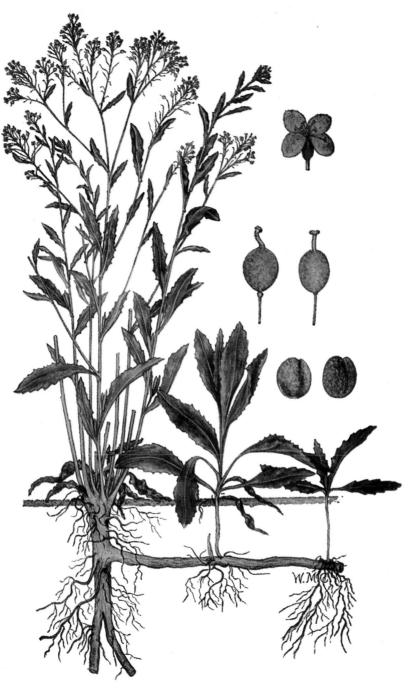

Fig. 138. Austrian field cress (*Rorippa austriaca*), showing habit, single flower, mature pod, seeds.

Tumbling mustard is an erect winter annual or biennial, 2 to 3½ feet tall, commonly widely branching above. It is almost smooth to somewhat hairy below. The lower leaves are divided and rather large, especially the terminal lobes, the margins entire to toothed. The upper leaves are reduced, with narrowly linear segments. The yellowish-white

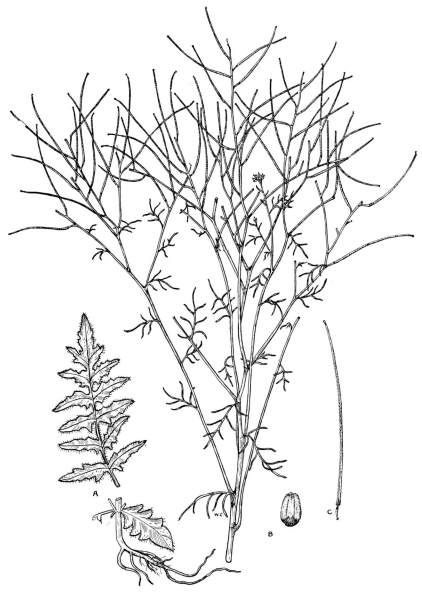

FIG. 139.   Tumbling mustard (*Sisymbrium altissimum*), showing habit. **A**, basal leaf ; **B**, seed ; **C**, pod.

FIG. 140.   London rocket (*Sisymbrium Irio*).

petals are about ¼ inch long. Pods are about 2½ to almost 4 inches long, rather thick, on spreading stems approximately ¼ inch long. The oval seeds, about $\frac{1}{16}$ inch long, are amber tinged with dark reddish-brown at the tip. The cotyledon foldings are indicated by 2 dark lines or depressions. The seed is often carried in impure commercial seeds.

LONDON ROCKET (*Sisymbrium Irio* L.) (Fig. 140)

This European weed is becoming widespread and common, often being quite prevalent as an orchard weed in coastal southern California, especially Riverside to Los Angeles. It extends northward to Modoc County. London rocket is an annual, reproducing by seeds. The plant is erect, 1½ to 2 feet tall, and smooth. The leaf blades are 1 to 4 inches long, usually divided, with a large terminal lobe and 1 or 2 pairs of smaller lobes below narrowing to a stem (Fig. 140). The yellow flowers are borne in a dense spike-like inflorescence. The narrow pods, 1¾ to 2 inches long, are divergent from the main stem, the whole fruiting spike becoming elongated and loose in age.

HEDGE MUSTARD (*Sisymbrium officinale* (L.) Scop.) (Fig. 141)

This species, introduced from Europe, occurs almost throughout North America, and in California is a common weed of waste places, vacant lots, roadsides, pastures, gardens and wet places up to about 2,500 feet, especially west of the Sierra Nevada. Hedge mustard is an annual, reproducing by seed. The stem is rigid, 1 to 4 feet high, with divergent upper branches; the herbage is roughish throughout. The leaves are deeply divided, the coarse pointed teeth sometimes turning toward the base of the leaf. The lower leaves, 4 to 10 inches long, are more or less in the form of a rosette. The yellow flowers are about ⅛ inch in diameter and are borne in tiny clusters at the tips of the elongating pod-bearing branches. The erect pods, pressed against the stem, are cylindrical, about ½ inch long and somewhat hairy (Fig. 141A). The upper portion of the plant often turns dull purple in age. The seeds are greenish-brown, about $\frac{1}{16}$ inch long, irregularly oval, with a single dark green line indicating cotyledon foldings. The surface is roughened by elongated inconspicuous pits.

ORIENTAL HEDGE MUSTARD (*Sisymbrium orientale* L.)

This species has been reported from the San Francisco Bay area. It differs from *S. altissimum* in having larger and less divided upper leaves, which are almost entire to hastately lobed, and spreading, long rigid pods which appear continuous with the equally thick pedicels.

DESERT CANDLE (*Streptanthus inflatus* Greene)
Other common name: Squaw cabbage.

Although of practically no importance as a weed, desert candle is of interest because of its peculiarly inflated stem and rather bright flowers. The plant occurs on the dry hills and plains from the Mojave

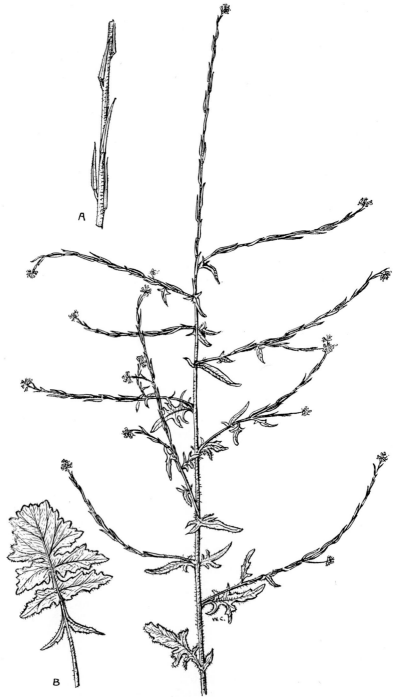

Fig. 141. Hedge mustard (*Sisymbrium officinale*) habit. **A**, erect,
appressed pods; **B**, lower leaf.

desert north to the upper San Joaquin Valley and through the inner Coast Range to western Fresno County. It is an annual, reproducing by seed. The plant has a simple erect stem 1 to 2½ feet tall, strongly inflated and becoming hollow. The leaves are smooth, rarely slightly

FIG. 142.   Left, thale cress (*Arabidopsis Thaliana*) showing habit. **A**, pod ; **B**, flower. Right, tansy mustard (*Descurainia pinnata*) showing habit. **A**, pod.

hairy, with margins entire to toothed. The flower spike appears somewhat compact, the petals and calyx purple or purple tinted.

SHAGGY THELYPOD (*Thelypodium lasiophyllum* Greene) (Fig. 144)

Of some ten species of *Thelypodium* in California, shaggy thelypod is perhaps the only one of importance as a weed. It occurs in the open foothills throughout southern California north to Washington, especially in good soil. It is frequent on grassy slopes and in washes, where is is conspicuous because of its height and strongly deflexed pods.

FIG. 143.   Flixweed (*Descurainia Sophia*) showing habit. **A**, leaf ;
B, mature pod and seed.

Shaggy thelypod is erect, from 6 inches to 6 feet tall, simple or branching above. The herbage is sparsely hairy or almost smooth, the lower leaves much cut or divided into segments, the upper less lobed or only toothed. The flowers are densely borne on branches, which become much elongated when in fruit. The petals are pale yellow, white or pink-tinted, about ⅛ of an inch long; the sepals are somewhat shorter. The pods are 2 to 4 inches long, straight or curved and deflexed (Fig. 144). The seeds are about $\frac{1}{12}$ of an inch long, dull gray-brown and strongly pitted, and foldings within the seed may be distinguished through the outer coat as a faint line. This weed is markedly variable as to size, leaf form, hairiness, flower color and shape, pod size and form. Occasionally seed of *Thelypodium* occurs as an impurity in grain.

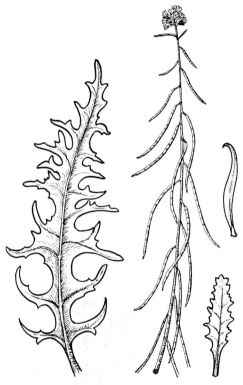

PENNY CRESS (*Thlaspi arvense* L.) (Fig. 145)

Other common names: Field penny cress, Frenchweed, fanweed.

Penny cress, introduced from Europe, is now abundant and widespread, especially in the prairie regions of the

FIG. 144. Shaggy thelypod (*Thelypodium lasiophyllum*), showing at left and right (bottom) two types of basal leaves; upper right, an upper leaf, and center, fruiting branch.

Northwestern States and Canada. In California it is largely restricted to Los Angeles, Modoc, Lassen, and Siskiyou counties, where it is found in grain fields, grasslands, gardens, and waste places. It is considered a serious weed pest in the Northwestern States in grain fields.

The weed is an erect annual 6 to 15 inches tall, simple, or sometimes branched above. The plant is smooth throughout. The leaves are about ½ to 2 inches long, not divided, and clasping the stem with ear-like projections. The small white flowers are borne in terminal branching clusters. The pod, about ½ inch in diameter, is shaped like a palm-fan with prominent margin notched at the top. The very short style is apparent in the notch. The flattened seed is 1.5 to 2 mm. long, ovate in outline, rounded at the top and pointed at the scar.

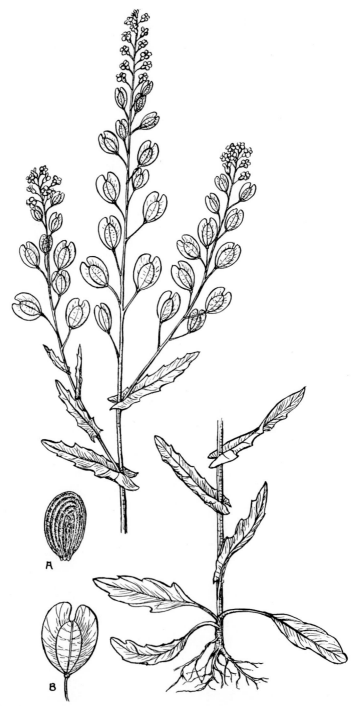

Fig. 145. Penny cress (*Thlaspi arvense*), showing habit. **A**, seed; **B**, pod.

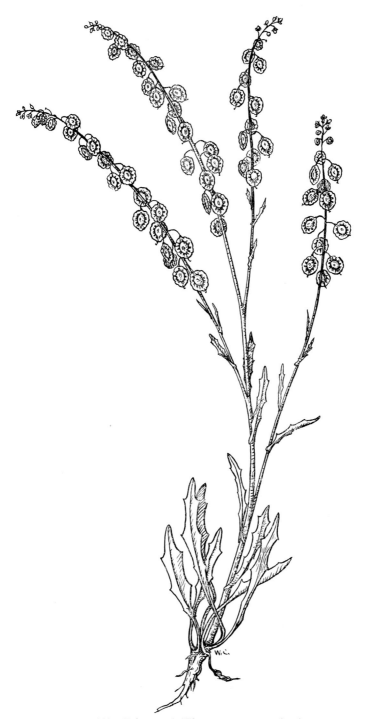

FIG. 146. Fringe-pod (*Thysanocarpus curvipes*).

The faces are roughened with from 5 to 7 concentric ridges (Fig. 145A). The color is very dark reddish-brown to black, dull to slightly glistening.

FRINGE-POD. *THYSANOCARPUS*

This genus comprises the fringed or lace pods, slender annuals with very small white or purplish flowers and flattened disk-like pods surrounded by a winged margin. The name is from the Greek, *thysanos*, fringe, and *karpos*, fruit.

KEY TO WEEDY SPECIES OF THYSANOCARPUS

Pod stems more or less recurved their whole length, rays of the wings broad
  Basal leaves in rosette, toothed or divided_____*T. curvipes*
  Basal leaves not in rosette, entire or with spreading segments_____*T. laciniatus*
Pod stems straight or recurved only at the tip rays of the wings narrow____*T. radians*

FRINGE-POD (*Thysanocarpus curvipes* Hook.) (Fig. 146)

Fringe-pod is widely distributed and frequent on open hill country west of the Sierra Nevada. It is a slender annual, 1 to 1½ feet high, somewhat hairy. The stem leaves are narrow, clasping the stem with ear-like lobes. The basal leaves narrow at the base to a stem; the blades divide into somewhat triangular lobes. The roundish pods are hairy or smooth, ¼ inch in diameter or less, often convex on one side. The wing is narrow and well filled by the broad rays. The wing commonly is not perforated, but in rare instances perforations do occur.

SOUTHERN LACE-POD (*Thysanocarpus laciniatus* Nutt.)

Southern lace-pod occurs on the open hills in southern California west of the mountains (occasionally a form on the Mojave Desert) north to central California. It is an annual 8 to 15 inches tall, usually smooth, or sometimes the stems slightly hairy. The leaves are quite narrow, cylindrically toothed or deeply cut into narrow segments. Stem leaves are not clasping the stem, or only slightly. The fruiting racemes are 1 to 8 inches long. The pods, on slender spreading or deflexed stems, are more or less eliptic. The wings bordering the pods are without rays.

SPOKE-POD (*Thysanocarpus radians* Benth.)

This plant is widely scattered but infrequent on the low hills and rolling plains of the north Coast Ranges, Sacramento Valley and bounding foothills. It is an annual, 6 to 18 inches tall, the lower leaves divided, with the segments curved backward. The stem leaves are lance-shaped, with projections at the base which clasp the stem. The pods are about ⅓ inch in diameter, smooth to hairy, with a membranous wing in which the spokes fade out just within the margin of the wing. The pod stems are straight, spreading and recurved at the tip.

DOBIE POD (*Tropidocarpum gracile* Hook.) (Fig. 147)

Dobie pod is often found in dense colonies spotted over valleys and surrounding hill slopes of the Great Valley, south Coast Ranges and south

through the desert to San
Diego County. The plant
is an erect annual, simple
to diffusely branched and
spreading with many
stems from below. The
height of the stem varies
from 3 to 15 inches, and
is soft hairy throughout.
The lower leaves are up
to 4 inches and more long,
divided into pinnate-like
segments; the stem leaves
are much smaller. The
pale yellow flowers are
mustard-like in form and
borne singly on rather
slender stems in the axils
of the leaves. The seed
pods are narrow, from 1
to 2½ inches long, tipped
by a beak about ⅛ inch
long. The seeds are dark
reddish-brown, flattened,
oval and somewhat nar-
row toward the base
which bears a small white
appendage.

ROSE FAMILY
(Rosaceae)

The rose family is a
large and important one,
possessing herbs, shrubs
and trees. Many useful
plants, from the food and
ornamental standpoints,

FIG. 147.   Dobie pod. (*Tropidocarpum gracile*).

belong to the family; for example, *Spiraea*, raspberry and blackberry
(*Rubus*), strawberry (*Fragaria*), roses (*Rosa*), stone fruits (*Prunus*),
apple and pear (*Malus*), quince (*Cydonia*), *Cotoneaster Pyracantha*, and
mountain ash (*Sorbus*).

LADY'S MANTLE (*Alchemilla arvensis* (L.) Scop.) (Fig. 148)

This naturalized plant from Europe is common throughout California, occurring on low hills and plains. It is a very small annual herb,
1 to 3 inches high, with scant, soft hairy herbage, palmately-lobed leaves

¼ inch or less long, and small, greenish flowers clustered in the axils. The calyx is pitcher-shaped, corolla none, stamens 1 to 4, pistil 1, and the fruit an achene enclosed by the lower part of the calyx. The seed is about 1.5 mm. long, dull, rough, yellowish-brown; pointed egg-shaped, flattened laterally, with a tail-like appendage at the broad end.

WESTERN CHOKECHERRY (*Prunus demissa* (Nutt.) (Dietr.)

This species occurs on mountain slopes and in canyons, from 500 to 7,500 feet, in the Sierra Nevada, Coast Ranges, and southern California. Western choke-cherry is a deciduous shrub or small tree up to 20 feet tall, or more. The leaves are simple, finely toothed, oblong-oval, sharp-pointed, the blades 1 to 3½ inches long, the petioles about ½ inch long; at the base of the leaf blade on the petiole are 1 or 2 glands. The flowers are white, and in racemes 2 to 4 inches long, at the ends of more or less leafy peduncles. The flowers are of the plum or cherry type: a 5-cleft calyx, 5 petals, 15 to 30 stamens, and a single pistil. The fruit is a drupe (stone-fruit), red or dark-purple in color, about ¼ inch in diameter, and bitter and astringent in taste.

Western chokecherry is poisonous to livestock, the toxic substance being found in the leaves, bark, and stones of the fruit. The pulp of the fruit is not poisonous.

FIG. 148. Lady's mantle (*Alchemilla arvensis*).

CALIFORNIA WILD ROSE (*Rosa californica* C. & S.)

This attractive native is scattered throughout the State, along river and creek banks, at lower and middle altitudes, becoming a pest in certain parts of the Coast Range where it forms extensive, dense thickets.

Stems 3 to 6 feet high with few to numerous recurved prickles. Leaflets 5 to 7, commonly ½ to 1½ inches long, more or less soft-hairy, especially beneath, stipules narrow with lanceolate tips. Flowers few to many, 20 to 40 in a panicle, petals ¾ to 1 inch long, rose-pink. Pedicels hairy to glandular; hips globose or ovoid, $\frac{1}{3}$ to $\frac{2}{3}$ inch broad, somewhat constricted below the calyx lobes.

BLACKBERRY. *RUBUS*

There are several species of *Rubus* native to California. The most common native is *R. vitifolius* (California blackberry). The cultivated common blackberry (*R. laciniatus*), and Himalaya berry (*R. procerus*) are frequently escapes, becoming troublesome weeds along fences and ditches, and occasionally in orchards and fields.

All the species of *Rubus* are bushes with long trailing or climbing stems. The leaves are usually compound with 3 to 5 leaflets. The calyx is 5-parted, the petals 5 and separate, the stamens numerous, and the pistils many, and crowded on a receptacle. The fruit is the receptacle together with the numerous drupelets which are attached thereto. The seeds are commonly $\frac{1}{8}$ inch or less long, rounded at one end and slightly curved toward a point at the other, and much flattened.

COMMON BLACKBERRY (*Rubus laciniatus* Willd.)

This cultivated species is naturalized in northern California. It is an evergreen shrub from 4 to 8 feet tall; stems angled, stiff and very prickly; leaflets 5 to 15, deeply laciniate and cut-toothed, greenish or slightly grayish beneath; flowers about 1 inch across, rose-colored; fruit globular, black.

HIMALAYA-BERRY (*Rubus procerus* P. J. Muell.)

This introduction from Europe is abundantly established in the coastal counties of northern California. Sprawling evergreen shrub; stems up to 10 feet long, angled and prickly; prostrate stems rooting at the nodes; leaves 5-foliate, the leaflets 4 to 5 inches long and nearly as broad, serrate, strongly whitened below; flowers in conspicuous terminal panicles, roseate to white; fruit black, large subglobose to elongate.

CALIFORNIA BLACKBERRY (*Rubus vitifolius* Cham. & Schlecht.)

This species is widely distributed in California. It is an evergreen bush, with a few short, erect stems, and several that may trail and climb for a distance up to 15 or more feet; leaves mostly 3- to 5-foliate, some of them simple; stems and leaves very prickly; flowers white, up to $1\frac{1}{4}$ inches broad; fruit oblong, black.

ANNUAL BURNET (*Sanguisorba annua* Nutt.)

This burnet is a native of California, occurring mostly at higher altitudes. It is an annual, with oblong greenish spikes. The stigmas are brush-like and the fruiting calyx is narrowly 4-winged; faces of the achenes are smooth between the angles. It differs from *S. minor* in having leaflets about $\frac{1}{2}$ inch long sharply cleft into narrow lobes.

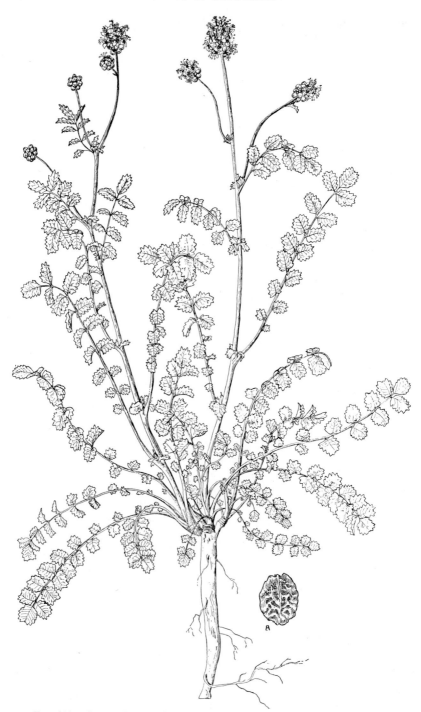

FIG. 149. Garden burnet (*Sanguisorba minor*), showing habit. **A,** achene.

GARDEN BURNET (*Sanguisorba minor* Scop.) (Fig. 149)

This native of Europe thus far occurs only sparingly in California. It is a perennial herb, branching near the base to form a basal clump of foliage. The stems are 12 to 24 inches high. The leaves are unequally pinnate, consisting of 6 to 10 pairs of nearly round or oblong, finely-toothed leaflets. The flowers are small, and crowded in a dense spike or head at the end of a long naked stalk. The calyx consists of 4 petal-like lobes, the corolla is lacking, stamens 2 to 4, and pistil 1. The fruit is an achene about 3 mm. long enclosed by the 4-angled, dry calyx tube, rough between the angles.

GREAT BURNET (*Sanguisorba officinalis* L.)

This species is a perennial, introduced from Europe and now established to a limited extent near the coast in the northern part of the State. The leaves are merely serrate and the fruiting spikes are purple.

PEA FAMILY (Leguminosae)

The pea family is of wide geographical distribution, occurring both in temperate and warm climates. It is the second largest family of flowering plants, having over 12,000 species. Probably no family is of greater agricultural importance than this one, unless it is the grass family. To it belong beans, peas, vetches, clovers, alfalfa and other medics, cowpea, soy bean, and peanut. Other well known members of this family are *Acacia,* honey locust (*Gleditsia*), Sesbania, lupines (*Lupinus*), *Genista, Lotus,* sweet pea (*Lathyrus*), sennas (*Cassia*), red bud (*Cercis*), and wild licorice (*Glycyrrhiza*).

Members of the pea family commonly have compound leaves, and characteristic irregular flowers with a butterfly-like shape. The petals are usually 5, including a broad upper one (the standard or banner) 2 lateral ones (the wings), and 2 lower ones more or less united, forming a keel (Fig. 2f). The fruit is a legume or pod, and the seeds usually have thick cotyledons filled with food.

KEY TO GENERA AND SPECIES OF LEGUMINOSAE (PEA FAMILY)

Stamens distinct; corolla orange-red_____Pignut (*Hoffmannseggia densiflora*)
Stamens with filaments all united, or 9 united and 1 separate (Fig. 2f2)
  Calyx deeply 2-lipped (Fig. 160b)
    Flowers yellow
      Leaves simple, or branches leafless; densely spiny shrub
                        Furze or gorse (*Ulex europaeus*)
      Leaves 3-foliate, or branches leafless; shrub not spiny
                        Scotch broom (*Cytisus scoparius*)
    Flowers mostly blue or purple
      Plants annual _____*Lupinus pusillus*
      Plants perennial
        Flower stalks short and stout_____*Lupinus leucophyllus*
        Flowers slender
          Wing petals very hairy_____*Lupinus laxiflorus*
          Wing petals not hairy_____*Lupinus onustus*

KEY TO GENERA AND SPECIES OF LEGUMINOSAE (PEA FAMILY)—
Continued

Stamens with filaments all united, or 9 united and 1 separate (Fig. 2f2)
  Calyx not deeply 2-lipped (Fig. 160e)
    Leaves simple ; low spiny shrub_____Camel thorn (*Alhagi camelorum*)
    Leaves compound
      Leaves 3-foliate
        Flowers in a head (Fig. 160C)
          Corolla white or yellowish white_____White clover (*Trifolium repens*)
          Corolla yellow
            Heads small, about ¼ inch broad_____Shamrock (*Trifolium dubium*)
            Heads larger, about ½ inch broad___Hop clover (*Trifolium procumbens*)
          Corolla pink, rose-colored, red or red-purple
            Flowers in spike-like heads, much longer than thick
                    Crimson clover (*Trifolium incarnatum*)
            Flowers in globular or ovoid heads, sometimes somewhat longer than
            broad
              Flowers with a pedicel_____Alsike clover (*Trifolium hybridum*)
              Flowers sessile_____Red clover (*Trifolium pratense*)
        Flowers in a raceme
          Pods small, ovoid
            Flowers white_____White sweet clover (*Melilotus alba*)
            Flowers yellow
              Pods with strongly wrinkled, non-hairy coat
                    Yellow melilot (*Melilotus indica*)
              Pods with somewhat pubescent coat
                    Yellow sweet clover (*Melilotus officinalis*)
          Pods curved or coiled
            Pods 1-seeded, not spiny_____Black medick (*Medicago lupulina*)
            Pods several-seeded
              Pods with prickles_____*Medicago apiculata*
              Pods without prickles
                Stems pubescent ; purple spot in center of each leaflet
                    Spotted bur clover (*Medicago arabica*)
                Stems smooth ; no purple spot in center of each leaflet
                    Toothed bur clover (*Medicago hispida*)
  Leaves pinnate
    Leaves odd-pinnate (Fig. 152)
      Herbage glandular dotted_____Wild liquorice (*Glycyrrhiza lepidota*)
      Herbage not glandular dotted
        Pods strongly inflated (Fig. 152)
          Pods with a stipe (Fig. 160a)_____*Astragalus leucophyllus*
          Pods without a stipe
            Pods densely pubescent_____*Astragalus Hornii*
            Pods smooth or sparsely pubescent
              Plants not more than 1 foot tall_____*Astragalus lentiginosus*
              Plants 1 to 6 feet tall
                Leaves 2½ to 5 inches long_____*Astragalus Menziesii*
                Leaves 3½ to 7 inches long_____*Astragalus oocarpus*
         Pods not strongly inflated
          Leaves 1¼ to 2½ inches long_____*Astragalus Purshii*
          Leaves 3 to 5 inches long_____*Astragalus Mortonii*
    Leaves equally pinate (Fig. 159)
      No tendrils_____*Sesbania macrocarpa*
      Tendrils present_____*Vicia* species

CAMEL THORN (*Alhagi camelorum* Fisch.) (Fig. 150)

Camel thorn grows wild throughout Turkestan, and also in European Russia, particularly in the highlands along the Volga. It is more or
less extensively established in several counties : Merced, Madera, Fresno,
Kern, Kings, Riverside, Imperial, San Diego and Tehama Counties. In

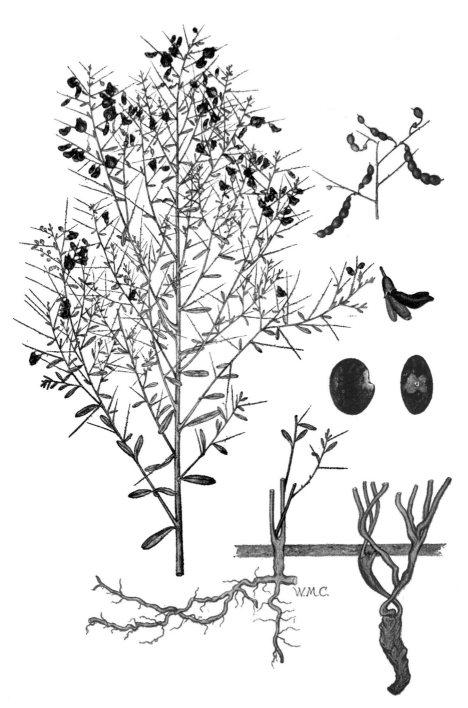

FIG. 150. Camel thorn (*Alhagi camelorum*)

most of the areas infestations have been greatly reduced through control measures.

Camel thorn is a somewhat woody bush 1 to 3 feet tall. The stems are armed with thorns. Leaves simple, petioled, entire and smooth, varying in size from very small ones at top of plant to those ¾ inch long lower down. Flowers are maroon. The fruit is a slender pod, twisted in various forms, and pinched in here and there so as to appear like a string of beads. Usually a small spine occurs at the end of each pod. The seeds resemble large clover seeds, yellowish- or greenish-brown with dark mottling, to dark brown. Camel thorn blooms in June and matures pods in July.

Camel thorn has a well-developed root system which often extends to a depth of 6 or 7 feet. There is a tendency for the rootstocks to branch at the 3 to 4½ foot level, and from these branches aerial stems arise. The rootstock system of camel thorn may be very extensive, spreading in all directions from a mother plant to a distance of 25 feet or more.

Camel thorn gained entrance into California in two ways: (1) in early shipments of Turkestan alfalfa seed, and (2) in the packing around date offshoots. The former is undoubtedly the chief source. A number of years ago, in the development of the lands belonging to Miller and Lux, large acreages in the lower San Joaquin Valley were planted to alfalfa. Much of this was Turkestan, the seed of which was imported. Scattered infestations of camel thorn occurred throughout this area. While apparently the plant does not spread rapidly by means of seeds, probably due to the difficulty of the seedlings in becoming established, it spreads rapidly in a vegetative manner. Many of the infestations are circular in form, varying in size from less than one to several acres. These areas maintain their circular form, and rapidly increase in diameter. The outlying plants are from rootstocks, rather than from seeds.

Browsing animals have been a factor in disseminating camel thorn in the State. On the dry lands of Kern County, in the areas infested with the weed, one may find large numbers of seed in the droppings of both horses and cattle. Tests show this seed to be viable.

In its native land camel thorn is grazed and used as a forage plant. Camels, cattle and horses eat and apparently relish the plant in spite of its thorns.

LOCO WEED. ASTRAGALUS

Jepson's Manual of the Flowering Plants of California describes 62 species of *Astragalus* or loco weed.

The loco weeds are annual or perennial herbs with compound, odd-pinnate leaves, flowers in racemes, spikes, or heads, and hairy or smooth herbage. The calyx is 5-toothed and the corolla of the ordinary pea type (5 petals—1 large standard, 2 wings, and a keel of 2 united petals). The corolla is usually long and narrow with the keel obtuse. The fruit is a pod, often bladder-like and inflated or flat and compressed. The seeds are irregularly wedge-shaped, squared off and notched at the narrow edge. The differentiating characteristics of some of the more important species are brought out in the key to the genera and species of Leguminosae.

None of the California species has been tested by experimental feeding to determine whether or not it is toxic. However, there is some evidence that a few of the native species cause injury to livestock. It is probably well to regard with suspicion all the species of *Astragalus*.

FIG. 151.   Woolly-leaved loco (*Astragalus leucophyllus*) showing leaves, bladdery fruits on a long stipe. A, single flower; B, seeds.

SHEEP LOCO (*Astragalus Hornii* Gray)

Sheep loco extends from the San Bernardino Valley, Kern and Inyo Counties, through the Mojave Desert to the upper San Joaquin Valley. It is a perennial, about 3-4 feet tall, widely spreading, rather sparsely appressed-hairy or the stems and top surface of the leaves smooth. The leaves are about 3-5 inches long with about 21 narrowly oblong leaflets, obtuse at the apex and about ⅓ to ⅔ inch long. The yellowish-white flower spike is dense, as is the pod-bearing spike. The pods are strongly inflated, rather densely pubescent, not extended on a stipe or stalk-like base. The pods are broadly ovate, slender pointed at the apex about ½ inch long, 2-celled.

Sheep loco is infrequent, but is reported poisonous to sheep.

SPOTTED LOCO (*Astragalus lentiginosus* Dougl.)

The plant is a perennial, about 1 foot tall and branching from the base, sparsely hairy or smooth. The leaves are 1 to 2½ inches long with 11-21 leaflets which are oblong and about ¼ to ½ inch long. The flower bearing stems are shorter than the leaves, the flowers densely crowded, white or purplish. In this loco weed the pod is strongly membranous inflated, not produced on a stipe or stalk-like projection. The pods are broadly ovate, 2-celled, about ½ to ⅔ inch long, straw colored or often purple-mottled, rather shiny, more or less grooved on each side at the joining.

WOOLLY-LEAVED LOCO (*Astragalus leucophyllus* T. & G.) (Fig. 151)

The plant is a perennial, erect, 1 to 3 feet tall, silvery-hairy but in age becoming green. The leaves are 2½ to 5 inches long, with 17 to 29 narrow to oblong leaflets. The yellowish-white flower spikes are about 2 to 4 inches long. This species has a strongly inflated pod, extended on a hairy stipe or stalk-like process which is more than twice as long as the calyx. The pod is oblong to ovate, abruptly short-pointed, 1⅛ to 1¾ inches long, 1-celled, the sides slightly unequal. Woolly-leaved loco occurs on low hills in the inner Coast Ranges from Solano to Monterey County and in Madera County.

GRAY LOCO (*Astragalus Menziesii* Gray) (Fig. 152)

The plant is a perennial, 1 to 4 feet tall, erect or somewhat spreading from the base, somewhat grayish-hairy or later becoming green and smooth. The leaves are about 2½ to 5 inches long, with many crowded oblong leaflets about ½ to ¾ inch long. The whitish flower spike is about 2 to 4 inches long, dense, borne on strong stems almost as long as the leaves. In gray loco the pod is much inflated, but not produced on a stipe or stalk-like base. The pods are membranous 1½ to 2 inches long, not depressed along the seam where valves join, 1-celled. This species occurs mostly on the sandy slopes near the coast from San Francisco to Monterey.

MORTON'S LOCO (*Astragalus Mortonii* Nutt.)

The plant is a perennial, 1 to 2 feet tall, often widely branching from below, herbage flat-hairy. The leaves are 3 to 5 inches long with 13 to 21 leaflets about $\frac{1}{2}$–$\frac{3}{4}$ inch long, obtuse or acute. The greenish white or yellowish flower spikes are 1 to $2\frac{1}{2}$ inches long, crowded in flower and in fruit. In Morton's loco the pods are not strongly inflated, about $\frac{1}{2}$ inch long or less, fine hairy and not on a stipe or stalk. They are somewhat cylindric, grooved along one side and the joining prominent on the other, incompletely 2-celled. The pods are erect. This species occurs on the east side of the Sierra from Mono to Modoc and eastward.

FIG. 152. Left, gray loco (*Astragalus Menziesii*). Right, smooth loco (*A. oocarpus*). Pods without stipe.

SMOOTH LOCO (*Astragalus oocarpus* Gray) (Fig. 152)

The plant is perennial, 4 to 6 feet high, nearly smooth to somewhat hairy, the leaves $3\frac{1}{2}$–7 inches long with 19 to 23 narrowly oblong leaflets, leaflets commonly $\frac{1}{2}$–1 inch long. The flower-spike bearing stems are shorter than the leaves. In this species the pod is strongly inflated but not produced on a stipe or stalk-like extension at the base of the pod. The pods are ovoid and turgidly much inflated, 1-celled, about 1 inch long and gradually sharp-pointed at the apex.

TUFTED LOCO (*Astragalus Purshii* Dougl.)

The plant is perennial, forming dense tufts 2 to 4 (or more) inches tall from a long taproot. It is white-woolly, leaves 1½ to 2½ inches long, leaflets 9 to 19 bluntly oblong, ¼ to ½ inch long. The flower spike is few-flowered, at the end of stems shorter than the leaves. The flowers are white or blue and white. In this species the pods are not strongly inflated and not produced on a stipe or stalk-like process. They are 1-celled, oblong or ovate, about ½ to ¾ inch long, densely covered with white or yellowish hairs so that they appear quite woolly. This species and its varieties range from Mendocino to Siskiyou and Modoc; on the east side of the Sierra to Inyo; also on the south Coast Ranges.

SCOTCH BROOM (*Cytisus scoparius* Link) (Fig. 153)

This species was introduced from Europe as an ornamental, and plantings are found throughout the State. It has escaped from culti-vation in many places and become a pest. Particularly it is a pest in west Sonoma County, at Millbrae in San Mateo County, and in Placer and El Dorado counties. In the last mentioned county not only has it interfered with the establishing of young trees, but it has spread into pear orchards. Scotch broom is a perennial shrub, 3 to 6 feet high, with stiff, angled, broom-like green branches. Many of the branches may be leafless or only slightly leafy. The leaves are 3-foliate, the leaflets being small, and entire. The flowers are a bright yellow and usually borne in profusion. There are 5 sepals united to form a 2-lipped calyx, 5 petals of the pea type (a standard or banner, 2 wings, and a

FIG. 153. Scotch broom (*Cytisus scoparius*) showing habit of growth, flowering branches, and seeds bearing a light rounded appendage at the scar end.

keel formed of 2 fused petals), 10 stamens, the filaments of which are united, and a single pistil with a long spirally curved style. The fruit is a flattened pod, somewhat hairy along the margins, and several seeded. The seed is oval, about ⅛ inch long, very dark greenish-brown with a shiny surface and light rounded appendage at the scar end.

WILD LICORICE (*Glycyrrhiza lepidota* (Nutt.) Pursh.) (Fig. 154)
Other common names: Devil's shoestring, sweet root, licorice.

This species is a native of the Pacific Coast States, occurring chiefly in the coast counties of California, but becoming abundant in the Central Valley and Sierra foothills. It is rapidly attaining prominence as a weed in agricultural soils. Its importance as a weed has not been recognized generally, but field observations show that its vegetative spread is quite rapid. It does not yield readily to cultivation and hence should be looked upon as a serious pest.

Wild licorice is a perennial herb with thick, sweet roots, which may reach a length of several feet. The herbage is glandular and sticky and sometimes with minute scales. The plants are 2 to 3 feet tall. The leaves are compound, composed of 11 to 15 leaflets, and glandular-dotted. The leaflets are short-stalked, 1 to 1½ inches long, and with a prominent midrib. The flowers are in axillary spikes. The flowers are of the pea type, about ½ inch long, the calyx very glandular and 5-cleft, the corolla yellowish-white and longer than the calyx. The pod is about ½ inch long and bur-like, being covered with hooked prickles, red-brown in color, tipped by the long persistent style, and containing 2 to 6 seeds. The seed is somewhat flattened, circular in outline, about $\frac{1}{16}$ inch in diameter with an irregular obtuse notch at the scar.

PIGNUT (*Hoffmanseggia densiflora* Benth.) (Fig. 155)

Pignut occurs for the most part in alkaline soils. It is found sparingly in the San Joaquin Valley and quite generally throughout the Mohave and Colorado deserts, and in the Imperial Valley. With its deep-seated tuberous roots, from which the plant freely sends up stems to the surface, which are difficult to remove from the soil, pignut is a weed which should be watched carefully and prevented from gaining headway. Small infestations should be grubbed out, taking care to remove the tuberous, nut-like roots. This plant is an herb, the stems of which are 8 to 12 inches high, with a tuft of leaves at the base. The leaves are twice divided, 3 to 5 inches long, and usually with 3 to 5 pairs of leaflets. The leaflets are oblong in shape, and from 1/12 to 1/4 inch long. The leaves have characteristic glandular dots. The flowers are of the pea-type, yellow or orange-red, and about one-half inch long. The ovary of the flower is covered with peculiar tack-shaped glands. The pods are flat, about 1½ inches long, and few to several seeded.

Fig. 154.   Wild licorice (*Glycyrrhiza lepidota*). **A,** habit showing foliage and inflorescence characters, x ⅜ ; **B,** single flower, x 8 ; **C,** fruit, x 5, covered with brownish, hooked prickles and superficially resembling a cocklebur ; **D,** leaf, x 2.

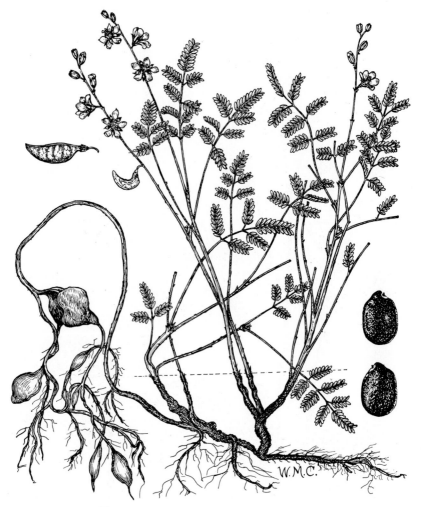

Fig. 155.　Pignut (*Hoffmanseggia densiflora*)

LUPINE. *LUPINUS* (Fig. 156)

In Jepson's Manual of the Flowering Plants of California descriptions are given for 65 species of *Lupinus*.

There are both herbaceous and woody species of lupine. The leaves are characteristically palmately compound, with petioles swollen at the base, and with from 3 to 17 leaflets. The flowers are in racemes, mostly blue or purple, rarely white, yellow, or red. The flowers are often arranged in distinct whorls. The calyx is deeply 2-lipped, the corolla of the usual legume type (a banner, 2 wings, and 2-parted keel). There are 10 stamens, all united by their filaments, 5 long and 5 short. The fruit is a flattened pod. The seeds vary in size, but the general form is somewhat flattened oval, with a raised smooth light colored area bordering an oval depressed scar.

The following described species occurring within our borders have been proved poisonous as the result of controlled feeding experiments. It is altogether likely that other species are equally toxic; at any rate, it is well to regard all lupines as possible stock-poisoning plants.

FIG. 156.   Lupine (*Lupinus* species), showing flowering and fruiting branches and palmately compound leaves.

GRASSLAND LUPINE (*Lupinus laxiflorus* Dougl.)

This widely distributed lupine is an erect perennial from 12 to 30 inches tall. The stems and leaves are clothed with minute appressed hairs. There are from 7 to 9 leaflets, $1\frac{1}{4}$ to 2 inches long. The petals are blue, rose, or pale yellow. The pods are about 1 inch long, bearing 4 to 6 seeds.

This species is known to be poisonous to livestock.

WESTERN LUPINE (*Lupinus leucophyllus* Dougl.)

This species is quite common in the mountains of northern California, at altitudes from 3,500 to 5,000 feet. It is a stout, erect perennial, up to 30 inches tall. The herbage is densely hairy, the leaves more or less woolly. There are from 7 to 9 leaflets, which are from 1 to 2 inches long.

The petals are white, pinkish, bluish or purple, and often turn brown when drying. The pods are woolly, up to 1 inch long.

Feeding tests indicate western lupine is poisonous.

WOODLAND LUPINE (*Lupinus onustus* Wats.)

This perennial lupine occurs chiefly in open pine forests of Plumas, Lassen and Siskiyou Counties, at altitudes between 5,000 and 9,000 feet. It is a slender plant, seldom taller than 10 inches. The leaves have long petioles, smooth above and appressed silky hairy below. Leaflets vary from 5 to 8, and are from 1 to $1\frac{1}{2}$ inches long. The flowers are deep blue, the pods from $1\frac{1}{4}$ to $1\frac{1}{2}$ inches long.

This species is regarded as poisonous to livestock.

LOW LUPINE (*Lupinus pusillus* Pursh.)

This species occurs only in the eastern part of the State—Inyo to Modoc Counties. It is an annual species, 4 to 8 inches tall. The leaves are smooth above, soft hairy beneath, and with 5 leaflets. The petals are bluish to white, the pods hairy, oblong, and 2-seeded.

Low lupine is poisonous to livestock.

MEDICK. *MEDICAGO*

KEY TO WEEDY SPECIES OF MEDICAGO

Plants annual, flowers yellow
  Pods several seeded, spirally coiled
    Pods armed with prickles
      Edge of pod sharp, not grooved between prickles_____*M. hispida*
      Edge of pod grooved between prickles_____*M. arabica*
    Pods not armed with prickles_____*M. apiculata*
  Pod 1-seeded, not coiled, prominently nerved, black when mature_____*M. lupulina*
Plants perennial, flowers blue_____*M. sativa*

Medicago apiculata Willd.

This is an annual medick naturalized from Europe, and widely distributed in the State, although nowhere very abundant. It is very similar to bur clover but the pods are unarmed or with very short spines.

SPOTTED MEDICK (*Medicago arabica* All.)

This is a native of Europe and Western Asia, which has been introduced into the United States and now occurs on the Atlantic, Gulf, and the California coasts from Eureka to San Francisco Bay. It is being used to a limited extent as a pasturage crop, is palatable and though not as common as the other medicks, is a valuable forage plant. Rarely it occurs as a weed of minor importance. This bur clover is a smooth annual with procumbent stems. The leaflets have a characteristic dark purple spot in the center. The pods are in long clusters, twisted into 3 to 5 spirals, and the edges bear numerous grooved spines which interlock. The seeds are kidney-shaped, and about $2\frac{1}{2}$ mm. long, golden brown in color.

BUR CLOVER (*Medicago hispida* Gaertn.)

This is a naturalized species from Europe that has become very common throughout California. It is the most common bur clover in this

State. It finds use as a pasture, hay, cover and green-manure crop, and as a weed is quite common in lawns. It was introduced into California during the Mission Period. Bur clover is a smooth, annual plant with procumbent stems, from a few inches to 2 feet long. The leaflets often have small whitish and dark red spots scattered over the surface, which disappear with age. The flowers are yellow. The pods are netted veined, twisted spirally, and spiny. There is a double row of more or less hooked and curved prickles along the edge of the pod. The seeds are somewhat waxy, light to brownish-yellow, kidney-shaped and not slightly twisted as is alfalfa seed, and about 3 mm. long.

Bur clover is a notable example of an aggressive introduced plant which has considerable forage value. The burs, which have high nutritive value, may mat in the wool of sheep and decrease the value of the fleece.

BLACK MEDICK (*Medicago lupulina* L.) (Fig. 157)
Other common names: nonesuch, trefoil, black clover, hop medic, hop clover.

This species is a native of Eurasia. It is found throughout the greater part of the United States and other temperate regions where it has often become a weed in fields, waste places, gardens, and lawns. It is sometimes planted on poor soil, and has some use as a green manure. It is highly regarded as a forage plant and because of this has been given the name "nonesuch," indicative of superiority. Black medick is usually annual, sometimes perennial. The stems are 4-angled, hairy, and branched at the base, and branches being prostrate and spreading. The leaves are 3-foliate, the central leaflet stalked; the leaflets have rounded tips, with margins minutely toothed. The flowers (of the pea-type) are small, yellow, in dense oblong or cylindrical heads, which are on stalks 1 to 3 inches long. The fruit is a flattened pod, black, curved, strongly veined, and 1-seeded. The seeds are a frequent impurity in alfalfa seed.

ALFALFA (*Medicago sativa* L.), a native of Europe, occasionally becomes established when it escapes from cultivation. It is readily distinguished by its purplish-blue flowers and perennial habit. The seed is similar to the bur clovers, but more angularly kidney-shaped, twisted when viewed edgewise, and a darker more greenish-brown in color, particularly when seen in bulk.

WHITE SWEETCLOVER (*Melilotus alba* Desr.)
Other common name: White melilot.

This species is an annual or biennial, rarely perennial, introduced from Europe. White sweetclover is cultivated somewhat for forage, but it has a slightly bitter taste which cattle must become accustomed to before they will eat it readily. Its value as a forage plant is below that of alfalfa. American beekeepers have long recognized the importance of sweetclover as a honey plant. It has become a common roadside and waste-place weed.

White sweetclover is an erect and smooth-stemmed plant attaining a height of 3 to 6 feet. The leaves have thick, oblong, finely toothed leaflets

Fig. 157. Black medick (*Medicago lupulina*), showing habit, and black, curved, strongly-veined pods.

which are narrow at the base, and truncate, notched, or rounded at the apex. The flower groups are numerous, slender, and often one-sided. The flowers, of the pea-type, are white. The pods are ovoid and slightly netted. The seed is flattened egg-shape, more convex on one edge and notched at the other, a light line running in from the scar parallel to the straight edge of the seed. The color is yellowish-green to brownish-yellow, with surface dull.

ANNUAL YELLOW SWEETCLOVER (*Melilotus indica* All.) (Fig. 158)
Other common names: Bitter clover, sour clover.

This introduction from Eurasia is a common cover crop in California, particularly the southern part. The flowers are yellow and it has smooth strongly wrinkled rather than hairy pods. This species is an annual and widespread, but not abundant, as a weed in gardens, fields, waste places and roadsides. It is a shorter growing plant than the other two sweetclovers, commonly about 1½-3 feet high. The seed is rounded egg-shape, somewhat flattened, drab- to greenish-brown, the surface definitely roughened.

YELLOW SWEETCLOVER (*Melilotus officinalis* Lam.)

This species is rare within our borders. It resembles white sweetclover, but the flowers are yellow instead of white, and the plants are less robust. The leaflets of this species are ovate, the flowers are large, and the pod is somewhat pubescent. The seeds are very similar to those of white sweetclover; they may be a plain golden-brown or a golden-brown mottled with dark brown or maroon.

HONEY MESQUITE (*Prosopis chilensis* (Molina) Stuntz)

Honey mesquite is a common shrub or small tree in washes and low places usually below 3,000 feet, on the Colorado and Mohave Deserts and in cismontane southern California. It is found locally in the upper San Joaquin and Sacramento Valleys, particularly in the vicinity of railroad stockyards.

A much branched shrub, 6 to 10 feet high, or a small crooked branched tree, 15 to 20 feet high. Thorns 1 or 2, axillary, ¼ to 1¼ inches long, rarely absent. Leaves usually with 2 pinnae about 2 to 4 inches long, each pinna with 18 to 36 linear entire leaflets ⅜ inch to 1 inch long; petioles enlarged and glandular at base. Flowers small, greenish yellow, in slender cylindrical spikes 2 to 3½ inches long, pods linear, 3 to 8 inches long, ⅓ to ½ inch wide, curved, flat or becoming thickened, irregularly constricted between the seeds, in drooping clusters of 1 to 6. Seeds smooth, about ¼ inch long.

SCREWBEAN or TORNILLO (*Prosopis pubescens* Benth.)

This shrub or small tree is similar to the honey mesquite, and the range is roughly the same as for that species. The pods, however, coil tightly into spirals 1½ to 2½ inches long.

Fig. 158.   Annual yellow sweetclover (*Melilotus indica*).

COLORADO RIVER HEMP (*Sesbania macrocarpa* Muhl.) (Fig. 159)
Other common names: Wild hemp, large indigo weed, pea-tree, long-podded sesban.

This plant is a native, being very abundant in overflow
land from the lower California
region east to the Atlantic. In
the Imperial Valley, where it
is grown as a cover crop, it has
spread along irrigation canals
and into adjacent fields, and
has appeared as a weed of rice
fields.

Sesbania is annual, attaining a height of 3 to 10 feet.
The stems are smooth, branching, and bear large compound
leaves which may be close to a
foot in length. Each leaf has
from 13 to 41 pairs of leaflets
which are about 1 inch long
and $\frac{1}{4}$ inch wide. The flowers
are one to several on slender
stalks. The flowers are of the
pea-type, about $\frac{1}{2}$ inch long,
the corolla yellowish, sometimes
reddish, and often mottled. The
pod is slender, jointed, 4 to 9
inches long, and contains many
brown-spotted seeds, about $\frac{1}{4}$
inch long, squarish on the ends.

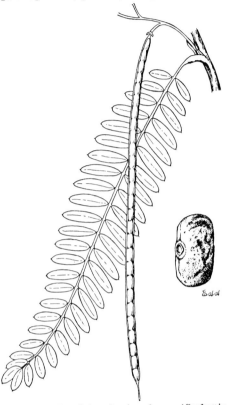

Fig. 159. Colorado river hemp (*Sesbania macrocarpa*), showing long, pinnate leaf, elongated pod, and seed.

CLOVER. TRIFOLIUM *

The true clovers (*Trifolium* species) are all herbs with palmate
3-foliate leaves. The flowers are of the pea-type, and occur usually in
dense heads. The pods are small, membranous, mostly 1-seeded, and
usually do not break open at maturity. None of the natives or the introduced species are of importance to us as weeds, except in very special
situations. Rarely certain of these, especially white clover, comes in
lawns where it may not be wanted. On the other hand, the seed of white
clover is frequently mixed with that of grasses, the clover-bluegrass
mixture being desired. All the clovers are valued as forage and some
are commonly used in tame grass mixtures. Jepson reports 41 species
of *Trifolium* as occurring in California, most of which are natives, one
of the most important being sour clover (*T. fucatum* Lindl.) (Fig. 160c).

*See key, page 252, for distinguishing characteristics of *Trifolium* species.

PINOLE CLOVER (*Trifolium bifidum* Gray)

This species sometimes occurs as an impurity in commercial lots of oats, wheat, and barley. It is a slender native, annual plant about 8 inches to 1½ feet high, with leaflets notched at their apex, often with a prominent tooth in the notch. The purplish to pale pink flower heads are small, the flowers turned downward in age, the flower stems hairy at the base of the heads.

SUCKLING CLOVER or SHAMROCK (*Trifolium dubium* Sibth. and *T. procumbens* L.)

These are introductions from Europe frequent in Humboldt, Del Norte, Nevada, and Calaveras counties, and also the San Francisco Bay region. (Low hop-clovers.)

ALSIKE CLOVER (*T. hybridum* L.)

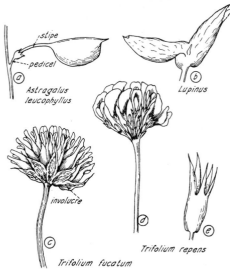

FIG. 160. Botanical characters of certain legumes. (a) fruit of woolly-leaved loco; (b) flower of lupine, showing deeply 2-cleft calyx; (c) flowering head of sour clover; (d) flowering head of white clover; (e) calyx of white clover.

This introduced species is planted as a forage and pasture crop, escaping from cultivation. It occurs in mountain meadows of the Sierra Nevada and in Humboldt and Siskiyou Counties.

CRIMSON CLOVER (*T. incarnatum* L.)

This is naturalized from Europe and has been found at Healdsburg, and at scattered sites to the north.

RED CLOVER (*T. pratense* L.)

This is a valued forage plant which has become naturalized in mountain meadows throughout the State to a limited extent.

WHITE CLOVER (*T. repens* L.) (Fig. 160d)

This is usually found where lawns are planted, the seeds often being used in lawn grass mixtures. It has escaped from cultivation.

GORSE (*Ulex europaeus* L.) (Figs. 161 and 162)
Other common name: Furze.

This is an introduced ornamental from Europe. In the coastal counties of California from Marin County to Humboldt County it has escaped from cultivation and in places forms dense thickets. It has spread over farm lands, rendering them almost worthless. It comes in on burned-over timber or brush areas, keeping out the native forage species as well as pine and spruce, thus interfering greatly with reforestation.

Gorse is a densely branched and spiny shrub, 2 to 4 feet high, which reproduces both by seeds and from creeping roots. The stems are stiff, dark-green in color, and without foliage leaves. The leaves are mere spines or scales. The flowers are yellow and showy, and usually clustered at the ends of the branches. The calyx is yellow, and deeply 2-lipped, as described under *Cytisus,* the filaments of the 10 stamens are united, and the fruit is a hairy pod about ½ inch long. The seed is rounded at one end, broader and shallowly notched at the other, with a conspicuous light colored appendage over the scar. The color is olive-green to brownish, the surface smooth and shiny.

FIG. 161. Gorse (*Ulex europaeus*).

NARROW-LEAF VETCH (*Vicia angustifolia* L.)
Other common name: Smaller common vetch.

This is naturalized from Europe and widely established as a weed in temperate regions. In California it is widely scattered but not common as a weed in fields and waste places. It is an annual or winter annual, and is similar to common vetch, except for its more slender leaflets and shorter flowers, about ¾ inch long. The seeds are more truly globular than common vetch, and smaller.

PURPLE VETCH (*Vicia atropurpurea* Desf.)
Purple vetch is reported at Point Reyes, at Hydesville, in Monterey County, and in the Sacramento Valley.

HUNGARIAN VETCH (*Vicia pannonica* Crantz)
Hungarian vetch is found in Rincon Valley, Sonoma County.

COMMON VETCH (*Vicia sativa* L.)

Other common names: Spring vetch, tare.

This vetch, a native of Europe, is a common forage and cover crop plant in many parts of the world. It has escaped from cultivation, although as a weed it is of little importance except under certain conditions, as in the grain fields of the Delta, where it is often troublesome. It is an annual climbing plant which branches freely. The leaves are pinnately compound with about 7 pairs of leaflets and a terminal tendril. The flowers (of the pea-type) occur singly or in twos in the leaf axils; they are about 1 inch long, short stalked and reddish-purple in color. The hairy pods, 1½ to 3 inches long, have 5 to 12 smooth, somewhat flattened globular gray or marbled seeds.

HAIRY VETCH (*Vicia villosa* Roth.)

Hairy vetch is an occasional fugitive at Fontana near Rialto, and in the Sacramento Valley.

Fig. 162. Gorse (*Ulex europaeus*) showing spiny nature of plant. **A**, single flower; **B**, seeds with a conspicuous light-colored appendage over the scar.

WOOD SORREL FAMILY *(Oxalidaceae)*

This is chiefly a tropical family, although a number of species occur in higher latitudes. Members of the family are mainly herbs with a sour sap. The principal genus is *Oxalis* in which there are around 175 species. The three following species are weeds.

BERMUDA BUTTERCUP *(Oxalis cernua* Thunb.) (Fig. 164)

This weed, a native of South Africa, is found in the San Francisco Bay Peninsula, where it occurs in truck gardens, and in southern California. Near Colma, in San Mateo County, some cabbage fields are golden when it is in flower, suggesting the common name, Bermuda buttercup. In southern California it is a common weed of walnut and orange groves. Bermuda buttercup produces bulbs, thus differing from *O. corniculata*, with its running rootstocks. The flowers of *O. corniculata* usually do not exceed $\frac{1}{4}$ inch in diameter, whereas those of *O. cernua* are from 1 to $1\frac{1}{2}$ inch across and showy.

YELLOW OXALIS *(Oxalis corniculata* L.) (Fig. 163)

This plant is a native of Europe. It is distributed quite generally throughout the State, being found chiefly in lawns and greenhouses. Under favorable conditions it will spread and completely take a lawn. It prefers shaded situations.

This oxalis is a perennial herb from running rootstocks. The stems are decumbent or ascending, 3 to 6 inches long. The leaves are compound, being composed of 3 heart-shaped leaflets, thus resembling somewhat a

FIG. 163.   Yellow oxalis *(Oxalis corniculata)*, showing habit and seeds.

FIG. 164. Bermuda buttercup (*Oxalis cernua*).

clover leaf. The leaflets are green, rarely tinged with purple, about $\frac{1}{2}$ to $1\frac{1}{4}$ inches long, and somewhat hairy. The flowers are solitary or in groups of 2 to 6. There are 5 overlapping sepals, 5 yellow petals which are about twice the length of the sepals, 10 stamens, and a single pistil with 5 styles. The fruit is an oblong capsule about $\frac{1}{2}$ inch long, hairy, and many seeded. The seed is 1-1.2 mm. long, flattened egg-shape and pointed at one end, broken by white-tipped transverse ridges, amber to dark brown in color.

The variety *atropurpurea* Planch. is similar to the above in all particulars except that it is generally not so tall, has deep red-purple stems and leaves, and a much thickened, more persistent type of root.

ROSE OXALIS (*Oxalis rubra* St. Hil.)

This introduction from Brazil has escaped from cultivation and become naturalized, particularly in Marin County. The purplish-rose, rarely white, flowers are borne in an umbel; petals slightly pubescent on the under side. Leaves and stems arise from the crown of a thickened tuberiform stem.

GERANIUM FAMILY (Geraniaceae)

This is a family of about 11 genera and 650 species. The best known representatives are the geraniums, the storksbill (*Pelargonium*) often grown in homes and gardens under the name geranium, and filaree (*Erodium*).

FILAREE. *ERODIUM*

There are five fairly common species of *Erodium* within our borders. Three of these (*E. Botrys, E. moschatum*, and *E. cicutarium*), are introduced from the Mediterranean region, and are now widespread throughout California, whereas two species, (*E. texanum* and *E. macrophyllum*), are native and relatively less abundant.

The three introduced species mentioned above have become valued forage plants on the ranges of our State, but in some places may assume the role of weeds. They are favored hosts for the beet leafhopper, serving as an over-wintering host in the coastal foothills adjacent to the Great Valley.

KEY TO WEEDY SPECIES OF ERODIUM

Sepals not tipped by short bristles, leaves more or less heart shaped at base
  Leaves round ovate, palmately deeply cleft or parted_____*E. texanum*
  Leaves somewhat kidney-shaped, bluntly round toothed or lobed__*E. macrophyllum*
Sepals bristle-tipped, leaves not cordate at base, pinnatified or divided into toothed or cleft lobes
  Leaves cleft into broad blunt-toothed lobes, beak 2-5 inches long
    Concavities at top of fruit subtended by 1 fold, beak of fruit 2 to $3\frac{1}{2}$ inches long
                           E. obtusiplicatum
    Concavities at top of fruit subtended by 2 folds, beak of fruit $3\frac{1}{2}$ to $4\frac{3}{4}$ inches long
                                E. Botrys
  Leaves pinnate, beak $1\frac{1}{2}$-$1\frac{3}{4}$ inches long
    Leaflets toothed, petals with naked claws, stipules large, obtuse____*E. moschatum*
    Leaflets pinnatified, petals with row of hairs on claw, stipules commonly small and acute _____*E. cicutarium*

BROAD-LEAF FILAREE (*Erodium Botrys* (Cav.) Bertol.) (Fig. 166)

This is a leafy plant, with stems $\frac{1}{2}$ to $2\frac{1}{2}$ feet long, coarse white-pubescent herbage, simple deeply-lobed leaves, sepals tipped with 1 or 2 short bristles, and with glands of the flowers greenish. This species has a beak of the fruit 3 to 5 inches long, consisting of a spirally-coiled portion and a terminal flail-like part, whereas, in its two close relatives the beak is but $1\frac{1}{2}$ to $1\frac{3}{4}$ inches long. In this species the spiral has numerous turns,

FIG. 165.   Red-stem filaree (*Erodium cicutarium*).

the flail-like tip with short grayish white hairs. The body of the fruit is club-shaped, sparsely hairy, gradually thickened upwards from a very pointed base, 7-10 mm. long. There is an oval scar-like area with raised rim borne slantwise at the apex. The seed, free from the flat-hairy coat, is pinkish-tan, smooth, club-shaped but rounded at both ends, with elongate scar at one side near the base.

RED-STEM FILAREE (*Erodium cicutarium* L'Her.) (Figs. 165 and 166)
Other common names: Alfilaria, pin clover, pin grass, storksbill, heronsbill.

Red-stem filaree is the most common and widespread of all our *Erodium* species. In Fremont's early report, he states that in 1844 this species "covered the ground like a sward," and that in the lower San Joaquin Valley he found "instead of grass, the whole surface of the country closely covered with it."

Red-stem filaree is an annual or biennial herb, with erect, spreading or prostrate stems 3 to 12 inches long. In the early stages the leaves form a rosette close to the ground. The leaves are hairy, dark-green, $\frac{1}{2}$ to 4 inches long, finely dissected, with small acute stipules. The flowers are similar in structure to those of *Geranium* although smaller, there being 5 sepals, each tipped with 1 or 2 (or 3) long, bristle-like hairs, 5 petals, rose-purple in color, 10 stamens with but 5 anther-bearing, and a 5-parted pistil with 5 united styles. The glands of the flowers are brownish or

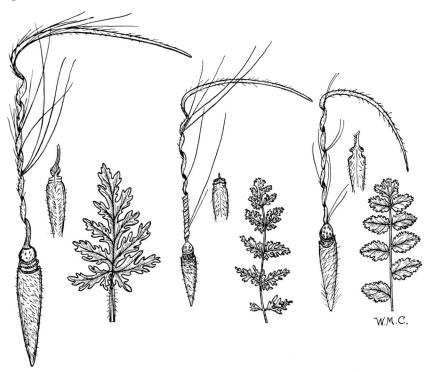

FIG. 166.   Fruits and leaves of *Erodium* species. Left, broad-leaf filaree; center, red-stem filaree; right, white-stem filaree.

reddish. The fruit becomes divided into 5 one-seeded parts, each with its persistent style developed as a twisted, hairy tail that coils when moistened. The flail terminating the spiral is about 15 mm. long. The body of the fruit is 4-5 mm. long, the slant-wise ''scar'' at apex circular and inconspicuous. The pinkish-tan free seed is slender club-shaped, with elongate scar on the side near the base.

This plant is regarded highly as forage for all classes of livestock, being under our conditions an excellent winter and early spring feed.

Erodium cygnorum Nees, an adventive and native of Australia, is reported by Parish as being locally established at a single station near San Diego.

LARGE-LEAF STORKSBILL (*Erodium macrophyllum* H & A)

This is a native species relatively rare in California, but recorded from the Sacramento-San Joaquin Valley, south Coast Ranges and southern California. The leaves are large, mostly basal, somewhat kidney-shaped with a blunt toothed margin, and often shallowly lobed. The petals are about ½ inch long, white, with sepals almost equaling the petals. There is also a larger variety with reddish-purple petals (var. *californicum* Jepson). The seeds are about ⅓ inch long, very blunt at the apex and densely covered with silky hairs. The spiral usually has only 2-3 turns.

Erodium malachoides (L.) Willd. has been collected by Mason on the Berkeley campus, also on Mt. Diablo and at several points in the northern Sacramento Valley. This species is from the Mediterranean region.

WHITE-STEM FILAREE (*Erodium moschatum* L'Her.) (Fig. 166)

This resembles red-stem filaree in its general habits of growth and in flower and fruit characters. It differs from it in that the plants are usually more robust, the stems are generally whitish, the leaves are larger (sometimes as much as a foot long), the leaflets are merely toothed (not deeply cleft), the herbage is very glandular, the stipules are large and obtuse, and the sepals are tipped with very short bristles (Fig. 166). It is a common plant of orchards and vineyards. The fruit is 4-5 mm. long, the slant-wise scar at apex large and conspicuous, the flail-like tip of spiral short, 10-12.5 mm. long.

ERODIUM OBTUSIPLICATUM (Maire, Weiller and Wilczek) (J. T. Howell)

This native of North Africa is reported by Howell as being widely distributed and rather common in weedy places about towns in Marin County. It has simple, deeply lobed leaves, concavities at top of fruit subtended by a single fold, upper part more or less hairy, and beak of fruit 5-9 cm. long.

TUFTED STORKSBILL (*Erodium texanum* Gray)

This native species is found particularly in sandy soils, often very low growing. The plant is silvery appressed-hairy, leaves round- to oblong-ovate, somewhat heart-shaped at the base and palmately lobed. The purple petals are large and showy early in the season, becoming much smaller later. The seeds are sparsely hairy. The fruit is 7-10 mm. long, the spiral about 4 turns, the flail-like tip 22 mm. or more, and tawny hairy.

CRANESBILL. GERANIUM

There are several species of *Geranium* in California which are weeds of minor importance. All these species are herbs with forking stems and swollen stem nodes. The leaves are palmately parted. The flowers are fairly large, with 5 sepals, 5 petals, 10 stamens, and a single pistil with 5 united styles. The fruit consists of 5 parts, each one-seeded, which separate at maturity from below by curling upward, bearing the twisted or spirally coiled styles as tails.

Geraniums are of some value as forage plants, especially in the spring, when the herbage is grazed by sheep. They are not usually eaten by other livestock.

KEY TO WEEDY SPECIES OF GERANIUM

Carpels smooth ; stems and petioles covered with soft spreading hairs_____*G. molle*
Carpels hairy ; lower parts of stems covered with hairs which turn downward
  Perennial _____*G. pilosum*
  Annual
    Flowers light pink_____*G. carolinianum*
    Flowers purple _____*G. dissectum*

CAROLINA GERANIUM (*Geranium carolinianum* L.) (Fig. 168)
Other common name : Carolina cranesbill.

This is an annual, naturalized from eastern United States, which is not common but rather widely distributed throughout California. The herbage is pubescent, the leaves palmately 5-7 parted, the segments again dissected into rather broad divisions. The inflorescence is usually gland-less, the petals light pink ; the carpels enclosing the seed are hairy and usually black. The seeds are oval, broad at the base and apex, covered with an elongate network.

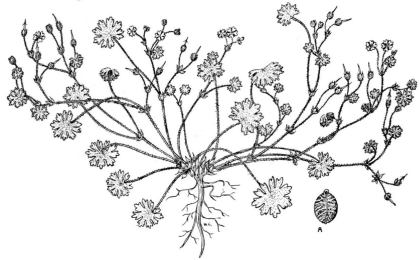

FIG. 167. Doves-foot geranium (*Geranium molle*), showing habit. **A**, seed.

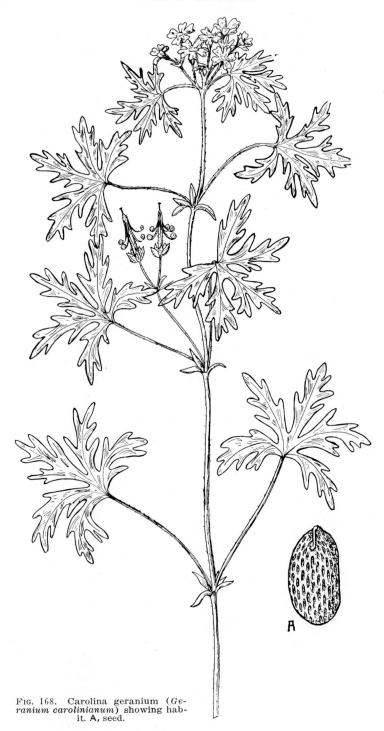

Fig. 168. Carolina geranium (*Geranium carolinianum*) showing habit. A, seed.

CUT-LEAVED GERANIUM (*Geranium dissectum* L.)

This introduction from Europe is an annual resembling *G. carolinianum*. It occurs in the Coast Ranges and is frequent in the San Francisco Bay region. It differs from it, however, in having a glandular inflorescence, narrow leaf divisions, purple flowers, and netted seeds, the walls of the network being thick and thereby giving the surface of the seed a pitted appearance.

DOVES-FOOT GERANIUM (*Geranium molle* L.) (Fig. 167)

This is an introduced annual from Europe, which occurs infrequently in the coastal region. It is a slender species 12 to 20 inches tall, with rose-pink flowers, the stems and leaf stalks clothed with soft, spreading hairs which are sometimes glandular. The transversely wrinkled carpels enclose smooth seeds, which are pinkish-tan in color.

TRAVELER'S GERANIUM (*Geranium pilosum* Forst.)

This introduction from Australasia is sparingly naturalized along the coast. The hairs on the stem are downwardly spreading; the deep purple petals are little longer than the sepals; the seed is overlaid with a coarse network.

MILKWORT FAMILY *(Polygalaceae)*

The principal genus in this family is *Polygala*, which has about half of all the species in the family. There are three species of *Polygala* in California, all natives.

MILKWORT (*Polygala cornuta* Kell.) (Fig. 169)

This species is native, from Fresno County to Siskiyou County, on wooded or brush-covered slopes. It is a perennial herb with a milky juice. The stems are 1 to 3 feet high, usually many from the crown. The leaves are alternate, simple, petioled, the blades oblong or elliptic and $\frac{1}{2}$ to $1\frac{1}{2}$ inches long. The flowers are in terminal racemes and in form suggest those of the pea family. There are 5 sepals, the two lateral being much larger than the others, 3 petals, one of which is hooded above and encloses the 8 united stamens, and the single pistil. The fruit is a 2-celled capsule. The seeds have a conspicuous caruncle, or wart-like appendage.

SPURGE FAMILY *(Euphorbiaceae)*

This is one of the largest of the plant families. It contains herbs, shrubs, and trees, often with an acrid and milky sap. The cactus-like plants of the African deserts are euphorbias. Many spurges are of economic importance such as *Ricinus* (castor-bean plant), *Hevea brasiliensis*, which is the source of Para rubber, *Manihot utilisissima*, the tapioca plant, and *Euphorbia pulcherrima*, the poinsettia. Unfortunately, many representatives of the family have weed characteristics.

FIG. 169.   Milkwort (*Polygala cornuta*), showing flowering and fruiting branches.

TURKEY MULLEIN (*Eremocarpus setigerus* Benth.) (Fig. 170)
Other common names: Woolly white drouth-weed, doveweed, yerba del pescado.

Turkey mullein is a native of the Pacific Coast, and is widely distributed in California. It occurs from Oregon to the Sacramento and San Joaquin valleys, the dry valleys of the Coast Range, and south to the Imperial Valley and San Diego County. It is found in dry open areas, especially in stubble fields and summer-fallowed land.

Turkey mullein is a low annual which forms prostrate mats 1 to 2 or more feet across, and varies in height from an inch or two to a foot. The stems and leaves are clothed with a dense coating of forked,

Fig. 170.   Turkey mullein (*Eremocarpus setigerus*). **A**, habit of plant ; **B**, seedling ;
C, seed ; **D**, staminate flower ; **E**, pistillate flower.

bristly, star-shaped hairs, which give to the plant a harshness to the
touch and a light gray color. The leaves are thick, 3-nerved, oval to
round in outline, ⅓ to 1½ inches long, on leafstalks of about the same
length. The flowers are small and inconspicuous. There are two sorts
of flowers on the same plant—staminate (stamen-bearing), and pistillate
(pistil-bearing). The staminate flowers have 5 or 6 sepals, no petals,
and 6 or 7 stamens, which in the bud are bent inward and downward.
The staminate flowers occur in flat-topped clusters at the ends of stem
branches. The pistillate flowers have no calyx or corolla, but a single,
densely hairy ovary and style. The pistillate flowers are usually solitary,
sometimes in 2's and 3's, in the axils of the lower leaves. The fruit is a
2-valved oblong capsule containing smooth, shining, mottled seed, 2 to 5
mm. long, rounded on the back and obscurely obtuse-angled on the front.
    The seeds are eaten by turkeys and turtle-doves. The stems and
leaves contain a narcotic poison, but birds and animals are not known

to be poisoned by the plant. Occasionally sheep and hogs eat the plant, and as a consequence "hair balls" may form in the digestive tract. The cases of death from eating turkey mullein are probably due to these indigestible balls rather than to the narcotic in the plant. California Indians threw broken stems and leaves of this plant into streams in order to stupefy fish.

SPURGE. EUPHORBIA

In California 18 species of *Euphorbia* are recorded. Several of these are weeds. The flowers of *Euphorbia* are characteristic. They occur in small groups enclosed by a circle of bracts, the so-called involucre. The involucre has 4 or 5 teeth or lobes, between which glands occur. Included in each involucre, which itself resembles a flower, are several staminate flowers and one pistillate flower. The staminate flowers are very simple, each consisting of a single stamen, often with a minute scale at the base. The pistillate flower has a long stalk, which extends the ovary well out of the involucre, and a 3-celled ovary with 3 bifid styles. The fruit is a 3-celled capsule, each cell containing 1 seed; seeds rounded on the back and more or less flat on the two other faces.

KEY TO WEEDY SPECIES OF EUPHORBIA

Stems prostrate, rarely ascending, forming mats
  Herbage smooth, leaves green
    Leaves serrate to almost entire
      Glands flat, seed 4-angled, with short indistinct crossribs and pits
                                              E. serpyllifolia
      Glands depressed in middle, seed notched at angles, crossribs sharp
                                              E. glyptosperma
    Leaves entire, thickish, seeds round ovate_____ *E. ocellata*
  Herbage slightly hairy, leaves red-blotched in one
    Capsule hairy, seed with low transverse ridges
      Hairs minute, flattened, style cleft $\frac{1}{3}$ to $\frac{1}{4}$ to base, leaves red-blotched _*E. supina*
      Hairs spreading, style cleft nearly to base, leaves green _____*E. prostrata*
Stems erect to ascending
  Perennial, leaves entire, seeds smooth_____*E. Esula*
  Annual, seeds wrinkled or pitted
    Leaves entire
      Leaves elongate, opposite, sessile in subremote pairs_____*E. Lathyris*
      Leaves obovate to roundish, alternate, petioled_____*E. Peplus*
    Leaves more or less toothed
      Leaves serrulate, blotched, seeds obtusely angled, faces wrinkled __*E. maculata*
      Leaves finely serrate, seeds ovoid to subglobose, surface honeycombed
                                             E. Helioscopia

LEAFY SPURGE *(Euphorbia Esula* L.) *(E. virgata* Wald. and Kit.) (Figs. 172-173)

This spurge is a serious agricultural pest in Iowa, Minnesota, the Dakotas and northward into Canada, having been introduced into the United States from Europe at some time prior to 1827, at which date it was recorded from Massachusetts. In California leafy spurge is limited to the northeastern corner of the State in Siskiyou, Modoc and Lassen Counties.

Leafy spurge is a deep-rooted perennial, attaining a height of from 1 to 3 feet. The stems are erect, commonly simple or somewhat branched above. The leaves are narrowly lance-like, ⅛ to ½ inch wide and approximately 1½ to 4 inches long, irregularly disposed along the stem. They taper toward the base, but are stemless, smooth and slightly bluish-green in color. The umbel-like inflorescence terminates the stem and is subtended by a whorl of leaves somewhat broader than those of the stem proper. Each branch of the umbel bears a terminal flower cluster, from the sides of which two forking branches arise. Each of these forks bears a terminal inflorescence which again gives rise to forked branches. This forking continues until there are a dozen or more branchlets extended beyond the first flower cluster, each with an inflorescence in the fork and one at the end of each branchlet. The individual inflorescence is enclosed in 5 bracts, and between these bracts are 4 crescent or shield-shaped glands which bear what appears to be brownish horns. Yellowish-green flowers of themselves are inconspicuous, but upon coming into full bloom the entire inflorescence, including the subtending bracts, turns a rather bright yellow. This yellowing, combined with the fact that leafy spurge grows in dense clumps or patches, makes the weed stand out against other vegetation so that it can be detected and the size of the infestation judged at a considerable distance.

The fruit consists of a 3-valved capsule, each valve containing one seed. Seed yellowish to dark chestnut in color with whitish appendage or caruncle at the base. When the capsule segments split they often eject the seed forcibly to some distance. One large undisturbed plant is capable of producing hundreds of seeds. These germinate readily, although the seedlings at first are not very vigorous.

The root system of leafy spurge is extraordinarily efficient. Roots have been found at depths slightly over 15 feet and they are often relatively numerous at 8 and 12 feet. In addition there are abundant surface feeding roots and spreading rhizomes. Because of the great depths to which the roots descend they are assured of an adequate and relatively constant supply of moisture. This advantage, together with a well developed food storage system, enables leafy spurge to persist over long periods and under adverse conditions. When the environment is favorable numerous adventitious buds develop and these give rise to new sprouts when brought close to the surface. In late summer small pink scaly buds appear just below the surface of the ground. These often extend far down on the root and show up conspicuously in contrast to the dark-brown of the roots.

When broken, the herbage exudes a milky, sticky sap which, because of its acrid taste, renders the plant unpalatable to livestock. Leafy spurge has long been suspected of causing livestock poisoning. In Iowa, however, sheep and cattle were pastured in areas where the plant was abundant with no fatalities resulting.

ENGRAVED SPURGE (*Euphorbia glyptosperma* Engelm.)

This species which occurs in the Imperial Valley, east to Arizona and south to Mexico, is an annual, similar to *E. serpyllifolia*. It differs in having commonly narrow, oblong leaves with a broad semicordate base, margins almost entire. The seeds are notched at the angles and sharply cross-ribbed.

WARTWEED (*Euphorbia Helioscopia* L.) (Fig. 171)

This Old World species has been found near El Monte in Los Angeles County, in Mendocino County, and also in San Francisco on the southeastern slope of Twin Peaks. It is an erect annual plant, 8-16 inches, with alternate, smooth, finely-toothed leaves. There are 4 rounded stalked glands. The pods are smooth.

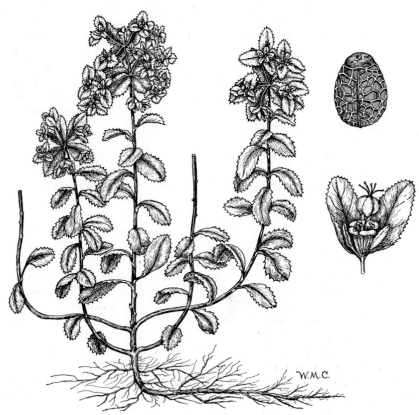

FIG. 171. Wartweed (*Euphorbia Helioscopia*)

CAPER SPURGE (*Euphorbia Lathyris* L.) (Fig. 173)

This is a native of the Mediterranean region, and occurs sparingly in California, usually in moist situations. It is a tall annual or biennial, 1 to 3 feet high, with smooth, glaucous stems and an acrid, milky juice. The stem leaves are thick, narrow, and arranged in 4 vertical rows on the stem. The leaves among the flowers are broader, and heart-shaped at the base. The glands of the involucre are crescent-shaped. The capsules at first are smooth, becoming rugose; seeds wrinkled.

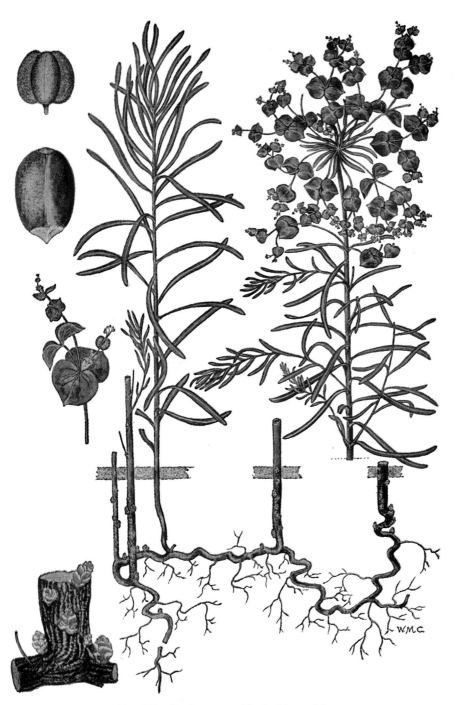

FIG. 172. Leafy spurge (*Euphorbia esula*)

Caper spurge sometimes poisons cattle. It is the so-called "gopher-plant" or "mole plant" of literature.

UPRIGHT SPOTTED SPURGE (*Euphorbia maculata* L.)

Spotted spurge is an erect or ascending annual, with a milky juice. The stems are often reddish, 1-2 feet high, much branched. The leaves are opposite, oblique at the base, oblong, $\frac{3}{4}$-$1\frac{1}{4}$ inches in length, toothed, and usually with a red blotch in the center. There are 4 spreading, white to reddish involucral glands which look like small petals. Each compartment of the 3-lobed capsule contains a single finely wrinkled seed.

OCELLATED SPURGE (*Euphorbia ocellata* D. & H.)

This native spurge is widely distributed in California. The stems are prostrate, and from 5 to 13 inches long. Leaves are delta-shaped, rather thick, unequal or cordate at the base, entire, and from $\frac{1}{4}$ to $\frac{1}{2}$ inch

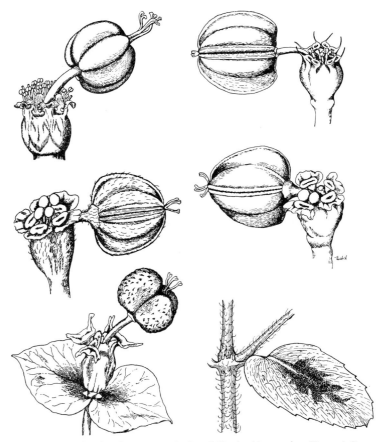

FIG. 173. Showing involucres and fruits of *Euphorbia* species. Upper left, caper spurge (*E. Lathyris*); center left, spotted spurge (*E. supina*); lower left, leafy spurge (*E. Esula*); upper right, petty spurge (*E. Peplus*); center right, thyme-leaf spurge (*E. serpyllifolia*); lower right, leaf of spotted spurge.

long. The glands of the involucre are yellowish or purplish, and 2 to 4 in number. Seeds are red-brown, and either smooth or wrinkled.

This species is regarded with suspicion by sheep men.

PETTY SPURGE (*Euphorbia Peplus* L.) (Fig. 173)

This is an introduction from Europe, which is frequently found in moist shady places in gardens and in greenhouses. This species is a smooth, erect annual 4 to 7 inches tall, with slender, yellow-green stems. The lower leaves are ½ to 1 inch long, broadly ovate or round, the upper oval; all the leaves are entire and more or less crisped or wrinkled. There are 4 involucral glands, crescent-shaped, and each with a long spreading horn. The capsule is globular with 2 crests on the back of each lobe. The seeds are oblong, ash-colored and pitted.

PROSTRATE SPURGE (*Euphorbia prostrata* Ait.)

This is widely distributed in the southern United States and occurs as a garden weed in Mill Valley, Marin County, and has been reported from the Ojai Valley, Ventura County. The herbage is pubescent, capsules hairy about the angles, and the seeds, 1 mm. long or less, are transversely wrinkled by sharp narrow ridges.

THYME-LEAF SPURGE (*Euphorbia serpyllifolia* Pers.) (Fig. 173)

This is a native of the Western States, occurring in moist situations, especially about ponds, in the Sacramento and San Joaquin Valleys and in the Coast Ranges. It is a smooth, dark-green annual, with stems which

FIG. 174. Prostrate spotted spurge (*Euphorbia supina*).

branch profusely, forming prostrate mats 1 to 3 feet in diameter. The leaves are opposite, oblique at the base, more or less finely-toothed toward the apex, and often with a red spot on the upper surface. The glands of the involucre are 2 to 4, usually with a petal-like white or reddish appendage. The seeds are 4-angled, smooth or faintly wrinkled, and clay-white in color.

PROSTRATE SPOTTED SPURGE (*Euphorbia supina* Ait.) (Figs. 173 and 174)

This is introduced from eastern United States. It is scattered almost throughout the State, both along the coast and inland. On garden walks, in sparse spots in lawns, and in flower beds, spotted spurge is aggressive and persistent, forming flat mats, or ascending. It produces an abundance of seed which sprout throughout the season.

This spurge has been suspected in stock-poisoning cases.

CASTOR BEAN (*Ricinus communis* L.)

This native of the warmer parts of Asia and Africa is grown as an ornamental in California. Sometimes it escapes from cultivation, and becomes a weed, although one of little importance, chiefly because it is so readily killed by low temperatures. It is a tall stout herb, with large palmately-lobed leaves, and numerous small greenish flowers of two sorts, staminate and pistillate, on the same plant. The staminate flowers have a 3-5 parted calyx, and numerous stamens; the pistillate flowers have an early deciduous calyx, a 3-celled ovary, and 3 red styles united at the base. The fruit is a large, more or less globular capsule, often spiny, which separates into 3 two-valved carpels. The seeds are usually mottled.

This species is known to cause poisoning in livestock, including poultry. In humans, local irritation may result from handling the seeds, and they are toxic when eaten.

DESERT STILLINGIA (*Stillingia linearifolia* Wats.)

This native of the desert regions has become a weed along railroads and rights-of-way in San Bernardino and Orange Counties. It is an erect, smooth, rush-like perennial herb. The stems are slender and attain a height of 3 feet. The leaves are usually entire, narrow, and 1 to 1½ inches long. The flowers are in terminal spikes which are staminate above and pistillate below. The calyx of the staminate flowers is papery and 2-parted; stamens 2. Pistillate flowers have no calyx; ovary of three 1-ovuled cells. Fruit a capsule, the lobes of which are deciduous.

CALTROPS FAMILY (Zygophyllaceae)

Most representatives of this family are shrubs or subshrubs, although a few are herbs or trees. The principal genera are *Tribulus*, *Kallstroemia*, *Fagonia*, and *Larrea*. *Larrea tridentata* is the creosote bush of the Mojave and Colorado deserts.

CALTROP (*Kallstroemia californica* (Wats.) Vail)

This is an annual which occurs rather sparingly in southeastern California. It resembles puncture vine in general appearance; fruits not long-spined. The plant is white hairy; 5 to 7 pairs of leaflets; petals yellow; fruit breaking up into numerous 1-seeded nutlets.

PUNCTURE VINE (*Tribulus terrestris* L.) (Figs. 175 and 176)

This is an introduction from the Mediterranean countries which has become widespread in California, and a weed of major importance. It is an annual, bright green, commonly prostrate. The stems radiate from the crown, branching freely. In open ground the habit is prostrate, exposing the maximum number of burs to the feet of passing animals or the tires of vehicles. Where the growth is very dense, the ends of the stems turn upward, and in the shade of alfalfa the plant may grow almost erect. When growing along fences and other obstacles it may trail like a vine.

The root system of puncture vine consists of a simple tap root branching into a network of very fine rootlets, which so surround the soil particles as to take the utmost advantage of the soil moisture. This root habit enables the puncture vine to live under conditions of drought survived by few other plants.

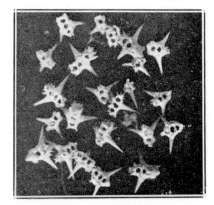

FIG. 175. Puncture vine *(Tribulus terrestris)*. Left, single bur and leaf ; right, burs cut open to show position of seed cavities.

The leaves grow in pairs on opposite sides of the stem. They are composed of several pairs of small oval leaflets. The stems frequently have a reddish color; like the foliage they are densely covered with silky hairs, which no doubt serve as a protective covering from heat and drought, and which give the entire plant a silvery appearance. The flowers, which are borne in the axils of the leaves, are bright yellow. The petals are usually open only in the morning, closing shortly after noon, except in cloudy weather. The fruit consists of a cluster of 5 spiny nutlets or burs. The nutlets, which fall apart at maturity, are adapted to dissemination by animals or rubber-tired vehicles because one of the two spines usually points upward whichever way the bur lies on the ground. The seeds, enclosed within the horny tissue of the bur, are protected by the spines and by the warty protuberances on the outer side of the nutlet or bur. Within the bur the seeds lie one above the other, separated by the same hard, horny tissue that composes the outer walls of the bur. The seed nearest the stylar end is the largest and usually sprouts first, the other seeds following in the order of their position in the bur. If there is sufficient moisture to germinate but one of the seeds in the bur, the others may remain dormant until conditions are favorable for germination.

The grade of wool is lowered by the presence of puncture-vine burs in large quantities. Mechanical injuries to animals are frequent. Cattle, horses, sheep, swine, and dogs have all been known to receive wounds from puncture vine burs. Mouth injuries are occasionally noted, but not so frequently as might be presumed from the prevalence of the weed in certain sections. Authentic cases of serious injury to livestock in California from feeding infested hay are rare.

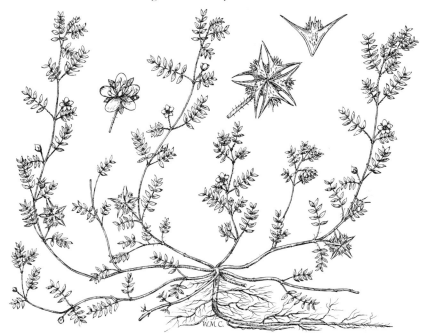

FIG. 176. Puncture vine (*Tribulus terrestris*).

SYRIAN BEAN CAPER (*Zygophyllum Fabago* L. var. *brachycarpa* Boiss.) (Fig. 177)

This is an introduction from southwest Asia, which is reported from a few localities in California: Mojave Desert, Antelope Valley, and Stanislaus County. It is a much-branched, somewhat shrubby plant

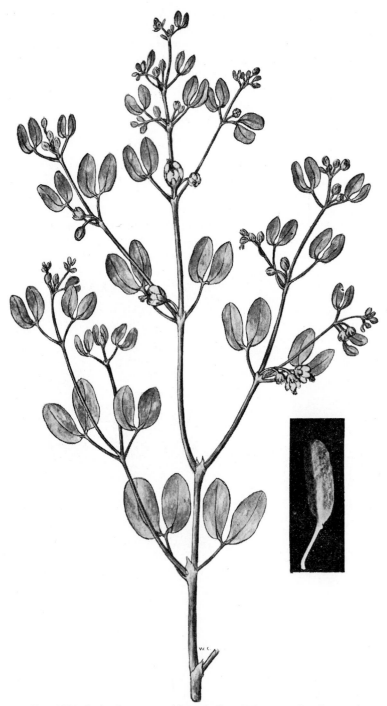

FIG. 177.   Syrian bean caper (*Zygophyllum Fabago* var. *brachycarpa*) showing habit, and single fruit.

with a deep, strong root. The leaves are opposite, thick, with one pair of leaflets, which are from ½ to 1½ inches long. The flowers are borne in the leaf axils, coppery to butter-yellow in color; the calyx 5-parted, petals 5, stamens 10, each with a scale at the base. The fruit is a 5-celled and 5-valved capsule with 1 seed in each cell. The seed is about ⅛ inch long, oval in outline and somewhat pointed toward the scar, much flattened. It is a silvery gray in color and has a rough surface.

AILANTHUS FAMILY *(Simarubaceae)*

This is a family of tropical and warm-temperate trees and shrubs, usually with pinnate leaves and a bitter bark. The best known representative with us is the tree-of-heaven.

TREE-OF-HEAVEN *(Ailanthus altissima* (Mill.) Swingle) (Fig. 178)

This tree, which in some localities has become a pest, is introduced from China. It is planted as an ornamental and shade tree, and has escaped from cultivation. It is naturalized in Pleasants Valley, Solano County, Marin County, and is recorded from Berkeley, Vacaville, Petaluma, San Andreas, Angels Camp and Columbia, and elsewhere throughout the Sacramento Valley.

FIG. 178. Tree-of-heaven *(Ailanthus altissima)*, showing fruits, and compound leaf.

Tree-of-heaven attains a height of from 20 to 60 feet. The leaves are pinnately compound, often being 2 feet long. There are from 1 to 4 coarse teeth near the base of each leaflet, and at the base of each tooth is a conspicuous circular gland. The leaves have a disagreeable odor when bruised. The flowers are small, greenish, and occur in large terminal panicles. Some of the flowers have both stamens and pistils, other flowers have pistils only, whereas others have stamens only. There is a 5-parted calyx and 5 petals; the staminate flowers have 10 stamens, the pistillate a deeply 2-5 parted ovary. The staminate flowers are very ill-scented. The fruit is of 1 to 5 distinct oblong samaras (winged fruit), about 1½ inches long, greenish yellow at first, and becoming a pinkish or reddish-brown.

SUMAC FAMILY *(Anacardiaceae)*

The representatives of this family are deciduous or evergreen trees or shrubs with resinous bark. Well known members are *Pistacia,* and the various species of *Rhus,* including the poison sumac *(Rhus vernix* L.) and poison ivy *(R. Toxicodendron* L.) of the Eastern States (Fig. 179). In California there are 6 species of *Rhus,* the only one of importance from our standpoint being poison oak.

POISON OAK *(Rhus diversiloba* T. & G.) (Figs. 179 and 180)

This plant is a very widely spread native, occurring up to 5000 feet elevation. It is more widely spread in California than any other

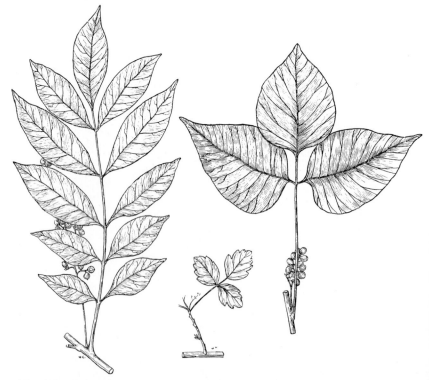

FIG. 179.   Left, poison sumac *(Rhus vernix)* ; center, poison oak *(R. diversiloba)* ;
right, poison ivy *(R. Toxicodendron).*

shrub. Poison oak is an erect, deciduous shrub which may climb over other shrubs and trees, holding on by adventitious rootlets. The leaves are 3-foliate, the leaflets glistening, variable in shape, 1 to 4 inches long, entire or irregularly toothed. The flowers are small, greenish, and occur in panicles. The flowers appear with the foliage in early spring. Each flower is about $\frac{1}{8}$ inch long, with a 5-parted calyx, 5 petals, 5 stamens and a single pistil. The fruit is a drupe (stone-fruit), whitish in color, the flesh marked with black fibers.

Poison oak, like its close relatives, contains a nonvolatile oil which acts as a skin irritant. Bees visit the flowers of poison oak, but the honey therefrom contains no poison.

Fig. 180.   Poison oak (*Rhus diversiloba*), showing fruiting branch, and two mature fruits, enlarged.

MALLOW FAMILY (Malvaceae)

The mallow family possesses one of our most valuable economic plants—cotton (*Gossypium*). Another crop plant is okra or gumbo (*Hibiscus esculentus*). *Althaea officinalis* is the marsh mallow, the roots of which are used principally for mucilage or for medicinal purposes. Ornamental representatives are hollyhock (*Althaea rosea*), mallow (*Malva* spp.), *Abutilon*, and *Hibiscus*. The stamens are characteristic features of the family, being numerous, and united to form a long tube enclosing the styles.

KEY TO GENERA OF THE MALLOW FAMILY

Fruit a capsule_____*Hibiscus*
Fruit (and ovary) composed of a single ring of carpels that separate from
    the central axis at maturity
    Style branches thread-like, stigmatic surface along the sides_____*Malva*
    Style branches ending in a head-shaped or flattish stigma
        Ovules, and usually the seeds, 2 or more in each carpel
            Bractlets present _____*Modiola*
            Bractlets absent _____*Abutilon*
        Ovule 1 in each carpel
            Annuals _____*Anoda*
            Perennials _____*Sida*

COUNTRY MALLOW (*Abutilon pauciflorum* St. Hil.) (Fig. 181)

This species, a native of the tropics, is an attractive plant which occurs as a weed particularly in gardens. It is very similar in general aspect to velvetleaf, but differs in the rather stiffish conspicuously downward hairs on the stems, the leaf blades acutely reflexed on their petioles, larger more orange-yellow petals and in the form of the carpel tips. The tips are short, rather erect, not abruptly at right angles to the carpels. The seeds are more narrow than those of velvetleaf.

VELVETLEAF (*Abutilon Theophrasti* Medic.) (Fig. 181)

This species, introduced from Asia, is sparingly reported from southern California and north to Yuba County, occurring as a weed particularly in orchards. It is a stout, erect, velvety annual, about 3 feet tall. The leaves are simple, alternate, heart-shaped, coarsely-toothed, palmately-veined, and velvety. The flowers are borne on short stalks. Each has 5 sepals, united at the base, 5 separate, yellow petals, and numerous united stamens. There are from 9 to 15 separate, hairy carpels arranged in a disk, their beaks long and conspicuously spreading. The seeds are unequally heart-shaped, with a strap-like appendage extending from the higher lobe into the notched scar. The dark gray or black surface is roughened by wart-like protuberances. They retain their viability for more than fifty years when stored in a dry place or when buried in the soil.

ANODA (*Anoda lavaterioides* Medik.)

This species occurs sparingly from Placer County southward. Its natural range is from western Texas to southern Arizona, extending to

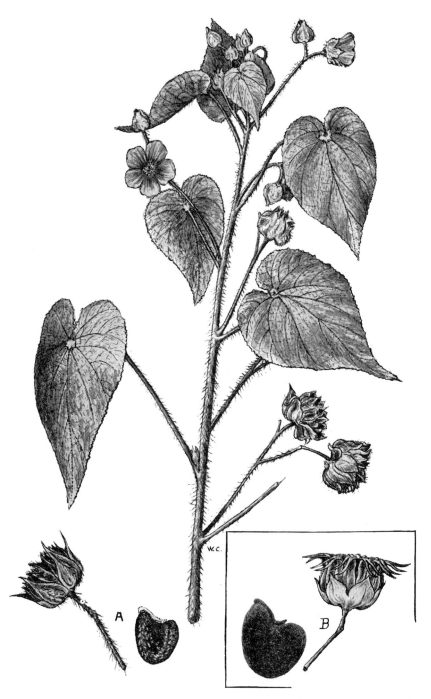

FIG. 181. Country mallow (*Abutilon pauciflorum*) showing leafy branch. **A,** fruits surrounded by calyx and single seed; **B,** velvetleaf (*A. Theophrasti*) showing the fruits surrounded by calyx and a ·single seed.

South America. It is a variable species, in size and shape of leaf blades. Often the upper leaf blades are hastate at the base. Stems and petioles are sparsely hairy, some of the hairs fine, others long and spreading. Petals purple. The fruit consists of several to many carpels which at maturity usually separate from one another and from the axis.

FLOWER-OF-AN-HOUR *(Hibiscus Trionum* L.) (Fig. 182)

This is an introduction from Europe, reported by Parish as a waif in an orange orchard at Riverside, 1917; also collected in Ventura and Butte Counties. This plant is widespread as a weed in eastern North America, especially southward. It is annual, with erect or spreading hairy stems 8 to 20 inches tall. The leaves are alternate, simple, petioled and pinnately veined, the upper ones 3-parted, the lower pinnately-lobed or parted. The flowers are solitary or two or three in the upper leaf axils, and each one remains open but a few hours. The calyx is bladdery-inflated and of 5 united sepals which are pale-green with a dark veining. The corolla consists of 5 sulphur-yellow petals, which have a purplish center and dark veining. The stamens are numerous, united for more than half their length and forming a column about the pistil. The fruit is a capsule enclosed in an inflated calyx. The seed is 2.5 mm. long, almost kidney-shaped to rounded-triangular in outline, with a strap-like appendage extending into the notch. There are yellowish-brown, warty protuberances on the surface.

KEY TO WEEDY SPECIES OF MALVA

Petals only slightly longer than the calyx
    Calyx lobes usually spreading under or about the mature fruit; margins of fruit
      winged _____*M. parviflora*
    Calyx lobes usually closed over the mature fruit; margins of fruit not winged
                                                           M. pusilla
Petals much longer than the calyx
    Flowers reddish-purple_____*M. sylvestris*
    Flowers pinkish_____*M. nicaeensis*
    Flowers pale blue_____*M. rotundifolia*
    Flowers white_____*M. verticellata*

BULL MALLOW *(Malva nicaeensis* All.) (Figs. 183 and 184A)

This species is a native of Europe, naturalized as a weed particularly about towns and cities. It is an erect plant with leaves resembling those of *M. rotundifolia.* The petals are pinkish, the corolla surpassing the calyx. The carpels are not hairy at maturity, but netted in a honeycomb fashion on the back. The calyx lobes close over and almost entirely cover the carpels. *(M. borealis* of California references. Howell.)

CURLED MALLOW *(Malva verticellata* L. var. *crispa* L.)

This is a smooth, erect annual, 4 to 6 feet tall; European, adventive in Marin County. Leaves are roundish in outline, with 5 to 11 shallow, toothed lobes, the margins crisped or wrinkled. Flowers white, clustered in the leaf axils, the petals 1 to 2 times the length of the calyx.

CHEESEWEED (*Malva parviflora* L.) (Fig. 184C)

This plant is naturalized from Europe. It is very abundant throughout California, being a weed of waste places, gardens, orchards, and vineyards. It is utilized as a cover crop in orchards. Cheeseweed is a coarse biennial 1½ to 3 feet tall. The leaves are roundish in outline, 1 to 5 inches broad, with a red spot at the base of the blade, with 6 to 7 shallow lobes, and with leaf-stalks more than twice the length of the blades. The flowers, in dense clusters in the leaf axils, have a structure similar to those of other *Malva* species. The involucral bracts are narrow, the petals pinkish, and notched at the apex, the pistil of 11 or 12 carpels. The petals are only slightly longer than the sepals, thus differing from *M. rotundifolia*. The calyx lobes usually spread under or about the mature fruit.

The plant and seed of cheeseweed when eaten by chickens cause pink whites of eggs.

DWARF MALLOW (*Malva rotundifolia* L.) (Fig. 184B)

Other common names: Round-leaved mallow, cheeses, low mallow.

Dwarf mallow is an Old World immigrant which is widely spread throughout the United States. It is usually found in gardens, farmyards and waste places, and occasionally in cultivated ground and new lawns. Dwarf mallow is an annual or biennial herb with procumbent stems 1 to 2 feet long, arising from a large deep root. The

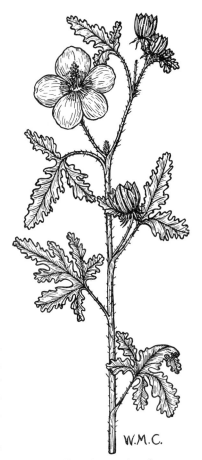

FIG. 182.   Flower-of-an-hour (*Hibiscus Trionum*).

plant is hairy throughout and leafy. The leaves are simple, rounded, heart-shaped at the base, slightly lobed, with rounded or blunt teeth, and with slender petioles several times longer than the leaf blade. The flowers are solitary or in clusters in the leaf axils, and each flower is subtended by 3 bracts. There are 5 calyx lobes, 5 petals which are much longer than the sepals, notched at the apex, and pale blue or whitish, numerous stamens united in a tube around the style, a single

FIG. 183.   Bull mallow (*Malva nicaeensis*).

pistil with 7 to 10 style-branches. The pistil is composed of 14 or 15 parts (carpels), and it ripens into a circular and flattened fruit, consisting of the 14 or 15 1-seeded carpels, arranged in a ring, thus suggesting the common name "cheeses." The carpels are not distinctly honeycombed, but hairy on the back.

HIGH MALLOW (*Malva sylvestris* L.)

This is an occasional escape which has been found northeast of Sacramento, at Guerneville and Redlands. It is a tall biennial with reddish-purple flowers 1 to 1½ inches broad. The petals are 2 to 4 times the length of the calyx.

M. pusilla Smith, a plant similar to cheeseweed, has been found at Alton, Humboldt County, and at San Pedro. The calyx lobes usually close over the mature fruit, thus differing from cheeseweed. Both of these species are of European origin.

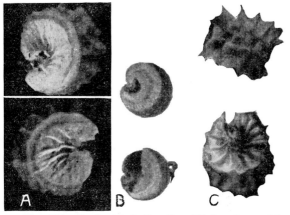

FIG. 184. Seeds of **A**, bull mallow (*Malva nicaeensis*); **B**, dwarf mallow (*M. rotundifolia*); **C**, cheeseweed (*M. parviflora*).

BRISTLY MALLOW (*Modiola caroliniana* G. Don.) (Fig. 185)

Bristly mallow is an introduction from the southeastern United States, established in scattered locations almost throughout California. It has recently become established in locations where ladino and white clover plantings have been made.

Bristly mallow is a low perennial, with spreading stems, 6 to 18 inches long. The leaves are rounded, coarsely-toothed, palmately-lobed, and from 1 to 1½ inches broad. The flowers are small, dull to brick red in color, and subtended by 2 or 3 narrow bractlets; they differ from those of *Malva* in that the stigma is at the tip of the style, rather than lengthwise on the inside of the style. The fruit is a low circle of 15 to 30 bristly carpels, each with 2 seeds. The seeds are about 1.5 mm. in diameter, rounded in outline, definitely notched on one side, and flattened.

ALKALI MALLOW (*Sida hederacea* (Dougl.) Torr.) (Fig. 186)
Other common names: Creeping mallow, star mallow.

Alkali mallow is quite generally distributed throughout California at lower altitudes and is a weed of major importance in many locations. In certain sections of the San Joaquin Valley it has become a serious pest in grain and cotton fields. It occurs in orchards, cultivated fields and waste places. The plant thrives in soil of alkaline reaction, although by no means is it confined to such soils.

The plants are low, scurfy, whitish, perennial herbs. The scurfiness is due to scale-like hairs and to forked yellow hairs which cover both stems and leaves. The stems are ½ to 1 foot long, and may be either erect or somewhat decumbent on the ground, in which case they rise at the end. The leaves are roundish or kidney-shaped, toothed along the margin, ¾ inch to 2 inches broad, and on stalks ½ to 1 inch long. The flowers stand singly or in small clusters in the leaf axils. The flowers are cream-colored, the petals 5 in number, being about ½ inch long. There are numerous stamens, the stalks of which are united for a distance to form a tube, at the top of which are the anthers. There is a single pistil composed of 6 to 10 carpels, each bearing a single seed. When ripe, the ovary splits into one-seeded, somewhat triangular fruits. The seed is short kidney-shaped, one lobe rounded, the other more pointed and extending in a somewhat thumb-like form.

Fig. 185. Bristly mallow (*Modiola caroliniana*), showing habit. **A,** group of seeds; **B,** 2 seeds; **C,** single carpel.

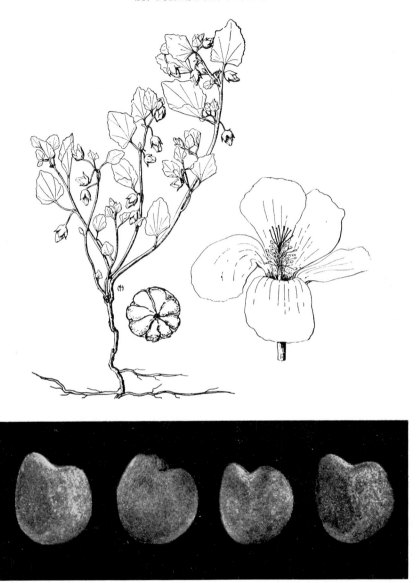

FIG. 186. Alkali mallow (*Sida hederacea*).

ST. JOHNSWORT FAMILY *(Hypericaceae)*

GOLD-WIRE (*Hypericum concinnum* Benth.) (Fig. 188)

This is a native species which occurs on mountain slopes and flats in the Coast Ranges as far south as Marin County, and in the Sierra Nevada from Mariposa County to Butte County. It is commonly in scattered patches rather than in extensive dense stands. The stems are wiry and very numerous from a woody crown, about 6 inches to 1 foot tall. The leaves are narrow, ¾ to 1¾ inches long, usually folded. The flowers are about 1 inch broad, in rather dense clusters at the ends of the stems. The capsule is definitely 3-lobed, the seeds cylindric, conspicuously larger than those of Klamath weed, transversely roughened.

KLAMATH WEED (*Hypericum perforatum* L.) (Fig. 187)
Other common name: St. Johnswort, Goatweed.

This weed is a native of Europe where it is not regarded as a troublesome weed. Although it is quite generally spread throughout northern and eastern United States, it has not attracted attention as a pest. In California the heaviest infestations are along the north coast, Humboldt County, thence south and east, with extensive heavily infested areas in Sonoma County. No menacing infestations are established south of Santa Clara County.

Klamath weed, or St. Johnswort, is an erect perennial plant, growing to a height of from 1 to 5 feet. It is more or less woody at the base but herbaceous above. Under our local conditions it dies down to the crown with approach of cold weather. A characteristic feature of this plant is the occurrence of many sterile or barren shoots at the base. In addition to erect stems, there are horizontal stems (runners) which run at or just below the surface of the ground. There is a highly branched, extensive root system. The young stems are 2-edged and have a pair of narrow wings on the sides. The leaves are numerous, opposite, light-green in color, somewhat rolled, sessile. They possess characteristic dark glands which appear as small translucent or pellucid dots along the leaf margins; the leaves are from ½ to 1 inch long and about ⅛ inch wide. The flowers are yellow and occur in showy clusters. Each flower is from ⅔ to 1 inch broad, and has 5 yellow petals with conspicuous black dots, 5 green lanceolate sepals which are much shorter than the petals, numerous stamens in groups of 3 to 5, and a single ovary divided into three locules, with 3 spreading styles. The fruit is a pod which at maturity breaks into three parts: usually the stamens and petals are attached to the pod. The seeds which are produced in large quantities are very dark-brown in color, small, cylindrical and pitted. (Fig. 187)

In certain parts of the world, chiefly in Australia and in northwestern United States, the plant has found conditions highly favorable for rapid spread and in these regions it has become a weed of major importance. Our chief concern with Klamath weed in California is that it has invaded natural grazing lands, sometimes completely destroying their value as forage. Over-grazing has made it easy for the plant to invade grasslands, and after a few years these areas may become an almost solid stand of the weed.

Klamath weed is also somewhat poisonous to livestock, both sheep and cattle. Although death caused by eating Klamath weed is rare in California, the poor condition of flesh and health of the animals which graze upon infested areas result in much loss to stockmen. The cattle and wool men of Humboldt County have suffered the greatest loss due to Klamath weed.

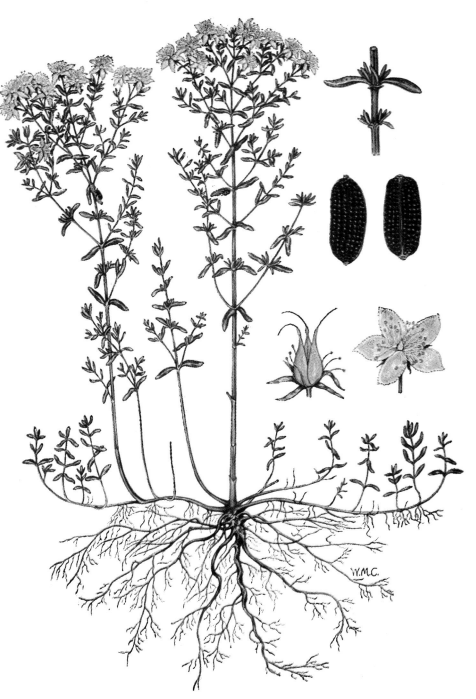

FIG. 187. Klamath weed (*Hypericum perforatum*).

PALE ST. JOHNSWORT (*Hypericum Scouleri* Hook.) (Fig. 188)

This native species is frequent in wet places at higher altitudes, but occurs almost throughout the State at from 500 to 6,000 feet elevation. It is similar in general appearance to Klamath weed, is also perennial from running rootstocks, but the leaves are generally broader, the petals larger and of a paler more dull yellow, the sepals ovate. It lacks the

FIG. 188. Left, Pale St. Johnswort (*Hypericum Scouleri*). Right, Goldwire (*H. concinnum*).

aggressive weediness of the introduced *H. perforatum*.
(*H. farmosum* HBK. var. *Scouleri* (Hook.) Coulter of authors.)

WATERWORT FAMILY *(Elatinaceae)*

There are only about 40 species of this family in the world. They are aquatic or marsh herbs. There are but two genera, *Elatine* (waterwort) and *Bergia*.

BERGIA (*Bergia texana* Seubert) (Fig. 189)

This representative of the waterwort family, a native from California and east to Texas and Missouri, is reported from a few localities in California—Sacramento, Merced, Murietta Hot Springs, and Elsinore. It is a diffusely branching annual, glandular-hairy stems. The leaves are opposite, oval or lance-shaped, tapering at the base, finely toothed at the apex, and ¼ to 1¼ inches long. There are 5 pointed sepals, ¼ to ½ inch high

FIG. 189.   Bergia (*Bergia texana*).

with thickened midrib and papery margins, and 5 whitish petals. Stamens vary from 5 to 10. The fruit is a 5-celled globular capsule with leathery walls.

FRANKENIA FAMILY *(Frankeniaceae)*

This family is composed of perennial herbs, low growing, with small opposite leaves. Leaves also often crowded in the axils. The flowers are sessile and solitary, or appearing clustered by reduction of the upper leaves.

ALKALI HEATH (*Frankenia grandifolia* C. & S. var. *campestris* Gray)

This weed occurs extensively in the interior plains of the Great Valley, and south to southern California, in alkaline situations. It is a perennial, erect or spreading and tufted, about 6 inches to 1½ feet high. The herbage is smooth to somewhat hairy, particularly at the nodes. The leaves are about ⅓ inch long or less, slender spatulate in outline and strongly rolled back or revolute on the margin. The petals are small, extending about 1/12 inch beyond the calyx tube. The style is 3-cleft. The capsule, with a persistent calyx, is linear and angled, many seeded.

YERBA REUMA (*Frankenia Palmeri* Wats.)

This species occurs along the coast of southern California and is similar to the preceding. It is more compact and shorter growing, commonly about 6 inches tall, with the leaves densely borne along the branchlets. The margins of the thickish linear-oblong leaves are strongly rolled back, appearing almost cylindric, slightly short hairy. The petals are small and whitish, the style 2-cleft, and the seeds few in number.

TAMARISK FAMILY
(Tamaricaceae)

Members of this family are trees or shrubs with small juniper- or cedar-like leaves. There are four genera, the largest genus being *Tamarix,* of about 75 species.

FRENCH TAMARISK, SALT CEDAR (*Tamarix gallica* L.)

This is a Eurasian species which is used extensively in California as a windbreak, and as an ornamental shrub. It is sometimes an escape from cultivation, and now occurs as such at widely scattered localities from Lake County to the Colorado Desert. Tamarisk is a densely branched shrub or small tree, attaining a height of 5 to 20 feet. It has long, slender branches which bear numerous, very small leaves pressed closely to the stem. There are numerous small pink flowers which occur in long terminal panicles. There are 5 sepals, 5 petals, few to 10 stamens, and a simple pistil with 3 to 5 styles. The fruit is a many-seeded capsule.

SMALL FLOWER TAMARISK, SALT CE- DAR (*Tamarix parviflora* D. C.)

This native of Europe has escaped from plantings and become naturalized, as in San Benito and San Diego Counties. The flower clusters are lateral; flowers with their parts in 4's.

MIGNONETTE FAMILY
(Resedaceae)

This is a small family of about 65 species, mostly from the Mediterranean countries, the principal genus being *Reseda.*

There are four species of *Reseda* in California, all of which are occasional escapes from gar-

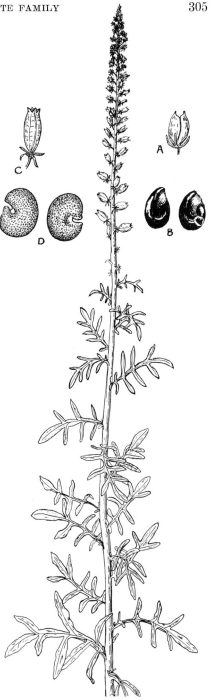

FIG. 190. White cut-leaved mignonette (*Reseda alba*). (Left), **C**, capsule; **D**, seeds of same. (Right), **A**, capsule; **B**, seeds of yellow mignonette (*R. lutea*).

dens. They are herbs with simple, alternate leaves and inconspicuous irregular flowers. There are from 4 to 8 sepals, 4 to 7 toothed or cleft petals, 8 to 40 stamens, inserted on a disk on one side of the flower, and a single, 1-celled pistil. The fruit is a 3- to 6-lobed, horned capsule, opening at the top before the seeds mature.

WHITE CUT-LEAVED MIGNONETTE (*Reseda alba* L.) (Fig. 190)

This species is similar to yellow mignonette, except that the petals are white and all of them are cleft or divided. The seed is light in color, not glossy. It is adventive and sometimes perennial in southern California.

YELLOW MIGNONETTE (*Reseda lutea* L.) (Fig. 190)

This is an annual which occurs as a garden escape about Los Angeles and near Poway in San Diego County. The stems are erect, clustered and from 4 to 12 inches high. The roots and stems have a pungent or peppery taste. The leaves are once or twice pinnately compound or parted, and bear small, gland-like stipules. The flowers are in long, slender racemes. There are 6 sepals, 6 pale yellow petals, 3 or 5 of which are divided, and 15 to 20 stamens on one side of a disk. The fruit is a 3-lobed capsule. The seed is oval in outline and flattened slightly, about 1 mm. long, shiny dark green to black with a depressed lighter area extending past the middle on one face, much smaller on the other.

DYER'S ROCKET (*Reseda Luteola* L.)

This European species, formerly cultivated for its yellow dye, is reported as an escape near Poway in San Diego County, and at Sausalito, Marin County.

COMMON MIGNONETTE (*Reseda odorata* L.)

A native of North Africa, this annual differs from yellow mignonette in having mostly entire 3-lobed leaves, and very fragrant flowers with deeply 5- to 8-cleft petals. It is an occasional escape from cultivation, as in Marin County, and at San Diego and Ocean Beach.

DATISCA FAMILY (Datiscaceae)

This is a small family of plants, the only representatives in California being the Durango root, described below.

DURANGO ROOT (*Datisca glomerata* Brew. and Wats.) (Fig. 191)

This is a native species of dry stream beds or washes. It is found in the Coast Ranges, the Sierra Nevada up to 5,000 feet, and in southern California. It is an erect, perennial herb, 2½ to 8 feet tall. The leaves are alternate, 5 to 6 inches long, divided and more or less toothed. The flowers are in clusters in the axils of branches. Pistillate and staminate flowers occur on different individuals. There is no corolla in either type of flower. In pistillate flowers the calyx is about ⅓ inch long, tubular, somewhat 3-angled and 3-toothed; the ovary is inferior, 1-celled, and the styles 3.

Sometimes there are a few stamens in pistillate flowers. In staminate flowers the calyx is but $\frac{1}{12}$ inch long, subtending an indefinite number of stamens. The fruit is a capsule, which opens at the apex between the styles. The seed is oblong, with collar-like scar off center at one end. The surface has characteristic rows of somewhat squarish pits. The color is yellowish-brown.

Feeding tests have shown that this plant is very poisonous to cattle and horses. It was used as a fish poison by the Indians.

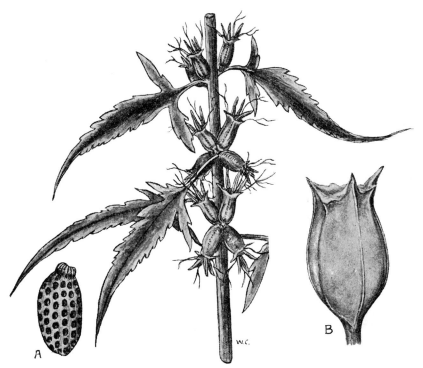

Fig. 191.   Durango root (*Datisca glomerata*), showing clusters of flowers in leaf axils.
A, seed ; B, capsule.

GOURD FAMILY *(Cucurbitaceae)*

There are about 700 species of ''cucurbits,'' mainly tropical. A number of species are of economic importance, chief of which are the pumpkin, squash, watermelon, muskmelon, and cucumber. The wild cucumber (*Echinocystis lobata* Torr. & Gray) and the star cucumber (*Sicyos angulata* L.) are sometimes planted as ornamental vines. Only a few species are of any importance as weeds.

KEY TO GENERA OF GOURD FAMILY

Fruit melon or gourd-like ; flowers large
  Corolla 5-parted nearly to the base_____ *Citrullus*
  Corolla bell-shaped, 5-lobed to middle or a little more_____*Cucurbita*
Fruit not melon or gourd-like ; flowers small, whitish_____*Echinocystis*

FIG. 192.   Calabazilla (*Cucurbita foetidissima*), showing branch bearing leaves, flowers and developing fruits, and (inset) seeds.

CITRON (*Citrullus vulgaris* Schrad.)

The citron is a form of the common watermelon in which the flesh is white, hard, and inedible. The rind is used for making preserves. The plant has the general appearance of the watermelon but it is easy to distinguish the fruit from that of the cultivated watermelons by the characters given above. In those districts of the State where watermelons are grown for seed the occurrence of a few citron plants in the neighborhood may be disastrous, in that the watermelon and citron hybridize readily, and the progeny is commercially undesirable.

GOURD. CUCURBITA

KEY TO WEEDY SPECIES OF CUCURBITA

Leaf blades triangular ovate_____*C. foetidissima*
Leaf blades palmately 5-cleft or 5-divided
  Blades 6 to 12 inches long, cleft nearly to base; lobes lanceolate to very narrow
                                                      C. digitata
  Blades not over 5 inches long, cleft not nearly to base; lobes deltoid_____*C. palmata*

FINGER-LEAF COYOTE MELON (*Cucurbita digitata* Gray.)

This species occurs from New Mexico to Arizona and the desert region of southern California. It is a perennial trailing vine with large roots, and grayish, rough foliage. The leaves are 5-parted to the base, the lobes entire or with one or two smaller lobes near the base, greener above than beneath, the midveins being whitish. The flowers are yellow, and the fruits globose.

CALABAZILLA (*Cucurbita foetidissima* H. B. K.) (Fig. 192)
Other common name: Chili coyote.

This native plant occurs throughout southern California and north to the San Joaquin Valley. It is a plant of sandy soil. It is a rough, perennial vine with a large, carrot-shaped root. The stems are 5 to 15 feet long, equipped with tendrils, and may strike root at their joints. The leaves are triangular in shape, more or less heart-shaped at the base, hairy below, and 4 to 12

FIG. 193. Common man-root (*Echinocystis fabacea*), showing leaves, tendrils, flowers, and spiny fruit.

inches long. The flowers are yellow or yellowish, usually solitary and of two sorts: staminate and pistillate, both occurring on the same plant. The corollas are 3 to 4 inches long. The staminate flowers have 3 stamens, the anthers of which are long and more or less intertwined. The pistillate flowers have a single 3-celled ovary, to which the calyx tube is adherent, and 2 or 3 stigmas. The fruit is a dry, round, smooth gourd, 3 to 4 inches in diameter, containing numerous seeds.

COYOTE MELON, MOCK ORANGE (*Cucurbita palmata* Wats.)

This species has a similar geographical distribution and is closely related to calabazilla. It differs from calabazilla in having palmate (5-cleft) leaves, smaller flowers (1¾ to 2¾ inches long) and a 5-celled fruit.

WILD CUCUMBER. *ECHINOCYSTIS*

KEY TO WEEDY SPECIES OF ECHINOCYSTIS

Corolla wheel- or saucer-shaped; many flowers in the staminate flower-groups
    Corolla greenish white; fruit globular_____*E. fabacea*
    Corolla clear white; fruit oblong_____*E. macrocarpa*

Corolla bell-shaped; relatively few flowers in the staminate flower-groups
    Herbage green; abortive stamens in pistillate flowers; spines usually minutely
      hairy _____*E. oreganus*
    Herbage whitish; no abortive stamens in pistillate flowers; spines without pubes-
      cence _____*E. Watsonii*

COMMON MAN-ROOT (*Echinocystis fabacea* Naud.) (Fig. 193)

This is a native species of central California attracting attention because of its enormous root, which may attain the size of a man's body; thus the origin of the name, common man-root or "Old Man in the Ground." The plant is perennial with trailing or climbing stems 10 to 30 feet long, bearing branched tendrils. The leaves are thin, deeply 5- to 7-lobed, and 2 to 4 inches across. The flowers are small, white or greenish-white, and of two kinds: staminate and pistillate, occurring on the same plant. The staminate flowers are in few-flowered clusters, the pistillate usually solitary. The corolla is rotate or somewhat saucer-shaped, and of 5 to 7 lobes. The fruit is about 2 inches in diameter, rounded, spiny, the spines being stout and ⅓ to 1 inch long. There are usually 4 seeds in each fruit, which are ½ to 1 inch long, oval and slightly flattened toward the scar end and bordered by a shallow groove or darker line.

CHILICOTHE (*Echinocystis macrocarpa* Greene)

This species occurs along the coast from central California southward. It has clear white flowers, leaves 3 to 8 inches broad, oblong, spiny fruits 3 to 4 inches long and 2 to 3 inches in diameter, containing from 12 to 14 seeds.

HILL MAN-ROOT (*Echinocystis oreganus* Cogn.)

This species occurs in the hills from Santa Clara County north to Oregon. The fruit is 2 to 3½ inches long, somewhat tapering at each end, nearly smooth or sparsely covered with short, weak spines, and usually containing 6 seeds.

WATSON'S MAN-ROOT (*Echinocystis Watsonii* Cogn.)
This is found in the north Sierra Nevada foothills and north Coast Ranges. It differs from the other species in having smooth foliage covered with a "bloom."

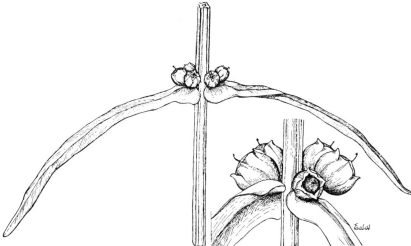

FIG. 194. Red-stem (*Ammannia coccinea*), showing fruits clustered in leaf axils.

LOOSESTRIFE FAMILY (Lythraceae)

This family of about 400 species is most abundantly represented in the American tropics, although widely distributed over temperate regions. The species of *Lawsonia* and *Lagerstroemia* are cultivated as ornamentals. In California there are three species of *Lythrum* (loosestrife), one of *Rotala* (tooth-cup), and one of *Ammannia* (red-stem).

RED-STEM (*Ammannia coccinea* Rottb.) (Fig. 194)
This is a native of California which has become an abundant weed in rice fields. It is recognized by its reddish stems, especially at harvest time. Red-stem is an erect annual with 4-angled stems, attaining a height of 4 to 14 inches. The leaves are opposite, broadly linear, sessile by a broad auricled base, and 1 to 2 inches long. The flowers are in whorls of 2 to 5. The calyx is bell-shaped, the tube being 8-ribbed and 4-toothed, sometimes with small teeth between. The corolla consists of 4 small, purplish petals; sometimes they are wanting. There are 4 stamens, and a single pistil. The fruit is a small globular capsule, which bursts open irregularly. The seeds are minute, suggesting grains of red pepper. The fruit of this weed is known as "Redberry" by the rice industry.

CALIFORNIA LOOSESTRIFE (*Lythrum californicum* T. & G.)
This is a native stoloniferous perennial found in low valley and marshy lands throughout the foothills and low-altitude valleys of California. The stems are erect, often attaining a height of 3 to 6 feet. In contrast to grass poly, the flowers are distinctly pedicled, rather than sessile, and are bright purple rather than pale purple or whitish.

GRASS POLY (*Lythrum hyssopifolia* L.)
(Fig. 195)

This species occurs throughout California and is frequently a weed in cultivated grounds. It is an erect annual, glabrous herb, usually 4 to 9 inches high, sometimes up to 2 feet, with 4- or 5-angled stems. The leaves are sessile, alternate, linear or oblong, and from $\frac{1}{4}$ to $\frac{1}{2}$ inch long. The flowers are solitary in the axils. The calyx is tubular, cylindric, 8- to 12-ribbed, and about $\frac{1}{6}$ inch long. There are 5 or 6 petals, usually less than $\frac{1}{12}$ inch long, pale purple or whitish, and inserted with an equal number of stamens on the calyx. The fruit is a 2-celled capsule. The seeds are about 1 mm. long, rounded at the apex and tapered toward the scar end. The back is rounded, with two somewhat flattened faces with a light central line terminating in a small but conspicuous scar. It is pale straw color.

EVENING PRIMROSE FAMILY
(Onagraceae)

Members of this family are widely distributed over the world, but are well represented in America. Most of them are herbs, a few, shrubs. A number of species are found in gardens and hot-houses as ornamentals, such as certain of the evening primroses (*Oenothera*), fuchsias, and godetias. In our flora species of *Epilobium*, *Clarkia*, *Godetia* and *Oenothera* are particularly well represented. A few are weeds. The seeds of *Boisduvalia, of Godetia*, and of *Oenothera* occasionally occur as impurities in commercial samples of wheat, oats, and barley.

FIREWEED (*Epilobium angustifolium* L.)
(Fig. 196)

Other common names: Great willow-herb, burntweed, flowering willow.

This is a common plant of burnt-over areas, occurring at higher elevations throughout the Sierra Nevada and north Coast Ranges. It is generally distributed throughout northern United States and Europe. There are some 13 different species

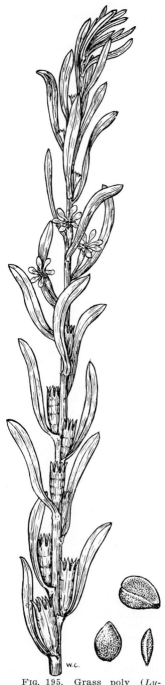

FIG. 195. Grass poly (*Lythrum hyssopifolia*), showing leafy branch with flowers and fruits below; also the seed in three views.

of *Epilobium* within our borders but this species is one which is markedly weedy in nature. It is one of the most important range plants from the forage standpoint, being especially good sheep feed. It is also an important bee plant.

Fireweed is a perennial herb from creeping rootstocks. The stems are erect, 2 to 6 feet high, somewhat reddish, and smooth below but more or less finely-hairy above. The leaves are alternate, simple, lance-shaped, very short-stalked, 2 to 6 inches long, and entire or very minutely toothed. They resemble the leaves of willow, hence the common name, willow-herb. The flowers are in long terminal racemes, and each flower is subtended by a small slender bract. The flowers are lilac-purple in color, petals spreading. There is a tubular calyx, 4-cleft at top, 4 petals, 8 purple stamens, and a single central pink style, exserted, and bearing a 4-lobed stigma. The ovary, which is below the other flower parts, matures to form a 4-celled capsule, 2 to 3 inches long, containing numerous minute brown seeds, each bearing a tuft of fine white hairs, which aid in seed dispersal. The calyx tube is not prolonged above the ovary.

PANICLED WILLOW-HERB (*Epilobium paniculatum* Nutt.) (Fig. 197)

This native species is common on open ground throughout California. It differs from the preceding in its small, inconspicuous flowers and the calyx tube prolonged above the ovary.

FIG. 196. Fireweed (*Epilobium angustifolium*).

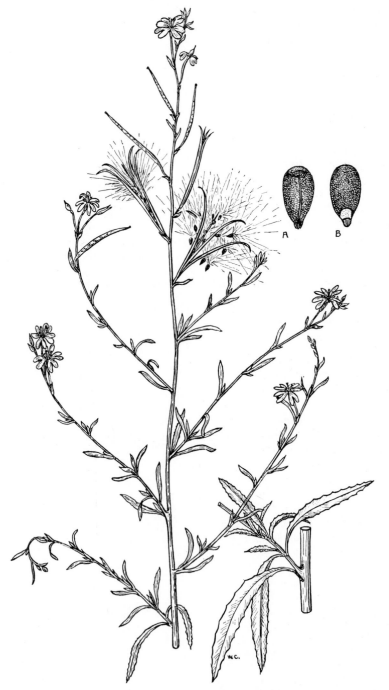

Fɪɢ. 197.   Panicled willow-herb (*Epilobium paniculatum*), showing habit.
A, B, two views of seed.

SCARLET GAURA (*Gaura coccinea* Nutt.*) (Fig. 198)

This species is a native, extending into Canada and Mexico. It is established at several stations in southern California. Scarlet gaura is a perennial, stems about 6 inches to 2 feet tall. The leaves are numerous, ¾ to 1½ inches long, the lower leaves broadly or narrowly oblong, the upper very slender. They are soft hairy to smooth. The floral bracts are persistent, 3-6 mm. long, or longer. The flower spikes are simple, about 2 to 7 inches long, nodding at the tip. The sepals are separately reflexed and the petals, which are 3-6 mm. long are white, pink or red, becoming red in age. The fruit is short-ovoid, about 7 mm. long, strongly 4-angled in the upper half, tapering like a pyramid to the apex and narrowed into a short very stout rounded base.

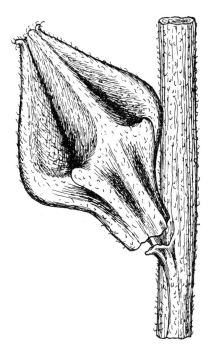

FIG. 198. Fruit of scarlet gaura (*Gaura coccinea*).

SCENTED GAURA (*Gaura odorata* Sesse) (Fig. 200)

This native of the southwest ranges from Texas to Mexico, is also established in southern California and at scattered sites in central California. The plant is branched from the base, about 8 inches to a foot high. The plant is very similar to *G. coccinea* from which it differs chiefly in the broader, shorter, and early deciduous floral bracts and the shape of the fruit. The fruit is broadly pyramidal and sharply angled in the upper part and narrows gradually to a rounded rather slender base, about ½ the length of the fruit, or often shorter. The fruit is usually about 10 mm. long.

VELVET WEED (*Gaura parviflora* Dougl.)

Velvet weed is a native of western United States which has attracted attention in the Imperial Valley as a weed of cotton fields. It is an annual herb with whitish, hairy herbage. The stems are erect and 2 to 3 feet high. The leaves are alternate, oval-lance-shaped, entire or very shallowly wavy-margined, sessile or nearly so, the upper 2 to 3 inches long, the lower 3 to 4 inches long, and on a narrowly winged leaf-stalk. The flowers are in dense terminal, leafless spikes, 6 to 12 inches long. The calyx forms a tube and is 4-cleft at the apex, and finally deciduous. The petals are 4 in number, and reddish. The fruit is spindle-shaped, nut-like, 4-ridged, indehiscent, and 2 to 4 seeded.

WAVY-LEAFED GAURA (*Gaura sinuata* Nutt.) (Fig. 201)

This is a native of the plains of United States and Mexico, established in southern California and north to San Mateo. It is perennial, approximately 1 to 3 feet tall, stem simple or branched from the base, glabrous or nearly so, the basal leaves soft-hairy on the edges. The stem leaves are often crowded, spatulate to lance-like or often quite narrow. The floral bracts are lance-shaped, or wider and narrowing to a slender

FIG. 199.   Yellow water-weed (*Jussiaea californica*). Above, capsule with persistent calyx lobes ; below, single flower.

Fig. 200. Scented gaura (*Gaura odorata*).

Fig. 201.   Wavy leaf gaura (*Gaura sinuata*).

tip. The inflorescence is simple or branched, with naked stems 4 inches long, or more. The sepals are grayish hairy, turned back or reflexed separately. The petals are ¼ to ½ inch long, white at first and becoming red. The fruit is slender spindle-shape, about ¼ inch long, very slightly hairy to smooth.

YELLOW WATER-WEED (*Jussiaea californica* (S. Wats.) Jepson) (Fig. 199)

Other common name: Water Primrose

This species is widely distributed in central and southern California, an inhabitant of stagnant or slow-running water and muddy banks. It sometimes causes clogging of ditches and streams. The yellow water-weed is a smooth, rather fleshy, perennial herb, the stems of which may reach a length of 6 feet. The leaves are alternate, 1 to 2 inches long, and oblong in shape, except the floating ones which are elliptic to almost round, stipules minute, soft. The flowers are a conspicuous deep yellow, long-stalked, with an elongated calyx tube formed of 5 sepals and enclosing the ovary; there are 5 petals about ½ inch long, 10 stamens, and a single pistil with a 5-celled ovary. The fruit is a spongy capsule about 1 inch long, bearing numerous seeds. The 5 pointed lobes of the calyx are persistent on the fruit.

WATER PRIMROSE (*Jussiaea repens* L.)

This similar plant, which occurs in streams of the upper San Joaquin Valley, can usually be readily distinguished from the preceding by its hairy herbage and large firm dark green stipules.

CARROT OR PARSLEY FAMILY *(Umbelliferae)*

This family possesses plants of food value such as carrot, parsnip, coriander, fennel, caraway, celery and parsley, and also a number which are weeds. The flowers (except in *Eryngium*) are in groups called an umbel which is characteristic of this assemblage of plants and suggests the name ''Umbelliferae,'' literally meaning umbel-bearing. The flower groups or inflorescences may be compound, in which case the smaller groups of flowers are designated umbellets. The umbel as a whole is subtended by an involucre, composed of slender bracts (leaf-like structures). The umbelliferous fruit is very characteristic. It is a dry fruit of two parts (carpels) which separate at maturity along the midline into two one-seeded halves. The two halves remain attached for a time after splitting by a forked stalk. Each half of the mature fruit bears, on the outside, 5 longitudinal membranous or corky ribs, and in some cases there is one smaller rib in each of the four furrows or grooves between the main ribs. Within the grooves, as is best seen by a cross-section, are oil tubes running lengthwise the fruit. These tubes contain secretions of balsams, resins, and volatile oils. It is usually necessary to have the mature fruit in order to make a positive identification of a species.

KEY TO GENERA OF UMBELLIFERAE

Fruit bearing prickles, bristles, scales, or tubercles (Fig. 206A)
  Ribs on fruit none (Fig. 207B)
    Flowers greenish-white or blue in dense heads_____Eryngium
    Flowers white, in compound umbels_____Anthriscus
  Ribs on fruit present (Fig. 206A) ; flowers white
    Fruit with a beak several times longer than the body (Fig. 211)_____Scandix
    Fruit without a long beak (Fig. 212)
      Bristles of fruit hooked at tip_____Torilis
      Bristles of fruit not hooked at tip_____Daucus
Fruit not bearing prickles, bristles, scales or tubercles
  Ribs of fruit not winged (Fig. 203b)
    Flowers white or pinkish, never yellow
      Stems purple-dotted _____Conium
      Stems not purple-dotted
        Petals conspicuously unequal_____Coriandrum
        Petals essentially equal
          Umbels almost sessile in the forks and terminal on the branches_____Apium
          Umbels terminal on the branches
            Upper leaves ternate_____Ammi
            Upper leaves pinnate or bipinnate
              Fruit corky throughout_____Berula
              Fruit corky on ribs only
                Fruit broadly oval or roundish_____Cicuta
                Fruit almost cylindrical_____Oenanthe
    Flowers yellow _____Foeniculum
  Some or all of the ribs of the fruit winged
    Lateral ribs winged, the dorsal and intermediate ones filiform (Fig. 203e)
      Leaves pinnately compound_____Pastinaca
      Leaves ternate
        Flowers white _____Heracleum
        Flowers yellow _____Anethum
    Lateral, dorsal and intermediate ribs all winged or very prominent
      Umbellets in compact heads (Fig. 203f) _____Sphenosciadum
      Umbellets not in compact heads_____Angelica

BISHOP'S WEED (*Ammi majus* L.) (Fig. 202)

This is a European weed that has become naturalized in the Napa Valley, occurring in low, wet places. It is a slender, erect, smooth branching biennial herb, 1¼ to 2½ feet high. The basal and lower leaves are once pinnate with 3 to 7 leaflets, ¾ to 3 inches long; the upper leaves are twice or thrice pinnate, the divisions about ½ to 2 inches long. The flowers are in compound umbels, there being 25 to 30 rays, ¾ to 2 inches long. The fruit is oval, and less than 1/12 inch long.

This weed is suspected of being deleterious to cows when eaten in quantity.

TOOTHPICK WEED (*Ammi Visnaga* Lam.)

This is a European weed naturalized in the Santa Clara Valley and at Long Beach. It is a stouter plant than Bishop's weed, attaining a height of nearly 3 feet. The seed is about 2 mm. long, convex on the back, with 3 raised light nerves, flat on the front face.

This species has been considered the cause of scours in cows.

F1G. 202.   Bishop's weed (*Ammi majus*), showing flowering branches, and (right) fruit.

ANGELICA (*Angelica tomentosa* Wats.)

This is a stout perennial, 2-5 feet tall, with leafy stems, leaves fine soft hairy to almost smooth, pinnate or three- to five-divided, or compoundly so. The leaflets are ovate and acute or long pointed, sometimes varying to lanceolate or roundish, coarsely and irregularly toothed. The leaf stems or petioles are strongly dilated at the base. The rays are more or less unequal, flowers white, the umbels large and terminal. The fruits are strongly compressed, elliptic-oblong in outline. The ribs are prominent, the lateral broadly winged, the others often narrowly winged, about $\frac{1}{4}$ to $\frac{1}{3}$ inch long. This species occurs in coastal southern California north through the Coast Ranges to Humboldt County.

DILL (*Anethum graveolens* L.)

This is a garden plant from the Old World which has occasionally escaped from cultivation. It is recorded from San Bernardino, Long Beach, Los Angeles, and Oakland. Dill is a slender, usually branching annual 1 to 3 feet tall. The stems are leafy, the leaves finely dissected. The flowers are yellow, and in compound umbels. Both involucre and involucels are lacking. The fruit is elliptical, flattened dorsally, and the lateral ribs are narrowly winged.

BUR CHERVIL (*Anthriscus vulgaris* (L.) Pers.)

This is an adventive weed from Europe which is thus far rare in California. It is a slender annual herb, 1½ to 3 feet high, with bipinnate leaves and bipinnatifid leaflets. The flowers are white, the rays few (3 to

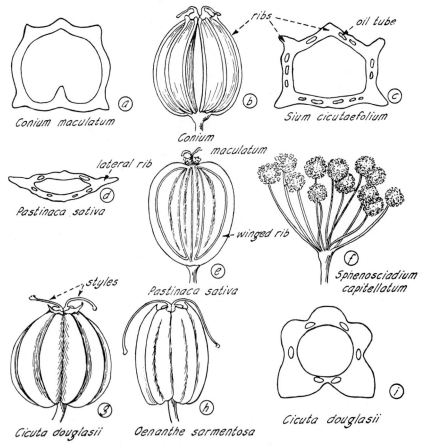

FIG. 203.   Botanical characters illustrating keys to various members of the carrot family. (a) cross section fruit of poison hemlock; (b) external view of fruit of same; (c) cross section of fruit of water parsnip; (d) cross section fruit of wild parsnip; (e) external view of fruit of wild parsnip; (f) umbellets of *Sphenosciadium;* (g) external view of fruit of western water hemlock; (h) external view of fruit of water parsley; (i) cross section fruit of western water hemlock.

6), $\frac{1}{2}$ to 1 inch long, the involucre lacking, and the fruit somewhat compressed and covered with short, hooked bristles.

COMMON CELERY (*Apium graveolens* L.)

Common celery is a garden plant, naturalized from Europe, which frequently escapes from cultivation, becoming a weed along streams and in marshy places. It is an erect, smooth biennial herb with fibrous roots, and forking stems 2 to 4 feet tall. The leaves are compound, the lower ones long-stalked and composed of 5 to 10 leaflets, the upper ones short-stalked or sessile and composed usually of 3 leaflets. The leaflets of upper leaves are 1 to 3 inches long and as wide, or wider, coarsely toothed or 3-cleft, or even 3-divided. The flowers are white or greenish-yellow, in compound umbels which are opposite the leaves, or terminal, or in the forks of the

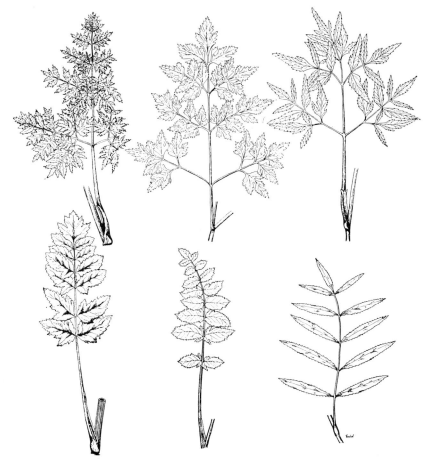

FIG. 204. Leaves of various species of carrot family. Upper left, poison hemlock (*Conium maculatum*); upper center, water parsley (*Oenanthe sarmentosa*); upper right, western water hemlock (*Cicuta Douglasii*); lower left, wild parsnip (*Pastinaca sativa*); lower center, cut-leaved water parsnip (*Berula erecta*); lower right, water parsnip (*Sium cicutaefolium*).

stems. The fruit is small, about $\frac{1}{12}$ inch long, egg-shaped, and finely 5-ribbed, the ribs being slightly winged.

CUT-LEAVED WATER PARSNIP (*Berula erecta* (Huds.) Cov.) (Fig. 204)

This is a plant of wet places, up to 8000 feet altitude; widespread but not abundant. It is a perennial from 12 to 40 inches tall, with simple-pinnate leaves composed of 5 to 9 pairs of serrate leaflets, 2 to 4 inches long.

Although known to be poisonous, cut-leaved water parsnip has seldom caused trouble.

KEY TO POISONOUS UMBELLIFERAE AND RELATED PLANTS WITH WHICH THEY MAY BE CONFUSED

A. Fruits strongly flattened dorsally, the lateral ribs broadly winged.
> B. Flowers yellow_____*Pastinaca sativa*
> BB. Flowers white.
>> C. Umbellets capitate; pedicels none_____*Sphenosciadium capitellatum*
>> CC. Umbellets loose; pedicels present.
>>> D. Marginal flowers of inflorescence irregular, central flowers regular; oil tubes of fruit visible externally, extending part of the length of the fruit_____*Heracleum lanatum*
>>> DD. Flowers all similar; oil tubes not visible externally, extending the entire length of the fruit_____*Angelica* spp.

AA. Fruits terete to somewhat compressed laterally, none of the ribs truly winged, although sometimes ridged.
> B. Fruits several times as long as broad, pubescent, caudate at base
>> *Osmorhiza* spp.
> BB. Fruits not more than twice as long as broad, obtuse at base.
>> C. Biennial; stem purple spotted; dried foliage "mouse-scented"; fruit ribs undulate_____*Conium maculatum*
>> CC. Perennials; stems not conspicuously purple-spotted; dried foliage not strongly scented; fruit ribs straight, prominent to obsolete.
>>> D. Involucre prominent, usually reflexed; leaves pinnate, the leaflets often variably dissected.
>>>> E. Fruit ribs narrow, prominent, plants erect from fibrous roots _____*Sium suave*
>>>> EE. Fruit ribs obscure in the corky pericarp; plants spreading, rooting at lower nodes_____*Berula erecta*
>>> DD. Involucre none, or of one or (at most) a very few inconspicuous bracts; leaves mostly bipinnate, the leaflets usually serrate entire or lobed.
>>>> E. Leaflets shallowly toothed or lobed, with rounded or acute teeth; fruits cylindrical, twice as long as broad; styles slender, in mature fruit usually about $\frac{1}{2}$ as long as the body of the fruit_____*Oenanthe sarmentosa*
>>>> EE. Leaflets usually rather narrow, sharply serrate to entire; fruits orbicular to oblong, not twice as long as broad; styles short_____*Cicuta* spp.

WATER HEMLOCK. *CICUTA*

WATER HEMLOCK

All of the *Cicuta* species occurring in California are tall, smooth, branching perennial herbs. The leaves are twice or thrice pinnate. The flowers are white and in compound umbels. The fruit is flattened laterally, broadly oval to roundish, with corky distinct ribs. The *Cicuta* species have short, erect or horizontal rootstocks and thick spindle-shaped roots. Both the rootstocks and roots contain a yellow oily secretion which does not occur in the other species with which it is likely to be confused. The rootstocks are further characterized by being divided internally into chambers by cross-partitions.

All parts of the plants are poisonous, though the underground are the most toxic.

SALT MARSH WATER HEMLOCK (*Cicuta Bolanderi* Wats.) This species occurs in marshes about Suisun Bay.

CALIFORNIA WATER HEMLOCK (*Cicuta californica* Gray) occurs in the coast region from Mendocino to Monterey County.

WESTERN WATER HEMLOCK (*Cicuta Douglasii* (DC.) C and R.) (Figs. 203 and 204) is widely distributed along streams throughout the mountains of the State.

OREGON WATER HEMLOCK (*Cicuta vagans* Greene)

Oregon water hemlock occurs in Nevada County on the east side of the Sierra Nevada.

POISON HEMLOCK (*Conium maculatum* L.) (Figs. 203 and 204)
Other common names: Deadly hemlock, snake-weed, poison parsley, wode thistle, poison stinkweed.

This plant is a native of Europe which is now widespread throughout California at lower altitudes. It usually occurs in shady or moist ground, behaves as a weed in pastures, along ditches and fences.

Poison hemlock is a tall, branching biennial herb, sometimes attaining a height of 10 feet. It has a long, white, often branched tap root. The stem is stout, smooth, and dotted with purple marks. The herbage has a mouse-like odor. The leaves are thrice-compound, 1 to 2 inches long or more, the segments toothed or deeply cut. The flowers are white and in large, open, compound umbels, the flower stalks being from ¾ to 1¼ inches long. The fruits are oval, granular, and have prominent wavy ribs. There are no oil tubes in the fruit.

All parts of the plant are poisonous. The degree of toxicity varies, and the plant is seldom eaten.

CORIANDER (*Coriandrum sativum* L.) (Fig. 205)

This is an introduction from the Mediterranean region, and is an occasional escape from cultivation. It is a slender, smooth, strong-smelling annual plant from 1 to 2½ feet high. The leaflets of the lower leaves are roundish or oval, cleft and toothed, ½ to 1¼ inches long; the upper leaves are finely dissected, the leaflets with narrow divisions. The inflorescence is a compound umbel, the flowers white or rose-tinted. The involucre is lacking, and the involucels consist of a few narrow bractlets. The fruit is almost globular.

WILD CARROT (*Daucus Carota* L.) (Fig. 206)
Other common names: Bird's-nest plant, devil's plague, Queen Anne's lace, "peanuts."

Wild carrot is a European plant which has escaped from gardens and become fairly widespread as a weed throughout California. It occurs in waste places, in pastures and meadows. It is an erect biennial herb from a fleshy, cone-shaped root. The main stem is 2 to 3 feet tall, hollow, ridged, and bristly-hairy. The basal leaves are large, long-petioled, and many times dissected, the upper smaller, less divided, and sessile with a sheathing base. The flower groups (umbels) are 2 to 4 inches across and flat-topped, becoming concave as the fruit matures. The flowers are small,

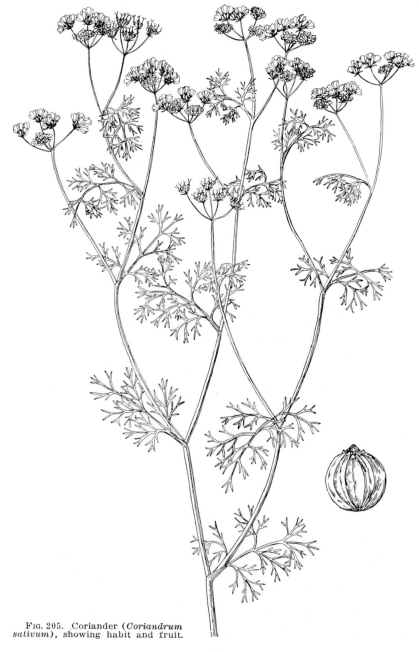

FIG. 205. Coriander (*Coriandrum sativum*), showing habit and fruit.

white or rarely pinkish. The fruit is dry, bristly, ribbed, and about $\frac{1}{6}$ inch or less long.

ERYNGO. *ERYNGIUM*

In California there are 11 species of *Eryngium* recorded. They are known commonly by the names "coyote thistle" or button snakeroot. They can not be regarded as pernicious weeds, although now and then certain of them may be troublesome in pasture lands, especially in the swales and areas of poor drainage.

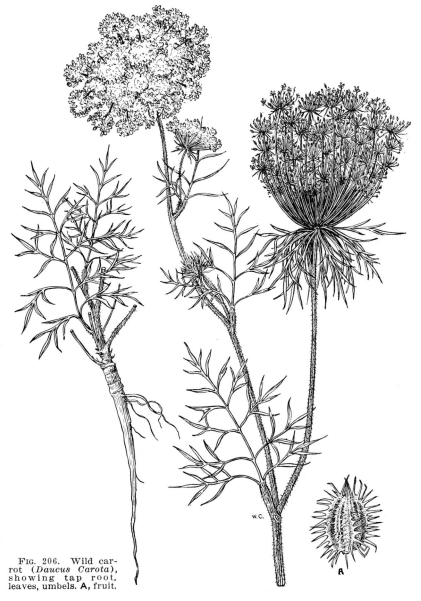

W.C.

Fig. 206. Wild carrot (*Daucus Carota*), showing tap root, leaves, umbels. **A**, fruit.

All the species of *Eryngium* are perennials with clustered coarse fibrous roots. The stems usually have a forked branching. The leaves are opposite, or the upper sometimes alternate, usually somewhat toothed or incised around the border, and spiny. The flowers are greenish-white or bluish, and condensed in heads, which are at the ends of branches or on short stalks in the forks of the stems. The bracts of the flowering heads are conspicuous and spined. The calyx lobes are prominent, sometimes spine-tipped, and persistent on the fruit. The fruit is covered with whitish thin scales, the ribs are absent, and oil-tubes are none or obscure.

BEE THISTLE (*Eryngium articulatum* Hook.)
Other common name: Blue thistle.

This species is erect, forkedly branched above, usually with a head in the forks. It attains a height of 2 to 3 feet, and has a strong disagreeable odor. The lower leaves are elongated, jointed and hollow, sometimes with a blade at the apex. The upper leaves are more or less cut at the edges, sometimes opposite. The heads are very blue, about $\frac{1}{3}$ to $\frac{2}{3}$ inches long. This species occurs in the San Joaquin and Sacramento Valleys, north to Siskiyou and Modoc.

COYOTE THISTLE (*Eryngium Vaseyi* C. & R.) (Fig. 207)

This species is found in low places in fields in the Sacramento Valley, west Mendocino County and south to Monterey County. The plant is gray-green and has two stages of growth: early slender hollow jointed leaves, which disappear when the swales dry up and are followed by upright leafy branching stems commonly 8 to 13 inches high. The lower leaves are lance-like, somewhat cut along the edges and spiny, often lobed below, and 4 to 8 inches long. The heads are about $\frac{1}{4}$ inches long, spiny toward the base of the bracts.

FENNEL (*Foeniculum vulgare* (L.) Gaertn.) (Fig. 208)

This plant is naturalized from Europe. It has become quite abundant in California, especially in the central and southern parts, where it frequents waste places. It is a stout, erect, and smooth perennial, with dark green aromatic herbage. The stems are streaked, branching, and rise to a height of $2\frac{1}{2}$ to 7 feet. The leaves are decompound and very finely dissected into numerous thread-like segments. The leafstalks are inflated and clasp the stem. The flowers are small, yellow, and in large compound umbels; each ray of the primary umbel is terminated by a secondary umbel of 12 to 20 flowers. The fruit is oblong with prominent ribs.

COW PARSNIP (*Heracleum lanatum* Michx.) (Fig 209)

This is a native plant rather widely distributed throughout California at middle elevations in both the Coast Range and Sierra Nevada. It may become weedy in pasture lands and along streams and fences. Cow parsnip is a stout perennial from thick, horizontal rootstocks. The stems are 3 to 5 feet high, ridged, hairy, and sometimes an inch in

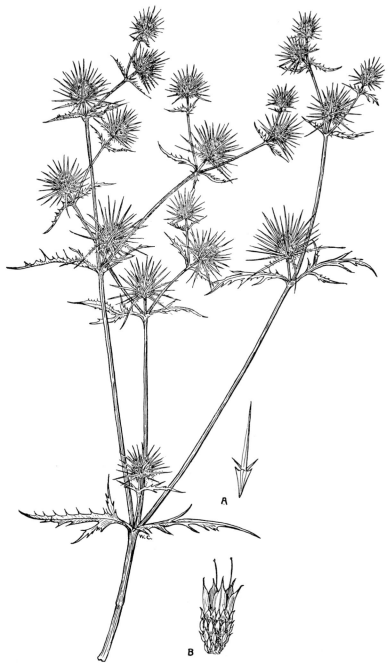

FIG. 207. Coyote thistle (*Eryngium Vaseyi*), showing habit. **A**, single bractlet; **B, fruit.**

diameter at the base. The leaves are compound, each composed of 3 leaflets which are broadly lance-shaped in outline, 3 to 6 inches broad, the margins lobed and sharply toothed. The leafstalks are whitish, much inflated and sheath the stem joints. The flowers are white, in large compound umbels which are usually 3 to 6 inches broad, sometimes more. The rays of the umbel are stout, 10 to 30 in number, and 2 to 4 inches long, each supporting a small umbellet of 8 to 12 flowers. The fruit is strongly flattened, winged, and almost circular in outline.

FIG. 208.   Fennel (*Foeniculum vulgare*).

FIG. 209. Cow parsnip (*Heracleum lanatum*), showing single compound leaf, and umbels.

There is some belief that it is poisonous to livestock but definite evidence of this is lacking.

PENNYWORT (*Hydrocotyle umbellata* L.) (Fig. 210)

This native perennial is a weed in lawns, particularly in southern California. It spreads from slender, creeping rootstocks. The leaves are round in outline, with wavy margin, about $\frac{1}{2}$ inch in diameter. The flowers are in small, many-flowered umbels on stems about $\frac{1}{2}$ inch long. The fruit is about $\frac{1}{12}$ inch long, notched at base and apex; dorsal rib is prominent.

FIG. 210. Pennywort (*Hydrocotyle umbellata*).

WATER PARSLEY (*Oenanthe sarmentosa* Presl.) (Figs. 203 and 204)

This species occurs in shallow ponds or slowly running water in the Coast Ranges, and north Sierra Nevada. The stems are succulent, glabrous, 2 to 4 feet tall, arising from thick rootstocks. The lowest leaves are mostly pinnate, 1 to 3 feet long, whereas the majority of the leaves are bipinnate; leaflets are oval-shaped, toothed or incised, ¾ to 2 inches long. The fruits are cylindrical, thus distinguishing the species from *Cicuta* with its orbicular to oblong fruits.

Water parsley is not known to be poisonous.

WILD PARSNIP (*Pastinaca sativa* L.) (Figs. 203 and 204)

This European plant has escaped from cultivation and become naturalized, being found now as a weed along ditches and roadsides, and in low-lying marshy areas. It is a branching biennial 2 to 4 feet tall, with a single, thick tap root, and not a cluster of roots as have the water hemlocks. The stems are branching and angular or fluted. The leaves are imply pinnate and often large, the lower ones often 1 to 1½ feet long; the leaflets are oval, with blunt ends, somewhat lobed and toothed, and 1 to 3 inches long. The flowers are yellow and in compound umbels, the primary ray 10 to 20 in number and 1 to 2½ inches long. The fruit is oval, strongly compressed, ribbed, and with conspicuous dark lines caused by the oil tubes (Fig. 203e).

SHEPHERD'S NEEDLE (*Scandix Pecten-Veneris* L.) (Fig. 211)
Other common names: Devil's darning-needle, Venus' or Lady's comb, Adam's needle, needle chervil.

This is a fugitive from Europe which is rather common in eastern United States, and in California has been found from the San Francisco Bay region to Santa Barbara County. It is an annual, erect, hairy herb, 5 to 16 inches high, with leaves 2 or 3 times pinnately dissected, the segments of the leaves being very narrow and pointed. The flowers are small, white, and grouped in compound umbels. The stalks of the small umbels are about ½ to 1 inch long. The involucre is lacking or only of 1 bract. The fruit is about ⅓ inch long, ribbed, and tipped by a characteristically straight, flat beak "needle" 1½ to 2 inches long, its edges rough with stiff bristles.

The "needles" may cause sores in the mouths of animals.

WATER PARSNIP (*Sium cicutaefolium* Gmel.) (Figs. 203 and 204)

This is a smooth, perennial herb of ponds and sloughs in northern California. The stems are 2 to 3½ feet tall, and arise from a cluster of fleshy roots. The leaves are simply pinnate, up to 3½ feet long, the leaflets 5 to 13 in number, toothed, 2 to 4 inches long. The flowers are white, in compound umbels.

SPHENOSCIADIUM (*Sphenosciadium capitellatum* Gray) (Fig. 203)

This is a perennial with very stout stems 3 to 5 feet high, and leaves which are large and glabrous; leaflets or division toothed, or more or less coarsely and saliently few-toothed above, entire below. There are 4 to 8 rays or more, unequal, 1-2 or 4 inches long, the flowers white or purple tinged, pubescent. The fruit is oblong wedge-shaped, about ¼ inch long, flattened and slightly hairy to smooth. The ribs are prominent, winged above, the dorsal and intermediate ones narrow, the lateral broader. This species occurs in the Sierra Nevada from Kern County to Modoc and thence to Siskiyou.

FIG. 211. Shepherd's needle (*Scandix Pecten-Veneris*).

HEDGE PARSLEY (*Torilis nodosa* (L.) Gaertn.) (Fig. 212)
Other common name: Knotted hedge parsley.

This plant is introduced from Europe, and is becoming widespread within California, although no place very abundant. It is an erect, slender, slightly branched annual, 7 to 13 inches tall. The stems and leaves are rough and hairy. The leaves are twice pinnate, the lower 3 to 5 inches long, including the leaf-stalk, the upper successively shorter. The flower groups are scattered along the stems, opposite the leaves at the nodes. The fruits on the outside of the flower-group are densely covered with hooked bristles, whereas those on the inside are warty and without prickles.

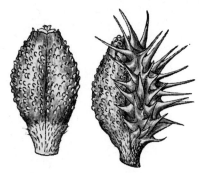

FIG. 212. Hedge parsley (*Torilis nodosa*). Left, fruit from inside of flower group; right, fruit from outside of flower group.

FIG. 213. Red pimpernel (*Anagallis arvensis*), showing habit. A, seeds; B, capsule splitting open.

PRIMROSE FAMILY *(Primulaceae)*

This is a cosmopolitan family, best represented in the Northern Hemisphere. A number of the genera possess species which are in ornamental use, such as primrose (*Primula*), cyclamen and shooting star (*Dodecatheon*).

RED PIMPERNEL (*Anagallis arvensis* L.) (Fig. 213)

Other common names: Poorman's weatherglass, red chickweed, eye-bright, shepherds-clock, poison chickweed, scarlet pimpernel.

Pimpernel, a weed from Europe, has become naturalized in California, chiefly along the coast, but is also frequently found in the interior valley. It occurs in damp soil about habitations, by roadsides, and in meadows. It flowers throughout the year in the coastal area.

Pimpernel is a low, spreading, branched annual herb, with 4-angled stems up to 1 foot long. The leaves are opposite, or sometimes in whorls of 3, about ⅓ inch long, oval or pointed, thin and light green, and glandular-dotted beneath. The flowers are salmon-colored or brick-red, solitary in leaf-axils, and about ¼ inch broad. They open only under a clear sky. The calyx is deeply 5-cleft and persistent on the fruit. The corolla is wheel-shaped, deeply 5-parted, the segments being minutely glandular-hairy at the apex. There are 5 stamens, with bearded anthers, and a single pistil with one style. The fruit is a smooth, globular, many-seeded capsule which splits open around the middle, the upper half coming off like a lid and freeing the seed. The seeds are elliptical, 3-angled, brown, and finely pitted.

Red pimpernel is included in the literature on toxic plants, and has been suspected of causing death among horses in California.

BLUE PIMPERNEL (*A. arvensis* var. *coerulea* Ledeb.) is recorded from a few localities: Fallbrook, Los Angeles, and Mt. Diablo. The corolla is blue.

DOGBANE FAMILY *(Apocynaceae)*

In this family are about 1100 species, distributed widely. Like the milkweed family, members of this family have a milky sap. The best known horticultural representative is oleander *(Nerium oleander)*. In California, growing without cultivation, there are 4 genera: *Amsonia, Vinca, Apocynum,* and *Cycladenia.*

MOUNTAIN HEMP (*Apocynum androsaemifolium* L.) (Fig. 215)

This species, closely related to dogbane, is a thickly branched plant 5 to 8 inches high with greenish leaves, pale, and with dense matted soft hairs below. The corolla is bell-shaped with the opening of the corolla much wider than the base. The coma or silky appendage on the seed is tawny. The follicles are commonly pendulous.

This species contains an acrid milky juice which may poison livestock.

DOGBANE (*Apocynum cannabinum* L.) (Figs. 214 and 215)

This is a native widely distributed in California, especially on river banks and along streams. It is an erect plant 2 to 4 feet tall, with light yellowish-green smooth herbage. The leaves are oval to lance-shaped, 2½ to 4 inches long, sessile or short-stalked, and yellowish. The flowers are small and in terminal clusters. The calyx is small and deeply 5-cleft; the corolla is greenish, bell-shaped, 5-lobed, and bears 5 small triangular awl-shaped appendages alternate with the stamens; corolla segments are shorter than the calyx-lobes. The fruit is a slender follicle 2 to 7 inches long, bearing numerous flat seeds.

It is occasionally a weed in cultivated ground and in pasture lands, and is poisonous to cattle.

OLEANDER (*Nerium oleander* L.)

This shrub, which occurs from the Mediterranean to the Orient, is widely utilized as an ornamental in California and sometimes persists about abandoned dwelling sites.

All parts of the oleander are highly toxic and it occasionally causes the death of stock which eat the foliage.

FIG. 214.   Dogbane (*Apocynum cannabinum*).

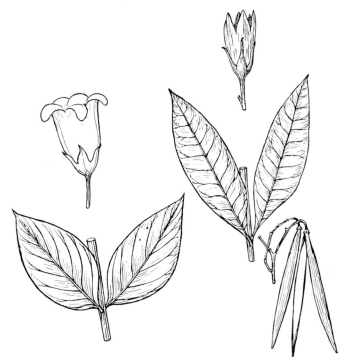

Fig. 215. Leaves and flowers of (left) mountain hemp (*Apocynum androsaemifolium*), (right) dogbane (*A. cannabinum*).

PERIWINKLE (*Vinca major* L.)

This native of Europe has escaped from gardens, especially about the San Francisco Bay region, and grows without cultivation along water courses in protected places. It is an evergreen herb, with short, erect flowering stems and trailing nonflowering stems. The leaves are oval, from 1 to 2 inches long, and rather long-petioled. The flowers are solitary in the leaf axils; they are blue in color, 1 to 1¼ inches broad, with a characteristic stigma, the apex of which is densely covered with clusters of hairs. The style is thread-like, bordered below by a reflexed membranous collar. The fruit is a follicle. The seeds are less than ⅛ inch long, very dark brown and roughened on the surface.

MILKWEED FAMILY *(Asclepiadaceae)*

This is a very large family of plants containing about 2,000 species. They include perennial herbs, vines, or shrubs with a milky juice. The principal genus in California is *Asclepias*, of which there are some 11 species.

BLADDERFLOWER (*Araujia sericifera* Brot.) (Fig. 216)

Bladderflower is established in numerous sites scattered from Riverside County in the south to Placer County in the north.

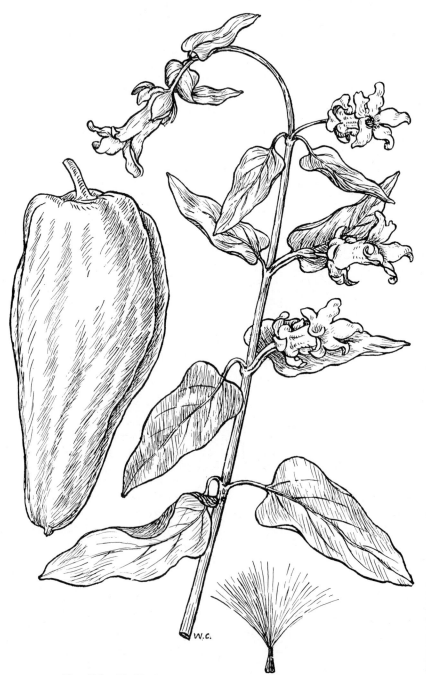

W.C.

Fig. 216. Bladderflower (*Araujia sericifera*) (*natural size*).

Bladderflower is a native of Peru. It was introduced into South Africa more than 40 years ago where it escaped and is now widely spread through the south coastal districts, Natal and parts of the Transvaal. In Ventura County this rapid growing twiner has been the cause of concern among some of the citrus growers.

Bladderflower is a twiner which grows up into the tops of high trees. The stems exude a milky sap. The plant is simple to sparingly branched with stems slender, one-eighth to one-fourth inch in diameter, their surface finely hairy. The opposite leaves are 2 to 4 inches long, broad and commonly squarish below, narrowed above to a short apical point. The petioles are slender, one-fourth to three-fourths of an inch long and finely hairy, those on the young growth commonly reflexed. The pairs of leaves are disposed from three to seven inches apart along the stem. The upper surface of the leaf is dull, dark green, the lower paler or grayish, with a minute pubescence. The flowers are solitary or two at the nodes on stems one-half to one inch long. The five-lobed greenish calyx is conspicuous and surrounds the base of the corolla. The corolla is white, the tube about one-half inch long, inflated at the base and topped by five lobes which are

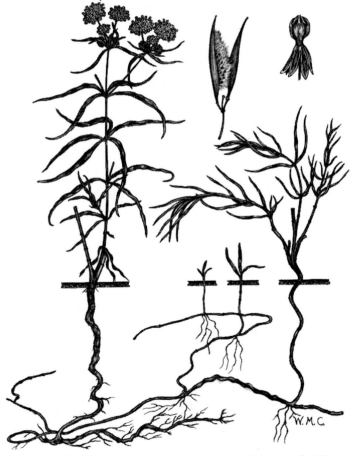

Fig. 217.   Mexican whoried milkweed (*Asclepias fascicularis*).

about one-half inch long and overlap toward the right in the bud. There are five scales attached to the throat tube. The pod is somewhat pear-shaped, three to four and one-half inches long, light, gray-green. It resembles the chayote in gross aspect. At maturity the pod splits, revealing numerous club-shaped dark brown seed, topped with the tuft of long silky hairs characteristic of the milkweed group.

MILKWEED. ASCLEPIAS

There are numerous common plants which contain a milky juice, chief of which are wild lettuce, sow thistles, and the true milkweeds. The latter, belonging to the family Asclepiadaceae, have plant characteristics quite different from those of other plants with a milky juice.

The species of *Asclepias* in California are all perennial herbs arising from deep-seated roots or rootstocks. The leaves are opposite or in whorls. The calyx is 5-parted, corolla 5-lobed, stamens 5, and the pistils 2. The stamens of this group are unusual; the filaments are united into a tube which joins above with the style, and the anthers are also united and bear appendages (hoods). There is a circle of 5 hoods, in some species containing an incurved horn. The fruit is a follicle (pod-like dry fruit which splits open along one side) containing flat seeds which are provided with a tuft of hairs.

The three most important species of *Asclepias* in California from the weed or poisonous-plant standpoint are *A. fascicularis*, *A. eriocarpa* and *A. speciosa*. *A. fascicularis* differs from the others in its smooth herbage and its long slender leaves which are in clusters at the stem joints.

WOOLLY-POD MILKWEED (*Asclepias eriocarpa* Benth.)

This species occurs in the Coast Ranges and Sierra Nevada foothills, south to coastal southern California. Woolly-pod milkweed has stems 1½-3 feet high, more or less sharply angled below. The plant is hoary with matted short white hairs which are often shed in age. The leaves are broadly oblong, broad or heart-shaped at the base, some of them in whorls of 3 or 4, 4 to 7 inches long and borne on very short petioles. The flower umbels are in clusters toward the top of the plant, flowers creamy white and about ¼ inch long. The hoods are pink or purplish. The seed pods are not spiny.

The leaves and stems of woolly-pod milkweed appear to be equally toxic, and they are dangerous in the dry as well as the fresh, green state. Apparently when dry, woolly-pod loses its disagreeable flavor, and thus may be dangerous when found in hay. This species of milkweed is regarded as the most poisonous.

MEXICAN WHORLED MILKWEED (*Asclepias fascicularis* Decne.) (Fig. 217)
Other common name : Narrow-leaf milkweed.

The Mexican whorled or narrow-leaf milkweed ranges from southern Mexico through western Arizona, California, and western Nevada to Washington and eastern Idaho. In California it is distributed at low altitudes, whereas the other two species mentioned above extend from low altitudes up to 4000 or 5000 feet. It occurs along roadsides, on ditch banks, on railway embankments, on gravelly stream beds and slopes, and not infrequently in gardens and cultivated fields. It usually grows in full sunlight.

The plant grows to a height of 2 to 3 feet. It is erect and has perennial underground stems. The stems and leaves are smooth. The leaves occur in characteristic whorls or clusters of 3 to 6 at the nodes, or the uppermost and lowermost may be opposite. The leaves are long and narrow, and lance-shaped at the tip. They are 3 to 6 inches long and from $\frac{1}{6}$ to $\frac{1}{2}$ inch wide. The flowers are many, in umbels. Each flower is on a long stalk. They are greenish-white, sometimes tinged with purple; they have a peculiar cup-like structure (hood), inside of which is a horn. The fruit is a slender pod, bearing numerous seeds. The seeds are flat, brown, and bear a silky tuft of hairs at the end. The plant spreads by means of its seeds, which are readily blown by the wind and are carried in water. The plant also spreads by means of its shallow, horizontal underground stems, and it is this habit which makes it a weed of some importance. *A. mexicana* of California references.

Mexican whorled milkweed is apparently only one-fourth as toxic as woolly-pod milkweed. Like the woolly-pod, it is also dangerous when dried, hence is a menace in hay.

SHOWY MILKWEED (*Asclepias speciosa* Torr.)
Other common name: Creek milkweed.

This native is distributed from Minnesota to Arkansas and westward to the Pacific Coast. It occurs in the Coast Range of California from the Bay region north to Siskiyou County and in the Sierra Nevada foothills from Fresno County to Plumas County. As a weed it is found in pasture lands, meadows, and in waste places.

This milkweed is a stout perennial, 2 to 4 feet tall, with soft, woolly herbage. The leaves are opposite, thick, oval-pointed or oblong, 4 to 5 inches long and $1\frac{1}{2}$ to 2 inches wide, short-petioled, and with prominent veins. The flowers are pink or reddish-purple, in umbels at the tops of the stems or terminating lateral branches in the axils of the upper leaves. The stamen tube bears hoods from each of which protrudes a curving horn. The hoods are 2 or 3 times the length of the anther column. The fruits (follicles) are large, thick-skinned, soft-spiny, and contain numerous light-brown flattened seeds, each with a tuft of long hairs at one end.

With showy milkweed, large amounts of the leaves are required to cause poisoning symptoms. The empty pods are more toxic than the leaves, while the seeds are the most dangerous of all parts. There is some evidence that this species loses some of its toxicity when dried in the field.

MORNING-GLORY FAMILY *(Convolvulaceae)*

The representatives of this family occur chiefly in warm climates. A number are of economic importance, among which may be mentioned the sweet potato (*Ipomoea Batatas*), garden morning-glory (*Ipomoea purpurea*), and cypress vine (*Quamoclit Quamoclit*). Most members of the family are twining or trailing herbs; some tropical species are shrubs or trees, often with a milky juice. The principal genera in which weed species occur are *Convolvulus, Cressa, Cuscuta* (dodder), and *Dichondra.*

MORNING-GLORY. CONVOLVULUS

Most of the species of morning-glory in California are native to the State, but the definitely weedy *Convolvulus sepium* (hedge bindweed), *C. arvensis* (wild morning-glory) and *C. althaeoides* (Althaea-leaved morning-glory), have been introduced.

Although the species of *Convolvulus* contain a toxic milky juice in the roots, no well-authenticated cases of poisoning have been reported. There is evidence, however, that "hair-balls" in sheep are largely composed of the fibers of these plants.

KEY TO WEEDY SPECIES OF CONVOLVULUS

Corolla more than ½ in. long, perennial
  Bracts smaller and narrower than sepals, more or less distant
    Bracts inserted less than their length below calyx, corolla cream-white, 1-2 inches long; climber_____*C. occidentalis*
    Bracts at least more than, or more than twice, their length below calyx, prostrate_____*C. arvensis*
  Bracts large, calyx-like, embracing the calyx
    Herbage densely velvety, leaf blades triangular-hastate, basal lobes usually toothed; low trailing_____*C. villosus*
    Herbage not as above
      Stems short, 1-15 in. or almost stemless; not twining
        Bracts ovate-obtuse, embracing but not enclosing calyx_____ *C. subacaulis*
      Stems long, twining or trailing
        Upper leaves deeply cut to pinnatifid, corolla deep rose-pink ___*C. althaeoides*
        Leaves, not deeply cut or pinnatifid
          Bracts cordate, ovate, completely enclosing calyx, corolla white to roseate_____ *C. sepium*
          Bracts not cordate
            Bracts loosely investing calyx, membranous purple, corolla white, the folds often purple-striped, rarely pinkish
              Leaves fleshy, bracts sub-orbicular to broadly oval, usually well exceeding calyx, corolla 1½-2½ in. long (insular) __*C. macrostegius*
              Leaves not fleshy; bracts sub-orbicular to broadly oblong, about equalling calyx, corolla 1⅜-1⅝ in. long_____*C. cyclostegius*
           Bracts closely investing calyx, ovate-lanceolate, green or rarely slightly purple tinged, corolla commonly cream-white, ¾-1⅜ in. long_____*C. aridus*
Corolla less than ½ in. long, annual_____*C. pentapetaloides*

ALTHAEA-LEAVED MORNING-GLORY (*Convolvulus althaeoides* L.)

Introduced from the Mediterranean region, this attractive perennial, twining morning-glory is established in a few spots in southern California; Ventura and Orange Counties. Stems to about three feet long, lower leaves ovate-cordate, the upper variously lobed and, toward the ends of the stems, more or less deeply pinnatifid. Flowers about 1 inch long or more, 1 to 2 in the axils, deep rose-pink.

FIG. 218.   Wild morning-glory (*Convolvulus arvensis*), showing trailing stems, leaves, flowers, fruit, and seed. Inset at right, seeds enlarged.

ARID-LAND MORNING-GLORY (*Convolvulus aridus* Greene)

This native trailing perennial occurs on dry slopes in southern California: Orange and San Bernardino Counties. Besides the species there are three subspecies in which the degree of hairiness and the leaf form vary considerably. The ovate-lanceolate bracts closely invest the calyx. The corolla is cream-white, except in the very slender leaved *C. aridus tenuifolius*.

WILD MORNING-GLORY (*Convolvulus arvensis* L.) (Figs. 218 and 219)
Other common names: Orchard morning-glory, field morning-glory, field bindweed, European bindweed, corn-bind, creeping Jenny.

This is the only species within our borders which requires serious consideration from the weed standpoint. Wild morning-glory is a trailing perennial generally distributed throughout California at lower altitudes. A large portion of the cultivated lands of the State are subject to its infestation.

The leaves are on slender leaf-stalks, about $\frac{1}{2}$ to 1 inch long, their bases squarish to sagittate, the blades narrowing gradually upward to the rounded or blunt tip; when the plant is grown under adverse conditions, they are much narrower than when grown under favorable conditions. The flowers are borne on slender stalks in leaf axils. Each flower has 5 united blunt sepals, a funnel-shaped corolla, obscurely 5-lobed, and pale pink or white within and purplish on the outside, 5 stamens attached to the inner surface of the corolla, and a single pistil. The ovary is 2-celled and ripens into a capsule, normally containing 4 seeds. The seeds have a rough surface, are dark brown in color, flattened on one side and rounded on the other, about $\frac{1}{8}$ inch long.

Apparently there is some delayed germination in morning-glory seeds, due to a condition known as "hard seed." It is known that scarified morning-glory seeds have a higher percentage of germination than do unscarified. This delayed seed germination increases the difficulty of control, due to the fact that the seeds may lie dormant in the soil for several years. However, in soil infested with morning-glory plants which are allowed to go to seed, there is some germination and every year seedling plants appear.

We quote from Crafts regarding the growth habits of the wild morning-glory: "The morning-glory plant, if subjected to varying environmental conditions, occurs in a number of forms. Variation in size and form of the leaves and stems is usually associated with the supply of moisture, but may also result from frequent cutting, which tends to deplete the food reserves in the root. The form of development taken by the root system is frequently related to the soil type and water table. the taproot being primarily a storage organ, a large proportion of the tissue is alive and respiring. This necessitates an oxygen supply during the growing season, and it will be found that all old roots are of such form that only the current season's growth actually penetrates below the summer water level. Consequently, in localities where there is a high water table, the taproot may branch at a depth of two feet or less, while in other localities it may penetrate to a depth of 10 feet or more before branching profusely.

"The root system of this plant is characterized by the production of annual laterals in great numbers. These laterals develop adventitiously throughout the length of the taproot and its branches, and permeate the soil in all directions. Most of them die at the end of the season and are replaced by new ones each year; but any which have become favorably situated may make more than average growth and become so well developed that they persist as permanent branches. It is by means of these persistent laterals that spreading in a horizontal direction is accomplished. Shoot buds arise on these horizontal laterals and develop into rhizomes which, reaching the surface, establish new crowns.

"The unusual ability of the morning-glory plant to reproduce vegetatively is related to the form of its underground structures. The relatively large storage capacity of the root necessitates the existence of many living cells in close relation with a large supply of food, and an efficient system for absorbing mineral nutrients. These conditions favor bud formation, which is the most characteristic habit of the plant. Favorable growing conditions stimulate intense activity, and these buds may be produced by dozens or even hundreds, especially during warm weather and after a cultivation which has destroyed the top growth. The ability to produce buds, together with the food reserve of the root, favors vegetative reproduction and makes the plant persistent. The dense foliage and twining growth enable the plant to choke out competitors and present difficulties to thorough spraying.

"The rhizome, being below ground, is protected and persists along with the root to which it is attached. Starting from a small bud, it may develop into a structure as large as the root itself or even larger, in which case the juncture of the root and rhizome may be difficult to find. Certain characteristics, however, may enable the observer to identify it. The rhizome, except when very old, has leaf scales on the surface, a pith through the center, and leaf gaps penetrating the xylem. These are lacking in the root.

"Rhizomes may vary in length from a few inches to several feet. Roots severed at various depths below the surface of the ground by gophers, or partially killed by spraying, often give rise to rhizomes several feet in length. Rhizomes may give rise to lateral roots, and, if detached from the main root, may exist independently and develop into separate plants. Whenever the taproot has become broken or cut, as in deep cultivation or plowing, the structures which connect it to the growing tops are invariably rhizomes. In many instances, old roots that have been cut off successively for several years may produce a thousand or more slender rhizomes from the severed end and give rise to a peculiar and striking bunchy form of leafy growth above ground."

European authorities list this as somewhat poisonous because of purgative properties; American authorities as slightly toxic, if at all.

BIG-LEAVED COASTAL MORNING-GLORY (*Convolvulus cyclostegius* House)

This native perennial occurs along the coast from central to southern California. Its thinnish leaves and purple bracts which about equal the sepals, distinguish it from other species.

ISLAND MORNING-GLORY (*Convolvulus macrostegius* Greene)

This wiry-stemmed smooth trailing perennial, which is somewhat woody at the base, occurs on hill slopes from 5 to 1,500 feet on the islands off the coast of southern California. It has greenish to purple-tinged bracts which well exceed the sepals, and large white flowers.

WESTERN MORNING-GLORY (*Convolvulus occidentalis* Gray) (Fig. 219)

This native perennial which climbs and twines extensively occurs from 10-1,000 feet on brushy slopes west of the mountains from central California southward. The leaf blades, 1-2½ inches long, are sagittate, the basal lobes squarish and angularly lobed. The bracts are slender, usually about their length distant from the flower.

SMALL-FLOWERED MORNING-GLORY (*Convolvulus pentapetaloides* L.)

This is relatively unimportant in California, occurring in grain fields in Contra Costa County and in the lower San Joaquin Valley south to San Diego. It is distinguished from all other morning-glories by its small purplish-blue flowers about ⅓ inch long. It is an annual, introduced from the Mediterranean.

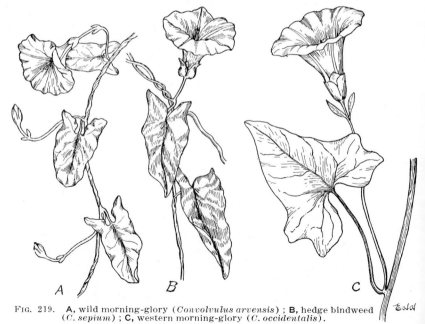

FIG. 219. **A,** wild morning-glory (*Convolvulus arvensis*) ; **B,** hedge bindweed (*C. sepium*) ; **C,** western morning-glory (*C. occidentalis*).

HEDGE BINDWEED (*Convolvulus sepium* L.) (Fig. 219)

This is not abundant in California, although it is a pernicious weed in eastern United States. It occurs in the neighborhood of Los Angeles and San Bernardino. It may be distinguished from *C. arvensis* by the pair of large bracts that encloses and conceals the calyx.

This is considered poisonous in Europe and has been suspected of poisoning pigs.

HILL MORNING-GLORY (*Convolvulus subacaulis* (H&A) Greene)

This low-growing and frequently almost stemless native occurs on dry open hills from Napa and Solano Counties to San Luis Obispo County. It often forms compact mats, its angular 5-lobed white corollas which are purple-tinted on the outside conspicuous above the commonly roundish-deltoid leaves.

WOOLLY MORNING-GLORY (*Convolvulus villosus* Gray)

This velvety-pubescent native, with stems 3-12 inches long from slender fleshy rootstock, is found on open hillsides, particularly on gravelly soil, from Siskiyou to northern Ventura County and from Shasta to Tulare County. The leaf blade is typically triangular-hastate, about 1 inch long; the bracts are about ½ inch long and enclose the calyx; the funnel-form cream-white corolla is about 1-1½ inches long.

ALKALI CLOVER (*Cressa cretica* L. var. *truxillensis* Choisy) (Fig. 220)
Other common name: Alkali weed.

This plant is especially common in alkali soils, and occurs throughout the Sacramento and San Joaquin Valleys, southward to southern California. It is especially abundant in the alkaline soils of the San Joaquin Valley. It is a low, white-hairy perennial herb, usually profusely branched from the base, forming sprawling, tufted plants 3 to 10 inches high. There are many leaves which are small, about ⅙ to ⅓ inch long, oblong or oval, and very short-stalked. The flowers are borne on short stalks in the axils of the upper leaves. The flowers are white, and have 5 separate sepals, a 5-parted corolla which is bell-shaped and silky-hairy on the outside, 5 stamens and a single pistil with 2 distinct styles. The fruit is a small, hairy capsule, usually 1-seeded. The seed is less than ⅛ inch long, broadly ovate, somewhat pointed at the scar end, and pinkish-tan in color, with smooth surface.

DODDER (*Cuscuta* spp.) (Figs. 221, 222, 223)
Other common names: Love-vine, strangle-weed, devil's-hair.

There are at least 7 species of dodder occurring in California, all parasitic on one or more species of flowering plants. Some of the dodder species have a rather limited host range, whereas others live on quite a variety of hosts. Alfalfa dodders are of the most concern to growers of seed.

Dodder plants have slender, thread-like stems of a yellowish or orange color which twine and coil about the host plants. It is extremely

FIG. 220.   Alkali clover (*Cressa cretica* var. *truxillensis*). Left. fruits and seeds.

difficult to detect the presence of dodder in a stand of young alfalfa plants, for example, as the threads are small and inconspicuous. The dodder seeds germinate about the same time as alfalfa seeds. As the alfalfa plants grow, dodder keeps pace, spreading and branching extensively. Soon the dodder in a field may be detected by the dense growth of yellow, tangled stems, or by the occurrence of patches of stunted alfalfa plants, and in severe cases, by a mat of dodder and alfalfa.

Dodder is a flowering plant and produces seed. The seeds resemble those of alfalfa, more or less, and occasionally it requires more than casual observation to detect the seeds of dodder among seeds of alfalfa. The seeds are produced in tremendous numbers, and fall to the ground or are harvested with the crop. They retain their vitality for at least five years under ordinary field conditions. Some of the dodder seeds may germinate the same season they mature while others rest over. The conditions favoring their germination are similar to those which are required for the germination of alfalfa seed.

The dodder seeds germinate in the ground, and the young plant is at first dependent upon food stored within the seed. A slender, yellowish, leafless stem is sent out, which swings slowly about in its growth, and if it comes in contact with a suitable support, it coils about it. Very soon small, wart-like suckers (haustoria) appear along the slender dodder stem, and these penetrate the tissues of the plant upon which the dodder is preying. Through these suckers the dodder draws nourishment from the alfalfa plant. Having established itself upon its host and derived food from it, dodder loses all connection with the soil by the shriveling up of the lower part of the stem. If the young seedling does not encounter a suitable host, it withers and dies. Thus, dodder is a parasitic, seed-producing plant. This is indeed rather unusual, for we know that practically all seed-producing plants draw nourishment from the soil, and possess green leaves which enable them to make their own food.

As dodder grows older it branches and rebranches, spreading from plant to plant. The older branches may die if the stems upon which they are fastened are used up, but new branches are continually formed. Any growing section of a dodder plant is independent of another, for it gains its nourishment locally, and is not dependent upon an older part of the stem to conduct its food supply from a remote distance. This habit makes it very difficult to eliminate from a field. After a period of growth, small white or cream-colored flowers are produced in clusters. Each bell-shaped blossom has the usual parts of a flower, and produces a seed pod which contains two or three seeds. Although a majority of the flowers appear simultaneously, there is a succession of these, so that flowers and seeds may be produced throughout a greater part of the growing season. Consequently, a quantity of seed-bearing pods is bound to be harvested with the alfalfa seed crop. It is entirely possible to harvest a hay crop before dodder seeds mature.

| *Cuscuta planiflora*
Little-seed alfalfa dodder | *Cuscuta campestris*
Field dodder | *Cuscuta indecora* x 10
Big-seed alfalfa dodder |

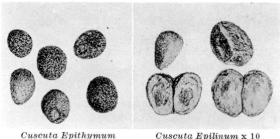

Cuscuta Epithymum   *Cuscuta Epilinum* x 10
Clover dodder   Flax dodder

FIG. 221. Seeds of the more common dodders.

Dodder, infesting clover, has been reported injurious, causing bowel trouble in horses and scours in cattle. Hay does not cure properly when dodder is present.

FIELD DODDER (*Cuscuta campestris* Yunck) (Figs. 221 and 222)

This is a native, widely distributed in the United States, especially the midwest and southwest on various low-growing plants, including clover and alfalfa. The capsules are globular, the corolla remains at the base of the mature capsule, and the corolla lobes are acute with inflexed tips. The seeds (Fig. 221) are dull pinkish or grayish tan, the surface relatively smooth. Scar a raised white line, surrounded by scar area of fine radiating lines. Seed 1.1 mm. long, 0.9 mm. wide; form ovate, rounded on the back, angles commonly distinct. (*C. pentagona* Engelm. of authors.)

FLAX DODDER (*Cuscuta epilinum* Weibe) (Figs. 221 and 223)

This species is introduced from Europe into northern United States. It is not yet reported from California, but may occur in seeds of flax. It resembles clover dodder, but the corolla scales are not incurved; and the flowers are yellowish-white. The seeds are grayish or chalky tan, the surface dull and scurfy-roughened. The scar is a raised point, the scar area distinct, flat and finely striate radially. The seeds are 1-1.5 mm. in diameter, broadly ovate, sometimes angled; they often stick together in pairs.

Field dodder (*Cuscuta campestris*);
right, flower detail. Left, *C. plani-*
flora, flower detail.

Big-seed alfalfa dodder (*Cus-*
cuta indecora); left, flower
detail.

FIG. 222.   Alfalfa dodders.

CLOVER DODDER (*Cuscuta epithymum* Murray) (Figs. 221 and 223)

This species is introduced from Europe, and has become abundant in northeastern United States. It is rare in California. It occurs in clovers, alfalfa, other leguminous crops, and a variety of low plants. The flowers are pinkish, the corolla scales with fine rounded teeth, the lobes strongly incurved. The capsule is circumscissile. The seeds (Fig. 221) are dull gray or grayish brown, like particles of earth, the surface coarsely granular, somewhat pitted. The scar is short, whitish, and line-like; the scar area is indistinct. Seeds 0.5 to 1 mm. in diameter, globular or tapering toward the base, sometimes angled.

BIG-SEED ALFALFA DODDER (*Cuscuta indecora* Choisy.) (Figs. 221 and 222)

This is a native of tropical America, now established from Illinois to Florida and westward. In California it occurs throughout the central valley, and in Lake and Mendocino Counties. It infests various hosts, chiefly legumes and sunflower. The flowers are whitish, fleshy, usually with purplish anthers and stigmas. The corolla lobes are spreading and with reflexed tips. The capsule is globular and covered with the withered corolla. The seeds are tan to reddish, grayish or greenish brown. The surface is coarse-scurfy, suggesting network. The scar is a short slit; scararea depressed, somewhat indistinct to scurfy. The seeds are 1-2 mm. in diameter; form circular, one face somewhat "dished."

LITTLE-SEED ALFALFA DODDER (*Cuscuta planiflora* Tenore) (Figs. 221 and 222)

This is introduced from Europe, widely distributed in the West. In California it occurs in the central valley, in Lake, Mendocino, and Modoc Counties. The capsule is 1- to 4-seeded, and opens by a lid. The seeds (Fig. 221) are yellowish or greenish brown, surface very finely roughened and appearing scurfy. Scar a raised point; surrounding scararea indistinct. Seeds 1 mm. long, 0.7 mm. wide; form oblong, rounded on the back, angles commonly distinct.

CHILEAN DODDER (*C. racemosa* Martius var.*Chiliana* Engelm.)

This dodder is an introduction from Chile, which may become a pest in alfalfa fields in the State.

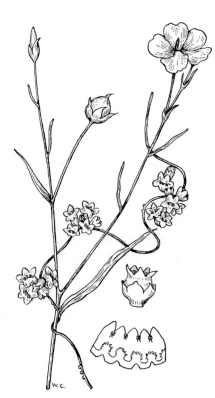

Clover dodder (*Cuscuta epithymum*).
Above, germinating dodder seed
Below, flower and at right a stem showing attached parasite

Flax dodder (*Cuscuta epilinum*);
right, flower detail.

FIG. 223.   Clover and flax dodders.

MARSH DODDER (*Cuscuta salina* Engelm.)

This dodder is a very conspicuous species. It occurs on saline herbs, chiefly *Salicornia*, and in spring colors the salt marshes with patches of gold turning to rust color. Marsh dodder does not attack crop plants.

CANYON DODDER (*Cuscuta subinclusa* Durand and Hilgard)

This species of dodder occurs almost throughout California on such hosts as *Ceanothus, Rhus, Prunus, Salix, Aesculus, Sambucus, Eriogonum* and *Quercus*. It frequently invades orchards and has caused appreciable damage in citrus groves in Orange and San Bernardino Counties; also on citrus nursery stock.

Cuscuta subinclusa differs from the other species of dodder which occur in California in having a relatively long cylindrical corolla, with the lobes spreading and scarcely more than one-half the length of the tube. The scales within the tube are about one-half its length and fringed. The capsule is ovoid and in age is covered by the withered persistent corolla.

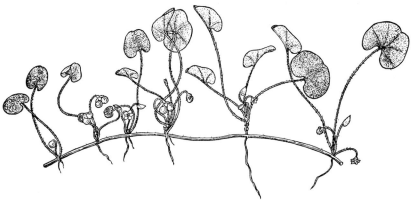

FIG. 224. Dichondra (*Dichondra repens*).

DICHONDRA (*Dichondra repens* Forst.) (Fig. 224)

This plant is naturalized from the tropics. It has been found in the foothills of El Dorado County, at San Francisco, Del Mar, San Joaquin, Los Angeles and San Diego. It is a perennial herb with slender, creeping, whitish-pubescent stems which root freely and form a matted ground cover, except in the shade where the leaf stems elongate. The leaves are kidney-shaped, entire, and ¼ to ½ inch wide, or under favorable conditions as much as 1½ inches wide. The stalks of the small inconspicuous flowers are long and bear two small bracts at the base. The calyx is deeply 5-parted, the corolla greenish white and 5-cleft. The ovary is deeply 2-lobed, densely white-hairy, and at maturity breaks into 2 one-seeded almost spherical, dark gray utricles.

The variety *occidentalis* has purple corolla and larger leaves.

MEXICAN MORNING-GLORY (*Ipomoea hirsutula* Jacq.)

This native of tropical America has become naturalized in coastal southern California. It is similar to the popular *I. hederacea* of gardens but the sepals are merely acute, not long drawn out to a slender point and recurved as in *I. hederacea*.

TALL MORNING-GLORY (*Ipomoea purpurea* (L.) Lam.)

This species, which is the most commonly planted ornamental morning-glory, is naturalized sparingly in California. In certain southern California counties this native of tropical America is often troublesome as a weed in orchards, vineyards and gardens.

PHLOX FAMILY (*Polemoniaceae*)

This family is well represented in the flora of western North America. To it belong such well known ornamentals as *Phlox*, *Gilia* and *Polemonium*. It furnishes us with no weeds of importance, with the exception of two native species of *Navarretia*. The seeds of *Colomia grandiflora* and *Gilia capitata* occur as impurities in commercial lots of oats, barley, and wheat.

NAVARRETIA (*Navarretia intertexta* (Benth.) (Hook) (Fig. 225)

This is sometimes a weed of cultivated areas. It is widely distributed in the Sacramento and San Joaquin Valleys, in the Coast Ranges and Sierra Nevada foothills. It is a native annual, with simple erect or branching stems 2 to 7 inches high, the herbage white-puberulent, the leaves bipinnatifid, the calyx tube densely white-woolly, the corolla white or lavender. The seeds are about 1 mm. long, covered with a loose network, a number of individual seeds often agglutinized into an aggregate, thus causing the seeds to be flattened or squared off on the contact side, rounded on the free side. The seed itself is dark, the covering lighter and more or less transparent. Individual seeds, or seed masses, occur as an impurity in commercial seed grain.

SKUNKWEED (*Navarretia squarrosa* (Esch.) H. & A.)

Skunkweed is common from Monterey County to Humboldt County. It is a small annual with rigid stems 8-16 inches tall. The leaves are alternate, pinnate or pinnatifid, the segments rigid and spine-tipped, the herbage hairy and glandular. The calyx is 5-angled, the tube being papery between the angles. The corolla is blue and funnel-form. There are 5 stamens, inserted on the corolla tube, a 3-celled ovary, and a 3-cleft style. The fruit is a 3-celled capsule, the seeds small and numerous.

PHACELIA FAMILY (*Hydrophyllaceae*)

This family includes a number of genera, three of which are widespread and of common occurrence in California, namely Yerba Santa

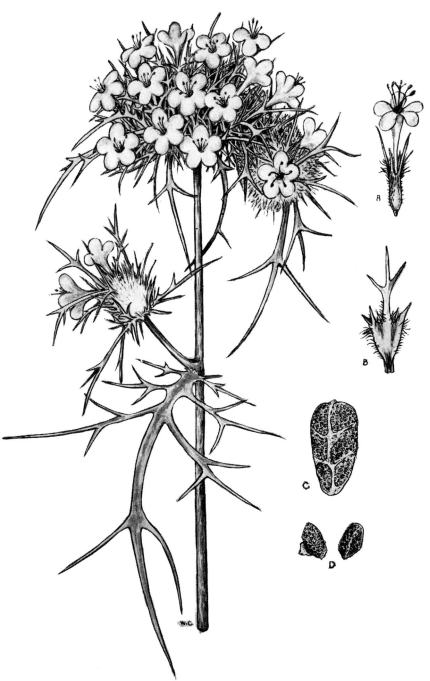

F<small>IG</small>. 225.   Navarretia (*Navarretia intertexta*).   **A,** single flower; **B,** bract; **C,** agglutinized seeds; **D,** individual seeds.

(*Eriodictyon californica* (H. & A.) Greene), baby blue-eyes (*Nemophila Menziesii* H. & A.), and over fifty species of *Phacelia*, one in particular of which is of importance as a weed.

ROCK PHACELIA (*Phacelia californica*)

This is sometimes a weed in flax. It is a coarse, erect perennial herb with stems 1¼ to 2 feet high, arising from a crown. The stems and leaves are stiff-hairy. The leaves are dissected, 2 to 4 inches long; usually there are 1 to several pairs of small leaflets below the large ones. Flowers purple.

FIDDLE-NECK (*Phacelia tanacetifolia* Benth.)

This weed occurs in cultivated fields and waste areas in the Sacramento and San Joaquin Valleys, the Sierra and Coast Range foothills and eastward, south to coastal southern California. It is an annual, erect and branching somewhat above, about 1½ to 4 feet tall. The leaves are divided into numerous lobes, giving the foliage a fern-like appearance. The flowering spike is about 4 inches long, with attractive blue, open bell-shaped flowers, with 5 somewhat spreading petals and long exserted stamens. Inside the corolla tube there are scales which are attached to the corolla throughout their length. The capsule is 2-valved, containing dull reddish-brown seeds which are rounded on the back, somewhat angled on the face, their surface deeply pitted.

BORAGE FAMILY *(Boraginaceae)*

There are well over 1500 species of this family in the world, most of which are rough with coarse hairs, which occur not only on stems and leaves but calyx and corolla as well. Several representatives are ornamentals, such as forget-me-not (*Myosotis*), bluebells (*Mertensia*), and heliotrope (*Heliotropium*), and a considerable number of species are weeds. In California there are about 94 species in the family, of which 5 are introduced.

KEY TO GENERA OF BORAGE FAMILY

Ovary not divided, or merely lobed_____*Heliotropium*
Ovary deeply 4-parted
  Nutlets provided with barbed prickles_____*Lappula*
  Nutlets not provided with barbed prickles
    Flowers white
      Leaves usually alternate_____*Cryptantha*
      Leaves (lower) opposite_____*Allocarya*
    Flowers yellow _____*Amsinckia*
    Flowers blue or purple
      Corolla tube curved at the middle_____*Lycopsis*
      Corolla tube not curved at the middle
        Fruiting calyx much enlarged, papery and veiny_____*Asperugo*
        Fruiting calyx not much enlarged
          Scar of nutlets small and marginless_____*Myosotis*
          Scar of nutlets large and excavated, bordered by a
            prominent vein_____*Symphytum*

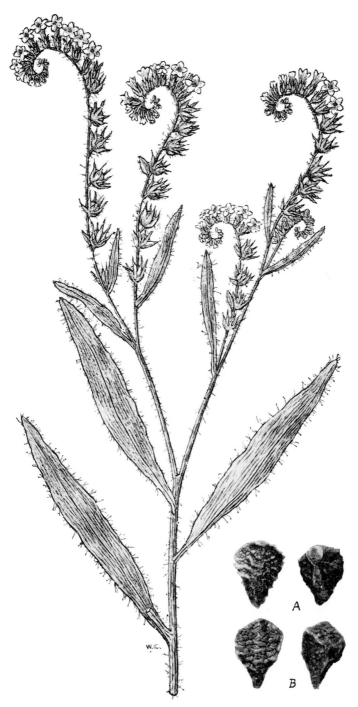

Fig. 226. Buckthorn (*Amsinckia Douglasiana*). **A**, seeds ; **B**, seeds of tesselate buckthorn (*Amsinckia tesselata*).

SCORPION WEED (*Allocarya* species)

These attractive native members of the borage family occur rather widely in California. They have white flowers borne on the typical spike-like stem, with unopened buds at the top curved inward in fiddleneck fashion. The crests in the throat of corolla are weakly developed or absent. The nutlets are broad or elongated club-shaped, quite pointed at the base and variously flecked with color, smooth, rugose or tuberculate on the back. The calyx is persistent and does not fall with the fruit.

BUCKTHORN (*Amsinckia Douglasiana* DC) (Fig. 226)
Other common names: Fiddleneck, yellow burweed, yellow tarweed, fireweed, yellow forget-me-not, zaccoto gordo.

This species is native to California, and widespread. It occurs in orchards and vineyards, along roadsides and in waste places, but does the greatest amount of harm as a weed in grain fields. It is very common in the interior valley, and the seed is a frequent impurity in oats, barley and wheat.

Buckthorn is a rough-hairy annual with erect, simple or branching stems, attaining a height of $1\frac{1}{2}$ to 4 feet. It is an extremely variable species. The leaves are alternate, ovate or strap-shaped, and very harsh-hairy. The flowers are numerous, orange-yellow in color, and grouped in characteristic one-sided, curling, spike-like inflorescences, 5 to 10 inches long. There is a 5-lobed caylx which is bristly-hairy, a 5-lobed funnel-form corolla, 5 stamens attached to the corolla tube, and a single pistil. The ovary is distinctly 4-lobed, and at maturity breaks apart to form 4 nutlets, each 1-seeded. The nutlets are keeled, and more or less roughened or wrinkled, transversely ridged, and grayish in color.

There are records of deleterious effect on hogs which have been fed large amounts of the seed, as in barley screenings.

COAST BUCKTHORN (*Amsinckia intermedia* F. & M.)

This species, also a native annual, is very similar to *A. Douglasiana,* but is less common and largely confined to coastal areas. The plant is in general lower growing, 1 to 2 feet, and the flowers a lighter yellow. The nutlets are brown to black, in form similar to the preceding species.

TESSELATE BUCKTHORN (*Amsinckia tesselata* Gray.) (Fig. 226)

This is another native annual species, similar to the two preceding species in general aspect. It occurs chiefly on the sandy plains and desert mesas in the Mojave and Colorado deserts, the Antelope Valley, north into the San Joaquin Valley, in the dry Coast Ranges and Inyo County. The nutlets in this species are distinctive; they are not keeled nor transversely ridged on the back, but flattish, having a tesselate, or uneven cobblestone pavement surface.

GERMAN MADWORT (*Asperugo procumbens* L.)

This borage was collected in 1947 in a hay meadow near Fort Bidwell, Modoc County. It is an adventive from Europe, long known as a

weed in waste places in eastern United States, and in recent years reported from Colorado, Utah, Oregon, and Washington. It is annual,
rough-hairy, low sprawling herb. The leaves are oblong, lance-shaped,
½ to 1½ inches long. The flowers are small, blue in color, and in fruit the
flower-stalk is recurved. The fruiting calyx is enlarged, papery and
veined.

NIEVITAS (*Cryptantha* species) (Fig. 227)

These "little snow" flowers, as in the scorpion weed, occur in drifts
on open hillsides and untilled grainlands almost throughout California.
The plants resemble miniature white forget-me-nots. There are definite
crests in the throat of the corolla. The 4, or 3, 2 or 1 nutlets are papillate
or muriculate, never rugose. The calyx usually falls with the fruit. ·

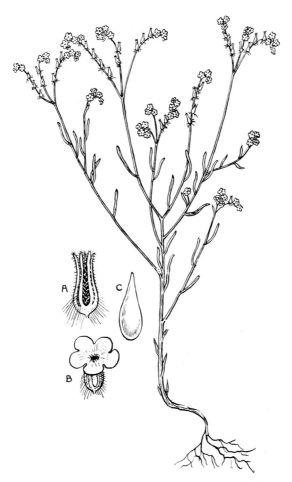

Fig. 227.   Nievitas (*Cryptantha flaccida*).   **A,** fruiting
calyx ; **B,** flower ; **C,** nutlet.

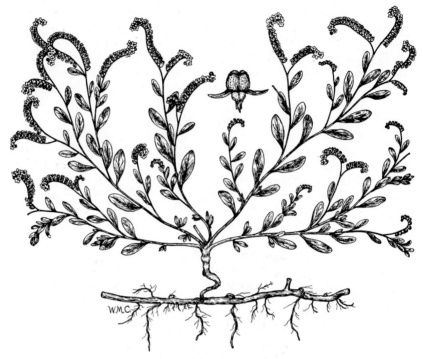

FIG. 228.   Heliotrope (*Heliotropium curassavicum* L.)

HELIOTROPE (*Heliotropium curassavicum* L.) (Fig. 228)
Other common names : Chinese pusley, alkali heliotrope, seaside heliotrope, white-
    weed, devil-weed.

This plant is widespread from Delaware southward and westward
to the Pacific Coast. It occurs mostly in low, moist or alkaline soils.
Under our conditions heliotrope is a perennial herb with branching,
prostrate stems that may attain a length of two or three feet. Both the
stems and leaves are fleshy, smooth and covered with a fine waxy-like
covering which rubs off easily. The herbage on the growing plant is a
soft ashy-green but, after picking, the entire plant quickly darkens to
a purplish-brown. This characteristic, peculiar to *H. curassavicum*, may
be found of value in recognizing the weed in the field. The leaves are
oblong in shape, 1 to 2 inches long, and conspicuously veined ; the lower
leaves have short stalks, whereas the upper leaves are sessile. The groups
of flowers form characteristic one-sided spikes which are mostly in pairs.
The corolla is tubular, with an open throat ; it is white in color and has
a yellow ''eye'' which may change to blue or purple. The stamens are
included within the corolla ; the stigma looks like a skull-cap, due to its
turning down over the ovary. The fruit is spherical, and forms 4 one-
seeded nutlets, or, by abortion, fewer. At maturity the nutlets separate.
They are about the size, shape and color of dodder seed, about 1 mm.
in diameter, light brown and scurfy on the surface, and when found in

alfalfa are sometimes confused with
dodder, which is an impurity of
major importance in the alfalfa
seed trade. Seed of alkali heliotrope
occurs frequently in alfalfa seed
from the Great Valley and southward.

Heliotropium europaeum L. is
recorded here from near Red Bluff,
Tehama County. Apparently not
persisting there.

STICKSEED (*Lappula echinata*
Gilib.) (Fig. 229)

This native of Eurasia, has
been found at Santa Monica and at
Upland. It is not otherwise known
from the State. It is a rough, hairy
annual, from 1 to 2 feet high.

SMALL BUGLOSS (*Lycopsis arvensis*
L.)

This weed, also a native of Europe, has been found at Upland, in
the San Bernardino Valley, the only
known occurrence in the State. It is
a coarse, bristly-hairy annual herb,
8 to 24 inches tall, with alternate,
lance-shaped, entire or wavy-margined leaves. The flowers are in
leafy, curved clusters. The calyx has
5 narrow lobes, and the corolla is a
curved, funnel-shaped pale-blue
tube, the throat of which is closed
by bristly scales. There are 5 sta-
mens inserted on the corolla, and a 4-parted ovary, which in fruit separates into 4 nutlets.

FIG. 229.   Stickseed (*Lappula echinata*).

FORGET-ME-NOT (*Myosotis sylvatica* Hoffm.)

This is a European garden plant sparingly naturalized at San An-
selmo, Mill Valley, Berkeley, and San Francisco. It is a leafy-stemmed
perennial about 1 foot high, with rough-hairy herbage, lance-shaped or
oblong entire leaves 1 to 4 inches long, and light-blue flowers.

YELLOW AND BLUE SCORPION-GRASS (*Myosotis versicolor* (Pers.) J. E.
Smith)

This species, closely related to the forget-me-not, has been found as
an adventive at Quincy and Eureka. It is a native of Europe.

Fig. 230.   Pop-corn flower (*Plagiobothrys Torreyi*).
A, nutlet.

POP-CORN FLOWERS (*Plagiobothrys* species) (Fig. 230)

Pop-corn flowers are rather slender annuals with soft pubescent herbage and alternate leaves, mostly toward the base in more or less of a rosette form. The corolla is white and short and has small crests at the throat. The nutlets are broadly ovate, roughened on the back and with a rounded raised scar where the seed breaks away from the receptacle.

ROUGH COMFREY (*Symphytum asperrimum* L.)

A native of Europe, this is adventive at Arcata. It is a coarse perennial herb 2 to 3 feet high, with oval to oblong lance-shaped entire leaves, 4 to 7 inches long, purple, tubular flowers in one-sided forked racemes, and a fruit which breaks into 4 nutlets at maturity.

VERBENA FAMILY *(Verbenaceae)*

The verbena family possesses herbs, shrubs, trees, and climbing forms. The last named are known as the lantanas. Our two chief genera are *Verbena* and *Lippia*, which contain weeds of importance. *Verbena hybrida* is a garden plant.

MAT-GRASS (*Lippia nodiflora* Michx.) (Fig. 231)

This is a widely distributed species, found across the continent, and in California, especially in the Sacramento-San Joaquin delta region. It is used as a ground covering where, on account of the absence of irrigation water, grasses do not flourish. It is also used as a soil binder on levees.

FIG. 231. Mat-grass (*Lippia nodiflora*), showing habit. **A,** single leaf; **B.** leaf of fog-fruit (*L. lanceolata*).

Mat-grass is a prostrate perennial with extensively creeping stems, 1 to 3 feet long. The stems root freely at the nodes. The leaves are opposite, simple, thickish, long-wedge-shaped at the base, sharply toothed toward the tip, and are 1 inch or less long. Both stems and leaves are finely hairy. The flowers are in dense oblong heads, subtended by closely overlapping bracts. The flower has a short, 2-cleft calyx, a white tubular corolla, the upper part of which is 2-lipped, and a single pistil. The fruit is globular or indistinctly 2-lobed.

FOG-FRUIT (*Lippia lanceolata* Michx.) (Fig. 231)

This creeper is closely related to *L. nodiflora* and has the same geographical distribution, but is not as abundant. It resembles *L. nodiflora* in general appearance, but has thinner leaves which are oval, and pale blue flowers.

L. filiformis Schrad. is an introduction from South America which is an occasional escape from cultivation in southern and central California. It is also a matted, creeping plant with leaves in clusters, and with ovoid flowering heads.

VERVAIN. *VERBENA*

Several of the species of *Verbena* occurring in California may be regarded as weeds. All of our verbenas are herbs with opposite or whorled leaves, and with flowers in dense, terminal, more or less leafy spikes. The calyx is tubular, 5-angled and 5-toothed; the corolla salverform, tubular, and 5-lobed; the stamens 4 in number in two pairs; the pistil 1, with a 4-celled ovary, and a 2-lobed stigma. The fruit is mostly enclosed by the calyx, and separates at maturity into 4 nutlets.

KEY TO WEEDY SPECIES OF VERBENA

Spikes short, dense, parallel and erect in a compact cyme_____*V. bonariensis*
Spikes mostly elongated, forming a loose panicle
  Bracts exceeding or at least equalling the flowers_____*V. bracteata*
  Bracts shorter than the flowers
    Spikes very slender, the flowers and fruit scattered on the axis
      Leaves serrate _____*V. scabra*
      Leaves pinnately cleft or incised_____*V. menthaefolia*
    Spikes densely-flowered, at least above
      Petioles winged _____*V. prostrata*
      Petioles not winged_____*V. hastata*

ARGENTINE VERVAIN (*Verbena bonariensis* L.)

This introduction from South America occurs sparingly in central California. It is an erect herb, $1\frac{1}{2}$ to 6 feet tall. The leaves are sessile, the blades $2\frac{1}{2}$ to $4\frac{1}{2}$ inches long, oblong, lance-shaped, and toothed. The flowers, lavender in color, are in short, dense spikes, which are clustered in a close compact cyme.

BRACTED VERVAIN (*Verbena bracteata* Lag. & Rodr.)

This species extends across the United States and southern Canada. It occurs chiefly in dry soil, sometimes a weed in pastures, lawns, and waste places. It is annual or perennial, diffusely branched, some of the branches being erect, some prostrate. The erect branches are $\frac{1}{2}$ to $1\frac{1}{2}$ feet tall. The leaves and stems throughout are rough-hairy. The leaves are wedge-shaped in outline, coarsely toothed or cut, and $\frac{1}{2}$ to 1 inch long. The flowers are in thick, leafy spikes, and only a few of them are in bloom

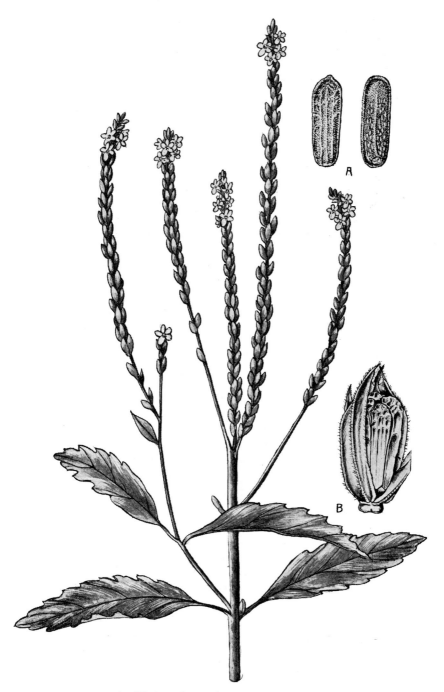

FIG. 332. Blue vervain (*Verbena hastata*). **A**, nutlets of same; **B**, fruit of prostrate vervain (*V. prostrata*).

at any one time. The corolla is a purplish blue. The flat face of the nutlet is roughened by rather sharp excrescences, the back ridged and netted above, cinnamon to drab in color, about 1.5 mm. long.

BLUE VERVAIN (*Verbena hastata* L.) (Fig. 232)

This is a native of the Eastern States and the Mississippi Valley, and has been found sparingly on the islands of the lower Sacramento River. It is a perennial with erect, angled, and coarsely grooved stems, 2 to 5 feet high. Stems and leaves are rough-hairy. The leaves are lance-shaped or oblong, taper-pointed, doubly toothed, dark green above and grayish-green beneath, and from 3 to 6 inches long. Some of the lower leaves have a pair of lobes at the base which are turned outward. The flowers are in dense spikes 2 to 3 inches long, the spikes grouped closely together. The corolla is a deep blue. The nutlets are about 2 mm. long, slender and rounded on the back, the margin more or less winged and with network toward the apex. The commissure or contact side is smooth with scattered white granules. The general color is reddish brown.

EUROPEAN VERVAIN (*Verbena menthaefolia* Benth.)
Other common name: Herb-of-the-cross.

This is an adventive from Europe, now found in southern California. It is an annual species with an erect, diffusely branched stem 1 to 3 feet high. The lower leaves are deeply cut to bipinnatifid, 1 to 1½ inches long, the upper lance-shaped, entire, toothed or deeply cut, all minutely hairy. The flowers are in slender, open spikes, white or purplish, and subtended by bracts which are shorter than the flowers. The seed is about 2 mm. long, ridged and netted on the back, granular-white on the commissure, white at the base.

PROSTRATE VERVAIN (*Verbena prostrata* R.Br.) (Fig. 232B)

This species occurs the length of the State in the coast region, on dry hillsides. It is sometimes a troublesome weed in pasture land. It is a diffusely branching and spreading perennial with stems 1 to 4 feet long. The stems and leaves are clothed with soft hairs, and grayish-green in color. The leaves are ovate or oblong, coarsely toothed, 1 to 2 inches long, and often wedge-shaped at the base. The lower leaves may be 3-parted or divided. The flowers are violet or blue, and in dense spikes, 4 to 12 inches long. Nutlets ridged on the back, scabrous with sharp excrescences on the commissure.

NETTLE-LEAF VERVAIN (*Verbena scabra* Vahl.)
Other common name: White vervain.

This species is widespread and abundant throughout eastern North America, and south to Texas and Mexico, but thus far is rare in California. It has been found in marshy land near Los Angeles and San Bernardino. It is an erect perennial, 1 to 3 feet high. The stems are slender, angled, and usually with scattered hairs. The leaves are oval or oblong-ovate, coarsely toothed and 1 to 3 inches long. The corolla is white or purplish. The nutlets are broader than the other species, the edges some-what winged, the commissures covered with irregular waxy granules.

MINT FAMILY (Labiatae)

Members of this family are aromatic plants, usually with square stems, mostly opposite leaves, and irregularly shaped flowers. The mint family is a large one, comprising many of economic importance such as thyme (*Thymus*), sage (*Salvia*), mint (*Mentha*), and *Coleus*. A considerable number are weeds.

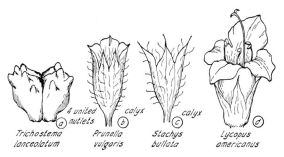

FIG. 233. Botanical characters of certain species of mint family. (a) four attached nutlets of vinegar weed; (b) calyx of self-heal; (c) calyx of hedge nettle; (d) flower of water horehound.

KEY TO GENERA OF MINT FAMILY

Ovary of 4 united nutlets; nutlets laterally attached_____*Trichostema*

Ovary of 4 distinct or nearly distinct nutlets; nutlets basally attached

  Corolla strongly 2-lipped

    Calyx with 10 spiny hooked teeth at tips_____*Marrubium*

    Calyx teeth not hooked at tip

      Upper pair of stamens longer than lower_____*Nepeta*

      Upper pair of stamens not longer than lower

        Calyx 2-lipped

          Upper calyx lip truncate_____*Prunella*

          Upper calyx lip not truncate_____*Salvia*

        Calyx 5-toothed, not 2-lipped, open in fruit

          Calyx teeth spine-tipped_____*Stachys*

        Calyx teeth not spine-tipped

          Corolla purplish red_____*Lamium*

          Corolla white_____*Molucella*

  Corolla regular or nearly so, or the lobes almost equal; herbs

    Flowers in terminal heads_____*Monardella*

    Flowers in axillary whorls

      Anther-bearing stamens 2_____*Lycopus*

      Anther-bearing stamens 4_____*Mentha*

DEAD NETTLE (*Lamium amplexicaule* L.) (Fig. 234)
Other common names: Henbit, blind nettle, bee nettle, giraffe head.

This is an introduced plant from Europe which is widespread throughout eastern United States. It is occasionally found in California, as a weed of gardens and cultivated fields. Dead nettle is a low annual or biennial, more or less decumbent at the base, with numerous upright branches, which are 4-angled, and which readily root at the lower nodes. The leaves are rounded, coarsely toothed or lobed, the upper sessile and clasping the stem, the lower with stalks; the leaves are less than an inch long and hairy. The flowers are in 1, 2, or 3 compact whorls in the leaf axils. The calyx is tubular with 5 nearly equal awl-shaped teeth. The corolla is pink to purplish, tubular and much surpasses the calyx; the corolla is 2-lipped, the upper lip hairy, the lower spotted. There are 4 hairy stamens, the upper pair being shorter than the lower. The nutlets are sharply 3-angled, grayish-brown in color, speckled with silvery-gray granules.

FIG. 234.   Dead nettle (*Lamium amplexicaule*), showing habit and (inset) seeds.

RED DEAD NETTLE (*Lamium purpureum* L.)

This native of Asia, naturalized in eastern and southern United States, Washington and Oregon, has been found by Howell as a garden weed near Kenwood, Sonoma County. It is an annual, similar to the preceding, from which it may be distinguished by the leaves, all of which are petioled.

WATER HOREHOUND (*Lycopus americanus* Muhl.) (Fig 235)
Other common name: Cut-leaf bugleweed.

This plant is a native which is distributed throughout the United States and southern Canada. In California it has been found in the San

FIG. 235. Water horehound (*Lycopus americanus*), showing habit and seeds.

Bernardino Valley, along the lower Sacramento River, and San Francisco. It occurs on low moist ground and is a weed of pastures and waste places.

This species is a bitter-tasting perennial from creeping rootstocks. The stems are erect, branching above, 4-angled, smooth or slightly hairy, often purplish below and 2 to 3 feet tall. The leaves are narrowly or broadly lance-shaped, coarsely-toothed, 1 to 2 inches long, and narrowed at the base into a slender petiole; the lower leaves are pinnatifid and green or purplish. The flowers are in dense axillary clusters. The calyx is bell-shaped, and 4 to 5 toothed. The corolla is tubular, white to pale purple, and filled with spreading hairs. There are 4 stamens, only 2 of which are anther-bearing. The nutlets are yellow to dark-brown, 2-angled, and toothed at the tip.

HOREHOUND (*Marrubium vulgare* L.) (Fig. 236)

This is a European species which has become widespread throughout the United States. It is one of the most common weeds in California. Here, it is a weed of roadsides, ditch banks, and waste places, also in meadows, pastures and old fields, and not infrequently on arid hills and mesas. It extends to fairly high elevations. It is sometimes gathered in quantity for the wholesale drug trade.

Horehound is a white-woolly perennial, with erect stems 10 to 30 inches tall. The stems are conspicuously 4-angled. The leaves are opposite, 1 to 2 inches long, petioled, roundish or ovate, green above, white-woolly underneath, the margins scalloped. Both stems and leaves have an intense bitter taste. The flowers are white, and grouped in dense clusters in the leaf axils. There is a tubular calyx with 10 spiny teeth which become recurved in fruit and, inasmuch as the calyx is persistent in the fruit, these teeth aid in fastening the seeds to the coats of animals. The corolla is 2-lipped, the upper lip 2-lobed, the lower 3-lobed. There are 4 stamens, and a single pistil with 1 style and a 4-lobed ovary. Each lobe of the ovary develops into a 1-seeded nutlet, which is rounded on the back and angled on the face, grayish-brown in color, with black or dark-brown granules over its surface.

MENTHA

There are several species of *Mentha*, occurring in California, none of which is of more than secondary importance as a weed with us.

All the species of *Mentha* are strongly aromatic perennial herbs, mostly with slender, creeping rootstocks, opposite leaves and 4-angled stems. The flowers are small and in distinct whorls. The calyx is short-tubular or bell-shaped, and usually 5-toothed. The corolla is also tubular, and 2-lipped. There are 4 nearly equal stamens, and a single pistil, with a 2-cleft stigma, and a 4-parted ovary. The seeds are rounded on the back, with two flat faces on the front, somewhat angled and raised in the center, pointed below and rounded above.

FIG. 236. Horehound (*Marrubium vulgare*).

KEY TO THE WEEDY SPECIES OF MENTHA

Whorls of flowers all axillary

    Branches leafy to the ends; leaves 2-7 cm. long; calyx-teeth
        similar and equal to nearly so_____*M. arvensis*

    Leaves toward the end of the branches reduced and inconspicuous;
        leaves 1-2 cm. long; calyx-teeth dissimilar, the 2 lower lance-
        awl-shaped _____*M. Pulegium*

Whorls of flowers in terminal spikes, or some in the upper axils

    Plants smooth or nearly so

        Leaves sessile or nearly so_____*M. spicata*

        Leaves petioled

            Leaves lance-shaped, acute; calyx hirsute_____*M. piperita*

            Leaves oval, obtuse; calyx glabrous_____*M. citrata*

    Plants hairy, at least at the nodes_____*M. rotundifolia*

TULE-MINT (*Mentha arvensis* L.)

    This is a native species which is common in marshes and meadows. Its stems are simple or branched, 1½ to 4 feet long, the herbage soft-hairy and hoary to greenish and almost smooth, the leaves ovate to oblong-lanceolate, tapering into a short stem. The whorls of flowers are often shorter than the leaf stems.

BERGAMOT MINT (*Mentha citrata* L.)

    This species is perennial, introduced from Europe, reported from Mecca, San Bernardino, Fresno, Berkeley, and Marin County. The lower leaves are broadly oval, squarish at the base.

PEPPERMINT (*Mentha piperita* L.) (Fig. 237)

    This mint has been found in the Bay area and at Los Angeles. It is naturalized from Europe, and is found along streams and in low fields. The stem is erect and commonly unbranched below the terminal flower spikes. The leaves are oblong, sharply few toothed, acute at the apex and glabrous or smooth. The spikes are dense and but slightly interrupted.

PENNYROYAL (*Mentha Pulegium* L.)

    Pennyroyal, naturalized from Europe, has been found on the islands of the lower San Joaquin, and in Sonoma and Marin Counties. The stems are 1-2 feet long, erect or rooting at the joints, the herbage pubescent with short white hairs. The leaves are 1-1½ inches long, toothed to entire, leaves more or less elliptic in shape, becoming smaller and inconspicuous towards the end of the branches.

ROUND-LEAF MINT (*Mentha rotundifolia* L.)

    This native of Europe is established locally at San Bernardino, Los Angeles and Mill Valley. It is soft-hairy or downy, the leaves sometimes white felty beneath, leaves round-ovate to broadly elliptical about 1 to 2 inches long.

SPEARMINT (*Mentha spicata* L.)

This is also a native of Europe which is fairly common in wet places about Berkeley, in the Napa Valley, Lake County, Marin County and in southern California. It is smooth, with leafy stolons and purplish stems. The spikes are leafless and about ½ inch thick. The leaves are oblong, ½ to 2 inches long, toothed on the margins.

Fig. 237. Peppermint (*Mentha piperita*).

SHELL-FLOWER (*Molucella laevis* L.)
Other common name: Molucca-balm.

This is an adventive which thus far has been found only in the foot-hills of west Colusa County. It is a native in western Europe, where it is a weed of roadsides and fields. This annual is sometimes cultivated as a curious plant in flower gardens and is called shell-flower and shell-balm because its peculiar green flowers bear some resemblance to shells. The plant is smooth throughout, 1 to 2 feet high, with rather stout branching stems. The leaves are roundish in outline with wavy margins. The flower has a white or pink-tinged corolla and a prominent net-veined, bell-shaped calyx, about $1\frac{1}{4}$ inches long, which appears very much like a green morning-glory flower. These large green calyces are persistent, finally turning whitish or straw color. They are subtended by spiny bracts. Each flower produces only 4 seeds, but the flowers are numerous, and a large proportion of them seem to have their full quota of well-developed seeds. The seeds are somewhat smaller than wheat grains, but large enough and heavy enough so that they would form a dangerous impurity in wheat.

MUSTANG MINT (*Monardella lanceolata* Gray) (Fig. 238)

This is a native species, which with its several varieties, is fairly widely distributed in California. The plant is an annual, $\frac{1}{4}$ to $2\frac{1}{2}$ feet high, with opposite, entire, oblong lance-shaped leaves $\frac{1}{2}$ to 2 inches long, and rose-purple flowers. The flowers are rather densely capitate, the corolla tube but slightly longer than the corolla limb, the bracts subtending, the heads greenish or purplish. The general structure of the flower is similar to that of coyote mint.

COYOTE MINT (*Monardella villosa* Benth.)

This native species and its several varieties occur generally throughout California in the agricultural sections, and not infrequently infest cultivated lands. It is a perennial herb, $\frac{3}{4}$ to $1\frac{1}{2}$ feet high, and somewhat tough and woody at the base. The leaves are opposite, simple, with resin dots more or less conspicuous on the lower surface, round-oval or oval to lance-shaped, somewhat toothed, $\frac{1}{2}$ to 1 inch long, and

FIG. 238.   Mustang mint (*Monardella lanceolata*).

with prominent veins. The flowers are in heads, each head being sub-tended by leaf-like, pinnately-veined bracts. The flowers have a narrow, tubular, 15-nerved calyx, the 5 teeth equal or nearly so, and hairy within; the corolla is purple to pink or dull white, with a 2-cleft upper lip and a 3-parted lower lip; there are 4 stamens, all fertile, and a deeply 4-parted ovary.

CATNIP (*Nepeta Cataria* L.) (Fig. 239)

This plant, a native of Europe, is widely distributed throughout northern United States. In California it occurs chiefly at moderate eleva-tions, being found occasionally in neglected places and in pasture lands. Catnip is a perennial, with 4-angled, downy-hairy stems 2 to 3 feet high. The leaves are triangular-ovate, heart-shaped at the base, scalloped on the margin, green above, whitish-downy beneath, and from 1 to 3 inches long. The flowers are in dense spikes 1 to 3 inches long. The calyx is tubu-lar with 5 equal teeth; the corolla is white, spotted with purple, 2-lipped, the upper lip 2-cleft, the lower 3-lobed; there are 4 stamens, the upper pair much longer than the lower; the ovary is deeply 4-lobed, and de-velops into four dark reddish-brown nutlets which have two white spots near the base.

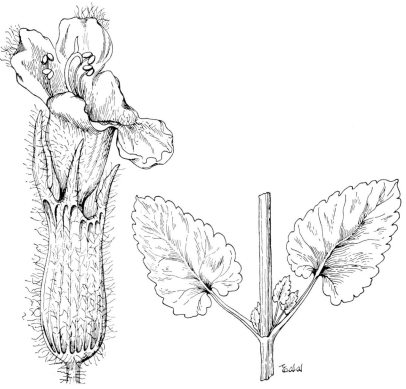

FIG. 239. Catnip (*Nepeta Cataria*).

GROUND IVY (*Nepeta hederacea* (L.) Trev.)

This species, sometimes planted as a ground cover, is closely related to catnip. It is a perennial with creeping and trailing stems, kidney-shaped leaves, and blue flowers.

SELF-HEAL (*Prunella vulgaris* L.) (Fig. 240)

This native of Europe now occurs almost throughout California as a weed in lawns and to a lesser extent in pastures and meadows. Self-heal is a low, perennial, more or less hairy plant, 4-10 inches high, which under some conditions takes on a bronzy hue throughout and so becomes quite unsightly in lawns. The leaves are oval or oblong, rounded at the base, obscurely toothed, 1-3 inches long, and petioled. The flowers are

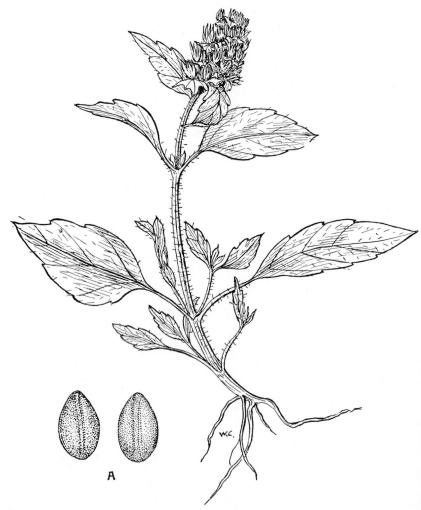

FIG. 240.   Self-heal (*Prunella vulgaris*), showing habit.   A, seeds.

violet, pinkish or lavender. The smooth seed is about 1.5 mm. long, oval, with a white point at the base; back rounded, front angled. There is a light line around the edge of each front face and down the center back. The general color is yellowish-brown to brown.

Var. *lanceolata* (Bart.) Fern. occurs in the Sierra Nevada and San Bernardino Mountains. In this variety the leaves are lance-shaped or oblong, gradually narrowing to a wedge-shaped base.

MEDITERRANEAN SAGE (*Salvia Aethiopis* L.) (Fig. 241)

This introduction from the Mediterranean region is now established in Texas, Arizona, and Oregon. In California it has been found in Modoc, Lassen, and Plumas Counties. Mediterranean sage is a biennial, forming a rosette of very large leaves the first season and a much-branched flowering stem the second season. The herbage is softly white-woolly, the whole presenting a sparsely felty appearance. In age the upper surface of the leaves often becomes more or less devoid of hairs and then the sage-like venation of the dull gray-green leaves is apparent. The squarish stems, opposite leaves, two-lipped corolla with conspicuously exserted stamens, are typical of the members of the mint family, Labiatae.

The flowering stems are about three feet tall, stout, and simple below, but divide again and again into silvery-bracted branchlets to form a spectacular inflorescence of many small white flowers. The seeds are borne in great abundance and have the form of the typical mint-sage group; rounded on the back and over the top, slightly flattened to an indistinct central ridge on the front face toward the basal scar. The surface is smooth and there is a color pattern describing an irregular venation. A quite interesting aspect of the plant, particularly from the weed dissemination standpoint, is the provision by which the seed-bearing top becomes detached at a natural joint and thereby free to roll about as a tumbleweed.

Mediterranean sage has recently developed as a troublesome and rapidly spreading pest on pasture lands.

STACHYS

Species of *Stachys* occurring in California are herbs, with rough or soft pubescence. Leaves opposite. The flowers are borne in whorls in the axils of the uppermost reduced leaves or bracts. The calyx is turbinate to tubular bell-shaped, 5 to 10-nerved or ribbed with 5 pointed teeth; corolla with cylindrical tube, the lower lip 3-lobed and longer than the upper lip; 4 stamens. Nutlets obtuse at apex.

There are 7 native perennial species, and one introduced annual species according to Jepson in "A Flora of California." The most important of these are distinguished in the following key.

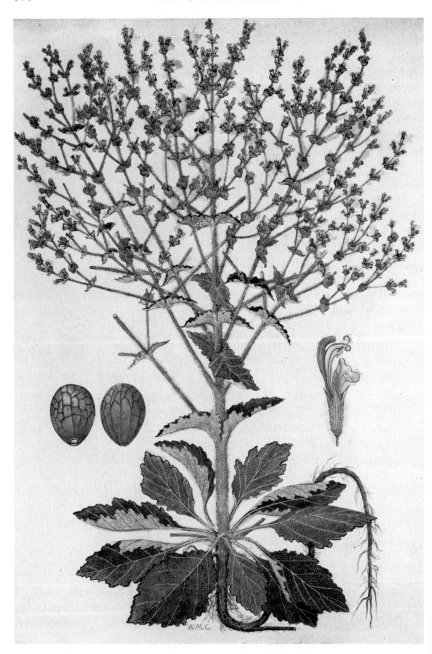

FIG. 241. Mediterranian sage (*Salvia Aethiopis*).

KEY TO WEEDY SPECIES OF STACHYS

Herbage white-woolly_____*S. albens*
Herbage hairy, but not white-woolly
  Annual _____*S. arvensis*
  Perennial
    Corolla tube 9-12 mm. long, with a horizontal hairy ring within near the base
                                                        S. bullata
    Corolla tube 5-7 mm. long, with an oblique hairy ring within about ⅓ of length
      of tube above the base_____*S. ajugoides*

WHITE STACHYS (*Stachys albens* Gray)

This species is widespread in the State, occurring from near sea-level to over 8000 feet elevation. Under favorable conditions the plants may attain a height of 8 to 10 feet; the usual height range is from 2 to 5 feet. The herbage is white-woolly; leaf blades are 1½ to 4 inches long, oval to lance-shaped, with wavy margins; spikes usually 3 to 6 inches long, dense, the number of whorls variable; corolla white, bearing within the middle an oblique ring of hairs; nutlets tuberculate.

AJUGA STACHYS (*Stachys ajugoides* Benth.)

This species is common throughout the central valley and the Coast Ranges. Plants 1 to 2 feet high, glabrous to densely hairy; leaf-blades 1 to 2½ inches long, oval to oblong; spikes 1 to 8 inches long, flower-whorls usually separated; corolla white or pinkish, the lip purple-dotted on center; corolla tube an oblique hairy ring below the middle.

Jepson recognizes a number of segregates as follows: var. *quercetorum* (Hel.) Jepson, var. *rigida* (Nutt.) Jepson and Hoover, and var. *cymosa* (Hel.) Jepson.

FIELD STACHYS OR HEDGE-NETTLE (*Stachys arvensis* L.)

This introduced annual from Europe has been collected in Humboldt, Del Norte, and Marin Counties. The plants are about 1 foot tall; stems and leaves thinly hairy; leaf-blades ½ to ¾ inch long, deltoid-ovate to elliptic, toothed; flower-whorls in upper leaf axils, and in short terminal spikes; calyx purple; corolla pale purple.

HEDGE-NETTLE (*Stachys bullata* Benth.) (Fig. 242)

This native occurs along the coast and inland at low altitudes, being found commonly along roadsides as a weed, although as such it is not of great significance. Hedge-nettle is a perennial plant with simple, erect, usually unbranched stems 1 to 2 feet high; stems 4-angled and rough-hairy, especially on the angles; leaf blades oblong-ovate or elliptic, more or less squarish at the base, coarsely scalloped along the margin, densely soft-hairy, and 1 to 3 inches long; the lower leaves have stalks 1 to 5 inches long; flowers in distinct, widely separated whorls at the top of the stem, with usually about 6 flowers in each whorl; sepals united for over half their length, and tipped by stiffly-pointed teeth; calyx persistent in the fruit; corolla purplish, tubular, more than twice the length of the calyx; lower lip of corolla bears on its inner surface a transverse hairy ring near the base; nutlets broadly and obtusely oval, rounded on the back and only slightly flattened on the front faces.

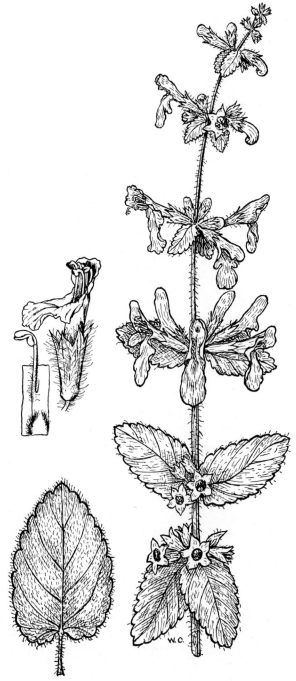

Fig. 242.   Hedge nettle (*Stachys bullata*). Note detail of flower structure and of single stamen.

VINEGAR WEED (*Trichostema lanceolatum* Benth.) (Fig. 243)
Other common names: Camphor weed, blue-curls.

This is an important bee-plant which is abundant and widely distributed throughout California up to 2,600 feet. It is an ill-scented annual herb, with very leafy stems which are 6 to 16 inches tall. The herbage is very hairy, and minutely glandular. The leaves are simple, opposite, lance-shaped, ¾ to 1¼ inches long, and sessile. The flowers are in axillary groups. The calyx is 5-cleft, the corolla slender tubular, and much larger than the calyx, and abruptly curved into an arc of a circle just below the 5-lobed limb. There are 4 stamens with filaments which are long exserted at maturity, curving outward and downward. There are 4 nutlets, attached by the sides. The seed is about 2 mm. long, broadly club-shaped, rounded on the back, the front faces flattened toward an angle. The back is irregularly ridged below, coarsely netted above, the network extended into more or less well-developed points around the edge and over the top.

POTATO FAMILY
(Solanaceae)

The potato family is a large one, chiefly tropi-

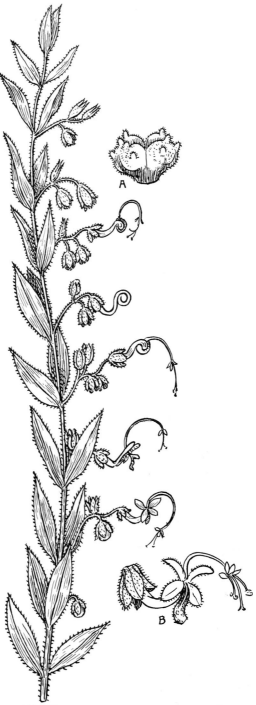

FIG. 243. Vinegar weed (*Trichostema lanceolatum*). A, four nutlets attached; B, flower.

cal. It has about 2,000 species. A number of these are important medicinal and food plants. Here are included such economic forms as red or Cayenne pepper, tobacco, common Irish potato, egg plant, tomato, belladonna, which furnishes the atropin of commerce, petunia, etc. There are also several noxious weeds in the family.

KEY TO GENERA IN POTATO FAMILY

Fruit a berry or at least not dehiscent
  Anthers coming together or converging around the style; anthers
    opening by a pore or slit near the tip_____*Solanum*
  Anthers not coming together or converging around the styles;
  anthers opening by a longitudinal slit
    Calyx in fruit large and bladdery; herbs_____ _____*Physalis*
    Calyx in fruit not large and bladdery; shrubs
      Plants spiny _____*Lycium*
      Plants not spiny_____*Salpichroa*
Fruit capsule-like, mostly dehiscent
  Capsule prickly; flowers very large_____*Datura*
  Capsule not prickly_____*Nicotiana*

KEY TO WEEDY SPECIES OF DATURA

Corolla large, 6 to 8 inches long; perennial_____*D. meteloides*
Corolla white or purplish-white, 2 to 4 inches long; annual
  Prickles numerous, subequal, relatively short_____*D. Stramonium and var.*
  Prickles few, the upper very long and heavy_____ _____*D. ferox*

CHINESE THORNAPPLE (*Datura ferox* W.) (Fig. 244)

This species recorded from Asia, occurs sparingly in California in the northern Sacramento Valley. The spines on the pod are wide at the base, few in number and over an inch long.

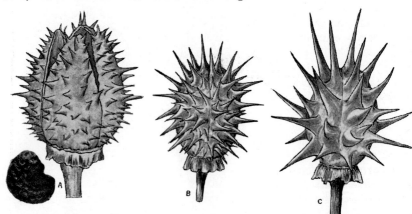

FIG. 244. Capsules of **A**, Jimson weed (*Datura Stramonium*); **B**, purple thornapple (var. *Tatula*); **C**, Chinese thornapple (*D. ferox*).

TOLGUACHA (*Datura meteloides* DC.) (Fig. 245)

This is a very conspicuous *Datura*, but of little significance as a weed. It is a native of the western and southwestern United States. The plant is an erect, branching perennial, 2 to 3 feet high, with large white flowers tinged with violet, the corolla often being 8 inches long and 3 to 6 inches wide. The capsule is globular, about 1 inch in diameter, and densely prickly. The seeds are light yellowish-brown in color, smooth, and bordered by a somewhat wavy, grooved margin.

This thornapple is regarded as poisonous to livestock.

FIG. 245. Tolguacha (*Datura meteloides*).

JIMSON WEED (*Datura Stramonium* L.) (Fig. 244)
Other common names: Stramonium, Jamestown-weed thornapple, mad-apple, stink-wort.

This is a naturalized tropical weed which is widely spread in the warmer parts of the State but is nowhere very abundant. It may be found along roadsides, in corrals, waste places, and in cultivated fields.

Jimson weed is a coarse, rank-smelling annual with erect, stout, greenish stems 1 to 5 feet high. The leaves are alternate, simple, smooth and thin, 3 to 8 inches long and about half as wide, unevenly toothed, and borne on stout stalks. The flowers are solitary in the axils of the leaves, white or purplish-white, and have a fetid odor. The calyx is 5-toothed and encloses the lower part of the corolla-tube. The corolla is funnel-form, 5-lobed, and 4 to 5 inches long. There are 5 stamens attached to the inside of the corolla tube, a single ovary, and a long style with a 2-lobed stigma. The fruit is a hard, prickly oval capsule, about 2 inches long filled with many dark-brown to black, flat seeds, rounded on the back and concave on the scar edge. The surface is minutely pitted and wrinkled with larger dimple-like depressions.

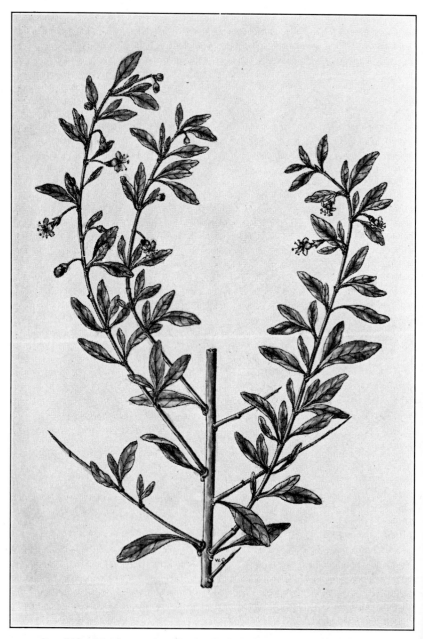

Fig. 246.   Matrimony vine (*Lycium halimifolium*) showing general habit.

It contains atropin and hyoscyamin, and is somewhat poisonous to animals. All parts of the plant are toxic, the seeds being the most so.

Purple thornapple (var. *Tatula* (L.) Torr.) has a purple-tinged stem, corolla lavender, prickles definitely subequal. This ill-scented toxic weed is generally avoided by livestock.

CHINESE MATRIMONY VINE (*Lycium chinense* Mill.)

Similar to the following, this east Asian species is reported as an escape in Solano County and elsewhere. It is usually without barbs, and has larger berries.

MATRIMONY VINE (*Lycium halimifolium* Mill.) (Fig. 246)
Other common names: Jacksonvine, boxthorn.

Matrimony vine, which was introduced from Europe, is established as a garden escape from Ontario to Virginia, Minnesota, and Kansas. It has been reported as noxious in scattered locations from Modoc to San Diego County. This escaped ornamental has attractive lavender flowers and small orange-red berries, both being present simultaneously and in great abundance under favorable conditions. Late in the summer the short lateral branchlets lose their leaves and become straw-colored and rigid. In this stage the plant may be described as having long trailing branches armed with strong sharp barbs. Vacant lots, edges of fields, and waste places occasionally present impenetrable spiny thickets. The seeds, borne in a small fleshy pear-shaped berry, are like very small tomato seeds, somewhat pointed at the scar end.

This plant contains an alkaloid that may cause poisoning of sheep and cattle.

TOBACCO. NICOTIANA

There are 5 species of *Nicotiana* in California, 4 of which are sometimes weeds or poisonous plants. All of them are heavy-scented plants, usually sticky and hairy, with entire, alternate leaves. The calyx is 5-toothed or 5-lobed and more or less invests the fruit. The corolla is funnel-form or salver-form and 5-lobed. There are 5 stamens attached to the corolla tube, and a single pistil with a 2-celled ovary, 1 style and a stigma which is entire or sometimes 2-lobed. The fruit is a 2-celled, smooth capsule containing many small seeds.

Tree tobacco, desert tobacco, and coyote tobacco are known to be poisonous to livestock.

KEY TO WEEDY SPECIES OF NICOTIANA

Shrub; flowers yellow; herbage smooth_____*N. glauca*
Annual herb; flowers white, cream or greenish; herbage sticky
    Leaves with ear-like lobes at the base; flowers open during the day__*N. trigonophylla*
    Leaves petioled or sessile, without ear-like lobes at the base; flowers open at night
        Limb of corolla less than ½ inch broad_____*N. attenuata*
        Limb of corolla ¾ to 1 inch broad_____*N. Bigelovii*

COYOTE TOBACCO (*Nicotiana attenuata* Torr.)

This is a sticky, ill-smelling annual herb, 2 to 4 feet high, with white or greenish flowers, the corolla tube of which is 1 to 1½ inches long and the corolla limb less than ½ inch broad. It is common throughout California up to 4,000 feet on dry stream beds and sandy flats. This, and the following species, were used by the Indians as a smoking tobacco and undoubtedly they cultivated them to some extent. Acc. Howell— *N. acuminata* (Grah.) Hook var. *multiflora* (Phil.) Reiche.

FIG. 247. Tree tobacco (*Nicotiana glauca*).

INDIAN TOBACCO (*Nicotiana Bigelovii* (Torr.) Wats.)

This is an annual, resembling the foregoing although it is usually less tall, being 1½ to 2 feet high. The flowers are fewer than in *N. attenuata*, the corolla tube about 1½ inches long, its limb 1 inch wide. It occurs throughout California in the valleys and foothills, on flood plains and occasionally in cultivated areas.

TREE TOBACCO (*Nicotiana glauca* Graham) (Fig. 247)

This is a soft, smooth evergreen shrub 6 to 15 feet high with large bluish-green leaves and yellow flowers, the corolla of which is about 1½ inches long. It is naturalized from South America and is widespread in the interior of California, occurring along stream beds and in waste places. Poisonous when eaten by livestock.

DESERT TOBACCO (*Nicotiana trigonophylla* Dunal.)

This tobacco is a slender, sticky-hairy annual herb 1 to 3 feet tall, with broadly oblong to ovate leaves, the upper sessile, the lower with a short-winged stalk. The flowers are cream or greenish-white, tube not much over ½ inch long, the limb less than ½ inch wide. It occurs in the Colorado and Mojave deserts on sandy or rocky soil. Toxic to livestock.

TOMATILLO (*Physalis ixocarpa* Brot.) (Fig. 248)
Other common name: Ground-cherry.

Tomatillo is naturalized from Mexico, and is now a fairly common orchard weed in central and southern California. This species is an annual, much branched, smooth or sparingly hairy on the young parts. The leaves are oval or heart-shaped at the base, deeply cut or entire on the margins, the stem about the same length as the blade. Flowers are borne singly in the leaf axils. The corolla is about ½ inch in diameter, with a dark purplish center. The large purple-tinged berry bursts the calyx.

This is sometimes grown for its edible fruits.

LANCE-LEAF GROUND-CHERRY (*Physalis lanceifolia* Nees.)

This annual ground-cherry is sometimes abundant in the rice fields of the northern Sacramento Valley, and extends to southern California and into Texas and South America. The plant is about 8 inches to 2 feet tall, herbage smooth, yellowish-green. The lanceolate leafblades are about 1 to 3 inches long, their margins subentire to shallowly toothed. The corolla is yellow, about ¼ inch broad. The greenish ''cherry,'' enclosed in the loose calyx, is about ½ inch in diameter.

NEW MEXICO HUSK TOMATO (*Physalis neomexicana* Rydb.)

This stout annual, a native of Colorado and Mexico, is rare in California; collected at Elsinore. The leaf blades are ovate, obtuse, 1 to 3½

FIG. 248.   Tomatillo (*Physalis ixocarpa*).

inches long, coarsely toothed or wavy on the margin, with a fine short pubescence. Peduncle ½ inch long in fruit; calyx ¾ to 1 inch long.

HUSK TOMATO (*Physalis pubescens* L.)
Common name: Ground-cherry.

Husk tomato has been introduced into California from the southeastern United States, and is less abundant than tomatillo. The plant is diffusely branched and angled, about 6 inches to over a foot tall, silky hairy. The leaf blades are ovate, oblique at the base with the margins almost entire, the petioles about the same length as the blade. The corolla is wheel-shaped, like that of a tomato flower. In fruit the calyx is membranous and bladdery-inflated and completely covers the berry. The corolla is yellow with a dark center; the small yellow berries are enclosed in the husk-like calyx.

LILY-OF-THE-VALLEY VINE (*Salpichroa rhomboidea* Miers) (Fig. 249)

Lily-of-the-valley vine is an ornamental which has recently been reported from Kern, Santa Cruz, Ventura, Los Angeles, San Luis Obispo,

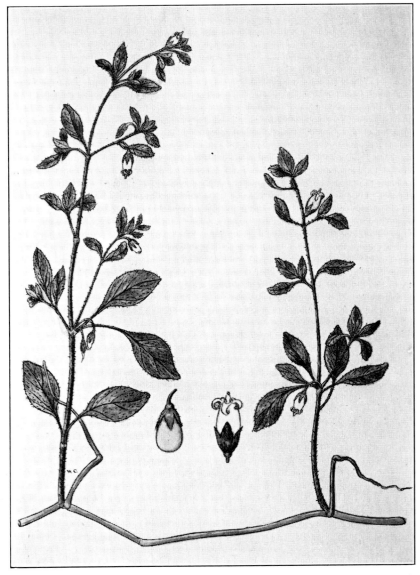

FIG. 249. Lily-of-the-valley vine (*Salpichroa rhomboidea*) showing general habit, with detail of fruit and flower.

and Yolo Counties, and as abundant in Golden Gate Park. Heretofore we have records of its establishment in San Francisco, San Diego, Sacramento, and San Joaquin Counties. This is a South American plant, with attractive dark-green foliage, graceful trailing habit and delicate white flowers, followed by yellowish or white berries, with small tomato-like seeds. It is possessed of a most tenacious root system which enables the plant to persist under adverse conditions and overrun garden areas or empty lots. It tolerates alkali and will thrive under intense heat and drouth.

NIGHTSHADE *SOLANUM*

KEY TO WEEDY SPECIES OF SOLANUM

Plants armed with spines
  Perennial, berry not enclosed by calyx
    Densely silvery-hairy, leaves slender, entire or the margin uneven _*S. elaeagnifolium*
    Sparsely stiff hairy, not silvery
      Leaves ovate or oblong, coarsely lobed or shallowly scalloped
        Calyx lobes gradually tapering to a slender point, berry
          1-1.5 cm. _____*S. carolinense*
        Calyx lobes broad, abruptly short-pointed, berry about 2 cm._____*S. Torreyi*
      Leaves lanceolate, spines sparse, obscure or rarely absent_____*S. lanceolatum*
  Annual, berry partly or wholly enclosed by the spiny calyx
    Corolla yellow, herbage densely stellate pubescent, spines subulate___*S. rostratum*
    Corolla whitish, herbage villous-pubescent with long viscid hairs,
      spines flattened _____*S. sisymbriifolium*
Plants not armed with spines
  Peduncles much shorter than the pedicels, or almost none,
    corolla blue-purple _____*S. Xantii*
  Peduncles as long as, or longer than, the pedicels, corolla whitish
    Leaves deeply pinnatifid_____*S. triflorum*
    Leaves entire, bluntly lobed or uneven on the margin
      Plants conspicuously hairy, calyx at maturity enveloping lower
        part of berry, ripe berry greenish_____*S. sarachoides*
      Mature plants sparsely pubescent or smooth, ripe berry black
        Peduncle deflexed at maturity, filaments unequal, mature berries
          immediately deciduous when ripe, straggling perennial_____*S. furcatum*
        Peduncle erect at maturity, filaments nearly or quite equal,
          mature berries persisting on plant when ripe
          Flowers large, corolla lobes 6-11 mm., style exserted, 2 mm.
            beyond anthers, stigma very slightly expanded, bushy_____*S. Douglasii*
          Flowers small, corolla lobes 3-7 mm., style barely exserted
            beyond anthers; stigma enlarged, capitate
            Leaves firm in texture, calyx lobes all distinct, reflexed at
              maturity _____*S. nodiflorum*
            Leaves thin in texture, calyx lobes unequal and some partly
              fused, not reflexed at maturity (cultivated) _____*S. nigrum*

CAROLINA HORSENETTLE (*Solanum carolinense* L.) (Fig. 250)

    Carolina horsenettle is a native in the southern United States. It was introduced into the Northeastern States and is spreading west and south. The pernicious nature of this *Solanum* is indicated by the fact that it is declared noxious by the seed laws of the following states: New Jersey, Pennsylvania, Indiana, Iowa, Minnesota and Oklahoma. It has been

FIG. 250.   Carolina horsenettle (*Solanum carolinense*).

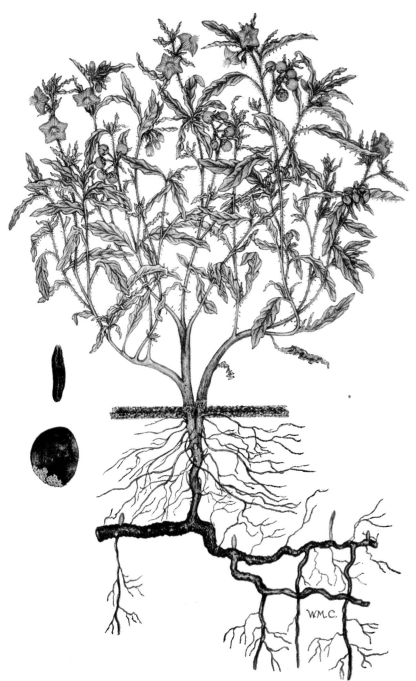

FIG. 251. White horsenettle (*Solanum elaeagnifolium*).

reported from Yuba, Stanislaus, Ventura and Orange Counties. Where the weed has become established it is found growing in both cultivated ground and pasture land, favoring sandy well-drained situations. It is a pest in pastures, becoming so dense as to crowd out other forms of vegetation. Because of the deep roots and creeping habit, this horsenettle is extremely difficult to eradicate once well established.

Carolina horsenettle is a strong perennial, spreading both by means of rootstocks and numerous seeds. It is an erect, loosely branching plant, from 1 to 4 feet tall. Branches, stems, and midveins, and sometimes even the lateral veins of the leaves, are armed with straight awl-like yellow spines. The leaves are roughened by fine star-shaped hairs, 4- to 8-rayed, which may be readily distinguished with the aid of a hand lens. The alternate leaves are about 2 to 6 inches long, oblong to ovate in outline, with unevenly lobed, wavy margins.

The flowers are borne in clusters along the sides of the stem, although at first they appear terminal. They are similar in shape to the potato, tomato and other solanaceous flowers, five-lobed and about $\frac{3}{4}$ to $1\frac{1}{4}$ inches in diameter. The corolla is bluish-white to pale violet, with the stamens on short filaments united into a conelike form, protruding from the center of the corolla.

The fruit is a smooth, globular, tomato-like berry, about $\frac{1}{2}$ inch or more in diameter, orange-yellow in color, with soft pulpy interior. The seeds are flattened laterally, pale yellow to golden brown in color, with what appears to the naked eye to be a smooth surface, but which is granular or pebbly-roughened when seen through a lens.

Sheep are the only animals which will graze on Carolina horsenettle; they feed chiefly on the berries, and thereby scatter the seed through droppings.

DOUGLAS BLACK NIGHTSHADE (*Solanum Douglasii* Dunal)

Solanum Douglasii is similar to *S. nodiflorum*, but is a perennial; bushy in habit. It is a native species and has been recorded from Sacramento County south to coastal southern California and eastward through the deserts. The herbage is minutely soft hairy. The flowers are white, in form quite like *L. nodiflorum*, but definitely larger, corolla lobes 6-11 mm. long. The mature berry is black, similar to *S. nodiflorum*, but larger, 6-9 mm. thick. They persist on the bush in the ripened condition.

This nightshade has been suspected in livestock poisoning.

WHITE HORSENETTLE (*Solanum elaeagnifolium* Cav.) (Fig. 251)
Other common names: Silverleaved nightshade, bull nettle, trompilla, sand brier.

White horsenettle is a native of western United States from Missouri to Arizona. It is quite generally distributed throughout the San Joaquin Valley, with particularly heavy infestations in Kern County. The coastal northern and southern counties have small and scattered infestations, confined largely to railroad rights-of-way. It was brought in with bedding in stock cars, and there is also evidence that the seed was brought in with feed stuffs.

White horsenettle is a perennial branching herb, from 1 to 3 feet high. The roots and rootstocks are deep-seated. The stems are usually provided with very slender, sharp prickles; sometimes, however, these are wanting. The leaves are lance-shaped, oblong or linear, being from 1 to 4 inches long and from ¼ to 1 inch wide; the leaves have a stalk or petiole and are often wavy-margined; all the leaves, as well as the stems, have a silvery appearance due to a dense, scurf-like hairy covering. Under the hand lens it will be observed that the hairs show 4 to 8 rays appearing like a star. The flowers are blue or violet in color, ¾ to 1 inch broad. The ovary of the flower is covered with white woolly hairs. An examination of the stamens shows that one of them, the lower, is much longer than the other four.

The fruit is a smooth berry, spherical in shape, dull yellow or orange in color and about ½ inch in diameter. There are a number of seeds in each berry. They are brownish-drab, slightly unevenly circular in out line, smooth and shiny appearing but minutely granular under a lens. Remnants of dried pulp often adhere to the seed, giving it a scurfy ap pearance.

SOUTH AMERICAN BLACK NIGHTSHADE (*Solanum furcatum*) (Fig. 252)

This straggly perennial, a native of South America, has been intro duced and is established mainly along the coast from Humboldt to San Mateo County. It is similar to *S. Douglasii*, but differs in the following respects. The fruiting pedicel is deflexed at maturity, and the mature berries are immediately deciduous when ripened. This nightshade spreads mainly through a slow but persistent enlargement of the straggly clumps.

LANCEOLATE NIGHTSHADE (*Solanum lanceolatum* Cav.)

This native of Mexico has escaped from cultivation and become a difficult weed pest in various garden sites from central to southern Cali fornia. It is a strong perennial, with extensively spreading deep-seated creeping root system. The lance-shaped leaves are relatively large, com monly 4-6 inches long. The stems and leaves are heavily clothed with star-shaped hairs, giving the plant a dark gray-green appearance. The showy corolla is violet-blue on the inner surface, densely white-pubescent on the outer. The calyx lobes are about ½ inch long, gradually narrowing to a greatly elongated apex.

AMERICAN BLACK NIGHTSHADE (*Solanum nodiflorum* Jacq.)

This member of the nightshade family, introduced from tropical America, is found throughout California. It is most common along the coast usually occurring in shady moist places. This nightshade may grow either as an annual or perennial. The leaves are firm in texture, flowers small, lobes 3-7 mm. from base of corolla; stigma enlarged and capitate. The stems subtending the berries are erect at maturity, the

berries retained in the ripened stage; glossy black. The sepals are separate from each other and reflexed at maturity. The seeds are smaller
than those of *S. nigrum*.

This species has been suspected in cases of livestock poisoning.

EUROPEAN BLACK NIGHTSHADE (*Solanum nigrum* L.)

This introduction from Europe probably occurs in California only
as a garden plant. It is low and spreading or sometimes tall, 1 to 3 feet
across. The leaves are dark green, 1-3 inches long with entire or wavy
margins. The flowers are whitish, or slightly purplish-tinged, in more or

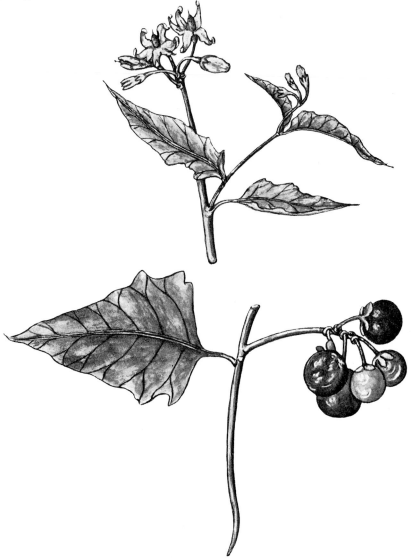

FIG. 252. South American black nightshade (*Solanum furcatum*) x 1½.

less drooping clusters, the corolla lobes 3-7 mm. long. The calyx is of 5 small lobes, more or less fused and not reflexed at maturity. The fruit is a depressed-globose berry, up to ½ inch or more in diameter on cultivated plants. The seeds are large, 1.7-2.2 mm. long.

This is the "Wonder-berry" or "Garden Huckleberry" of horticulture. The herbage and green fruits are considered toxic; the ripe berries reputedly edible.

BUFFALO BUR (*Solanum rostratum* Dunal.) (Fig. 253)
Other common names: Colorado bur, Texas thistle, sandbur, beaked nightshade.

This plant is a native of the Great Plains region from Nebraska to Texas; it is spreading rapidly westward and eastward. It has been found at widely scattered localities in California. It occurs in feed lots, in waste places, in fields and pastures.

Buffalo bur is erect, branched, annual, ½ to 2 feet high. The stems and leaf-stalks are covered with many stout yellow prickles ⅛ to ½ inch long. The leaves are 2 to 6 inches long, deeply cut, and covered with yellow, forked hairs, the veins and midribs, as well as the leaf-stalks being very prickly. The flowers are yellow, the calyx being densely prickly, and persistent, and enlarging in the fruit, the corolla wheel-shaped and 5-lobed. The fruit is a berry which is enclosed within the spiny calyx, forming a spiny bur. The seeds are dull, brownish-black, flattened and coarsely pitted.

The burs may cause mechanical injury to livestock, but the plant has not been proved poisonous.

HAIRY NIGHTSHADE (*Solanum sarachoides* Sendt.)

Hairy nightshade is similar in general appearance to black nightshade. It is an annual species, introduced from South America and recorded from widely scattered locations as at Eureka, Mono Lake, Vallejo, Santa Ana River. The herbage is conspicuously spreading-hairy. The apex of the pedicel and the calyx are strongly expanded at maturity, the calyx embracing the lower part of the berry, which is greenish when ripe.

This species contains a bitter alkaloid, *solanin*, which is poisonous to animals; green berries especially should be avoided. Feeding tests with poultry and guinea pigs demonstrated herbage and unripe fruits were toxic.

RED BERRIED OR VISCID NIGHTSHADE (*Solanum sisymbriifolium* Lam.)

This annual, adventive from tropical America, is reported from the San Marcos Pass, Santa Barbara County, and at other scattered sites in southern California. It has long and short prickles abundant on the calyx, as well as the stems, leaves and pedicels. The leaves are deeply pinnatifid, corolla bluish or white, the fruiting calyx loosely embracing the red berry.

TORREY'S NIGHTSHADE (*Solanum Torreyi*, A. Gray)

This species, which is very closely related to *S. carolinense* is troublesome and of frequent occurrence in the southwest. Torrey's nightshade, reported from Placer County and Ventura County, is very densely

FIG. 253. Buffalo bur, *Solanum rostratum*. Left, seed.

pubescent, felty to the touch, the hairs 8 to 12 rayed. The berry is bright yellow when ripe, about ¾ inch in diameter.

CUT-LEAVED NIGHTSHADE (*Solanum triflorum* Nutt.)

This is an annual species, native in the Great Plains and spreading westward. It has been reported in California from Los Angeles, San Luis Obispo and Lassen Counties. Cut-leaved nightshade is of erect habit, or prostrately spreading, 1 to 3 feet tall. The leaves vary from 2 to 4 inches in length and are deeply cut about half way to the midvein into from

7 to 9 rounded or pointed lobes. The plant is smooth to somewhat hairy with simple unbranched hairs. The flowers are borne in clusters of from 1 to 3 in the leaf axils, corolla white, slightly less than ½ inch across The berry is globose, green or yellowish, about ¼ inch in diameter. The dull light yellowish-brown seeds are unevenly circular, flattened and minutely pitted.

PURPLE NIGHTSHADE (*Solanum Xantii* Gray)

This native herbaceous perennial, including several varieties, occurs in the foothills and mountains from 100 to 4,000 feet scattered almost throughout California. The typically gray-pubescent, sometimes green stems arise from a woody rootcrown. The flowers are few in a cluster corolla light purplish-blue. This species is frequently reported from foothill and mountain range lands.

FIGWORT FAMILY *(Scrophulariaceae)*

Members of this rather large family vary considerably in habits Some forms are poisonous, a few medicinal, a number are weeds, and a large number are in ornamental use. Common ornamentals are snap dragon (*Antirrhinum*), beard-tongue (*Pentstemon*), *Calceolaria,* and foxglove (*Digitalis*).

KEY TO GENERA IN FIGWORT FAMILY

Anther-bearing stamens 5; leaves alternate; flowers regular_____*Verbascum*
Anther-bearing stamens less than 5; leaves alternate or opposite; flowers irregular
   Corolla with a spur at base of tube_____*Linaria*
   Corolla without a spur at base of tube
      Upper lip of corolla helmet-like; leaves opposite_____*Bellardia*
      Upper lip of corolla not helmet-like
         Stamens 5, 4 anther-bearing, the 5th sterile
            Flowers in whorls_____*Collinsia*
            Flowers not in whorls_____*Scrophularia*
         Stamens 4 or 2, 5th stamen entirely absent
            Leaves alternate; stamens 4_____*Digitalis*
            Leaves opposite, at least the lower
               Corolla 4-lobed; calyx 4-parted_____*Veronica*
               Corolla 2-lipped
                  Corolla tubular or funnel form_____*Mimulus*
                  Corolla bell-shaped_____*Bacopa*

ROUND-LEAF WATER HYSSOP (*Bacopa rotundifolia* (Michx.) Wettst.) (Fig. 254)

This perennial herb occurs in ponds and muddy situations in the San Joaquin and Sacramento Valleys. The creeping stems are lax, fleshy 10 to 14 inches long, smooth to soft hairy, forming floating mats. The leaves are opposite, round, sessile, with a fan-shaped venation; about ½ inch long. The flowers are solitary in the leaf axils, white in color, the corolla bell-shaped, the upper lobe 2-lobed, the lower 3-lobed. There are 4 anther-bearing stamens and a 2-valved capsule.

Where this water hyssop is thick in rice fields, it retards the growth of the young rice plants but usually disappears late in the season.

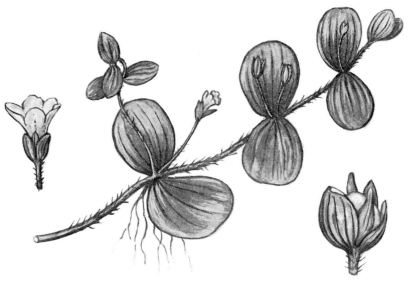

FIG. 254. Round-leaf water hyssop (*Bacopa rotundifolia*).

BELLARDIA (*Bellardia Trixago* (L.) All.) (Fig. 255)
This is a naturalized plant from Europe occurring in old fields at Pacheco, East Oakland, Berkeley, Mt. Diablo, and Napa. It is an erect, finely-hairy annual herb, ½ to 1½ feet high. The leaves are opposite, lance-shaped, and coarsely toothed. The flowers are in a dense, thick, somewhat 4-sided terminal spike. The flowers are white, the calyx deeply cleft before and behind, the corolla 2-lipped, the stamens 4 with broad filaments and the anthers densely short hairy near the margins. The fruit is a swollen capsule.

CHINESE HOUSES (*Collinsia bicolor* Benth.) (Fig. 256)
This is a native annual, widespread throughout the State, frequently occurring in cultivated fields. However, it is not a troublesome weed. The plants are ½ to 1½ feet tall, smooth or finely-hairy throughout, and

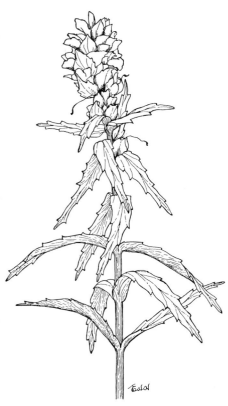

FIG. 255. Bellardia (*Bellardia Trixago*).

often sticky above. The leaves are opposite, broadly oblong, finely toothed, and 1 to 2 inches long. The flowers are in whorls, usually the whorls being widely separated, thus suggesting the common name "Chinese houses." The calyx is 5-cleft; the corolla is strongly 2-lipped, usually less than 1 inch long, the lower lip violet or rose-purple, the upper lilac or white. The fruit is a 2-celled capsule, usually with about 6 seeds in each cell.

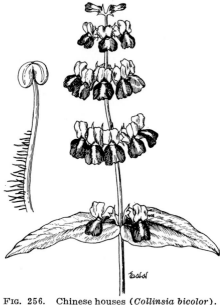

FOXGLOVE (*Digitalis purpurea* L.)

This European garden plant is naturalized in the coastal sections of Humboldt and Mendocino Counties. It is a tall hairy biennial herb, 2 to 6 feet tall, with alternate, broadly lance-shaped leaves with toothed margins; the lower leaves are 6 to 12 inches long and stalked, the upper smaller and sessile. The flowers are showy and grouped in long, terminal one-sided racemes. Each flower has. a trumpet-shaped, purple to white, drooping corolla, about ½ inch long, and red-spotted on the inside. The fruit is an oval capsule containing numerous rough, brown seeds.

FIG. 256. Chinese houses (*Collinsia bicolor*). At left is detail of single stamen.

When green or in hay, foxglove occasionally poisons horses.

DOPATRIUM (*Dopatrium junceum* (Roxb.) Buch.-Ham.)

This fragile aquatic plant is a native of southeastern Asia, reported from India, China and Japan. It is more or less abundant in the rice fields of the northern Sacramento Valley. The slender, strict, erect stems vary in length from a few inches to a foot or more. The leaves are opposite, relatively small and bract-like. The flowers are sub-sessile, the pedicel much shorter than the capsule. The calyx lobes are about one-half the length of the capsule; flowers violet. The capsule is loculicidal; the numerous minute seed, slender spindle-shape.

TOADFLAX. *LINARIA*

KEY TO WEEDY SPECIES OF LINARIA

Flowers solitary in the axils of the leaves
  Leaves triangular or hastate_____*L. Elatine*
  Leaves oval to round, heart-shaped or rounded at the base_____*L. Spuria*
Flowers in terminal racemes
  Flowers yellow; perennial_____*L. vulgaris*
  Flowers blue or white; annual or biennial_____*L. canadensis*

BLUE TOADFLAX (*Linaria canadensis* Dum.)

This is a native of North America and South America, and is widely distributed in California, although nowhere abundant. It is usually found growing in sandy soil. It is an annual or biennial, smooth, green herb, sometimes somewhat fleshy, the flowering stems 1 to 2 feet high. The lower leaves are opposite, the upper alternate. The leaves are entire, sessile, ½ to 2 inches long and strap-shaped. The flowers are in loose, terminal racemes. Each flower has a 5-parted calyx, a 2-lipped, blue corolla, the lower lip closing the opening to the corolla tube, 4 stamens in unequal pairs, and a single ovary. The fruit is a rounded capsule, many-seeded, and opens by pores or slits just below the tip.

SHARP-POINTED TOADFLAX (*Linaria Elatine* (L.) Miller) (Fig. 257)

This species is a prostrate and spreading hairy annual. It is an introduction from the Old World, occurring sparingly in California. It has been found in Orange County, at Wintersberg, and in Yolo County. The leaves are oval, short-petioled, ½ to 1 inch long, and triangular or hastate in shape. The flowers are spurred, and 2-lipped, the corolla being yellowish and somewhat purplish beneath. The fruit is a subglobose capsule, shorter than the calyx, and opens by 1 or 2 terminal slits or pores. There are numerous seeds, oval, mostly rough or tubercled, and wingless. (*Kickxia Elatine* (L.) Dumont.)

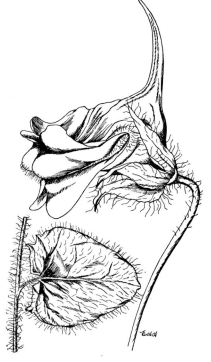

ROUND-LEAVED TOADFLAX (*Linaria Spuria* Mill.) (Fig. 258)

This species resembles *L. Elatine* except that the leaves are oval to round, and heart-shaped or rounded at the base. It is also an adventive from Europe, which occurs sparingly in California, chiefly the southern part. (*Kickxia Spuria* (L.) Dumont.)

BUTTER-AND-EGGS (*Linaria vulgaris* Mill.)

FIG. 257. Sharp-pointed toadflax (*Linaria Elatine*), showing detail of flower and leaf.

This European introduction, which is a bad weed throughout the Eastern States occurs sparingly in California. It is reported from the San Francisco Bay area, Sonoma County, and at Upland. It is a perennial with yellow flowers.

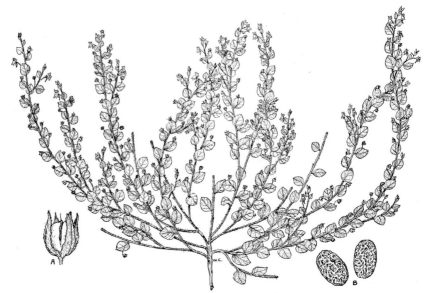

FIG. 258. Round-leaved toadflax (*Linaria Spuria*). **A**, capsule; **B**, seeds.

COMMON MONKEY-FLOWER (*Mimulus guttatus* DC.) (Fig. 259)

This native, which is represented by several varieties, occurs in moist places throughout the State up to 6,000 feet. It is occasionally a weed of moist meadows. It is an erect annual or perennial and rooting at the joints. The leaves are opposite, more or less elliptical, palmately-veined, thin, irregularly toothed, the lower petioled, the upper sessile. The inflorescence is a terminal raceme. The calyx is 5-angled and 5-toothed; the corolla is yellow with purple or brown dots, tubular, strongly 2-lipped, and ¾ to 1½ inches long; there are 4 stamens and a single pistil with a 2-lobed stigma; the fruit is an oval capsule with thin, hard walls.

FIGWORT (*Scrophularia californica* Cham.) (Fig. 260)

This native species occurs in the hills throughout California up to 6,000 feet. It is a rank-growing perennial herb, from 3 to 6 feet tall. The leaves are opposite, oval, heart-shaped at the base, and toothed. The flowers are arranged in a narrow, terminal panicle. The flowers are small, the corolla being about ⅓ inch long, and of dull-reddish color; a nectar disk occurs at the flower base. Each flower has a 5-parted calyx, a somewhat globular corolla tube, the two upper lobes of which are longer than the two laterals and the very short deflexed lower lobe, 4 fertile stamens, the fifth sterile, and a 2-celled ovary. The fruit is a many-seeded capsule, the seeds very small, rough and dark brown.

VERBASCUM

There are three species of *Verbascum* occurring in California, all of which are naturalized from Europe. They are tall annual or biennial herbs with long, slender erect stems and alternate leaves. The flowers are short-lived and occur in spikes or racemes. The calyx is 5-parted, the corolla wheel-shaped, 5-parted, and yellow or whitish. There are 5 stamens, all anther-bearing, with 3 of the filaments woolly. There is a single pistil, with a 2-celled ovary and 1 style. The fruit is a 2-valved capsule, containing numerous pitted or roughened seeds.

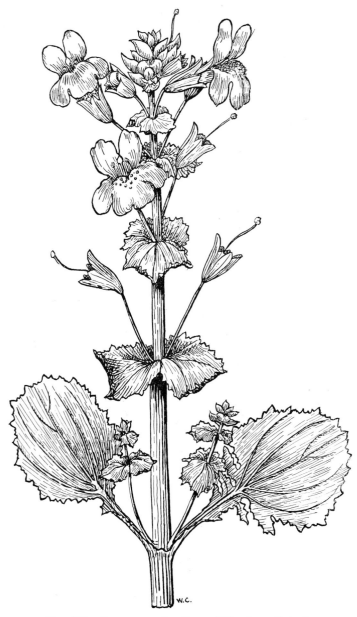

Fig. 259.   Common monkey-flower (*Mimulus guttatus*).

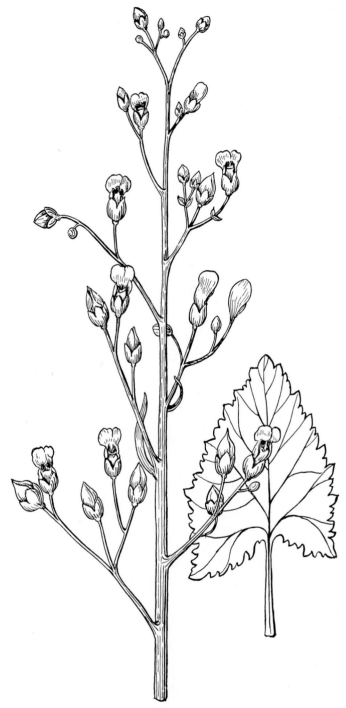

FIG. 260.   Figwort (*Scrophularia californica*).

KEY TO WEEDY SPECIES OF VERBASCUM
Plants very woolly ; flowers sessile_____*V. Thapsus*
Plants with green herbage ; flowers stalked
   Flowers usually solitary ; flower stalks longer than calyx_____*V. Blattaria*
   Flowers usually clustered ; flower stalks not longer than calyx_____*V. virgatum*

MOTH MULLEIN (*Verbascum Blattaria* L.) (Fig. 261)

   This species occurs in the foothills and valleys throughout California, but is nowhere very abundant. It may be seen in waste places about towns and cities. It is a slender plant, 2 to 4 feet high, with green, smooth herbage. The lower leaves have a short-winged petiole, and are 3 to 4 inches long, the upper ones are smaller and have heart-shaped clasping bases. The flowers are stalked, yellow or whitish, 1 inch broad, and usually occur singly. All the filaments are bearded with violet woolly hairs.

FIG. 261. Moth mullein (*Verbascum Blattaria*). A, capsule ; B, seeds.

COMMON MULLEIN (*Verbascum Thapsus* L.) (Fig. 262)

   This is very common in many of the foothill valleys of the west slope of the Sierra Nevada, also in the north Coast Ranges. It occurs about old farmsteads in corrals, pastures, and along dry stream beds. It is a stout, erect, densely soft-woolly herb, 3 to 6 feet high, its basal leaves 6 to 12 inches long, the upper smaller with their bases prolonged and surrounding the stem to the next leaf, thus making the stem 4-winged. The flowers are

FIG. 262. Common mullein (*Verbascum Thapsus*).

sulphur-yellow, unstalked, and occur in long spikes. The seeds, about .5 to .8 mm. long, are dark reddish-brown to olive-brown in color, squarish and broader at one end, more rounded at the other, marked with grooves as long as the seed and transversely pitted or ridged.

VIRGATE MULLEIN (*Verbascum virgatum* Stokes)

This species is 3 to 4 feet high, with green, although hairy, herbage. The upper leaves are sessile, unstalked, clasping, wavy-margined, 1½ to 3 inches long, the lower petioled and 6 to 12 inches long. The flowers are yellow or whitish, stalked, ¾ inch broad, solitary or in small clusters in the upper leaf axils.

VERONICA

Nine species of *Veronica* are recorded as occurring in California. Most of them are of wide geographical distribution. Four of the nine species may be regarded as weeds with us. Ours are either annual or perennial herbs, the flowers having a 4-parted calyx, a wheel-shaped, deeply 4-lobed corolla, 2 exserted stamens, and a single 2-celled pistil with 1 style and 1 stigma. The fruit is a 2-celled capsule containing numerous seeds.

KEY TO WEEDY SPECIES OF VERONICA

Perennial from rootstocks ; leaves opposite ; flowers in racemes_____*V. serpyllifolia*
Annual ; leaves alternate or the lowest opposite ; flowers solitary in the leaf axils
    Flower stalks longer than leaves_____*V. Buxbaumii*
    Flower stalks shorter than leaves
        Lower leaves oval or oblong, entire or slightly toothed_____*V. peregrina*
        Lower leaves oval, with rounded or blunt teeth_____*V. arvensis*

CORN SPEEDWELL (*Veronica arvensis* L.)

A native of Europe which has escaped from gardens, this species is not common in California. It is an annual or winter annual with slender, diffusely-branching stems, 3 to 10 inches long. Both stems and leaves are hairy. Most of the leaves are opposite, thin, ovate, wavy-margined, and about ¼ inch long. The flowers are a bright blue. The seed is about 1 mm. long, oval in outline, with a slightly convex dorsal side, flattish on the other, frequently somewhat twisted. From the middle of the scar in the concave side a protuberance extends towards the margin. The surface is finely tuberculate in wave-like ridges, the color light yellowish-brown and somewhat opaque.

BYZANTINE SPEEDWELL (*Veronica Buxbaumii* Tenore)

This native of Europe is an occasional escape from gardens, and has been found in the Eel River Valley, at Woodland, Newark and San Bernardino. It is an annual herb with stems ½ to 1 foot long. The herbage is covered with spreading hairs. The leaves are oval or roundish, often broader than long, about ½ inch long and deeply toothed at the base. The corolla is blue with a small white center. The flower stalks are longer than the leaves, thus differing from those of the two foregoing species, in which the flower stalks are shorter than the leaves. The seed is strongly convex on one side, saucer-shape on the other, circular in outline and amber in color.

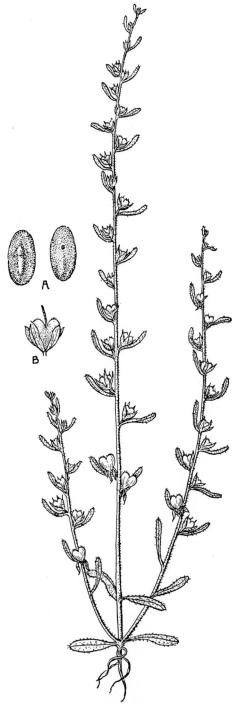

FIG. 263.   Purslane speedwell (*Veronica peregrina*).
A, seeds ; B, capsule.

PURSLANE SPEEDWELL (*Veronica peregrina* L.) (Fig. 263)
Other common name: Neckweed.

This species occurs throughout California up to 4,000 feet. It is a native annual herb, usually less than 12 inches high, with finely hairy glandular herbage. The leaves are alternate or the lowermost opposite, $\frac{1}{3}$ to 1 inch long, entire or toothed, mostly unstalked. The flowers are white. The seed is oblong, convex on one side and somewhat concave on the other, the surface smooth and dull, light tan and sometimes scurfy whitish.

THYME-LEAF SPEEDWELL (*Veronica serpyllifolia* L.) (Fig. 264)

This speedwell is widespread in the United States, and occurs throughout California from 3,000 to 6,000 feet. It is a creeping perennial, rooting readily at the nodes. The stems form dense mats. The lowest leaves are opposite, petioled, rather thick and smooth; the upper alternate, sessile and narrower. The flowers occur in a single terminal raceme. The corolla is pale-blue or bluish-white with darker stripes.

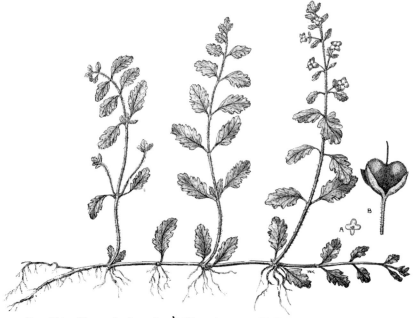

FIG. 264. Thyme-leaf speedwell (*Veronica serpyllifolia*). A, flower; B, fruit.

MARTYNIA FAMILY (Martyniaceae)

UNICORN PLANT, DEVIL'S CLAW (*Martynia louisianica* Mill.) (Fig. 265)

This native of the southern Mississippi Valley occurs in the Sacramento Valley and in southern California; sparingly established at Elsinore, Deep Well near Palm Springs. It is an annual, up to 2 feet tall, with rounded, heart-shaped leaves, 4 to 12 inches wide. The flowers are dull white or yellowish to pinkish purple, generally mottled or blotched with purple. The woody fruit is crested on one side, the spreading curved horns longer than the body.

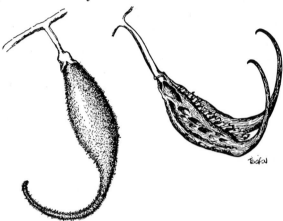

FIG. 265.   Unicorn plant (*Martynia louisianica*) showing unopen and opening fruits.

YELLOW DEVIL'S CLAW (*Martynia lutea* Lindl.)

This weed, a native of Mexico, is naturalized in the Sacramento and San Joaquin Valleys and southward. It is an annual with coarse roughish herbage in general appearance similar to squash. The leaves are rounded in outline or lobed, about 2-4 inches in diameter; the flowers are about 2 inches long, funnel form. On the outside they are pale greenish-yellow, the inside deep yellow with orange spots. The pod is a 4-celled capsule with an elongated terminal beak which splits into two recurved claw-like spines. The seed is about $\frac{1}{4}$ to $\frac{1}{2}$ inch long, and half as wide, irregular in form, but generally widest at the middle and narrowed at the ends, flattened laterally. The color is very dark grey to black, the surface dull and rough.

This plant has been cultivated for pickles. The hooked fruits are injurious to livestock; they also become entangled in the fleece of sheep.

PLANTAIN FAMILY *(Plantaginaceae)*

There are but 3 genera in this family, the principal one being *Plantago*, in which occurs a majority of the species. There are 14 species of *Plantago* in California, 6 of which are introduced, the remainder native. All are low herbs with flowers on long stems and leaves all basal.

PLANTAGO

The plantains are low herbs with flowers borne on a long leafless stem, all the leaves being close to the ground. The leaves are prominently 1- to several-ribbed or nerved. The flowers have 4 persistent sepals, a small, tubular, 4-lobed corolla, 2 or 4 stamens attached to the corolla tube, and a single pistil. The fruit is a capsule which at maturity splits at the middle with the upper part falling away like a lid.

BUCKHORN PLANTAIN (*Plantago lanceolata* L.) (Fig. 266)
Other common names: Ribwort, English plantain, narrow-leaved plantain, ribgrass, buck plantain, black-jacks.

Ribwort also is a species introduced from Europe which now occurs in most agricultural lands throughout the State, also in lawns, golf courses, parking-ways, and along roadsides. Hilgard (1890) considered it "with *Setaria glauca,* the most formidable enemy of irrigated grounds and pastures in the foothills of the Sierra and more or less in the adjacent portions of the Sacramento Valley." The plant resembles common plantain in its general growth habits. It is a perennial with dark green, somewhat hairy leaves, which are densely clustered at the top of the short, thick rootstock. The leaves are 3 to 12 inches long, entire, tapered below to slender, grooved leaf stalks, the bases of which are surrounded by brownish hairs; the leaf blades are prominently 3- to 5-ribbed. The flower stalks are often much longer than the leaves, angled, grooved and end in cylindrical flower groups, from ¾ to 2 inches long. The seeds are about 1.5 to 2.5 mm. long, smooth and shiny, mostly brown to greenish-brown in color, oblong in shape with a smooth convex side, the edges of which roll over the front face making that concave side appear as a rather narrow slit, the bottom of which is darker and roughish, with a scar about midway.

COMMON PLANTAIN (*Plantago major* L.) (Fig. 267)
Other common names: Broadleaf plantain, dooryard plantain.

This is naturalized from Europe and is common throughout the State, in dooryards, low fields, and waste places. According to Jepson, "it is called by the Indians 'White Man's Foot,' since it has closely followed the advance of civilization, springing up about the earliest frontier settlements." It has smooth herbage, the leaves are narrow to round-oval, 3 to 6 inches long, entire or toothed, and conspicuously 5- to 7-ribbed; the ribs converge at the base into a broad petiole which may be 4 to 5 inches long. The flower stalks bear a spike-like group of flowers 3 to 6 inches long. The seeds are about 1-2 mm. long, dull reddish-brown, irregularly angled, with lines appearing to radiate from the central scar. On the rounded side the fine parallel lines run the length of the seed.

FIG. 266. Buckhorn plantain
(*Plantago lanceolata*).

FIG. 267. Common plantain (*Plantago major*).

SAND PLANTAIN (*Plantago arenaria* Waldst. & Kit.), CROWFOOT PLANTAIN (*P. Coronopus* L.), FLAX-SEED PLANTAIN (*P. Psyllium* Nutt.), SLENDER PLANTAIN (*P. pusilla* Nutt.), and *P. virginica* L. are five other introduced species of *Plantago*, all of which have a very limited distribution in the State and thus far are of no significance from the weed standpoint, with the exception of the last-named which was found by Kay H. Beach infesting a lawn at the Tanbark Flat Laboratory of the San Dimas Experimental Forest, Glendora.

MADDER FAMILY (Rubiaceae)

The madder family is one of considerable economic importance. Here belong coffee (*Coffea*), *Cinchona* which yields quinine, and *Rubia tinctorium* from which is derived the artists' dye, alazarine. A number of genera possess ornamentals. Certain bedstraws (*Galium*) and field madder (*Sherardia arvensis*) are weeds. In *Galium* the flowers are solitary or in cymes, whereas in *Sherardia* they occur in heads subtended by an involucre.

GALIUM

The galiums are herbs with slender, square stems. The leaves are in whorls of 6 to 8 leaves each. The stipules are large and resemble leaf blades. The flowers have no calyx, a rotate corolla 3- or 4-cleft, 4 short stamens, and a 2-lobed ovary with 2 styles. The fruit has two globular halves, separating at maturity into 2 seed-like indehiscent 1-seeded carpels.

Jepson describes 24 species of *Galium* as occurring in California. Three of these described below, are introduced from Europe, and under certain conditions behave as weeds; all are annuals.

BEDSTRAW (*Galium Aparine* L.) (Fig. 268)
Other common names: Goose grass, cleavers.

This species is fairly well distributed throughout the State. The stems are weak and trailing, 4 inches to about 3 feet long, backwardly rough hairy on the angles of the stems; leaves 6 to 8 in a whorl, $\frac{1}{2}$ to 2 inches long. The flowers are white, in the axils of the upper leaves, fruit 2-3 mm. in diameter with stiff hooked bristles, borne on straight stalks.

CORN GALIUM (*Galium tricorne* Stokes) (Fig. 268B)

This species occurs in grain fields, particularly in Sonoma and Mariposa Counties. It is often present as an impurity in seed grain from those sections. The stems are not much branched, stout and about 6 to 18 inches long, the angles callous with recurved prickles. The leaves are narrow, in whorls of 6-8, also callous margined and bearing recurved prickles. The fruits are on stout recurved stems in the axils of the leaves, about $\frac{1}{6}$ inch broad and not hairy, but beset with small protuberances.

WALL GALIUM (*Galium parisiense* L.)

This species occurs in Sonoma, Humboldt and El Dorado Counties. The stem is much branched from the base, the branches very fine and slender, about 6 inches to a foot high, finely roughened. Leaves more or less lance shaped, about $\frac{1}{4}$ inch long. The flowers are whitish and very small, about $\frac{1}{32}$ of an inch, the fruit about as small as the flowers and hairy.

FIELD MADDER (*Shervardia arvensis* L.) (Fig. 269)

This representative of the madder family is a native of Europe which has become naturalized in pasture lands near the coast from

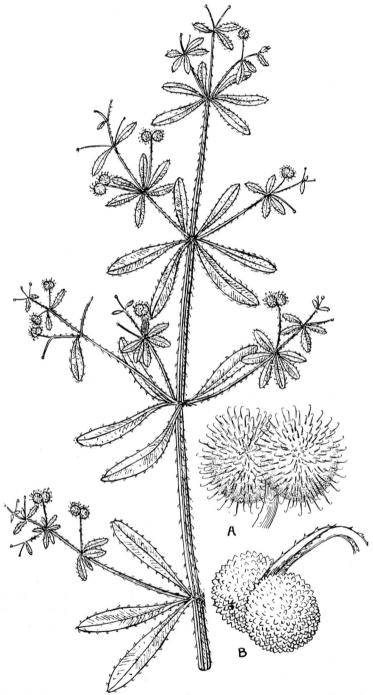

FIG. 268.   Bedstraw (*Galium Aparine*), showing habit.   **A**, mature fruit ;
B, fruit of corn galium (*G. tricorne*).

Marin County to San Mateo County. In the Eastern States it infests lawns, meadows and waste places. It is a slender annual herb, often closely matting the ground, with slender, square, hairy stems. The leaves are in whorls of 4 to 6, simple, entire, lance-shaped, and pungent. The flowers are small, blue or pinkish, in terminal clusters, which are surrounded by an involucre of fused bracts. There are 4 lance-shaped sepals, a tubular corolla of 4 or 5 lobes, 4 stamens, and pistil with a 2-lobed ovary and a 2-cleft style. The fruit is dry, 2-lobed, and splits at maturity into two 1-seeded indehiscent carpels. The seed is about 4 mm. long, broadest at the middle, tapering towards the base and the tip which continues into three spreading calyx teeth with scattered stiff

FIG. 269. Field madder (*Sherardia arvensis*). A, B, fruiting calyx.

hairs. There is a groove on the inner side, the outer strongly convex. The body of the seed is also covered with stiff upwardly turned hairs, the color grayish to dark brown. The calyx teeth are yellowish-brown.

HONEYSUCKLE FAMILY *(Caprifoliaceae)*

Representatives of this family are seldom troublesome as weeds. Many are grown as ornamentals for their flowers and foliage. Well known members of the family are the viburnums, elder (*Sambucus*), snow-berry (*Symphoricarpos*), bush-honeysuckle (*Diervilla lonicera*), and common honeysuckles (*Lonicera*).

JAPANESE HONEYSUCKLE (*Lonicera japonica* Thunb.) (Fig. 271)
Other common name: Chinese honeysuckle.

This is a naturalized species from eastern Asia which sometimes escapes from cultivation. It is a climbing or training, hairy shrub. The leaves are opposite, entire, short-stalked, oval, and from 1 to 3 inches long; the blade is acute at the apex, rounded at the base, green and smooth above, and pale and usually hairy beneath. The flowers are in pairs in the upper leaf axils; the flowers are white or pink, fading to yellow; the calyx is 5-toothed and the corolla has a tube nearly 1 inch long, the limb of which is 2-lipped; there are 5 stamens inserted on the corolla tube, and a single style which, with the stamens, protrudes from the corolla tube. The fruit is a black berry about ¼ inch in diameter.

FIG. 270. Blue elderberry (*Sambucus glauca*).

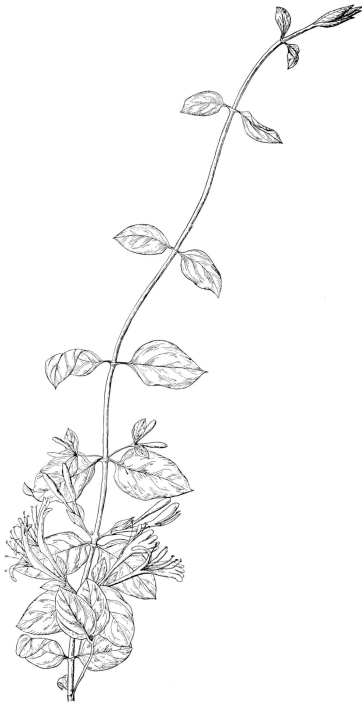

FIG. 271.   Japanese honeysuckle (*Lonicera japonica*).

BLUE ELDERBERRY (*Sambucus glauca* Nutt) (Fig. 270)

The blue elderberry is widely distributed in California up to 5,500 feet. Occasionally it forms a dense undesirable growth in waste places. It is usually a deciduous bush, 6 to 10 feet high, but may sometimes develop into a small tree and attain a height of 25 feet. The leaves are 1 to 3½ inches long, opposite, compound, odd-pinnate, with 5 to 7 leaflets; the leaflets are oval to oblong lance-shaped, sharply toothed except at the tip. The flowers are numerous in a flat-topped, compound cyme, which may attain a width of 8 or 9 inches. The flowers are white, with a 5-toothed calyx, a regular, rotate, deeply 5-lobed corolla, 5 stamens, and a 3- to 5-celled ovary. The fruit is berry-like, blue, 3- to 5-seeded, and usually somewhat less than ¼ inch in diameter.

TEASEL FAMILY *(Dipsaceae)*

This is a relatively small family, mostly of Europe and Asia. The best-known members in this country are teasel (*Dipsacus*), and *Scabiosa*. Certain of these are ornamentals, and may escape from cultivation.

FULLER'S TEASEL (*Dipsacus Fullonum* L.) (Fig. 272)

This weed is a native of Europe and has become established in California, especially near the coast, in low waste places, vacant lots, and pasture lands. Fuller's teasel is a coarse, stout, somewhat prickly, biennial herb, 3 to 6 feet tall. The leaves are large, opposite, sessile, those of the stem grown together about the stem, forming cups; the leaves are broad, oblong, somewhat sickle-shaped, the lower ones often a foot in length. The flowers are in a dense head at the ends of stems, and each head is surrounded by an involucre of spiny, unequaled bracts. The calyx is cup-shaped and 4-toothed, the corolla 4-lobed, the stamens 4 in number and inserted on the throat of the corolla, and the ovary 1-celled. The fruit is an achene about ¼ inch long, strongly 4-angled.

WILD TEASEL (*Dipsacus sylvestris* Huds.) is a naturalized species which has been found at San Francisco, and at Sisson, Siskiyou County.

SWEET SCABIOUS (*Scabiosa atropurpurea* L.)

This is another adventive species found infrequently in California. It is a native of the Mediterranean region, now found in the Sacramento and Napa Valleys, in Alameda County, and in San Bernardino County. Forms of this species are among the popular flower-garden annuals. The plant is about 2 to 3 feet high, the lower leaves lyre-shaped, the upper pinnately divided, lance-shaped, coarsely toothed or entire. The flower heads are about 1½ inches broad and subtended by an involucre. The flowers are black-purple to pinkish-white. The calyx is bristly, the limb of the corolla 4- to 5-cleft, the stamens 4, or rarely 2, and the fruit an achene, enclosed in the persistent involucre and bearing the calyx awns.

SCABIOSA (*Scabiosa stellata* L.), a native of the Mediterranean region, was collected at Altadena in 1893. It is a rare escape.

FIG. 272. Fuller's teasel (*Dipsacus Fullonum*).

VALERIAN FAMILY *(Valerianaceae)*

Members of the valerian family are herbs with opposite leaves. Species of *Centranthus* and *Fedia* are ornamentals. In our flora, the two chief genera are *Valeriana* and *Valerianella*.

RED VALERIAN *(Centranthus ruber* DC.) (Fig. 2k)

This garden plant, native of Europe and southwest Asia, occasionally escapes from cultivation. It is a smooth perennial, 1 to 3 feet tall, somewhat woody at the base, and usually forms a compact bushy growth. The leaves are simple, entire, or toothed at the base, oval to lance-shaped, up to 4 inches long, and sessile. The flowers are numerous, small, fragrant, deep crimson to pale red or white, and in dense terminal clusters. The calyx is divided into 5-15 narrow divisions, and the corolla has a slender 5-parted tube, with a spur at the base. There is a single stamen, and an inferior, 1-celled ovary which matures into an indehiscent achene-like fruit.

THISTLE FAMILY *(Compositae)*

The composite or thistle family is one of the largest of the plant kingdom, consisting of about 10,000 species, with a wide geographical distribution. It includes a few species of economic value, such as lettuce, Jerusalem artichoke, endive, and salsify; also such ornamentals as chrysanthemum, dahlia, marigold, and aster. Of special interest to us is the fact that within this family are numerous species of weeds.

A characteristic feature of the family is the flower-cluster (inflorescence), which is a head. In this the flowers, usually numerous, are mounted on a common receptacle which is subtended by an involucre, composed of a few to many small bracts (leaf-like structures). For example, a ''sunflower'' is not a single flower in the botanical sense, but a group or composite of individual flowers. The receptacle, the structure upon which the individual flowers are mounted, varies in shape from flat to convex or conical. The receptacle is smooth (naked) or there are

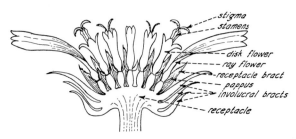

FIG. 273. Lengthwise median section of sunflower head.

chaffy scales subtending the flowers. The involucral bracts also vary greatly in shape, from narrow and spine-like to broad and leaf-like. (Fig. 273)

There are two types of flowers in the composite family: (1) disk or tubular, and (2) ray or ligulate. For example, in the sunflower head, there are numerous ligulate (strap-shaped) yellow flowers around the entire margin, and in the center is a larger number of smaller disk or tubular flowers. Each disk flower has a tubular, five-lobed corolla, attached at the tip of the ovary. Usually at the base of the corolla, and attached

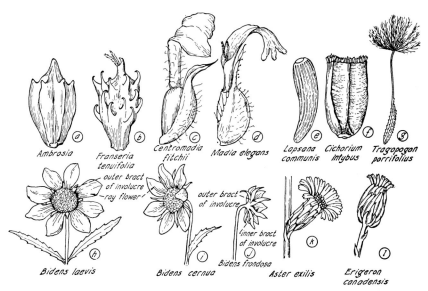

FIG. 274. Botanical characters illustrating keys to representatives in thistle family. (a) achene of ragweed; (b) achene of franseria poverty weed; (c) ray achene of Fitch's spikeweed; (d) ray achene of common madia; (e) achene of nipplewort; (f) achene of chicory; (g) achene of salsify; (h) flower head of bur marigold; (i) flower head of nodding bur marigold; (j) flower head of beggarticks; (k) flower head of slender aster; (l) flower head of horseweed.

to the tip of the ovary, is a structure known as the pappus, consisting of a few or a large number of bristles, awns, scales, or teeth. Inside of the corolla and attached to it are five stamens, whose anthers are united into a tube; and a single style. The ray or ligulate flowers usually are devoid of stamens.

The composite family is divided into two large groups. In the one group, represented by such weeds as dandelion, chicory, bristly oxtongue, cat's ear, and wild lettuce, the flowering head is composed wholly of ligulate or strap-shaped flowers possessing both pistil and stamens; there are no tubular flowers. In the other group, represented by such plants as sunflower, daisy, star thistle, etc., the head is composed of both disk and ligulate flowers. In both types of flowers the fruit is an achene, that is a dry, one-seeded, indehiscent fruit. The pappus is usually persistent at the tip of the fruit, serving as a means of dissemination by the wind. (Fig. 274)

KEY TO GENERA OF COMPOSITAE

Genera in which the heads are composed entirely of ligulate flowers.

Achenes without a pappus (Fig. 274, e) _____*Lapsana*

Achenes with a pappus

  Pappus chaff-like (Fig. 274, f)

    Flowers blue _____*Cichorium*

    Flowers yellow

      Plants thistle-like; heads sessile_____*Scolymus*

      Plants not thistle-like; heads long-stalked

        Woolly-hairy herbs with long fleshy tap root_____*Scorzonera*

        Not as above

          Bracts of involucre in 1 series_____*Rhagadiolus*

          Bracts of involucre in more than 1 series_____*Microseris*

  Pappus of bristles

    Pappus bristles plumose (Fig. 274, g)

      Achenes beakless _____*Stephanomeria*

      Achenes beaked

        Flowers purple _____*Tragopogon*

        Flowers yellow

          Receptacle naked; stems somewhat leafy_____*Picris*

          Receptacle chaffy; leaves basal_____*Hypochoeris*

    Pappus bristles smooth, or beset with very fine hairs or barbs; never plumose

      Achenes flattened

        Achenes with a beak (Fig. 320) _____*Lactuca*

        Achenes not beaked (Fig. 320) _____*Sonchus*

      Achenes not flattened

        Flower-bearing stem leafless; leaves all basal

          Achene spine-toothed above (Fig. 320) _____*Taraxacum*

          Achene not spine-toothed above

            Pappus persistent _____*Agoseris*

            Pappus falling away_____*Malacothrix*

        Flower-bearing stem somewhat leafy_____*Crepis*

Genera in which the heads are composed of both ray and disk flowers, or disk flowers only.

A. Receptacle covered with bristles or hairs; involucral bracts usually prolonged into spine or bristle

  Margins of leaves not prickly or spiny

    Leaves broad; bracts of involucre hooked at tip (Fig. 279) _____*Arctium*

    Leaves narrow; bracts of involucre not hooked at tip (Fig. 285) _____*Centaurea*

  Margins of leaves prickly or spiny (Fig. 284)

    Flowers yellow

      Outer bracts of involucre terminating in a simple spine_____*Cnicus*

      Outer bracts of involucre terminating in a leafy appendage (Fig. 284)

                                            Carthamus

    Flowers white, rose-colored or purple

      Leaves with conspicuous white blotches along the veins (Fig. 332) ____*Silybum*

      Leaves without conspicuous white blotches along the veins

        Achenes 4-angled _____*Cynara*

        Achenes not angled_____*Cirsium*

B. Receptacle naked, that is, without bristles or chaffy bracts; leaves alternate, or opposite in the genus *Eupatorium*

  Leaves opposite _____*Eupatorium*

Leaves alternate
1. Herbage scentless; bracts of involucre imbricated; disk-flowers yellow; pappus
of awns or bristles
  Staminate and pistillate flowers on different plants_____*Baccharis*
  Staminate and pistillate flowers on same plant, or flowers perfect
    Rays yellow or none
      Heads large and gummy_____*Grindelia*
      Heads not gummy
        Achenes not flattened
          Rays none
            Shrubs _____*Chrysothamnus*
            Herbs
              Leaves simple _____*Hymenothrix*
              Leaves pinnate _____*Tagetes*
          Achenes flattened _____*Heterotheca*
    Rays present, pink, white, blue or purple
      Pappus wanting; leaves all basal_____*Bellis*
      Pappus present
        Bracts of involucre in 2 or more series (Fig. 281)_____*Aster*
        Bracts of involucre in 1 or 2 series_____*Erigeron*
2. Herbage mostly white-woolly; bracts of involucre usually white or papery;
heads small; rays absent
  Receptacle chaffy
    Pappus none _____*Filago*
    Pappus present _____*Gifola*
  Receptacle naked
    Herbage not woolly_____*Pluchea*
    Herbage woolly
      Flowers all fertile, perfect and pistillate in same head_____*Gnaphalium*
      Flowers dioecious, that is, staminate and pistillate flowers in different
heads _____*Antennaria*
3. Herbage strong-scented or aromatic; bracts of involucre usually dry and
papery or with papery margins; flowers white, yellow or greenish; rays
present or none; leaves usually much divided
  Receptacle with chaff-like bracts
    Rays 14-20 _____*Anthemis*
    Rays 4 or 5_____*Achillea*
  Receptacle naked
    Outer series of flowers pistillate only and without corolla
      Heads peduncled _____*Cotula*
      Heads sessile _____*Soliva*
    All flowers with a corolla
      Rays many, conspicuous_____*Chrysanthemum*
      Rays none
        Heads solitary or in corymbs
          Flowers yellow _____*Tanacetum*
          Flowers greenish _____*Matricaria*
        Heads in panicles or somewhat spike-like_____*Artemisia*
4. Bracts of involucre scarcely imbricated, mostly in 1 or 2 series; disk and ray
flowers yellow; pappus bristles soft, usually white and copius
  Shrubs _____*Tetradymia*
  Herbs
    Annuals; leaves ear-like or lobed at base_____*Erechtites*
    Perennial or annuals; leaves not as above_____*Senecio*
5. Bracts of involucre reflexed, in 1 or 2 series; flowers golden yellow; achenes
ribbed; pappus of 5 to 12 papery short-pointed scales_____*Helenium*

C. Receptacle with chaffy bracts
1. Herbage usually with balsamic-resinous juice; bracts of involucre herbaceous or foliaceous, never papery; rays present and usually showy; pappus never of capillary bristles
     Inner bracts of involucre sac-like, that is, completely enclosing the achenes of ray flowers _____*Melampodium*
     Inner bracts of involucre not sac-like
         Rays white
             Disk corollas 4-toothed_____*Eclipta*
             Disk corollas 5-toothed_____*Galinsoga*
         Rays yellow or none
             Bracts of involucre unlike and in 2 series (Fig. 274, j)
                 Pappus of 2 to 4 barbed awns (Fig. 282) _____*Bidens*
                 Pappus, if present, never barbed, or none_____*Coreopsis*
             Bracts of involucre similar and in 2 or more series
                 Disk achenes strongly flattened (Fig. 340) _____*Verbesina*
                 Disk achenes thick, angled
                     Receptacle columnar (Fig. 327) _____*Rudbeckia*
                     Receptacle flat or convex_____*Helianthus*
2. Herbage usually glandular, viscid or heavy scented; bracts of involucre in a single series; rays always present
     Ray achenes half enclosed by involucral bracts which are rounded on back (Fig. 274, c)
         Receptacle conical or convex_____*Centromadia*
         Receptacle flat _____*Hemizonia*
     Ray achenes completely enclosed by involucral bracts which are flattened or keeled on back (Fig. 274, d)
         Herbage glandular-viscid _____*Madia*
         Herbage soft pubescent_____*Achyrachaena*
3. Coarse weeds or shrubs with small greenish or white heads; flowers unisexual; rays none; pappus none; fruit usually a bur
     Heads nodding, some of them containing both staminate and pistillate flowers; involucre of 4 or 5 bracts_____*Iva*
     Heads unisexual, both pistillate and staminate on the same plant; pistillate heads bur-like
         Involucre of pistillate heads maturing into a stout, extremely spiny bur (Fig. 341); involucral bracts of staminate heads distinct_____*Xanthium*
         Involucral bracts of staminate heads united
             Bur with a single beak at apex; a single row of short spines near the back (Fig. 274, a) _____*Ambrosia*
             Bur with 1 to 4 beaks; several rows of short spines near the back (Fig. 274, b) _____*Franseria*

MILFOIL OR YARROW (*Achillea Millefolium* L. var. *lanulosa Piper*) (Fig. 275)

This is a widely distributed species in California, especially in the mountains. It is a hairy, perennial herb, 2 to 3 feet tall, from rootstocks. The leaves are lance-shaped in outline but finely dissected, the deeply-lobed segments thickly crowded on the midrib. The flowering heads are numerous, small, and of white or yellow flowers grouped in flattened clusters at the ends of the stem branches. The involucre is composed of a few bracts with papery margins. The achenes are about 1.5 mm. long, .5 mm. wide, flattened oblong, pale to olive-gray with thin whitish margins, devoid of pappus.

Yarrow contains glucosides and bitter alkaloids. If consumed in quantity by sheep it occasionally produces gastric pains, with diarrhea and enuresis.

FIG. 275.   Milfoil (*Achillea Millefolium* var. *lanulosa*). Inset, achenes.

BLOW-WIVES (*Achyrachaena mollis* Schauer.) (Fig. 276)

This is a native species which is very abundant in central California, especially on adobe soils. It is a soft-hairy annual herb, 8 to 18 inches high, the branches erect, half-naked, and terminating in solitary, rather large flower heads. The rays are golden-yellow, becoming reddish-brown with age. The leaves are narrow, 2 to 5 inches long, with entire or finely-toothed margins; the lower leaves are opposite, the upper alternate. The involucre consists of green, lance-shaped bracts which at length fall away from the fruiting, rounded heads; the heads

FIG. 276.   Blow-wives (*Achyrachaena mollis*).

are $1\frac{1}{4}$ to $1\frac{3}{4}$ inches across. Pappus scales are silvery-shining and stand out stiffly from each other at the end of the slender, black-ribbed achene.

HAIRY AGOSERIS *(Agoseris hirsuta* (Hook.) Greene)
Other common name: False dandelion.

This species is rather abundant in the San Francisco Bay region. It is a perennial herb about 12 inches tall from a stout, woody tap root. The stem is erect, and the basal leaves are tufted. The leafy part of the stem is short, its naked and much longer upper part stalk-like, reddish, and supporting the head of flowers. The leaves are 2 to 4 inches long, usually compound but frequently merely toothed. The involucre consists of several series of green bracts. There are numerous flowers in each head, which are yellow at first, but turn reddish with age. The achene is about $\frac{1}{6}$ inch long, and tapers to a slender, thread-like beak, which is twice as long as the body of the achene; the beak is tipped by a crown of many soft fine hairs, dull white or faintly yellow in color.

COMMON RAGWEED *(Ambrosia artemisiifolia* L.)

This is an annual species, rather widespread throughout North America, particularly in the Eastern and North Central States. It occurs sparingly in California. It resembles the western ragweed in general appearance. The latter is perennial from rootstocks, and has much more harsh leaves.

WESTERN RAGWEED *(Ambrosia psilostachya* DC.) (Fig. 277)

This is a native of western United States, and in California is fairly widespread along roadsides, railroad rights-of-way, and waste lands. It is one of our principal late summer hay-fever plants. Western ragweed is a coarse, perennial, aromatic, erect herb, 1 to 2 or more feet high, from slender, running rootstocks. The leaves are alternate, the lower commonly opposite, deeply-lobed, or pinnatifid, and 2 to 5 inches long. Both leaves and stems are clothed with short, stiff hairs, giving the herbage a gray-green color. The flowers are inconspicuous, greenish, and borne in small hemispherical heads. There are two kinds of flowers, staminate and pistillate, borne on the same plant. There are numerous staminate, nodding, several-flowered heads which are in erect clusters (catkin-like racemes). The pistillate heads are few in number, one-flowered, and occur at the base of the staminate racemes. The fruit is about $\frac{1}{8}$ inch long, an achene-like, short, more or less pear-shaped bur, with a row of prickles near its summit and a central point at the apex.

SMALL RAGWEED *(Ambrosia pumila* Gray) which is of no importance from the weed standpoint, is another native species which occurs in the vicinity of San Diego. It is a low plant, $\frac{3}{4}$ to $1\frac{1}{2}$ feet tall, with leaves 2 to 3 times pinnatifid.

GREAT RAGWEED *(Ambrosia trifida* L.), a native of the Middle Western States and eastward, occurs in California. It is from 3 to 6 feet tall, stout, rough-hairy and coarse. The leaves are opposite, the lower ones

FIG. 277.   Western ragweed (*Ambrosia psilostachya*).   **A,** flower head ;
B, achene.

deeply 3-lobed, the upper ones 3-lobed or dentate or entire. The achenes, over ¼ inch long, are light in color, 5-6 ridged with ridges ending in stout projections near the summit, a single spine at the apex.

MAYWEED *(Anthemis Cotula* L.) (Fig. 278)

Other common names: Dog fennel, fetid chamomile, white stinkweed, stinking daisy, dill weed, manzanillo.

This species was introduced from Europe in the days of the early Spanish settlement. It is widespread throughout the State, occurring

FIG. 278.   Mayweed *(Anthemis Cotula)*.

in waste lands, pastures, along roadsides, in paths and dooryards. Dog fennel is a branching annual herb, 1 to 2 or rarely 3 feet high, with rank-smelling herbage and an acrid juice which is irritating to the skin. The leaves are alternate, numerous, and finely divided. The flowering heads are numerous and borne on naked stalks, $1\frac{1}{2}$ to 4 inches long. Each head is about 1 inch broad, and subtended by an involucre of several series of dry, blunt bracts. The ray flowers are 10 to 20 in number, white in color, and usually 3-toothed at the tip. There are numerous perfect disk flowers which mature 1-seeded dry fruits, interspersed with slender, awl-like bracts. Each achene is 10-ribbed, its surface roughened with numerous tubercles.

Mayweed is reported as blistering the skin of animals when eaten extensively.

FIG. 279.   Great burdock (*Arctium Lappa*).   Left, achenes.

GARDEN CHAMOMILE *(Anthemis nobilis* L.)

This is a perennial garden plant, closely related to the foregoing species, introduced from Europe, and found in California as an escape at Fort Bragg. It is an aromatic, hairy herb, 4 to 8 inches tall, having smooth achenes with a narrow membranous border.

GREAT BURDOCK *(Arctium Lappa* L.) (Fig. 279)

This is a native of Europe which is sparingly introduced in California, at Livermore, Niles, Aromas in San Benito Valley, Carmel Valley, Riverside, and Ferndale. It is a coarse biennial, 3 to 5 feet tall, with large, stalked, rounded, oval or heart-shaped leaves, 4 to 12 inches long, which are woolly hairy beneath. The flowers are in purple heads; the involucres are about 1 inch broad, and composed of bracts which are smooth, lance-shaped, rigid, and ending in long, spreading points hooked at the tip. The receptacle is densely bristly. The achenes are flattened, ribbed, and transversely wrinkled; the pappus has many short finely-barbed bristles.

COMMON BURDOCK *(Arctium minus* Benth.)

Closely related to the preceding, and also a native of Europe, it is now found on the bottom lands of the Eel River near Humboldt Bay, in Kings County, and at San Francisco Bay. It resembles the great burdock but differs from it in having smaller flowering heads and involucres which are from ½ to ¾ inch broad on short stalks.

Although rarely eaten by livestock, it is suspected of being poisonous.

AFRICAN DAISY *(Arctotis stoechadifolia* Berg.)

This native of South Africa is a bushy annual plant, 2 to 2½ feet tall, which occasionally escapes from flower gardens. The herbage is more or less white-woolly. The leaves are wavy-toothed. The heads are 2½ to 3 inches in diameter, on long stalks which far exceed the leaves. There are numerous imbricated involucral bracts, a bristly, honeycombed receptacle, and white or pale-violet rays.

BIENNIAL WORMWOOD *(Artemisia biennis* Willd.)

This species is an introduction from Europe, and occurs at numerous localities from southern California to Berkeley and the lower Sacramento River. It is a biennial, herbaceous or sometimes woody at the base, differing from California mugwort in being wholly smooth throughout.

COMMON SAGEBRUSH *(Artemisia tridentata* Nutt.)

This species has been suspected by stockmen as being mildly poisonous to sheep and horses, but evidence for such suspicion is very scant. It is a shrubby plant, 3 to 6 feet tall, with leaves mostly 3-toothed or the upper entire. Its range, including varieties, extends from Modoc and Siskiyou Counties to the Mojave Desert and southern California.

CALIFORNIA MUGWORT *(Artemisia vulgaris* L. var. *heterophylla* Jepson) (Fig. 280)

This is a native of California, and north to British Columbia and Saskatchewan, thence eastward to western Nevada and south to Lower California. It is widely distributed in the State, growing along streams, irrigation ditches, railroads, highways, and in moist pasture lands.

California mugwort is a perennial herb from running rootstocks. The stems are erect, woody at the base, and 3 to 6 feet high. The leaves are lance-shaped to oblong, oval or elliptic, sparingly cleft with downward-pointing incisions or the upper ones often entire; they are green above, white-woolly beneath, sometimes smooth, and 2 to 6 inches long. The flower heads are erect, and are arranged in dense spikes in an open or dense panicle, the main axis of which is leafy. The involucres are greenish and papery, smooth and usually enclose 20 to 30 flowers. Both marginal flowers and disk flowers are fertile. The achene is oblong, wholly devoid of pappus or appendage.

SLENDER ASTER (*Aster exilis* Ell.) (Fig. 281)

The slender aster is a native, occurring in the Sacramento Valley, south to coastal southern California and the Imperial Valley. It is a plant of river bottoms and of low wet waste lands, especially where the soil is saline. It also occurs in rice fields. The species is a slender, erect annual herb, 1 to 5 feet high. The stem is simple below, but branches freely above. The leaves are narrow, 2 to 4 inches long, entire, rarely

FIG. 280. California mugwort (*Artemisia vulgaris* var. *heterophylla*).

finely toothed, the upper leaves smaller than the lower. The heads are numerous, about ¼ inch high, and subtended by an involucre of narrow, long-pointed, papery-margined, green bracts. The rays are about 15 in number, light pink or purple in color; the disks are yellow. The achenes have a pappus of numerous long, white, fine, soft hairs.

PURPLE ASTER (*Aster Menziesii* Lindl.)

This native species is widespread in California, and sometimes behaves as a weed. It is an erect herb from a woody root, 1½ to 2 feet high. The leaves are rough-hairy, linear to lance-shaped, purple-veined on the lower surface, sessile, entire, somewhat heart-shaped at the base, and from 1 to 2½ inches long. The flowers are violet or purple, and the involucral bracts recurved in mature flower heads.

MEXICAN DEVIL-WEED (*Aster spinosus* Benth.)
Other common name: Wild asparagus.

This is a native of the Colorado Desert. It ranges from San Diego eastward through the Imperial Valley. In these sections it is a weed of considerable importance, often forming thickets along irrigation ditches. It infests cultivated fields, chiefly cotton and alfalfa. The Mexican devil-weed is an herbaceous perennial with widely spreading rootstocks, which may attain a length of 4 or 5 feet. There are numerous erect, slender, smooth, almost leafless stems varying in height from 3 to 9 feet. The leaves are green, few in number, the lower ones narrow, ¼ to 2 inches long, the upper awl-shaped or scalelike. Often there are spines, ⅛ to ½ inch long, in or above the leaf axils. The flowering heads are solitary or in loose clusters at the ends of the reed-like stems. The heads are about ½ inch broad and ½ inch high, subtended by an involucre of narrow, pointed, papery-margined, unequal bracts arranged in 2 or 3 series. The rays are white, drying brown, the disk yellowish or brownish. The achenes are smooth, and bear at the summit a pappus of numerous long, straight hairs.

DOUGLAS' BACCHARIS (*Baccharis Douglasii* DC.)

This native species is abundant in the salt marshes along the coast from San Francisco Bay to southern California and in the San Joaquin and lower Sacramento Valleys. It is a herbaceous perennial, woody at the base, the stems 4 to 5 feet tall. The stems and leaves are resinous. Leaves are lance-shaped or the lower lance-ovate, 3 to 4 inches long, and finely toothed. The flowering heads are numerous in compound, terminal cluster; involucral bracts are narrow, the margins papery, the centers green. The achenes are 5-nerved.

COYOTE BRUSH (*Baccharis pilularis* DC.)
Other comon name: Chaparral broom.

This is a common native species on the drier hillsides in the Coast Range from Los Angeles County north to Oregon. It occasionally gives trouble as a weed. It is a perennial evergreen shrub, 2 to 8 feet high. However, on wind-swept and exposed slopes it is often much lower, even

prostrate on the ground. The branches are angular. The leaves are
alternate, simple, sessile, broadly ovate or wedge-shaped, ½ to 1 inch
long, coarsely toothed, wavy-margined or sometimes entire. The flower
heads are ⅙ to ¼ inch long, solitary or usually clustered in the leaf axils
or at the ends of the branches. Ray flowers are absent. The staminate and
pistillate flowers are on different plants. The corollas are white. The
achenes are 10-nerved and bear a crown of hairs (pappus).

FIG. 281.   Slender aster (*Aster exilis*)   Left, achene.

MULE FAT (*Baccharis viminea* DC.)

This species is a native closely allied to the coyote brush. It is distributed in the Sierra Nevada foothills, the Sacramento and Napa Valleys south to coastal southern California. It occurs on flood beds of streams and rivers, often forming dense thickets, and it sometimes becomes a pest along irrigation ditches. It is a leafy shrub, 4 to 8 feet high with willow-like, smooth, dull-green leaves 1½ to 4 inches long and flesh-colored flowers. The achenes are 5-nerved.

ENGLISH DAISY (*Bellis perennis* L.)
Other common names: European daisy, marguerite, March daisy, bone flower.

This is a native of Europe, grown as an ornamental, which occasionally escapes from cultivation and becomes a weed. It occurs as such chiefly in the coastal region of California. English daisy is a low, perennial plant, all the leaves of which are basal. The leaves are oval, slightly toothed, and narrowed at the base to a margined leaf-stalk. The flowering stalks are about 4 inches tall, and each terminates in a flowering head. The ray flowers are white, tinged with pink, the disk flowers yellow. There are usually about 50 rays. The involucre is composed of 2 rows of equal, green (sometimes purple) bracts. The receptacle is conical, the achenes flattened, the pappus absent.

BUR MARIGOLD. *BIDENS*

These are herbs (ours annual) with opposite leaves, yellow flowers, and a characteristic achene which is flattened parallel with the involucral scales or is 4-sided, and bears 2 to 4 strong persistent barbed awns. The heads are many flowered and have from 3 to 9 rays (or sometimes absent). The involucre is composed of two series of bracts, the outer usually rather long and leaf-like, the inner elliptic or oval and membranous. The achenes are carried from place to place fastened in the hair of animals. In California there are four weedy species of *Bidens*.

KEY TO WEEDY SPECIES OF BIDENS

Leaves simple; rays 3 to 9, conspicuous; achenes with downward-pointing barbs on the margin
    Outer bracts of involucre scarcely longer than the disk; rays showy,
        golden yellow _____*B. laevis*
    Outer bracts of involucre leaf-like and longer than the disk; rays small,
        light yellow _____*B. cernua*
Leaves compound, 3 to 5-divided; rays inconspicuous or lacking; achenes with upward-pointing barbs on the margin
    Rays 1 to 5, inconspicuous_____*B. frondosa*
    Rays absent _____*B. pilosa*

NODDING BUR MARIGOLD (*Bidens cernua* L.)

This native annual is a weed of wet places, infrequent in California, and recorded from San Francisco, Mt. Shasta, and Yreka. It is about 8-20 inches tall, the leaves broadly lance-shaped, not divided into leaflets, the margins more or less irregularly toothed and the leaf blades mostly not joined to each other at their bases. The ray flowers are small and pale yellow, the heads nodding in fruit. The achenes are 4-angled and commonly 4-awned, the barbs pointing downward.

BEGGAR-TICKS (*Bidens frondosa* L.) (Fig. 282)

This is the most widespread of the species of *Bidens*. It occurs in wet soil throughout the San Joaquin and Sacramento Valleys. It is an annual, with erect stems 3-4 feet tall, smooth or slightly hairy. The leaves are divided into 3-5 divisions, coarsely toothed on the margins. The ray flowers are inconspicuous, and there are leaf-like outer bracts to the involucre. The 2-awned achenes are flat, rather bluntly oblong, with upward-pointing barbs on the margins. The heads are erect in fruit.

BUR MARIGOLD (*Bidens laevis* B. S. P.)

This is a native species which occurs in wet ground in the coastal region of southern California, and north in the San Joaquin and Sacramento Valleys. It is an annual, or in the south sometimes perennial, 1-3 feet tall, or up to 5 feet. The leaves are 3-8 inches long, lance-shaped, evenly saw-toothed on the margins. They taper toward the base and are more or less joined to each other where they are attached to the stem. The ray flowers are conspicuous, about 1 inch long, golden yellow. The

FIG. 282.   Beggar-ticks (*Bidens frondosa*). Left, achenes.

achenes are flattish, winged or keeled on the angles with downward pointing barbs on the margins and awns, which are usually 2 or 3. The heads are erect or nodding in fruit.

HAIRY BUR MARIGOLD (*Bidens pilosa* L.)

This native of the American tropics is now naturalized in California, where it is found along the coast in the south and as far north as central California. It is established along many streams and irrigation ditches and is a common weed in gardens and waste places in southern California. It is an annual, attaining a height of from 1-4 feet. The leaves are divided, with 3 to 5 ovate leaflets with toothed margins. The flower heads are inconspicuous, since the ray or marginal flowers are very small and whitish, or none. The achenes are long and slender, 4-sided, with 2-4 awns armed with upward pointing barbs.

THISTLE. CARDUUS

There are two European species of *Carduus*, naturalized in northern California, most frequently in moist draws or sheltered areas in hill lands. They are very similar in gross aspect and both known by the common name Italian Thistle. They are separable, however, according to Howell, into the two species described hereafter.

ITALIAN THISTLE (*Carduus pycnocephalus* L.) (Fig. 283)

This has been recorded from Sonoma, Contra Costa, San Francisco and Marin counties. The plant is an annual, 1-6 feet tall, bearing clusters of purplish-pink slender heads at the end of long spiny-winged stems. The spiny wings are often narrower and interrupted toward the heads, which are usually few—about 1-5. The involucral bracts are not membranous-margined. The margins and backs of the bracts of the heads bear small rough, upwardly appressed trichomes, especially on the midvein. The corolla lobes are commonly about 3 times as long as the throat. The achenes, about 5 mm. long, are of two types, a greenish-gray form with about 20 conspicuous longitudinal grooves, and a more smooth graybrown form. The pappus is dirty white, about 1.5 to 2 cm. long, minutely upwardly barbed. It is often early deciduous.

ITALIAN THISTLE (*Carduus tenuiflorus* Curt.)

This species is more widespread and abundant than the foregoing. It is recorded from Humboldt, Mendocino, Marin, San Francisco, San Mateo, Santa Clara, Contra Costa, Alameda, San Benito and Mariposa Counties; and recently from numerous sites scattered from Siskiyou to Riverside County. *C. tenuiflorus* is very similar to *C. pycnocephalus*, but the stem wings are commonly broader and extend uninterruptedly up to the heads. The heads are usually more numerous, 5-20, the involucral bracts more or less mebranous-margined. The small trichomes described in the preceding species are absent from the margins and midvein of the involucral bracts. These bracts are smooth except for a somewhat fringelike or ciliate margin. The achenes are about 4 mm. long similar to *C. pycnocephalus*, usually with 10-13 nerves, the pappus 1-1.5 cm. long. This species also has the light colored, conspicuously grooved form of achene and the darker, smoother brown type.

FIG. 283.   Italian thistle (*Carduus pycnocepnalus*).   Inset, achenes.

DISTAFF THISTLE (*Carthamus lanatus* DC.) (Fig. 284)

This is a native of the Mediterranean region, which has become adventive at San Francisco and Stockton. It is also reported from near Santa Ana, and as displaying vigorous and spreading habit in a canyon near San Luis Obispo, and elsewhere in southern California. It is an

FIG. 284.   Distaff thistle (*Carthamus lanatus*).   A, achene.

annual, 16 to 25 inches high, with rigid, prickly, pinnatifid, clasping leaves and yellow flowers. The outer bracts of the involucre end in a leaf-like appendage; the inner ones are more rigid, appressed and end in a spine tip. The achenes are pyramidal, with a wavy margin at the apex or broad end, and two kinds of pappus scales.

SMOOTH DISTAFF THISTLE (*Carthamus nitidus* Boiss.)

This species, an annual and closely related to the preceding species, is an introduction from Syria. It has been collected at Sonora, and Jacksonville in Tuolumne County and at San Luis Obispo. It is very similar to *C. lanatus* in all respects, even the achenes being difficult to distinguish.

SAFFLOWER (*Carthamus tinctorius* L.)

Safflower, a native of the Old World, occurs in the Antelope Valley, and in Kings, Sacramento, Tulare, and San Benito Counties. It has been grown to a limited extent since about 1920 as an oil seed crop. The plant attains a height of about 2 feet, has bright glossy and heavily veined foliage and a brilliant red-orange flower head. The achenes are smooth bone-white, about the size of a wheat kernel, somewhat angled and broader above with a slightly notched scar near the base.

CENTAUREA

To the genus *Centaurea* belong some 350 species, mostly natives of the Old World. All are herbaceous forms. In California, the species of *Centaurea* keyed below are the most common. In addition to these, the following species occur sparingly within our borders: pale flowered centaurea (*C. diluta* Ait.), black knapweed (*C. nigra* L.) brown knapweed (*C. Jacea* L.), and spotted centaurea (*C. maculosa* Lam.). These are European natives.

KEY TO WEEDY SPECIES OF CENTAUREA

Involucral bracts fringed, not definitely spiny
  Basal leaves divided, achene not notched, perennial_____*C. repens*
  Basal leaves entire, achene notched, annual_____*C. Cyanus*
Involucral bracts tipped with spines
  Flowers pinkish or purplish, stem wingless
    Achenes with definite pappus_____*C. iberica*
    Achenes devoid of pappus, or vestige of pappus only_____*C. Calcitrapa*
  Flowers yellow, leaf margins prolonged on stems as wings
    Spines slender, brownish purple, ½ inch long or less, pappus whitish, base of achene hook-like _____*C. melitensis*
    Spines stout, bright yellow, ½ inch long, pappus whitish, base of achene obtusely notched _____*C. solstitialis*
    Spines stout, blackish at base, pappus copious, black_____*C. sicula*

PURPLE STAR THISTLE (*Centaurea Calcitrapa* L.) (Figs. 285 and 287)

This species is a native of Europe. The name is derived from the word caltrop, an ancient instrument of war with four spinelike projections, used to impede the progress of mounted warriors.

Purple star thistle is particularly abundant in Solano County—Vallejo, Benicia to Vacaville and eastward—gradually spreading along lines of travel and encroaching laterally in uncultivated lands. It also occurs about San Jose, and in San Mateo and Humboldt Counties. The mature plant attains a growth of approximately 1 to 2 feet, densely and rigidly branched. It appears to be an annual or biennial under our conditions. The stems and leaves are covered with cobwebby hairs frequently becoming almost smooth in age. The leaf surfaces are sparsely pitted with minute clear globules, the leaves divided into narrowly-linear segments, or the uppermost narrow and undivided. The bracts of the flower head are tipped with a stout rigid straw-colored spine an

Fig. 285. Purple Star Thistle (*Centaurea Calcitrapa*).

inch long or less, with from 1 to 3 prickles at the base. The lobes of the flowers are deep rose-purple throughout, and the anthers, united into a tube and extending from the throat of the corolla, are paler in comparison. The achene or seed is 3 mm. long or less and from $1\frac{1}{2}$ to 2 mm. wide, without bristles. It is straw color, heavily mottled throughout with very dark brown, the mottling extending well down to the edge of the scar. Infrequently the seeds are pale. The notch is commonly greater than a right angle, one arm of the angle usually opening to the base of the achene.

CORN FLOWER (*Centaurea Cyanus* L.) (Fig. 286)

This species is well known as an ornamental of gardens, and has escaped to some extent in southern California, also in the northern part of the State. In Oregon the cornflower colors large acreages with its showy blooms. It is an annual, more or less woolly, 1 to 2 feet tall. The leaves are narrow, the heads solitary on the ends of long stems.

The flowers range from deep purple, through blue and pink to white. The achene is similar in shape to that of yellow star thistle, but larger and definitely yellowish about the scar, with the pappus bristles erect and brush-like.

PALE FLOWERED CENTAUREA (*Centaurea diluta* Ait.)

This species has been found at two locations in Los Angeles County: East Whittier and Watts. It is native to the Mediterranean region, and has not heretofore been reported as a weed in this country. The seeds occur as an impurity in canary grass seed.

FIG. 286.	Left, achene of corn flower (*Centaurea Cyanus*) ;
right, of Sicilian thistle (*C. sicula*).

IBERIAN STAR THISTLE (*Centaurea iberica* Trevir.) (Figs. 287 and 288)

This star thistle is now established in three widely separated localities in California. A vigorous grower of biennial habit, Iberian thistle is a native of Asia Minor, probably of Iberia, from whence its name is derived. It was first noted in 1923 from near Solvang, Santa Ynez Canyon, Santa Barbara County. In July, 1929, a considerable acreage was found near Santa Rosa. Two infestations near San Diego County, one approximately 80 acres in extent, were reported in August, 1932.

Mature plants are of bushy habit, much branched from below, 2 to 3 feet or more in height. The stems and leaves are sparsely covered with cobwebby hairs. The leaves, especially on the under surface, are pitted with minute clear globules. The lower leaves are deeply lobed or divided. The upper stem leaves are composed of a large terminal and two small lateral lobes, or the uppermost undivided and narrow. The bracts of the flower head are armed with a stout rigid straw-colored spine about 1 inch long or less, at the base of which are from 1 to 3, most commonly 2, small prickles. The lobes of the individual flowers of the head are purplish-pink at the tip, becoming paler toward the tube. Occasionally

the flower is al-
most white
throughout. The
anthers, which are
united and extend
conspicuously
from the tube of
the corolla, are
darker colored in
comparison to its
lobes, thus giving
the whole flower
head a quite pur-
plish-pink appear-
ance. The achene
is from 3-4 mm.
long and 1½-2 mm.
wide, crowned
with about 3 ir-
regular rows of
flattened micro-
scopically-toothed
bristles, the outer
shorter and broad-
er, becoming

FIG. 287. Achenes of (above) purple star thistle (*Centaurea Calcitrapa*) and (below) Iberian star thistle (*C. iberica*).

longer and narrower toward the innermost, which are about half the
length of the achene. Rarely the bristles are reduced to a single ring of
minute scales. The achene varies from straw color indistinctly lined with
gray to heavily linearly-mottled with very dark brown. Around the notch
and over the base the color is pale yellowish-white, without mottling. The
notch is commonly less than a right angle, usually both arms of the angle
opening to the side of the achene.

TOCALOTE (*Centaurea melitensis* L.) (Fig. 289)

Other common name: Napa thistle.

This species, naturalized from Europe, is a common impurity in
seed grain. It is especially abundant in counties of the San Francisco
Bay region and in the Sacramento Valley, and particularly obnoxious
in grain fields but has spread also into other agricultural lands, including pastured hills.

Tocalote or Napa thistle is an annual. It usually grows to a height
of 1 to 2 feet, and is much branched. A marked characteristic of the
plant is found in the leaves, the edges of which run down the stems,
forming wings. The lowest leaves are cleft while the upper ones are
narrow and without clefts or teeth. The flowering heads are either solitary, or in groups of 2 or 3 and are about ½ inch high. The bracts of the
heads are characteristic: the outermost bear a slender, divergent spine,

Fig. 288. Iberian star thistle (*Centaurea iberica*).

which is often branched below, with smaller spines at its base; the intermediate and inner bracts bear a rigid spine from $\frac{1}{6}$ to $\frac{1}{3}$ inch long. The flowers are yellow. At the tip of the seed are about 3 rows of bristles of unequal length. The base of the achene, with lateral notched scar, appears hook-like.

FIG. 289.   Tocalote (*Centaurea melitensis*).

RUSSIAN KNAPWEED (*Centaurea repens* L.) (Fig. 291)

Other common name: Turkestan thistle.

Russian knapweed is one of the major noxious weeds of California. It has now become well established throughout the warmer sections of the State, being a serious menace in cultivated fields, in orchards, and along roadsides and ditch banks. It is also found in many abandoned alfalfa fields. Russian knapweed is a native of southern Russia and Asia Minor to Altai and Afghanistan. A pernicious weed in the Crimea and other parts of southern European Russia, it was introduced into California between 1910 and 1914, in impure Turkestan alfalfa seed and also probably in sugar beet seed. Since 1914, no Turkestan alfalfa seed has been imported into California from foreign countries, although some is received in other states. It is very likely that its spread in California at the present time is not due to new infestations as the result of shipments of impure seed from outside California, but rather to movements of seeds, feedstuffs, etc., within the State. Also, it is spreading somewhat by natural means.

Russian knapweed is a perennial, very similar in its weed habits to morning-glory, Johnson grass, and hoary cress. It grows to a height of 1 to 3 feet, from creeping perennial rootstocks. The older rootstocks have a characteristic dark brown to black color; the younger ones are of a lighter color. The horizontal rootstocks are slender, except at the points where they turn abruptly downward, where they become ¼ inch or more in diameter. And, at this bend in the rootstock, a cluster of erect shoots usually arises; also, here, another rootstock runs horizontally for a distance before it bends downward. Rootstocks often extend to a depth of 2 to 4 feet, depending upon the quality of the soil. They branch frequently, sending off laterals, which may in turn give rise to vertical shoots. Close observation of these rootstocks shows small, narrow, appressed scale leaves, arranged alternately at regular intervals. These are usually darker in color than the stems, and clasping. On young rootstocks, however, the scales are light in color, quite long, and not so appressed to the stem. These scales on the underground stems are in reality leaves, and buds occur in their axils. It is from these buds that new shoots arise, when top growth is cut off. The stems are erect, stiff, and branched. Young stems are clothed with a soft, gray nap.

The leaves are of several types: the first leaves, those borne at the base of the plant, are thick, somewhat hairy, grayish blue-green in color, longer than wide and deeply notched. The typical stem leaves are thin, smoother than the basal leaves, and with margins entire or slightly toothed; the uppermost leaves, those on the flowering branches, are small, narrow, and entire margined. All types of leaves are more or less clasping to the stem and have an inconspicuous midrib. The leaves, as well as all other parts of the plant, have a pronounced bitter taste, which makes them unpalatable to livestock.

The flowers are in heads at the tips of branches; each branch of the flowering stem bears but a single flower head, and these branches are leafy up to the heads. The heads are small, about $\frac{3}{8}$ to $\frac{1}{2}$ inch in diameter, rounded in outline, and the flowers lilac colored. There are numerous flowers in each head, and all are alike. The head is subtended by numerous scale-like overlapping bracts, forming a structure known as the involucre. The outer and middle bracts are almost round, somewhat concave, and their margins and tips are thin and papery; the innermost bracts are long and lance-shaped, and also papery on margins and tips. The corolla is smooth and five-cleft. The pappus is white, and early deciduous. The bristles of the pappus are covered with barbs and are in several ranks, the innermost five being double the length of the others.

The seeds are oblong, somewhat larger than alfalfa seed, nearly white or ivory, marked lengthwise by inconspicuous fine lines. The mature seeds are not readily carried by wind as they are quite heavy, and devoid of pappus bristles. Moreover, since the seeds are borne in a cup-shaped head which does not open widely at maturity, ready dispersal by wind is prevented. However, this means of spread can not be entirely ignored.

SICILIAN THISTLE (*Centaurea sicula* L.) (Fig. 286)

This species, a native of the Mediterranean, was first noticed in 1923 in the vicinity of Alder Creek, southwest of Folsom. The limited infestation occurred near a bridge, adjacent to which the vegetation was burned off by the fire control crew of the State Division of Highways. The spread has been slight, away from the highway on both sides of the road, but not along the right-of-way except for one small patch north of Folsom near the highway.

The plant is an erect annual, 1-3 feet tall, the heads large and conspicuous at the ends of slender stems which are very narrowly winged by decurrent leaf margins. The ray flowers are lemon yellow, the bracts of the involucre tipped with a very dark brown to almost black spine. The achene is almost $\frac{1}{2}$ inch long, shiny dark brown with a bristly black pappus.

YELLOW STAR THISTLE (*Centaurea solstitialis* L.) (Fig. 290)

This species, also naturalized from Europe, is the most widely distributed of our star thistles. It occurs in cultivated fields, waste lands, along roadsides, and in the vacant lots of cities throughout the Sacramento Valley, the north Coast Range, about the Bay region and south. It is spread by many different agencies, but chiefly as an impurity in commercial seeds and hay, and by sheep.

Yellow star thistle is an annual. It usually grows to a height of 1 to $2\frac{1}{2}$ feet, and has rigid, spreading stems which are branched from the base; the stems are more or less whitened with a loose, cottony wool, as are the leaves. The basal leaves are 2 to 3 inches long and deeply lobed; the upper leaves are from $\frac{1}{2}$ to 1 inch long, entire, narrow, sharply pointed,

Fig. 290.   Yellow star thistle (*Centaurea solstitialis*).

Fɪɢ. 291   Russian knapweed (*Centaurea repens*).

and, as in tocalote, extend down the stem at the base to form wings, less broad than those of tocalote. The flowering heads are solitary at the ends of branches, about 1 inch long; the bracts of the head are armed with long, rigid spines; the spines of the lowest bracts are 3-pronged, those of the middle bracts simple, stout, yellow, and from $\frac{1}{4}$ to 1 inch long, whereas the uppermost bracts are spineless. The flowers are a bright yellow. There are two types of seed: a light-colored form with the lateral notch of the achene without a well-defined hook-like base, and with numerous, slender, white, soft bristles, and a small very dark to black-colored form devoid of pappus bristles. This latter form is difficult to separate from commercial seed when yellow star thistle occurs as an impurity.

FITCH'S SPIKEWEED (*Centromadia Fitchii* (Gray) Greene).

This has a general resemblance to common spikeweed. However, it is usually not over 20 inches tall and its herbage is dark-green, and distinctly ill-scented. The floral leaves are definitely longer than the rather conspicuous flower heads. The disk achenes have a linear pappus, whereas in *C. pungens,* the pappus is wanting. This is a native of California and Oregon and is becoming established as a weed in the San Joaquin Valley, and south to San Diego County.

COMMON SPIKEWEED (*Centromadia pungens* (T. & G.) Greene) (Fig. 292)

This is a native species which is abundant in southern California and northward through the San Joaquin Valley. In the latter region it covers many thousands of acres, often forming thickets 4 to 5 feet high, especially on alkaline or subalkaline soils.

Common spikeweed is a rigidly and freely branching annual herb, usually 2 to 3 feet high, but sometimes up to 5 feet. The herbage is yellow-ish-green. The stems are usually clothed with stiff, spreading hairs, which are glandular and secrete a sweet-scented substance. The lower leaves are 1 to 3 inches long, deeply lobed, the lobes or teeth needle-pointed; the upper leaves are entire, needle-like, $\frac{1}{2}$ inch or less long, the majority borne in dense globular clusters on short branches in the axils of the longer, spiny leaves. The floral leaves are scarcely longer than the flowering heads. The flowering heads are about $\frac{1}{2}$ inch or less broad, and occur at or near the ends of the stem branches. The involucre consists of a single series of narrow, pointed, spiny bracts. There are from 25 to 40 yellow rays, which are deeply cleft at the tip. Ray flowers are fertile, whereas disk flowers are sterile. The achenes are more or less triangular, roughened, somewhat 2-nerved on the back, and with a short lateral beak.

CHRYSANTHEMUM
KEY TO WEEDY SPECIES OF CHRYSANTHEMUM

Plants annual
    Rays golden yellow _____*C. segetum*
    Rays white _____*C. carinatum*
    Rays light yellow _____*C. coronarium*
Plants perennial
    Heads borne singly ; rays white_____*C. Leucanthemum*
    Heads borne in flat-topped dense clusters ; rays yellow_____*C. parthenium*

Fig. 292.　Common spikeweed (*Centromadia pungens*).

TRICOLOR CHRYSANTHEMUM (*Chrysanthemum carinatum* L.)

This is a native of Morocco, found growing without cultivation in the San Diego region. It is an annual, 2 to 3 feet tall; leaves are somewhat succulent, 2-pinnatifid; flowering heads solitary, $1\frac{1}{2}$ to $2\frac{1}{2}$ inches in diameter, rays yellow or ringed with yellow or red, the disk purple, thus giving the heads a tricolor effect; involucral bracts broad, the margins papery; achenes flat, winged.

GARLAND CHRYSANTHEMUM (*Chrysanthemum coronarium* L.)

This is a native of the Mediterranean region, and occurs along railway tracks and elsewhere in San Diego. It is an annual, smooth, leafy herb, 1 to 3 feet tall. The leaves are 1 to 4 inches long, bipinnatifid, the petioles winged. The flowering heads are solitary on leafy peduncles, and the flowers yellowish. The achenes are about 3 mm. long, 4 angled, one angle terminating in a tooth.

OXEYE DAISY (*Chrysanthemum Leucanthemum* L.) (Fig. 293)

This species is naturalized from Europe and has become established in fields in certain sections of the coast counties. In Europe

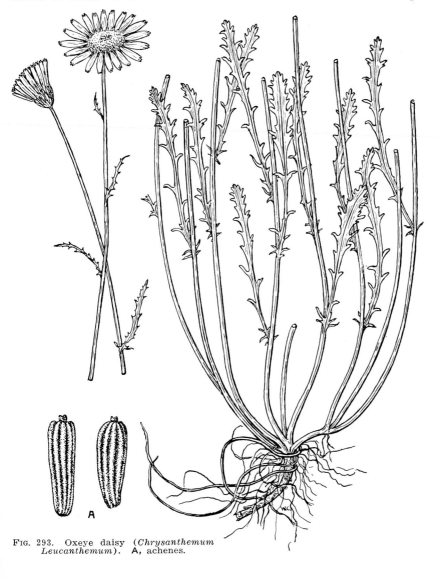

FIG. 293. Oxeye daisy (*Chrysanthemum Leucanthemum*). **A,** achenes.

and in the eastern United States it is regarded as a weed of considerable importance. Oxeye daisy is a perennial herb, with erect stem, 1 to 3 feet high, branching above. The lower leaves are roughly oval to spatula-shaped, coarsely toothed, and tapering to a long petiole; the upper leaves are lance-shaped, clasping, $\frac{1}{2}$ to $2\frac{1}{2}$ inches long, and toothed. The heads are terminal, $1\frac{1}{4}$ to 2 inches wide, the rays white, $\frac{3}{8}$ to $\frac{1}{2}$ inch long, with a tapering base which is inconspicuously notched

Fig. 294.   Corn chrysanthemum (*Chrysanthemum segetum*).   **A,** outer bract of head; **B,** disk achene; **C,** ray achene.

at the apex. There are 20-30 ray flowers and numerous yellow disk flowers. The achenes are 1-1.5 mm. long, narrowly obovate, dark brown to black with 10 white, conspicuously raised, rounded, vertical ribs.

FEVERFEW (*Chrysanthemum Parthenium* (L.) Pers.)

This species is sparingly established north of Spanish Creek, near Quincy, well away from human habitations. Collections have also been made in Diablo Canyon in San Luis Obispo County, on the north side of Mt. Shasta, and at Alta Loma Ranch in Napa County. This is a perennial herb from 1-2½ feet tall. Leaves are thin, up to 6 inches long, the lower petioled, the upper sessile, and pinnately parted, the segments toothed. There are numerous flowering heads, with white flowers, the rays of which are long persistent.

CORN CHRYSANTHEMUM (*Chrysanthemum segetum* L.) (Fig. 294)

This plant is naturalized from Europe, being reported in California at Berkeley, Caspar, and Mendocino City. We also have specimens from Santa Rosa, Fort Bragg, and Hydesville, and Siskiyou and Humboldt Counties. It occurs sparingly as a weed in open fields. It is an annual erect herb, 1 to 2 feet high. The lower leaves are incised or pinnatifid, the upper merely toothed, and with a clasping base. The attractive flower heads are 1¼ to 2 inches wide, the rays about ⅓ inch wide, deep yellow, with a broad base and conspicuously notched at the apex. The ray achenes are broad, 3-sided, the lateral angles winged and few-toothed; the disk achenes are cylindric and 5- to 10-ribbed.

CHICORY (*Cichorium Intybus* L.) (Fig. 295)
Other common names: Succory, blueweed.

Chicory is a garden plant introduced from Europe which has become naturalized throughout the State at lower altitudes. It is often common along roadsides and fences, and in waste places, occasionally troublesome in grain fields. Chicory is a perennial from a deep tap root. The stem is erect and 1 to 3 feet high. There are numerous basal leaves 3 to 5 or 8 inches long, which often spread on the ground; the upper leaves are smaller, lance-shaped or oblong, lobed and toothed or entire, clasping and ear-shaped at the base. The heads are in axillary clusters. The bracts of the involucre are in two series, the outer 4 or 5 spreading, the inner usually 8, erect. The flowers are blue. The achenes are 5-angled or 5-ribbed, beakless, and truncate. The pappus consists of a number of short fringe-like scales.

THISTLE. *CIRSIUM*

KEY TO SPECIES OF CIRSIUM

Heads with unisexual flowers_____*C. arvense*
Heads with perfect flowers
    Leaves and stems glandular pubescent_____*C. fontinale*
    Leaves not glandular pubescent
        Heads on peduncles, not with pronounced leafy bracts at base_____*C. occidentale*

FIG. 295.   Chicory (*Cichorium Intybus*).

Heads sessile or nearly so, leafy-bracted at base
  Leaves glabrous or hispid above, tomentose beneath
    Stems spinose-winged by decurrent leaf bases_____*C. lanceolatum*
    Stems not spinose-winged_____*C. edule*
  Leaves tomentose on both surfaces or later becoming glabrous above
                                                                    C. undulatum

CANADA THISTLE (*Cirsium arvense* Scop.) (Fig. 296)

Jepson records 19 species of *Cirsium* (true thistles) as occurring in California. Of these the most important from the weed standpoint is Canada thistle. While Canada thistle has a very limited distribution in California, it is a most troublesome weed and every effort should be directed to its recognition and eradication. The plant has been proclaimed one of the most serious weed pests known to agriculture and most states have laws directed towards keeping it out. It is found over the northern half of the United States, from the Atlantic to the Pacific, but does not thrive in the southern part. Throughout the agricultural sections of Canada, in Europe, in Australia and a number of other countries, the plant is a menace. A native of Europe, western Asia and northern Africa, Canada thistle possibly was introduced into Canada by early French settlers as an impurity in seed. Probably it was introduced into California in the same way.

Canada thistle is a perennial. The plant has an extensive root system, the main roots running horizontally, sometimes a distance of 15 feet or more. These so-called "runner roots" may store food, thus enabling the plant to live from year to year. It appears that any part of the root system is capable of giving rise to buds which develop into leafy shoots. It is well known that when the roots are cut into pieces by the hoe, plow, or other cultivating implements, each piece is capable of developing a separate plant. The roots, which are about ¼ inch in diameter, are light-yellow, or nearly white, and may go to a depth of from 2 to 2½ feet, quite beyond reach of the plow.

The stems are 1 to 4 feet tall, erect, slender, grooved and somewhat woody. The leaves are without a leaf stalk, usually somewhat clasping to the stem, often deeply cut and divided into irregular prickly lobes. However, there are some forms which have practically spineless leaves. The leaves are a vivid green on the upper surface and somewhat woolly on the under side. Canada thistle may live over the winter in the rosette stage and the leaves which compose this are rather long and irregularly shaped.

The individual flowers are very small and are grouped to form purple heads about ½ inch in diameter. There are two kinds of flowers: staminate and pistillate. The former are the male flowers and furnish the pollen; the latter are the female flowers and develop the seed. As a rule, all the flowers on one plant are either male or female. In other words, not all plants are seed-bearing. An entire patch of Canada thistle may be either staminate (nonseed-bearing) or pistillate (seed-bearing). This accounts for failure of seed production in some places. Seed production is dependent upon the presence of both kinds of plants. The flower heads of staminate plants are somewhat globular in form, while those of pistillate plants are more or less flask-shaped.

The seed is about ⅛ inch long, smooth, light-brown, finely grooved lengthwise, and usually somewhat flattened and curved; the tip is characteristically cupped with a small conical point in the center; the base of the seed is rounded. At the tip is a tuft of hairs, by means of which wind carries the seed long distances. Canada thistle seed, found as an impurity in commercial seed, is without the tuft of hair, which is easily brushed off. There is considerable variation in the amount of viable seed produced by a single plant. Apparently less seed is produced in the southern than in the northern part of its range. The seeds may retain their viability four years or more when buried in the soil.

Cirsium arvense var. *mite* has been found established in a beet field two miles south of Chualar, Monterey County. This weed grows more vigorously than beets, in some spots completely crowding out the crop. To date, no seed has been formed. The leaves of the main stem of var. *mite* are shallowly cleft, those of the branch stems almost entire or toothed, and minutely spiny.

INDIAN THISTLE *(Cirsium edule* Nutt.)

This native thistle occurs sparingly in southern California, more commonly in the Coast Ranges and northward. It is a robust but succulent biennial, 3 to 6 feet tall. The heads are leafy bracted, sessile or nearly so, with involucral bracts 1 to 1½ inches long, cobwebby or woolly. The heads are pale lavender to purple. The achene is smooth, the pappus dark or reddish tinged.

SPRING THISTLE *(Cirsium fontinale* (Greene) Jepson.)

This species, which is probably introduced, thus far has been found only in San Mateo County, at Crystal Springs. It is closely allied to bull thistle. It is a perennial, 1 to 2 feet high with glandular stems and leaves and nodding, dull white flower heads. As contrasted with the bull thistle, the stems are not spiny-winged, and the upper surfaces are not beset with stiff hairs.

BULL THISTLE *(Cirsium lanceolatum* (L.) Scop.) (Fig. 297)
Other common names: Spear thistle, plume thistle, bur thistle, common thistle.

This weed is a native of Europe and Asia. It has spread to all parts of the world and becomes troublesome in pastures and fields, along fences and in waste places generally. It is fairly common and often locally abundant at lower altitudes in California, especially in the northern part of the State.

Bull thistle is a biennial herb 2 to 4 feet tall. The stems are stout, branching, striated, and more or less woolly. The leaves are green above, lighter and somewhat hairy beneath, the midrib prominent and very hairy in the younger leaves; the leaf blades are coarsely toothed or deeply lobed almost to the midrib, the tips of the teeth or lobes armed with sharp, stout, yellow prickles. The lower leaves are from 6 inches to 1 foot long, 2½ to 4 inches wide, and stalked; the upper leaves are

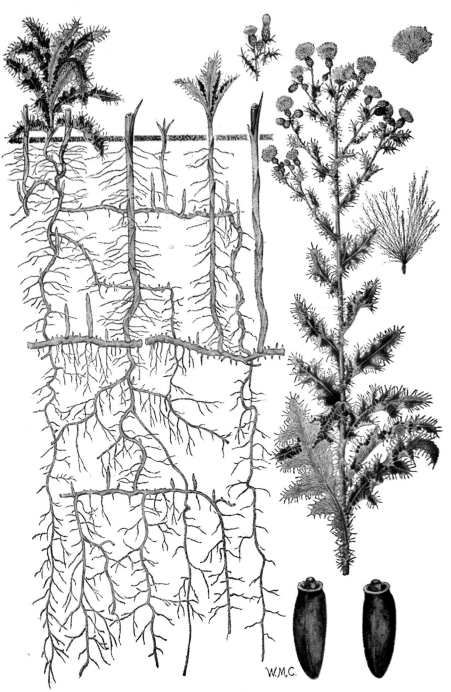

Fig. 296. Canada thistle (*Cirsium arvense*).

attached by the bases of the blades which are more or less continued down the stems as interrupted bristly wings. The flower heads are 1½ to 2 inches high and nearly as broad, occurring in clusters of 4 or 5 at the summits of stems. The involucre is composed of numerous slender, overlapping bracts, in many series, each bract ending in long, spreading, needle-like tips; the involucres at first appear cobwebby due

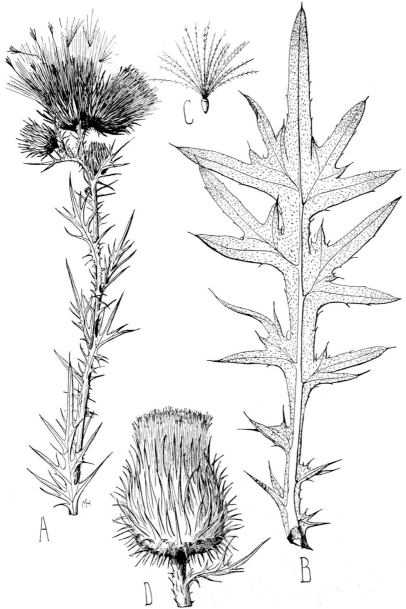

FIG. 297. Bull thistle (*Cirsium lanceolatum*). **A,** flowering stem; **B,** upper leaf; **C,** achene; **D,** head.

to white hairs which develop between the bracts. There are numerous flowers in each head, all alike, and all fertile, and rose-purple in color. The achenes are somewhat flattened, 3 to 4 mm. long; grayish, with obscure longitudinal maroon markings and yellowish at the collar. They bear at the summit numerous soft, white, plume-like bristles, which are united at the base and fall together from the mature achene.

WAVY-LEAVED THISTLE *(Cirsium undulatum* (Nutt.) Spreng.)

This is a native of the Great Plains and prairies to Kansas, New Mexico, and Arizona. It is a biennial, 1 to 3 feet high, densely white-woolly throughout. At maturity, the leaves may become smooth above. The leaves are lance-shaped or oblong lance-shaped, sessile or decurrent at the base, the margin wavy, lobed or dissected; they are beset with prickles. Outer bracts of the involucre are strongly prickly-pointed and sticky on the back. Flowers purple or pink.

WESTERN THISTLE *(Cirsium occidentale* (Nutt.) Jepson)

This is a native thistle which is fairly common and may behave as a weed. The western thistle runs into a number of varieties. They occur in the dunes or sandy hills along the coast from Mendocino County to San Diego, and also in the interior valleys and hills of the Coast Ranges; one variety also spreads into the Sierra Nevada. This species is a stout biennial 1½ to 3 feet tall, with herbage that is mostly white with a covering of cottony wool. The flower heads are 1½ to 2 inches high, the flower reddish or purple. The involucral bracts are straight, with short spines, and so densely enveloped by cobwebby hairs as to almost conceal the spines of the bracts. The achene is about 7 mm. long and 3 mm. wide,

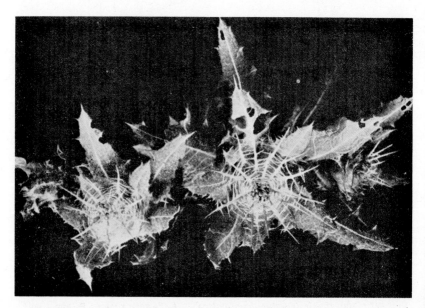

FIG. 298. Blessed thistle *(Cnicus benedictus)*, showing rosette habit of growth.

dark mahogany-brown with glossy smooth surface. The pappus is clear white and silky plumose throughout its length.

BLESSED THISTLE (*Cnicus benedictus* L.) (Figs. 298 and 299)

This thistle is naturalized from Europe, and is becoming distributed throughout the Sacramento Valley in certain points in the hills bordering. Specimens have also come from Bakersfield and Rosemead, and in San Diego County from Encinitas, Jamacha, and Glen Lonely.

It is an annual, prickly herb, 1 to 2 feet high. The stems are branching, juicy, and somewhat hairy. The leaves are alternate, thin, green, the lower ones stalked, the upper with clasping bases, all 3 to 6 inches long, their edges jagged with unequal teeth which are usually spiny. The flower heads are solitary at the ends of the branches, and are enveloped and almost concealed by the upper leaves. The heads are 1½ to 2 inches across, and about 1 inch long. The involucre is composed of several series of overlapping bracts, the inner equipped with long branching spines. There are numerous yellow flowers in each head. The achenes are conspicuously many-nerved, 10-toothed at the summit, and each has a crown (pappus) of dry scales arranged in two series, the outer long and yellow, the inner short and white.

FIG. 299. Blessed thistle (*Cnicus benedictus*).

GOLDEN COREOPSIS (*Coreopsis tinctoria* Nutt.) (Fig. 300)

This is a garden plant, introduced from central United States, which is, according to Jepson, an escape at Redding and Kaweah. It is an herb with a solitary, slender, erect stem 2 to 3 feet tall. The herbage is smooth, the leaves few and pinnately divided into 3 to 7 narrow segments. The flowers are yellow in showy heads. The involucre is hemispherical, the outer bracts oval, not more than $\frac{1}{12}$ inch long, the inner ones longer and

FIG. 300. Golden coreopsis (*Coreopsis tinctoria*).

broader, and often reddish. The achenes are flattened, wingless, and devoid of definite pappus.

AUSTRALIAN BRASS BUTTONS (*Cotula australis* Hook.) (Fig. 301)

Less common than common brass buttons is this allied species, a native from Australia, which occurs along the streets of many of our towns and cities. It is a slender, branching annual, usually 2 to 5 inches high. The herbage is not succulent, and is covered with soft spreading hairs. All the leaves are finely dissected into linear segments. The bracts of the involucre are brownish-tipped with papery margins. There are 2 or 3 outer rows of pistillate flowers. The marginal achenes are somewhat compressed, and minutely hispid on both faces.

FIG. 301.   Australian brass buttons
(*Cotula australis*).

COMMON BRASS BUTTONS (*Cotula coronopifolia* L.) (Fig. 302)

This is an immigrant from South Africa which is now found abundantly, especially in the coastal counties, in saline soil. It blooms nearly all the year round. It is a low, somewhat succulent, smooth, strong-scented, perennial herb. There are usually many stems clustered and spreading on the ground, $\frac{1}{2}$ to 1 foot long. The leaves are alternate, varying considerably in shape—linear, lance-shaped, oblong, entire, coarsely toothed or deeply lobed on the same plant; the leaf bases are dilated to form a short sheath around the stem. The herbage is yellowish-green in color. The flower heads are rounded-flattish, about $\frac{1}{3}$ inch broad, and borne on long,

Fig. 302.   Common brass buttons (*Cotula coronopifolia*).

naked stalks. The involucre is composed of two series of greenish bracts. Ray flowers are absent. There are numerous disk flowers, the single outer row pistillate and without corollas, the remainder with a 4-toothed yellow corolla and either fertile or infertile. The achenes are stalked and more or less winged on the margins.

SMOOTH HAWKSBEARD (*Crepis capillaris* (L.) Wallr.)

This is an adventive from Europe which is gradually enlarging its area of distribution in the State. It occurs in fields and pastures, and in waste places. The smooth hawksbeard is an annual or biennial herb 1 to 2½ feet high. There are one or more slender stems arising from the base. Most of the leaves are basal. The basal leaves are 3 to 6 inches long, 1 to 2 inches wide, deeply lobed or irregularly toothed, and with a winged petiole. The upper leaves are lance-shaped, sessile by a clasping base, and 1 to 2 inches long. There are numerous yellow flowering heads, subtended by an involucre of a single series of bracts. The receptacle is naked. The achenes are about ½ inch long, smooth, narrow-oblong, or narrowed equally at each end, 10-ribbed, and surmounted by a pappus of numerous soft hairs.

ROUGH HAWKSBEARD (*Crepis vesicaria* L. var. *taraxacifolia* Thuill.)

This is closely related to the smooth hawksbeard. It is introduced from Europe and is recorded as occurring infrequently on the Mendocino coast and near Los Angeles. It is an annual or biennial herb which resembles the smooth hawksbeard and may be distinguished from the latter by its upper leaves which have an arrowhead-shaped, toothed base, and by its beaked achenes.

Crepis bursifolia L., a native of southern France and Italy, is well established in the lawns on the campus of the University of California at Berkeley. *C. rubra* L., is a native of Italy and the Balkans, and reported from Belvedere in Marin County.

ARTICHOKE THISTLE (*Cynara Cardunculus* L.) (Figs. 303 and 304)

Artichoke thistle was introduced into the area near Benicia about fifty years ago. Probably it was imported from southern Europe where it was used as a food. It escaped from the gardens where it was first planted and spread over some 70,000 acres in and around Benicia and Cordelia. The heaviest infestations, covering 4,000 acres, were in the hills near Benicia. The plant had spread over the hills into the areas which were formerly used for grain to such an extent that the forage had been made useless. Due to the spiny nature and the spreading habit of the plant, cattle and sheep will not venture through thickly infested areas. Frequently, in order to save moving stock around a large, heavily infested area, it has been necessary to cut trails through. The infestations in and around Benicia and Cordelia have been largely eradicated in the last few years.

The plant is commonly called cardoon. It stems freely with branches 1½ to 2 feet in height. However, under growing conditions in this particular locality, these stems grow to a much greater height, in many cases higher than a man's head and spreading profusely from the crown. The stems and undersides of the leaves are whitish in color; the upper sides are green. Long spines are borne on the lobes and teeth of the leaves as well as on the head or floral part of the plant.

ARTICHOKE (*Cynara Scolymus* L.)

This garden plant from Europe is an occasional escape from cultivation. As early as 1897, Parish reported it as abundant over a hillside

FIG. 303. Artichoke thistle (*Cynara Cardunculus*), showing habit of growth in field.

FIG. 304. Artichoke thistle (*Cynara Cardunculus*).

pasture near Rincon, in San Diego County. It has also been found at San Bernardino, near a roadside, and at Laguna, Murrieta, and Orange. It resembles cardoon, or wild artichoke, from which it differs in that the leaf lobes are scarcely spiny, and the inner bracts of the involucre are not spiny.

FALSE DAISY (*Eclipta alba* Hassk.) (Fig. 305)

This is introduced from tropical America. It occurs from southern California to the Sacramento Valley; a weed of rice fields and the islands of the lower Sacramento River. This is a decumbent herb 1 to 2 feet high. The leaves are opposite, lance-shaped or oblong, finely toothed, somewhat hairy, the lower short-stalked, the upper sessile. The flowering heads are solitary in the upper leaf axils. The involucre is broad and composed of herbaceous bracts in about two series. The rays are short and white. The bracts of the receptacle are bristle-like. The achenes are thick, those of the ray flowers 3-sided, those of the disk flowers compressed and at maturity corky-margined.

FIG. 305. False daisy (*Eclipta alba*). **A,** achene.

NEW ZEALAND FIREWEED (*Erechtites arguta* DC.) (Fig. 306)

This species, introduced from New Zealand or Australia, has been found in redwood forests from Mendocino County to Del Norte County. It is a coarse, erect annual, 4 to 8 feet high, with a rank odor. The herbage

Fig. 306. New Zealand fireweed (*Erechtites arguta*).

is white hairy, soon becoming smooth, at least in parts of the plant. The leaves are alternate, oblong in outline, deeply pinnatifid, 3 to 4½ inches long, the leaf stalk winged and dilated at the base. The flower heads are numerous and in close groups. There are no ray flowers, but two kinds of yellowish-white disk flowers; central, perfect flowers, and marginal pistillate flowers. The pappus is of long, soft, fine bristles. The achenes are 5-nerved, roughened, and have a callus-like cup at the summit.

AUSTRALIAN FIREWEED *(Erechtites prenanthoides* DC.)

This is a native of Australia, said to have become naturalized in 1918 in Humboldt County, since which date it is spreading rapidly. It is 4 to 8 feet high with narrow lance-shaped finely-toothed leaves 3 to 6½ inches long. The leaves narrow down to the ear-lobed base. The flower groups are ½ to 1 foot across, and widely branched.

FLEABANE. *ERIGERON*

KEY TO WEEDY SPECIES OF ERIGERON

Rays inconspicuous, scarcely exceeding the disk
  Involucre smooth, pappus less than twice the length of achene_____*E. canadensis*
  Involucre densely hairy, pappus about twice the length of achene_____*E. linifolius*
Rays conspicuous, much surpassing the disk
  Nearly all stem leaves toothed_____*E. annuus*
  Stem leaves entire or only the lower toothed_____*E. ramosus*

ANNUAL FLEABANE *(Erigeron annuus* Pers.)

This is naturalized from the eastern United States, and now occurs sparingly in Humboldt County.

HORSEWEED *(Erigeron canadensis* L.) (Fig. 307)

Other common names: Canada fleabane, butterweed, pride weed, mare's tail.

This common weed is a native of eastern United States. It has spread throughout the greater part of the country. It is a well known weed along roadsides, ditch banks, in cultivated fields, and waste places. It is reported to be irritating to the nostrils of grazing animals.

Horseweed is a tall annual or biennial herb with slender, erect stems which vary considerably in height, from a few inches up to 8 or 10 feet. The stems branch near the top, bearing very many small flowering heads. The stems may be nearly smooth or rough-hairy. The lower leaves are 1 to 4 inches long, strap-shaped, the margins entire or toothed; the upper leaves smaller, and entire; all the leaves are usually hairy on both surfaces. The heads are small, ⅛ inch or less high, and are very numerous in a dense panicle. The involucre is composed of 2 or 3 series of very small, pointed, green, smooth bracts. The rays are very small and white, the disk yellow. The achenes are cylindrical, 1/16 inch or less long, squarish at the summit, and bearing 8 to 10 straight, brown-yellow, spreading hairs, each about 1½ times the length of the body of the achene.

FLAX-LEAVED FLEABANE *(Erigeron linifolius* Willd.) (Fig. 307)

This annual or biennial species is naturalized from the American tropics, and has become a pest in southern California, and in many localities in the northern part of the State. It often forms dense stands in company with *E. canadensis,* and may readily be distinguished from that species by the darker colored herbage and the greater diameter

FIG. 307. Left, horseweed (*Erigeron canadensis*); right, flax-leaved fleabane (*E. linifolius*).

of the fully matured head with pappus, which is globose and about ½ inch in diameter. The pappus is about 2 times or more the length of the body of the achene.

DAISY FLEABANE (*Erigeron ramosus* (Walt.) B. S. P.)

This species, also naturalized from the eastern United States, has been found in Humboldt and Plumas Counties, and Yosemite Valley. These two species, like the common fleabane, are annual or biennial.

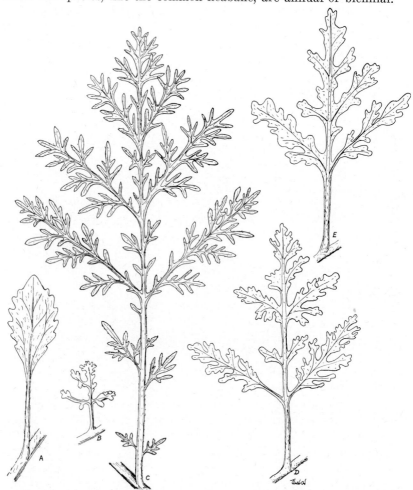

FIG. 308. Leaves of *Franseria* species. **A,** Chamisso's bur-weed (*F. Chamissonis*); **B,** burro-weed (*F. dumosa*); **C,** franseria poverty weed (*F. tenuifolia*); **D,** beach-bur (*F. bipinnatifida*); **E,** annual bur-weed (*F. acanthicarpa*).

WHITE THOROUGHWORT *(Eupatorium adenophorum* Spreng.)

This is a native of Mexico which is a rare escape in canyons near Monrovia, Pasadena, Santa Barbara, and Berkeley. It is a perennial herb with purplish, erect, simple or few-branched stems 12 to 20 inches tall, and mostly opposite leaves which are deltoid-oval, toothed, and

¾ to 1½ inches long. There are numerous flowering heads in small, compact clusters, the heads being about $\frac{3}{16}$ inch high. The bracts of the involucre are glandular, and finely hairy. The flowers are white, the achenes angular or striated, with a pappus consisting of a single row of capillary bristles.

FILAGO (*Filago gallica* L.)

This species, naturalized from Europe, is cited by Jepson from the Napa Range, Hydesville in Humboldt County, Ione, Milton, and Whiteside in Mariposa County. It is a low woolly annual, 5 to 7 inches high, with alternate, narrow, entire leaves, ½ to 1 inch long. The flowering heads are in small clusters. The heads are obconical, somewhat 5-angled, and about ⅙ inch high; the involucral bracts are concave or boat-shaped, and in series. Each bract subtends a pistillate flower, and in the center of the receptacle there is a cluster of sterile and fertile flowers. The achenes along the margin are completely enclosed by a bract which becomes hardened at the base.

FRANSERIA

There are 8 species of *Franseria* in California, five of which are weeds. The franserias or bur-weeds are herbs or low shrubs, with alternate leaves and small, inconspicuous, greenish, unisexual flowers in separate heads. The staminate heads, in more or less bowl-shaped nodding involucres, are in a terminal catkin-like spike, the pistillate in the axils of the upper leaves at the base of the staminate flower groups, or sometimes scattered throughout. The involucre of the staminate heads is bowl-shaped or top-shaped, that of the pistillate heads bur-like and enclosing 1 to 4 flowers.

ANNUAL BUR-WEED (*Franseria acanthicarpa* (Hook.) Cov.) (Figs. 308 and 309)

This is an inland species, rather common on the dry, sandy soils of the interior valleys. It is an annual herb 1 to 2 feet high, with broadly oval leaves, once or twice pinnatifid, and 1¼ to 3½ inches long. The burs are about ¼ inch long, smooth, and bear straight, flat, thin spines.

BEACH-BUR (*Franseria bipinnatifida* Nutt.) (Fig. 308)

The beach-bur is a plant of sandy beaches from Del Norte to San Diego. It is a perennial herb, the stems 2 to 3 feet long, somewhat hairy, spreading in all directions from the crown of the large, fleshy root. The leaves are gray-green, soft-hairy, 1 to

FIG. 309. Burs of *Franseria acanthicarpa* (left); *F. dumosa* (right).

4 inches long, the blades divided nearly to the midrib into narrow lobes which are irregularly margined or themselves deeply divided. The burs are more or less hairy, the spines thick, somewhat flattened, the tips of some being curved.

CHAMISSO'S BUR-WEED (*Franseria Chamissonis* Less.) (Fig. 308)

This bur-weed is abundant along the coast, on sandy soil, from Humboldt County to Santa Cruz County. It resembles *F. bipinnatifida* from which it is distinguished by the merely toothed leaves, or the lower more deeply cut.

BURRO-WEED (*Franseria dumosa* Gray) (Figs. 308 and 309)

Burro-weed is abundant on the Colorado and Mojave Deserts. It is a low rounded bush 10 to 20 inches high, with rigid, brittle branches. The slender branchlets end in an inflorescence, and the second year these appear as naked, spine-like structures. The stems are whitish, the foliage grayish, with fine, close hairs. The leaves are seldom over 1 inch long, and 1 to 3 times parted into a few short, obtuse lobes. The burs are 2-flowered and bear straight spines which taper from a broad, flat base.

FRANSERIA POVERTY WEED (*F. confertiflora* (DC.) Rydb.) (*Franseria tenuifolia* Gray) (Figs. 274b and 308)

This bur-weed occurs in coastal southern California, and eastward, being common on dry plains. It is also established in the north to a limited extent near Niles in Alameda County. It is a perennial, 1-2 feet tall, more or less spreading and minutely hairy throughout. The leaves are divided, the divisions again divided into narrowly oblong or linear lobes. There are small lobes along the main axis of the leaf and the ter-

FIG. 310. Galinsoga (*Galinsoga parviflora*).

minal lobes are elongated. The staminate heads are in spikes above, the pistillate involucres, usually 2-flowered, in clusters below. The bur is about $\frac{1}{10}$ inch long, minutely glandular-hairy, the spines broad at the base and incurved or hooked at the apex.

GALINSOGA (*Galinsoga parviflora* Cav.) (Fig. 310)

This plant, naturalized from tropical America, has been introduced into Europe as a weed, and in this country occurs in dooryards and waste places from coast to coast. In California it is reported from Los Angeles County, occurring along irrigation ditches and in waste places. Galinsoga is an annual herb, leafy almost throughout, 1 to 3 feet high. The leaves are opposite, sparsely rough-hairy, oval to lance-shaped, pointed at the tip, entire or toothed, thin, $\frac{3}{4}$ to 2 inches long. There are numerous small flowering heads, glandular-hairy throughout. The ray flowers are very small, fertile, white, and 4 or 5 in number. The disk flowers are yellow. The involucre is composed of two series of membranous bracts. The achenes are angled, or the outer ones flat. The pappus of disk flowers is of several short fringed scales, that of ray flowers of a few slender bristles, or none.

CUDWEED, COTTON ROSE (*Gifola germanica* L.) Dumort.

This species was reported (1938) between Hopland, Mendocino County, and Cloverdale, Sonoma County. It is a native of eastern United State. It is an annual, erect, cottony plant, 4 to 18 inches tall. The leaves are alternate, entire, simple, linear or lance-shaped, 3 to 12 inches long. The woolly flowering heads are in dense clusters. The receptacle is chaffy, the achenes are cylindric or somewhat compressed.

CUDWEED. GNAPHALIUM

This genus is represented in California by nine species, several of which behave as weeds. They are woolly herbs, all of which have small rayless flowering heads, with numerous papery involucral bracts, a pappus, and with both perfect and pistillate flowers in the same head.

Gnaphalium collinum Labill., an Australian species, is established in northwestern California.

Gnaphalium japonicum Thunb., has been collected at a number of stations in Humboldt County, and at Tracy; it is an Australasian species.

COTTON BATTING PLANT (*Gnaphalium chilense* Spreng.) (Fig. 311)
Other common name: Cudweed.

This is an annual or biennial, widely distributed in open ground in valleys and low hills. It is more or less white silky-hairy, stems $\frac{1}{2}$ to $2\frac{1}{2}$ feet tall, erect from a decumbent base, or single stemmed and erect. The leaves are narrow spatulate or the uppermost linear or lance-like, $\frac{3}{4}$ to $1\frac{1}{4}$ inches long with the bases somewhat auriculate or ear-like, or decurrent as wings on the stems. The heads are about $\frac{1}{4}$ inch long, borne in dense terminal clusters. The involucres, which are woolly only at the base, have a greenish-yellow tinge, becoming rusty. The pappus bristles are not united into a ring at the base, but fall separately.

Fig. 311. Cotton-batting plant (*Gnaphalium chilense*).

WHITE CUDWEED (*Gnaphalium luteo-album* L.)

This adventive from the Old World is a common weed of the San Francisco Peninsula in Santa Clara, San Mateo, and San Francisco Counties; also from the San Joaquin Valley to southern California where it occurs in alfalfa fields and along irrigation ditches. It is a white woolly annual 8 to 16 inches high. Leaves from 1 to 2 inches long, oblong-spatulate, woolly on both surfaces. The flowers are yellowish, turning to brown when mature, in terminal or axillary corymbs.

PURPLE CUDWEED (*Gnaphalium purpureum* L.)

This cudweed is a native, similar in general aspect to *G. chilense*. It is commonly 4-12 inches high, the herbage covered with a dense coating of white wool, the top surface of the leaves becoming green and smoother in age. The heads are crowded into an oblong spike-like inflorescence, the heads about ½ inch long, brownish or purple. The pappus bristles are attached to each other at the base and fall as a ring.

SPATULATE CUDWEED (*Gnaphalium spathulatum* Lam.)

It is an Old World species, and a common weed in southern California. It is an annual woolly herb, 8 to 16 inches tall, branched from the base, and leafy. The leaves are alternate, entire, petioled, ¾ to 1½ inches long and $\frac{3}{16}$ to ½ inch broad. The flowering heads are 3 to 4 mm. long and embedded in a mass of woolly hairs. The involucre consists of overlapping papery bracts. The pappus is a single series of capillary bristles.

GUM PLANT (*Grindelia camporum* Greene) (Fig. 312)

The most important gumweed from the weed standpoint is *G. camporum* which grows in southern California and along the inner Coast Ranges as far as San Benito County, and also on the open plains of the Great Valley as far north as Sacramento.

It is a perennial herb, 1 to 2 feet tall, with smooth, white shining stems. The leaves are light-green, sticky, 2 inches or less long, with toothed margins; lower leaves are oblong and blunt-pointed, upper ones with clasping bases and wider above the middle. The flowering heads are numerous and grouped in an open spreading panicle; unopened heads are whitened with a sticky secretion. The involucres are urn-shaped, the bracts green and broad-pointed. The flowers are bright yellow. The achenes are short, thick, each with a pappus of 2 to 8 stout awns or bristles.

Jepson describes six other species of *Grindelia* from California, none of which is of significance as a weed pest.

FRAGRANT RHAGADIOLUS (*Hedypnois cretia* (L.) Willd.) or (*Rhagadiolus Hedypnois* All.)

This is a native from Asia Minor which has been reported as occurring in a few California localities, namely Penn Valley, Nevada County, Oroville foothills, Atwater, Hornitos, Los Angeles, and San Diego. It is an annual herb, 5 to 13 inches tall, the stem usually branched from the base, the branches being diffuse and spreading. The basal leaves are stalked and often lobed, the upper narrow or lance-shaped, 1¼ to 5 inches long, entire, toothed or shallowly cleft. The involucre consists of a single series of bracts, which are narrow, incurved, spreading when the head is mature, and slightly stiff-hairy. The receptacle is naked. The achenes are cylindric, about ¼ inch long, 5 to 10-ribbed, the ribs barbed. The

Fig. 312. Gum plant (*Grindelia camporum*).

pappus of the inner achenes is double; the inner set composed of bristles, the outer of short scales, or sometimes none.

WESTERN SNEEZEWEED (*Helenium Hoopesii* Gray)

This species is a native of the Sierra Nevada from Tulare County to Tuolumne County, and also in the Warner Range of Modoc County. It is a stout, leafy perennial from 1¼ to 3 feet tall. When young the plant is quite hairy, but it becomes smooth with age. The leaves are alternate, entire, sessile, thick, the cauline ones 5 to 10 inches long, the basal 6 to 18 inches long, with tapering bases. The number of flower heads is from one to several, and each resembles a small sunflower. There are from 14 to 19 showy rays in each flower head. The bracts of the involucre slowly become reflexed. The achenes are top-shaped, densely tawny-hairy with a pappus consisting of 5 to 12 thin or papery, short-pointed scales.

The herbage is poisonous to sheep, but less so to cattle and horses.

ROSILLA (*Helenium puberulum* DC.)

This is a native of coastal California, Coast Ranges, and Sierra Nevada foothills in Butte County. It is an erect plant 2 to 5 feet high, differing from the preceding species in having leaves which are decurrent on the stem.

SUNFLOWER. *HELIANTHUS*

The sunflowers are easily recognized and widely distributed plants. Eight species are found in California, five of which are of a weedy nature.

All the sunflowers are stout, coarse herbs with simple, stalked leaves, and rather conspicuous yellow flowering heads, the so-called "sunflower." All but the lower or lowest leaves are alternate. The heads are solitary at the ends of branches or in terminal clusters. The rays are yellow, the disk yellow, brown, or purple. The involucre is composed of several series of closely overlapping bracts. The receptacle is flat or convex, low conical, its bracts persistent and enclosing the 4-angled achenes. The pappus consists of 2 scales or awns, or sometimes with 2 to 4 additional shorter ones, all of which fall off.

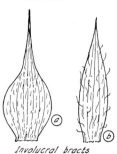

Involucral bracts
a - Helianthus annuus
b - Helianthus exilis

Receptacle bracts
c - Helianthus exilis
d - Helianthus bolanderi
e - Helianthus petiolaris

FIG. 313. Involucral bracts of (a) common sunflower, (b) slender sunflower. Receptacle bracts of (c) slender sunflower, (d) Bolander's sunflower, and (e) prairie sunflower.

Since all of the sunflowers, with the exception of blueweed, are more or less similar in gross aspect and habit, only blueweed is discussed at length.

KEY TO WEEDY SPECIES OF HELIANTHUS

Annual species, with flattened, brown or purple centers to the heads
　Involucral bracts broad at the base, and terminated by narrow pointed tips
　　　　　　　　　　　　　　　　　　　　　　　　　　　　　　　H. annus
　Involucral bracts narrow and tapering gradually to slender tips
　　Bracts of the receptacle shorter than the disk-flowers; rays ¾ to nearly 1 inch
　　long; mountain species _____*H. petiolaris*
　　Bracts of the receptacle equaling or surpassing the disk-flowers; rays ½ to ¾ inch
　　long; valley and coast species
　　　Stems rough to the touch; receptacle bracts with short awns which do not
　　　surpass the disk-flowers _____*H. Bolanderi*
　　　Stems stiff-hairy, especially near the heads; receptacle bracts with long awns
　　　which surpass the disk-flowers _____*H. exilis*
Perennial species, with yellowish, rounded centers to the heads
　Heads 2 to 3 inches broad_____*H. californicus*
　Heads 1 to 1½ inch broad _____*H. ciliaris*

COMMON SUNFLOWER (*Helianthus annus* L.) (Fig. 315)

This introduction from the Great Plains region is now well established in California. It is a common weed in cereals.

BOLANDER'S SUNFLOWER (*Helianthus Bolanderi* Gray)

This native is often abundant in the Sacramento Valley and west to the Coast; in the delta region it infests grain fields. (Fig. 313.)

CALIFORNIA SUNFLOWER (*Helianthus californicus* DC.) (Fig. 315)

This tall perennial grows shoulder high and is widespread in the State, occurring especially along streams and in low pasture lands.

BLUEWEED (*Helianthus ciliaris* DC.) (Fig. 314)

Blueweed is a native of the grasslands of the Southwest. For some time it has been known to occur in western Texas, Oklahoma, New Mexico, Arizona, and southward. According to Wooton and Standley, it is found in river valleys, usually in alkaline soil, in the Lower Sonoran Zone. In Mexico, where blueweed is common, it is known as Yerba Parda (dark gray herb), as the leaves and stems present a dark grayish or "smoky" appearance. In California it is established in Orange, Los Angeles, Ventura, San Luis Obispo and Tehama counties.

The five sites in California where blueweed has become established are so widely separated that it seems most probable the infestations arose from seed. Experiments on the viability of the seed, however, indicate that the germination is very low.

Blueweed is related to our common annual sunflower, but is a perennial with an extensive creeping root system. The horizontal roots or running rootstalks develop buds at irregular intervals, and these are capable of giving rise to new plants which seek the surface of the soil. Each of these plants is capable of maintaining itself as a separate individual. This fact should be borne in mind when control is attempted. When these plants are cut off, new growth arises from below and growth

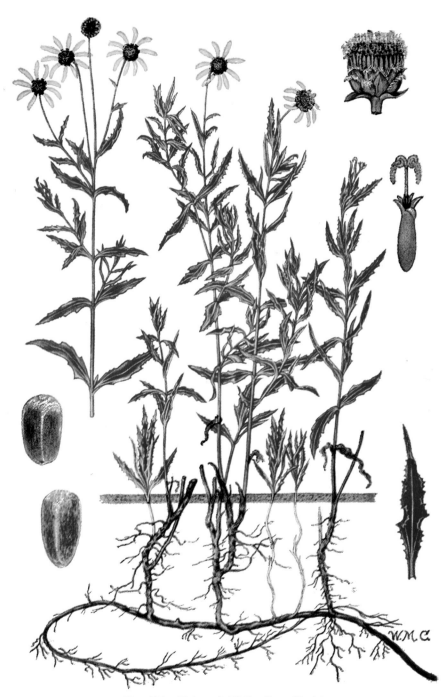

Fig. 314. Blueweed (*Helianthus ciliaris*).

and spread continue. While blueweed persists under dry soil conditions and on uncultivated land, its growth is especially favored where cultivation is practiced. Here the feeder roots penetrate to a greater depth, which makes eradication very difficult. The weed has a long growing season. It is one of the earliest weeds to resume growth in the spring and is persistent in its struggle to survive and mature seed.

The plants usually attain a height of from 1 to 2 feet. The stemless leaves are commonly alternate, sometimes opposite, particularly on the young growth. Leaf form is variable, from broadly lance-shaped with

Fig. 315. Common sunflower (*Helianthus annuus*). **A,** branch showing character of upper leaves and involucre; **B,** leaf of stem showing venation and heart-shaped base; **C,** achene; **D,** stem leaf of *A. californicus*.

irregular margins to narrowly linear with entire margins. The color varies from gray-green to blue-green, and often there are stiff little hairs on the margins and along the rather prominent veins of the under surface. The flower heads are borne singly or in groups of 3 or 4, each on the end of a rather long leafless stem. They are yellow and similar in form to the common sunflower, but much smaller, the diameter of the flower head being from 1 to 1½ inches. The center is dark purplish-brown and roughish, due to the toothed tips on the bracts which embrace the numerous individual seeds. The seeds are similar in shape to those of the common sunflower, about ⅛ inch long and a silvery gray-brown color. Some seeds are mottled with dark brown.

SLENDER SUNFLOWER (*Helianthus exilis* Gray) (Fig. 313) occurs in the Sacramento Valley, and in certain valleys of the Coast Range, also in the Sierra Nevada foothills from Amador County to Mariposa County.

PRAIRIE SUNFLOWER (*Helianthus petiolaris* Nutt.) (Fig. 313) is a native species and very common in certain valleys of the Sierra Nevada.

TARWEED. HEMIZONIA

There are 12 species of *Hemizonia* in California, 10 of which are annuals and 2 perennials. All have a sticky, heavy-scented herbage, which character has suggested the name "tarweed." The leaves are narrow, alternate (the lowest sometimes opposite), the lower usually toothed to pinnatifid. There are numerous flowering heads, either yellow or white. There are from 5 to many rays, 3-lobed or 3-toothed; ray flowers are fertile, the achenes being without pappus, thick, short, turgid, and half enclosed by the lower part of the involucral bract which falls with it. The disk flowers are surrounded by a circle of chaffy bracts, or the disk is chaffy throughout. Disk achenes may be sterile or fertile.

TARWEED (*Hemizonia congesta* DC.)

This is an annual, widely distributed in the Sacramento and San Joaquin Valleys and in the Coast Ranges. The stem is erect, branching above the base to a rather flatish top, 1 to 1½ feet tall. The leaves are narrowly linear to broader above, obscurely toothed to entire on the margins, and the plant is soft-hairy and slightly glandular throughout. The heads are in small clusters at the ends of the more or less leafy-bracted branches. The ray flowers are white and 3-toothed. The outer receptacle bracts are nearly separate or only lightly joined. The achenes are broad above, blackish, with a conspicuous inturned point or stipe below.

HAYFIELD TARWEED (*Hemizonia congesta* DC. var. *luzulaefolia* Jep.)

This is a widely branching to erect plant which arises from a rosette-like tuft of linear tapering leaves which are silvery gray in the young stage with flattened soft-silky hairs. The upper stem leaves are very much reduced. The rays of the flower head are white or pink-tinged and the outer bracts of the receptacle are joined to form a cup. The achene is glistening black with a very short point or stipe at the base.

FIG. 316.   Virgate tarweed (*Hemizonia virgata*).

COAST TARWEED (*Hemizonia corymbosa* (DC.) T. & G.)

This species is distributed on valley floors and hillsides from Humboldt County to San Luis Obispo and thence east to western Kern County. It also is an annual and is distinguished from *C. congesta* and *C. virgata* by the presence of a cup-like circle of bracts on the receptacle between the disk and rays, whereas in these two species the receptacle is chaffy

FIG. 317. Telegraph plant (*Heterotheca grandiflora*). **A**, habit of mature plant; **B**, seedling; **C**, head showing the involucre and curling rays; **D**, achene.

throughout. The flowers are bright yellow, rays 3-4 toothed and number-
ing 13 to 20. The ray achenes are beaked and the disk achenes have a
pappus of minute scales or none.

VIRGATE TARWEED (*Hemizonia virgata* Gray) (Fig. 316)

This annual species occurs in the Sierra Nevada foothills, the San
Joaquin and Sacramento Valleys, Lake County, and the south Coast
Ranges. It is particularly abundant along roadsides in the late summer, and bordering fence lines and grain fields. The plant is erect, 1-1½
feet tall, branching at about the middle into spreading branches at the
ends of which are numerous heads disposed on lateral branchlets. The
leaves are small, linear, and often crowded in groups in the leaf axils.
The leaves of the branchlets are squarish on the end, tipped by a saucer-
like gland. The ray flowers are yellow, 4 or 5 in number, the disk flowers
7-10. The involucre of the flower head is oblong, with 5 bracts which are
glandular on the back, the incurved tip ending in a squared-off gland.
The ray achenes are glistening black and have a strong beak.

TELEGRAPH PLANT (*Heterotheca grandiflora* Nutt.) (Fig. 317)

This is a native species especially abundant in the coast counties
of southern California, but extending as far north as the Santa Clara
and San Joaquin Valleys. It is a weed of late summer, occurring in waste
places and along roadsides.

The telegraph plant is a tall shaggy-hairy annual herb, with 1 to
several erect stems, 2 to 6 feet tall, arising from a long tap root. A
shorter-growing over-wintering form has also been observed. The leaves
are alternate, numerous, gray-green, oval in shape, 1 to 3 inches long and
⅓ to 1 inch wide; they are slightly toothed, and densely hairy on both
sides. The lower leaves are long-stalked, the upper sessile by a broad base.
The heads are arranged in a rather flat-topped cluster, each head solitary
at the tip of a branch or sometimes with a smaller head below supported
on a lateral shoot. The involucre is composed of numerous narrow, green
unequal bracts arranged in several series. Each head consists of about
30 ray flowers surrounding the numerous disk flowers. The achenes of the
ray flowers are triangular, and usually without a pappus; achenes of the
disk flowers are compressed, silky-hairy and surmounted by a persistent
brick-red pappus of simple, straight hairs.

Hymenothrix loomisii Blake.

This species, a native of central Arizona, has been found on the
Santa Fe right-of-way at San Dimas, Los Angeles County, and at
Riverside. It propagates by running rootstocks in the manner of west-
ern ragweed. It is a slender perennial herb with dissected leaves, and
with numerous flowering heads composed of pale yellow disk flowers.
Achenes are 4- or 5-angled, with a pappus of 12 to 20 papery paleae.

SMOOTH CAT'S-EAR (*Hypochoeris glabra* L.)

This is an annual, with smaller flowering heads, not more than ¼
inch broad, smooth herbage, and with inner achenes beaked, the outer

beakless. The smooth cat's-ear is an introduced European weed, which is widely distributed in California in cultivated fields and pasture lands.

IIAIRY CAT'S-EAR (*Hypochoeris radicata* L.) (Fig. 318)
Other common names: Gosmore, long-rooted cat's-ear, flatweed, coast dandelion.

This is an immigrant from the Old World which has become well established in cultivated fields and pasture lands in the coast counties of California. It is a perennial weed, with a thick, fleshy tap root, 8 to 24 inches long. There are from 1 to several stems, often thickening upward, smooth, slender, 1 to 2 feet tall. The leaves are in a cluster at the base of the plant; they are 1½ to 8 inches long, ⅜ to 1 inch wide, usually more or less lobed or toothed, with prominent midribs, and clothed on both surfaces with coarse yellow hairs. The flowering heads are yellow and about 1 inch broad. The involucre is composed of 2 or 3 overlapping series of distinct, green, erect, narrow bracts, the outer ones being successively shorter. At the base of each flower in the head is a narrow, pointed chaffy scale. The achenes are 10-ribbed, roughened by minute projections on its surface, and tipped by a slender, thread-like beak. The pappus consists of a tuft of white, silky, branched hairs.

POVERTY WEED (*Iva axillaris* Pursh.) (Fig. 319)
Other common names: Lesser marsh elder, small-flowered marsh elder, death weed.

Poverty weed is a native of western North America, occurring from the Canadian border south to Mexico. It is found principally in saline or alkaline soil. As a weed it often infests such agricultural lands, but is by no means confined to soils of this type. The largest infestation known in California is in Lassen County, where it is confined to an old lake bed used for pasture. This plant often comes in on overgrazed pastures and in the middle west has taken large areas of this type.

Iva axillaris is a coarse perennial herb with a rank, unpleasant odor. It develops horizontal woody roots from which buds may arise, a characteristic which adds to its ability to spread and resist eradication. The stems are 8 to 20 inches high and usually arise in clusters. The leaves are numerous, sessile, small, narrowly oval, gray-green, obtuse, faintly three-nerved, usually thick or even somewhat fleshy, and from ½ to 1½ inches long. The lower leaves are opposite on the stem, the upper alternate and smaller. The flowering heads are greenish and hang downward from the ends of their short stalks. The heads occur singly in the axils of the upper leaves, which character has suggested the specific name "axillaris." Each flowering head is subtended by a cup-shaped, toothed involucre. In this are numerous small greenish flowers of two kinds, pistillate and staminate. There are from 1 to 6 pistillate or seed-bearing flowers, situated around the margin of the flower group, and each has a short tubular corolla (sometimes corolla absent), and a single pistil. The staminate or non-seed-bearing flowers are 15 to 25 in number, with a funnel-shaped corolla, 5 stamens, and a reduced sterile ovary. The fruit is an achene, about 2 mm. long, obovoid, gray-brown to almost black, scurfy, without pappus.

Fig. 318. Hairy cat's ear (*Hypochoeris radicata*). A, habit; B, head; C, achene.

PUBESCENT POVERTY WEED (*Iva axillaris* Pursh. var. *pubescens* Gray) is a form of poverty weed in which the herbage is loosely hairy and the margin of the involucre almost entire. This is recorded from near San Francisco Bay, and recently was reported as an agricultural pest in San Benito County.

WOODY POVERTY WEED (*Iva Hayesiana* Gray) is another native species closely related to *I. axillaris*. It differs from the more common poverty weed in that the stems are definitely woody below and the bracts of the involucre are separate or distinct instead of being joined in a bowl-like structure. It occurs in alkaline or brackish soil in the extreme southern part of the State.

Fig. 319.   Poverty weed (*Iva axillaris*). Enlarged seed.

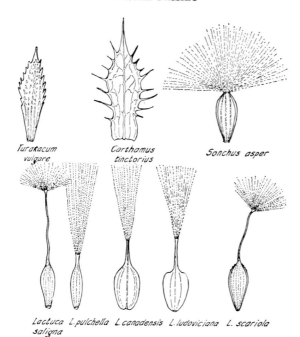

Taraxacum vulgare   Carthamus tinctorius   Sonchus asper

Lactuca L.pulchella L.canadensis L.ludoviciana L. scariola saligna

FIG. 320. From left to right, above, achene of common dandelion, bract of safflower, and achene of prickly sow thistle; from left to right, below, achenes of willow lettuce, blue lettuce, tall lettuce, western lettuce and prickly lettuce.

LETTUCE. *LACTUCA*

KEY TO WEEDY SPECIES OF LACTUCA

Achenes marginless, tapering to a very short beak about as long as the breadth of the body of the achene; flowers purple; perennial_____*L. pulchella*

Achenes margined, the beak about as long as, or longer than the body of the achene; flowers yellow or blue in var. *integrata;* annual or biennial

    Achenes several-nerved _____*L. scariola*
                                                  (and var. *integrata*)
    Achenes 1-nerved on each face
        Leaves narrow at base, the midrib not prickly_____*L. canadensis*
        Leaves broad at base, the midrib more or less prickly below____*L. ludoviciana*
Achenes about half as long as the beak; flowers yellow; annual or biennial___*L. saligna*

TALL LETTUCE or TRUMPET FIREWEED (*Lactuca canadensis* L.) (Fig. 320)
    This native of the eastern United States is of rather limited distribution and not important as a weed.

WESTERN LETTUCE (*Lactuca ludoviciana* DC.) (Fig. 320)
    This introduction from the eastern United States, has been found in Shasta County, but as yet has not become a weed in California.

BLUE LETTUCE (*Lactuca pulchella* DC.) (Fig. 320)
    This is a native North American species which has become a troublesome weed in Modoc and Lassen Counties and in the San Joaquin Valley. It is a perennial with an erect, leafy stem from 1 to 3 feet tall. The

purple flowers distinguish it from the other common species of *Lactuca*. The stems and leaves are smooth ; the leaves are 2 to 6 inches long, linear or long lance-shaped, entire to deeply cleft, and sessile, with a winged petiole. Achenes are marginless, oblong, and bear a very short beak, and short pappus.

WILLOW LETTUCE (*Lactuca saligna* L.) (Figs. 320, 321)

This species, naturalized from Europe, is a weed in certain parts of the Mississippi Valley and in California from Los Angeles County to Modoc and Lassen Counties, where it occurs in grain fields, pasture lands and in waste places. It is biennial, erect with ascending smooth or almost smooth stems, and glabrous slender leaves, entire or with pointed divergent lobes, sagittate at the base. The achene is very similar to that of *L. scariola*, but the beak is about twice the length of the body of the achene.

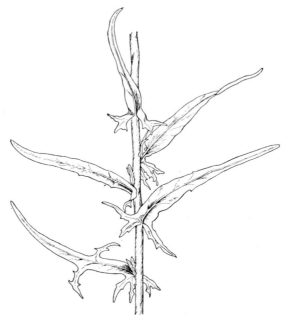

FIG. 321. Willow lettuce (*Lactuca saligna*).

PRICKLY LETTUCE (*Lactuca scariola* L.) (Figs. 320, 322)
Other common names : Common wild lettuce, English thistle.

This naturalized European weed is very common throughout California. It may be of importance in cultivated fields, in grain fields, in orchards and vineyards, and is widely distributed along roadsides, ditches, fence lines, and in waste places generally.

Prickly lettuce is an erect annual or biennial herb with a milky juice. The stems are somewhat rigid, nearly smooth above, sometimes prickly below, branching above, bluish-green in color, and may attain a height of 2 to 6 feet. The leaves are alternate. The lower leaves are 4 to 8 inches long, and 1 to 2 inches broad; they are usually deeply lobed. The margins are more or less prickly, the under sides with prominent whitish midribs beset with curved prickles, and with the leaf blade clasping the stem and somewhat twisted at its base; the upper leaves are smaller, usually entire, tightly clasping the stem, the bases with ear-like projections. The flower heads are numerous, cream yellow, and each head has from 9 to 14 flowers. The involucre is composed of 2 to 3 overlapping series of narrow, pointed, green bracts; the outer bracts are about ⅓ the length of the inner ones. The achenes are prominently ribbed, enlarging upward to above the middle and then abruptly contracting to a thread-like beak which is about as long as the body of the achene. There are usually a few short bristle-like teeth on the "shoulders." At the summit of the beak is the pappus, consisting of numerous soft, white, straight hairs.

LANCE-LEAVED PRICKLY LETTUCE (*Lactuca scariola* L. var. *integrata* Gren. & Godr.) (Fig. 322)

This form of prickly lettuce is very common in California, frequently occurring in extensive stands with the species. In the variety all the leaves are nearly entire, or minutely toothed, and from 2-6 inches long. The flowers are usually yellowish, although occasionally blue.

NIPPLEWORT (*Lapsana communis* L.)

This species, naturalized from Europe, occurs very sparingly in southwest Oregon and in Humboldt County, at Arcata. It is an erect annual with yellow flowers. One or a few stems arise from the base, attaining a height of 2 to 2¼ feet. The leaves and stems are stiff-hairy, or with soft, long hairs, or smooth above. The leaves are 1 to 1¾ inches long, oval in outline, coarsely toothed, and commonly there are one or two pairs of extra leaflets below the main blade. The involucre consists of from 7 to 9 linear-oblong bracts. The receptacle is naked. The achenes are oblong, somewhat flattened, narrowed above, rounded at the apex, and 20 to 30 nerved. The pappus is lacking.

WOOLLY-BASED LYGODESMIA (*Lygodesmia spinosa* Nutt.)

This native extends from the southern deserts north to British Columbia. It is a spinescent, rigid, divaricately branched perennial about 10 to 14 inches tall, almost leafless above, with inconspicuous rose to pink flowers terminal on the branchlets, each branchlet becoming spiny. There is a conspicuous tuft of tawny wool at the base of the stem. This weed is often reported spreading in grainfields and troublesome.

TARWEED. MADIA

There are 10 species of *Madia* in California, and these, in addition to the *Hemizonia* species, are known as tarweeds. In species of *Madia* the ray achenes are completely enfolded by the bracts of the involucre, and the achenes are either flattened or strongly keeled on the back; whereas in species of *Hemizonia* the ray achenes are only half enclosed

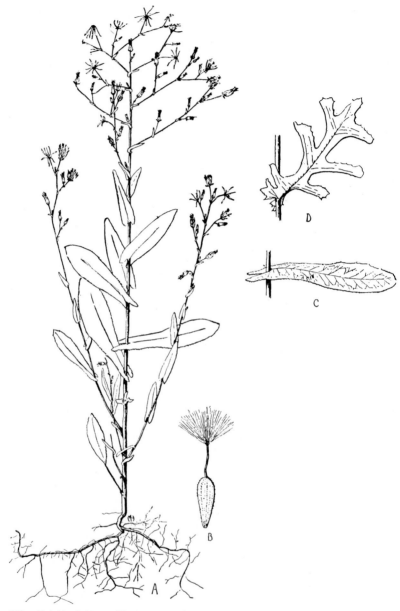

FIG. 322.   Prickly lettuce (*Lactuca scariola*).   **A,** habit; **B,** achene; **C,** leaf of var. *integrata;* **D,** leaf of typical form.

FIG. 323. Common madia (*Madia elegans*).

by the involucral bracts, and the achenes are rounded on the back. Like *Hemizonia* species, those of *Madia* have a sticky, heavy-scented herbage. The flowers of *Madia* are yellow and open in the evening, closing before noon of the next day.

COMMON MADIA (*Madia elegans* Don) (Fig. 323)
Other common name: Tarweed.

This is a native annual distributed from Oregon to Lower California, and occurring on dry hills and in valley fields. The plant is ¾ to 2 feet high, the disk flowers are few to many, the rays showy and conspicuous, the receptacle hairy. The ray achenes are only slightly curved, if at all, and the pappus is wanting.

CHILEAN TARWEED (*Madia sativa* Molina)

This is also an annual, quite likely introduced from Chile, and now widely distributed in the State, especially in the coastal counties, occurring in waste lots and fields. It is a stout plant 1 to 4 feet tall, in which the rays are inconspicuous, usually little or not at all exserted, the receptacle naked, and the ray achenes are curved about 4-5 mm. long, blackish over the main body and frequently mottled with a lighter color. A central nerve from base to apex of the achene is more or less pronounced.

QUILLWEED (*Malacothrix saxatilis* (Nutt.) T. & G.)

This native species occurs along the seacoast from Monterey County to Orange County, where it may invade cultivated fields. It is a perennial herb, somewhat woody at the base, from a stout root-crown. The stems are densely leafy, usually less than 2 feet high, but sometimes higher. Leaves are long lance-shaped, 1 to 5 inches long, entire or the lower coarsely toothed or deeply cleft. The flowering heads are ¾ to 1¾ inches broad, the corollas white or pinkish. Achenes are 10- to 15-ribbed, 5 ribs being much stronger than the others.

WESTERN PINEAPPLE WEED (*Matricaria occidentalis* Greene)

This species occurs in the Sacramento Valley, south Coast Range, and southward. It resembles the common pineapple weed, but is taller, being 1½ to 2 feet tall, with heads up to ½ inch high, and achenes with a broad, crown-like margin, or the crown lobed and one-sided.

PINEAPPLE WEED (*Matricaria suaveolens* Buch.) (Fig. 324)

This is probably a native species which is widespread throughout California, commonly found about old farmyards, along beaten roadsides, and in pasture lands.

Pineapple weed is a low, smooth annual 2 to 10 inches high, with sweet-scented herbage. The leaves are pinnately dissected. The heads are solitary or in loose groups, short-stalked, ⅙ to ⅓ inch high, and contain many yellowish-green flowers. The receptacle is long-conical and without scales. The bracts of the involucre are overlapping, broadly oblong, with papery margins and persistent. There are no ray flowers. The achenes are smooth, 3- to 5-nerved on the sides, rounded on the back, and with an obscure margin at its summit.

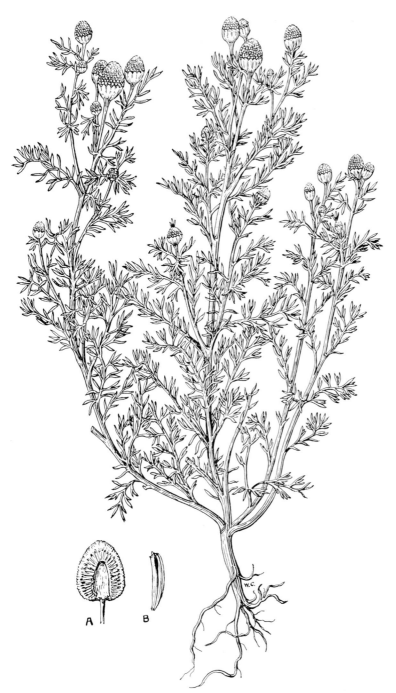

FIG. 324. Pineapple weed (*Matricaria suaveolens*). A, section through head ; B, achene.

MELAMPODIUM (*Melampodium perfoliatum* H.B.K.)

This species is introduced from Mexico. Thus far it has been found only in waste places about Los Angeles. It is a coarse, highly branched annual herb, 3 to 4 feet high. The leaves are opposite, 4 to 9 inches long, broadly oval, toothed, rough, pointed at tip, and narrowed below into a winged leaf-stalk; the bases of leaf-stalks of opposite leaves surround the stem. The heads are in leafy clusters. The involucral bracts are in two series, the outer of several broad, leaf-like bracts, whereas those of the inner series are smaller, hooded, and each encloses an achene. The pappus is absent. Ray flowers are yellow or white, disk flowers yellow.

MICROSERIS

This genus is a member of the Chicory Tribe of the Sunflower Family, a distinguishing characteristic of which tribe is the occurrence of heads composed entirely of perfect flowers with a strap-shaped corolla. There are 6 species of *Microseris* in California, all natives. All are low annual

FIG. 325.   Bristly oxtongue (*Picris echioides*).

FIG. 326. Arrow-weed (*Pluchea sericea*).

plants with basal leaves and naked, one-headed peduncles, thus resembling dandelions somewhat. The leaves and stems are glabrous or only very finely hairy. The leaves are deeply dissected into narrow lobes. The flowers are yellow. The receptacle is naked, the pappus chaff-like. The achenes are slender, spindle-shaped or cylindric, and ribbed.

BRISTLY OXTONGUE (*Picris echioides* L.) (Fig. 325)

Other common names: Bugloss, bugloss-picris.

This species is naturalized from Europe. It is widely established in California, growing in fields, vacant lots and waste places. Bristly oxtongue is a coarse, rough biennial herb, 2 to 3 feet tall. The stems are angled and clothed with barbed hairs. The basal and lower leaves are 2 to 6 inches long, $\frac{1}{2}$ to $1\frac{1}{2}$ inches wide, narrowly oblong in shape, the margin shallowly scalloped; the upper leaves are smaller, and clasp the stem. All the leaves are rough-hairy, especially on the undersides of the midribs. The flowering heads are about $\frac{1}{2}$ inch broad

FIG. 327.   Black-eyed Susan (*Rudbeckia hirta*).

and occur in clusters of 3 or 4 near the top of the stem, or solitary. The involucre is composed of 4 or 5 large, green, bristly outer bracts with broad bases and long, pointed tips, and about an equal number of narrower, long, pointed, densely bristly inner bracts, which are prominently keeled. The flowers are yellow. The achenes are oblong, orange-color, with surfaces ridged crosswise, and tipped by a beak as long or longer than the body of the achene. The pappus is abundant, composed of silky-white, branching hairs, united by their bases into a ring.

ARROW-WEED (*Pluchea sericea* (Nutt.) Cov.) (Fig. 326)
Other common name : Mock willow.

This species is native to California, Nevada, Arizona, and east to Texas. It is a plant of river bottom lands and is rapidly becoming a pest in the Imperial Valley and elsewhere in the newly irrigated districts of southern California, the plants often forming veritable cane-brakes impossible to penetrate.

It is a tall, slender, erect, willow-like shrub, 3 to 10 or even 15 feet high. The herbage is silvery-silky. The leaves are alternate, sessile, $\frac{1}{2}$ to 2 inches long and $\frac{1}{4}$ inch wide, the margins entire, and tapering to both ends. The flower heads are numerous, hemispheric, in clusters, and each contains many purplish disk flowers and no ray flowers. The involucre is composed of numerous bracts, the outer brown or purplish-tinged, and leathery in texture ; the inner thin and white, longer than the outer and soon deciduous. The achenes are 4- to 5-angled and crowned with a series of slender, rough bristles.

BLACK-EYED SUSAN (*Rudbeckia hirta* L.) (Fig. 327)

Black-eyed Susan is a native of eastern United States, where it is widely distributed as a weed. In California it has been introduced in the meadows of the Sierra Nevada from Mariposa County to Amador County, and is also occasionally found along irrigation ditches in Stanislaus County. In Iowa, certain species of *Rudbeckia* are considered poisonous to livestock. This is an erect, biennial herb, 1 to $2\frac{1}{4}$ feet high. The stems are 1 to several from the crown, and are branched above, the branches ending in single flowering heads. The stems and leaves are rough-hairy throughout. The leaves are thick, oblong to lance-shaped, somewhat 3-nerved, entire or sparingly toothed, $1\frac{1}{2}$ to 3 inches long, the upper leaves sessile, the lower narrowed into margined stalks. The heads are showy, 2 to 4 inches broad. The rays are $\frac{3}{4}$ to $1\frac{1}{4}$ inches long, and yellow. The disk is high conical, the disk flowers purple-brown. The involucre is of very hairy, spreading or reflexed bracts, sharp-pointed and narrow. Pappus is lacking. Achenes are 4-angled and obtuse or squarish at the apex.

GOLDEN THISTLE (*Scolymus hispanicus* L.) (Fig. 328)

This species is introduced from southern Europe, and thus far has been found at one locality in this state, Los Gatos, where it was found in abundance as early as 1893. It is a biennial with a thick tap root, and an erect stem 1 to 1½ feet high. The basal leaves are very spiny, toothed, or deeply cut, decurrent at the base, dark-green, marked with pale green spots. The flowering heads are bright yellow. The bracts of the involucre are in a few rows, papery-margined, and spine-tipped. The receptacle is chaffy. The pappus is a crown of papery, unequal scales.

BLACK SALSIFY (*Scorzonera hispanica* L.)

This plant, a native of central and southern Europe, is cultivated for its roots, and in instances

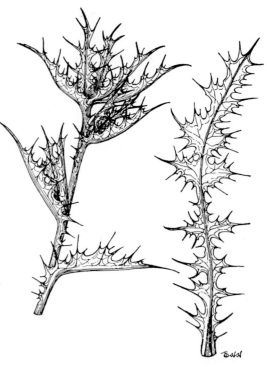

FIG. 328. Golden thistle (*Scolymus hispanicus*).

escapes from cultivation. It has become naturalized along roadsides in the upper Napa Valley, Knights Valley, and Ukiah Valley. It is a perennial, much-branched herb, 2 to 3 feet tall, and smooth or woolly-hairy throughout. It possesses a fleshy tap root, with black skin. The leaves are oblong to lance-shaped or sometimes linear, wavy-margined, and taper below into a long, winged petiole. The flowers are in large, long-stalked yellow heads. The bracts of the involucre are in several series, the outer much shorter than the inner. The achenes are nearly white, many-ribbed, and beakless.

TANSY RAGWORT (*Senecio Jacoboea* L.) (Fig. 329)

This European species is now abundant on the coastal flats of Mendocino and Del Norte Counties, and recently has been reported from south of Petaluma, Sonoma County, where in three years it has spread over about three acres.

The species is perennial, or biennial, in California. Stems up to 3 feet tall, cobwebby hairy, but early smooth; leaves deply bi- or tri-pinnatifid, cobwebby hairy beneath, 2 to 8 inches long, and 1 to 4 inches broad; flowers in a hairy corymb; involucre hemispherical; rays conspicuous, yellow.

Tansy ragwort is toxic to livestock, particularly cattle and horses.

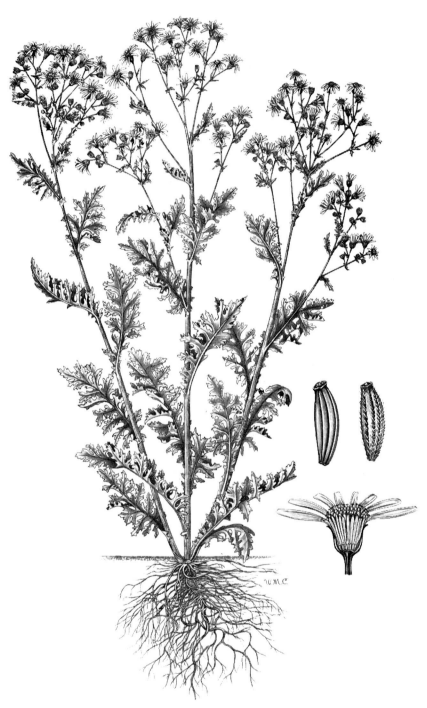

FIG. 329. Tansy ragwort (*Senecio Jacoboea*).

FIG. 330.   Common groundsel (*Senecio vulgaris*).   A, receptacle; B, achene.

COMMON GROUNDSEL (*Senecio vulgaris* L.) (Fig. 330)

Other common names: Grimsel, simson, ragwort, "Old Man of Spring."

This is a naturalized weed from Europe which is very common throughout California in waste places. Common groundsel is an annual, 6 to 15 inches tall, with simple or branching stems. The herbage is smooth or somewhat hairy. The leaves are alternate, pinnatifid, and with jagged margins. The lower leaves taper to a leaf stalk, the upper are attached directly to the stem by a broadened base. The flower heads are numerous. There are no ray flowers. Disk flowers are yellow. The involucre consists of about 20 equal black-tipped bracts with a number of conspicuously black-tipped small ones at the base. There are from 15 to 25 flowers in each head, all alike with tubular corollas. The achenes are somewhat hairy, finely ribbed, and tipped by a crown of silky, straight hairs.

It is reported that the herbage is poisonous to some animals.

DUSTY MILLER (*Senecio Cineraria* DC.), a native of the Mediterranean region, is reported locally common as an escape on the coastal bluffs at Santa Cruz.

PURPLE RAGWORT (*Senecio elegans* L.), a garden plant from South Africa, occurs at San Francisco. It has pinnatifid leaves and showy purple rays.

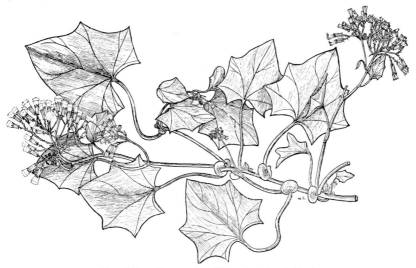

FIG. 331. German ivy (*Senecio mikanioides*).

GERMAN IVY (*Senecio mikanioides* Otto) (Fig. 331), a native of South Africa, has been found at several places along the coast. It is a twining perennial with bright-green ivy-like foliage and small heads of yellow flower.

WOOD GROUNDSEL (*Senecio sylvaticus* L.), is reported by Parish as having been collected along the waterfront at San Diego, and near Riverside. Jepson gives the distribution of this species as the woods of Mendocino and Humboldt Counties.

FIG. 332.   Milk thistle (*Silybum marianum*).

MILK THISTLE (*Silybum marianum* Gaertn.) (Fig. 332)

A native of the Mediterranean region, milk thistle has become very common in agricultural sections of California, occurring in cultivated fields, along fences and roadsides, on irrigation banks, and in pasture lands. Its spread has become rather rapid within the last ten years.

Milk thistle is usually a biennial under California conditions. The plant is erect, with simple or branching stems 2 to 6 feet high. The leaves are large, the lower 1 to 2 feet long and half as wide, the upper smaller. All the leaves are pointed, their bases clasp the stem, and the margins are wavy or the blades are more or less deeply lobed; they bear numerous yellow prickles $\frac{1}{8}$ to $\frac{1}{2}$ inch long, and the upper smooth and shining leaf surfaces are characteristically mottled with white blotches. The flower

Fig. 333. Perennial sow thistle (*Sonchus arvensis*).

heads are globose, 1 to 2 inches broad and armed with large, spreading or recurved stout spines which terminate the overlapping bracts of the involucre, these spines being $\frac{3}{4}$ to $1\frac{1}{2}$ inches long.

There are numerous purple flowers in each head. The achenes are about $\frac{1}{4}$ inch long, flattened, smooth and shiny, and bear several series of minutely barbed bristles which are united into a ring at the base and fall away from the achene together.

COMMON GOLDENROD (*Solidago californica* Nutt.)

This is a native species known to Spanish-Californians as ''Orojo de Liebre.'' It is widesperead on the west side of the Sierra Nevada, from low altitudes up to 4000-5000 feet, in dry situations.

FIG. 334.   Western goldenrod (*Solidago occidentalis*).

Common goldenrod is an erect, densely-leafy perennial herb 2 to 4 feet high. It is branched at the top where the yellow flowers are grouped in densely-clustered small heads, which form a narrow, compact panicle, 4 to 14 inches long. The leaves are oblong, entire or finely toothed, pointed at the tip and tapering below to a narrow base or short stalk; the lower leaves are frequently 4 inches long, the upper shorter. The bracts of the involucre are narrow and somewhat hairy. There are from 7 to 12 yellow ray flowers and about an equal number of disk flowers. The achenes are hairy.

Sheep have been known to be poisoned by eating the green or dried plants of goldenrod species.

WESTERN GOLDENROD. (*Solidago occidentalis* Nutt.) (Fig. 334)

This is also a native species, found in marshy places and along streams from Oregon to southern California. As a weed, it is of less importance than the common goldenrod. It is taller, the panicles are less dense, the leaves are covered with minute clear or dark dots, and the ray flowers are usually more numerous than the disk flowers.

SOLIVA (*Soliva sessilis* Rins. & Pav.) (Fig. 335)

This species is probably naturalized from Chile, and has become established at scattered points along the coast, occurring in moist

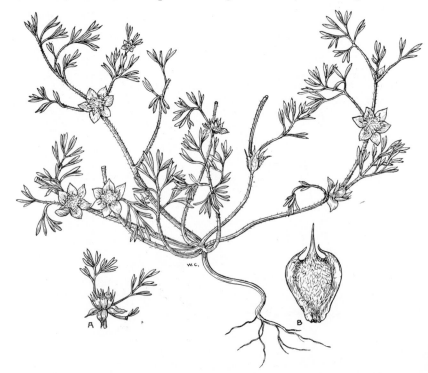

FIG. 335.   Soliva (*Soliva sessilis*). **A,** cluster of achenes; **B,** single achene.

ground. It has been collected in Mendocino County, Howell Mountain, Oakland, San Francisco, Santa Cruz Mountains, and Santa Barbara. It is reported as an objectionable lawn weed in Santa Cruz and Sacramento Counties.

This is a small depressed annual, 2 to 4 inches (or more) across, with rigid, short, somewhat tortuous branches. The herbage is very finely hairy. The leaves are stalked and pinnately dissected. There are from 1 to 3 flower heads sessile at the base. The involucre is of 7 or 8 oblong, hairy, greenish bracts. There is an outer series of 9 to 12 pistillate flowers, without corollas; the innermost flowers are perfect, but sterile, the corolla 4-toothed. The achenes are winged on the margin and pointed with a hardened persistent style.

SOW THISTLES. *SONCHUS*

In California there are four species of sow thistles, all naturalized from Europe, and weedy in nature. The two most abundant ones, and the most serious from the weed standpoint, are common sow thistle and prickly sow thistle.

The sow thistles are leafy-stemmed, coarse, succulent weeds with a milky juice. The leaves are alternate, mostly clasp the stem at the base, and are prickly-margined. The flowers are yellow, the receptacle flat and naked; the achenes ribbed and beakless; the pappus abundant, of cottony-white, soft, fine hairs, which usually fall off together.

KEY TO WEEDY SPECIES OF SONCHUS

Leaves when sessile, arrow-pointed at the clasping base, annual
  Achenes transversely rugose with lengthwise ribs_____*S. oleraceus*
  Achenes with lengthwise lines_____*S. tenerrimus*
Leaves when sessile, round-pointed at the clasping base
  Achenes flat, smooth, wing-margined with 3 lengthwise ribs on each face, annual
                                         S. asper
  Achenes oblong, with 5 lengthwise ribs on each face; perennial_____*S. arvensis*

PERENNIAL SOW THISTLE (*Sonchus arvensis* L.) (Figs. 333 and 336)
Other common name: Creeping perennial sow thistle.

This species, a native of Europe, is rare in California. It is perennial by deep roots and creeping rootstalks. The stems are 2 feet or more tall and branched, leafy below and almost naked above, smooth or glabrous throughout. The lower leaves are often almost a foot long, cut into backwardly curved lobes, the upper smaller and divided or almost entire, sessile and clasping. The heads are numerous, 1 to 2 inches broad and bright yellow. The achenes are about 3 mm. long with about 10 longitudinal thick ribs, transversely rugose.

PRICKLY SOW THISTLE (*Sonchus asper* (L.) Hill) (Figs. 336 and 337)

This annual species, naturalized from Europe, is usually associated with its close relative, *S. oleraceus*, which it resembles very closely. The clasping leaf bases are rounded rather than sharp-pointed, as in common sow thistle. Moreover, the upper part of the stem and the flower stalks of prickly sow thistle are usually furnished with spreading glandular hairs, although these parts may be smooth, as in common sow thistle. The achenes are flat, margined with a narrow wing; there are 3 longitudinal ribs on each face, the intervals between the ribs smooth, but the ridges and margins are transversely wrinkled.

COMMON SOW THISTLE (*Sonchus oleraceus* L.) (Fig. 336)

Common sow thistle, a naturalized species, has become widespread in California, occurring in fields, orchards, vineyards, along roadsides, ditches and waste places generally. It is an erect annual, 1 to 4 feet high. The basal and lower leaves are stalked, the upper sessile and clasping the stem; the leaves are divided into broad-toothed and spiny segments, the terminal segment being the largest and triangular in shape. The flowering heads are numerous, pale yellow, ¾ to 1¼ inches broad, with a smooth involucre. The achenes are flat, ribbed lengthwise, and transversely wrinkled.

SLENDER SOW THISTLE (*Sonchus tenerrimus* L.)

This annual, naturalized from Europe, is established in western San Diego County. The plant is about 1 to 2 feet tall, leafy up to the inflorescence. The achenes are small, about 2 mm. long and slender, longitudinally striate and transversely rugose.

FIG. 336. From left to right achenes of prickly sow thistle (*Sonchus asper*), perennial sow thistle (*S. arvensis*), and common sow thistle (*S. oleraceus*).

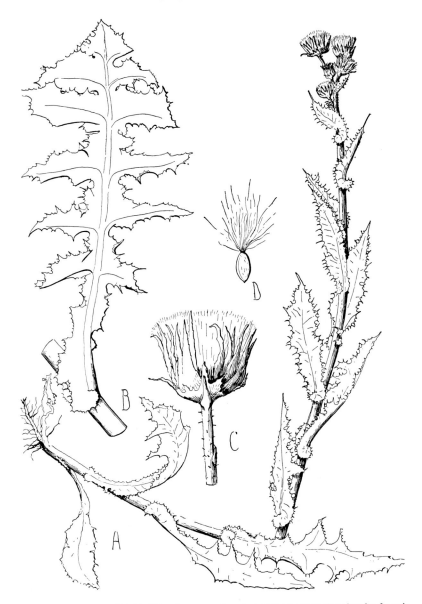

Fig. 337. Prickly sow thistle (*Sonchus asper*). **A,** habit of plant showing leaf variation and cluster of heads ; **B,** lower leaf ; **C,** head ; **D,** achene.

STEPHANOMERIA

Members of the genus are tall, slender herbs. The flowering heads are composed entirely of perfect flowers with strap-shaped flowers as in the genera *Picris* and *Tragopogon*. The flowers are pink. The receptacle is naked, and the achenes are 5-angled, the base broad and hollowed.

They are beakless and possess a bristle-like pappus, plumose at least above the middle.

There are several species of this genus in California. Both of the following are sometimes troublesome weeds.

PLUMED PTILORY (*Stephanomeria exigua* Nutt.)

This native annual is from ½ to 4 feet high, the stems bearing scattered gland-tipped hairs. The leaves are 1 to 2 inches long, and clasp the stem. The pappus is plumose only above; achene 5-angled, a double row of tubercles between the angles.

VIRGATE PTILORY (*Stephanomeria virgata* Benth.)

This native annual which is generally distributed and often troublesome in grain growing sections in late summer, is 1 to 4 feet high, the stems and leaves usually smooth. The leaves are 1¼ to 6 inches long, the upper entire and linear, the lower oblong or spatula-shaped and sometimes cleft. Pappus white, plumose almost throughout. Achene rugose-tuberculate between the 5 angles.

TAGETES (*Tagetes minuta* L.)

This is a native of South America which is reported as naturalized at Riverside. It is annual, 12 to 32 inches high, with mostly alternate, compound leaves 2 to 6 inches long, each with 11 to 17 leaflets, and conspicuously glandular dotted; the leaflets are narrowly lance-shaped, sharply toothed and ¾ to 2 inches long. The flowering heads are numerous and congested. The involucre is cylindric, about ¾ inch long, and composed of 5 united bracts with gland-dots.

TANSY (*Tanacetum vulgare* L.) (Fig. 338)

This European species is well established at Quincy. It has also become naturalized in Humboldt County along the road between Fortuna and Fernbridge. It is an erect, strongly aromatic perennial herb, 1½ to 3 feet tall. The leaves are alternate, pinnately divided or deeply incised, the lobes acute and usually toothed. Basal leaves are often 12 inches long. There are numerous flowering heads, ¼ to ½ inch broad, usually devoid of ray flowers. The involucre is low, hemispheric, its bracts appressed in several series, and slightly pubescent. The receptacle is flat, the flowers yellow, the achenes 5-angled, the pappus a short crown.

RED-SEEDED DANDELION (*Taraxacum laevigatum* (Willd.) DC.)

This is an introduced species that is found sparingly in the San Francisco Bay region. It resembles the common dandelion, from which it is distinguished by its red achenes, and shorter beak, which is 1½ to 2 times the length of the body of the achene.

COMMON DANDELION (*Taraxacum vulgare* (Lam.) Schrank.) (Fig. 320)

This well-known plant is introduced from Europe. It is usually found wherever man has settled. It is now well established throughout

FIG. 338.   Tansy (*Tanacetum vulgare*).

the State, chiefly as a pest in lawns, golf courses, and pasture lands. In some instances it has invaded native meadow lands.

Common dandelion is a perennial herb, stemless, with a basal cluster of deeply and irregularly lobed leaves, 2 to 10 inches long. The flowering heads are yellow, 1 to 2 inches broad, and borne at the top of hollow stalks. The involucre is composed of numerous narrow green bracts, the outer being much smaller than the inner. The achenes are greenish or light-brown, spindle-shaped, spinulose above and tapering into a slender beak two or three times the length of the body of the achene. The pappus consists of many soft, white hairs.

SPRING RABBIT-BRUSH (*Tetradymia glabrata* Gray)

This species is a native which occurs in desert-like situations from the Mojave Desert north along the east side of the Sierra Nevada. It is

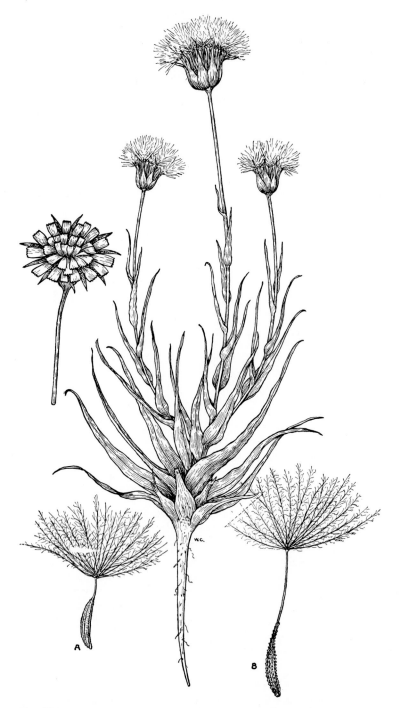

FIG. 339.   Salsify (*Tragopogon porrifolius*), showing habit and single head.
B, achene.   A, achene of meadow salsify (*T. pratensis*).

a low, rounded bush from 1 to 3 feet tall. The herbage is white-woolly, sometimes glabrate. The primary leaves are rigid, short-pointed, and early deciduous; the axillary leaves are in bundles of 3 to 6, soft, persistent, and somewhat less than ½ inch long. Usually by the middle of June the plant has made all of its growth, being dormant the remainder of the year.

The young buds and leaves are known to be poisonous to sheep.

SALSIFY (*Tragopogon porrifolius* L.) (Figs. 274 and 339)

This species, an introduction from Europe, is rather widely distributed throughout California, at lower altitudes, although nowhere abundant. It occurs especially in waste places about cities and towns.

Fig. 340.   Crownbeard (*Verbesina encelioides* var. *exauriculata*).

Salsify is a stout, smooth, somewhat succulent biennial or perennial herb from a stout tap root. The stems are 2 to 4 feet high, and generally unbranched. There are numerous narrow, smooth, grass-like green leaves, 8 to 12 inches long, with clasping bases. At the end of the stem is a single large head of purple flowers. The stem is swollen and hollow just below the flower head. The flower heads are 2 to 4 inches broad, and usually open in the early morning, closing by mid-day. The involucre is composed of a single series of long-pointed, green bracts. The receptacle is naked. The body of the achene is oblong, about ½ inch long, 5- to 10-ribbed, and long-beaked. The pappus consists of a crown of about 5 brownish, slender, plumose bristles.

MEADOW SALSIFY (*Tragopogon pratensis* L.) a European introduction has been collected at Loyalton in Sierra County, and elsewhere. The achene has a shorter beak than the preceding species. (Fig. 339A) The flowers are yellow.

CROWNBEARD (*Verbesina encelioides* Gray var. *exauriculata* Rob. & Greenm.) (Fig. 340)

Crownbeard has been introduced into California from eastern United States, where it is recognized as a weed. In California it has been found along the Salinas River, at Glendale, Cahuenga Pass, and Riverside, growing in summer beds of winter flood streams and on low plains.

This is an erect, branching annual herb, 1 to 4 feet high. The stems are grayish-white and covered with fine white hairs. The leaves are oval lance-shaped to broadly oval, toothed, white-hairy below, green above, 1¼ to 4 inches long on petioles about ⅓ as long. The heads are usually on elongated flower stalks. The bracts of the involucre are in 2 or 3 series, lance-shaped, and about ¼ inch long. There are 12 to 15 orange-colored rays which are deeply 3-toothed and about ½ inch long. The disk flowers are also yellow. The achenes are strongly flattened, broadly winged on each edge, the wings becoming corky-thickened. The pappus consists of two short awns, one on each edge of the achene.

XANTHIUM

The genus *Xanthium* is represented by about 15 species, only 2 of which are of special interest to California agriculture; these are common cocklebur (*Xanthium canadense*) and spiny clotbur (*X. spinosum*). Both species are annual, coarse-growing plants with widely branching and stout stems. The outstanding distinguishing mark of both is the "bur" which is covered with hooked prickles and which contains two black fruits. The bur sticks to the hair of animals, and the seed is thus disseminated. Spiny clotbur has stout, rigid, three-pronged spines about 1 inch long by the sides of the leaves; these spines are absent in the common cocklebur.

Fig. 341. Left, cocklebur (*Xanthium canadense*) ; right, spiny clotbur (*X. spinosum*).

COCKLEBUR (*Xanthium canadense* Mill.) (Fig. 341)
Other common names: Sea burdock, hedgehog bur-weed, sheep bur, button bur, clotbur, ditch bur.

This is an immigrant from the Old World tropics which is exceedingly abundant in California along neglected irrigation ditches and in low or marshy lands, and in moist pastures. It can withstand a certain amount of alkali.

Common cocklebur is a coarse, stout annual, 2 to 4 feet high. The stems are rough, more or less angled, tinged with red or brown, or more or less irregularly spotted. The leaves are 1 to 4 inches long, somewhat heart-shaped at the base, nearly entire or 3- to 5-lobed. The margins coarsely toothed, roughened on both surfaces with minute bristles, dark-green above but lighter beneath and conspicuously 3-nerved from the base. The leaf stalks are as long or longer than the blades. The flowers are very similar to those of the spiny clotbur. The burs are oblong or elliptic in shape, $\frac{1}{2}$ to 1 inch long, and covered with hooked bristles or spines, the lower parts of which have short, glandular hairs. Each bur ends in a pair of stout beaks somewhat converging over the end or hooked at their tips. Each bur contains two black achenes.

This, and the other species of Xanthium described herein, are poisonous to cattle, sheep, horses, hogs and chickens. They are most poisonous in the seedling stage. The seeds are also toxic. The burs cause serious mechanical injury, and lower the value of wool.

SPINY CLOTBUR (*Xanthium spinosum* L.) (Fig. 341)

Spiny clotbur grows to a height of 1 to 3 feet. The stems are covered with minute hairs. The leaves are 2 to 5 inches long, lance-shaped or narrowly oval, 2- or 3-lobed or cut, and narrowed at the base into a short leaf-stalk; they are thick in texture; the upper surface is dark-green with a conspicuous whitish midrib, and the lower surface is white with woolly pubescence. At the base of the leaf-stalk on one side is a 3-pronged spine about 1 inch long. The flowers are greenish and unisexual, the two kinds of flowers occurring on the same plant. The staminate or male flowers occur in almost globular heads, and in the terminal cluster; the pistillate or female flowers are usually situated lower on the plant than the male flowers, and are in the leaf axils. Each group of male flowers is subtended by an involucre; each male flower consists of a tubular corolla, mostly 5 stamens and a rudimentary ovary. The female flowers are usually in groups of two, surrounded by a closed involucre, which is covered with hooked spines; pistillate, or female flowers, have 1-celled ovary, a 2-cleft style, but no corolla. The "bur" is from $\frac{1}{3}$ to $\frac{1}{2}$ inch long, about $\frac{1}{8}$ inch in diameter, hairy, with two inconspicuous beaks at the tip, and beset with many short spines. There are two seeds in each bur. They retain their vitality for many years, lying dormant in the thick-walled bur.

Obnoxious in pastures, as the preceding. Also because the burs become tangled in the manes and tails of horses and tails of cattle.

WEEDS OF SPECIAL CROPS AND ENVIRONMENTAL CONDITIONS

Many weeds grow under a variety of situations, infesting various kinds of crops, and thriving equally well along roadsides, on ditch banks, and in waste places. However, there are weeds that commonly infest a certain type of crop or attain their best development under special environmental conditions. For example, the weeds of lawns and golf courses constitute a fairly distinct class, as do those of rice fields, or of alfalfa, or of pasture lands, or of the small cereals—wheat, oats, and barley. There follow herewith lists of weeds which are most commonly found in certain crops or in special situations in California.

IMPORTANT WEEDS OF ALFALFA

Achyrachaena mollis—Blow-wives
Allocarya spp.—Scorpion weed
Amaranthus blitoides—Prostrate pigweed
Amaranthus retroflexus—Rough pigweed
Amaranthus spp.—Amaranth
Amsinckia spp.—Buckthorn
Atriplex spp.—Saltbush
Avena fatua—Wild oat
Brassica arvensis—Wild mustard
Brassica nigra—Black mustard
Bromus spp.—Bromegrass
Cenchrus pauciflorus—Sandbur
Centaurea melitensis—Tocalote
Centaurea solstitialis—Yellow starthistle
Centromadia Fitchii—Fitch's spikeweed
Centromadia pungens—Common spikeweed
Chenopodium leptophyllum—Narrow-leaf goosefoot
Chenopodium spp.—Goosefoot
Cuscuta spp.—Dodder
Cynodon Dactylon—Bermuda grass
Echinochloa Crusgalli—Watergrass
Eremocarpus setigerus—Turkey mullein
Eryngium spp.—Button snakeroot
Grindelia spp.—Gumweed
Helianthus sp.—Sunflower
Heliotropium curassavicum—Alkali heliotrope
Hordeum spp.—Wild barley
Lactuca scariola—Prickly lettuce
Lepidium nitidum—Common peppergrass
Lepturus cylindricus—Thintail
Malva parviflora—Cheeseweed
Malva rotundifolia—Dwarf mallow
Malva sp.—Mallow
Matricaria suaveolens—Pineapple weed
Melilotus indica—Sour clover
Melilotus spp.—Sweet clover
Montia perfoliata—Miner's lettuce
Penicum capillare—Witch grass
Paspalum distichum—Joint grass
Phacelia spp.—Curly bloom, fiddle-neck
Phalaris minor—Mediterranean canary grass
Phalaris paradoxa—Gnawed canary grass
Picris echioides—Bristly oxtongue
Plantago lanceolata—Buckhorn plantain

Polygonum argyrocoleon—Silver-sheathed knotweed
Polygonum aviculare—Knotweed
Polygonum spp.—Smartweed
Polypogon monspeliensis—Rabbitfoot grass
Raphanus sativus—Wild radish
Rumex spp.—Dock
Salsoli Kali var. tenuifolia—Russian thistle
Setaria spp.—Bristlegrass
Sisymbrium officinale—Hedge mustard
Solanum nigrum—Black nightshade
Solanum spp.—Nightshade
Trianthema portulacastrum—Horse-purlane
Trichostema lanceolatum—Bluecurls
Trifolium bifidum—Pinole clover

COMMON WEEDS OF CEREAL GRAINS (EXCLUDING RICE)

Amaranthus graecizans—Tumbling pigweed
Amsinckia spp.—Buckthorn
Anthemis Cotula—Mayweed
Atriplex spp.—Saltbush
Avena fatua—Wild oat
Brassica incana—Short-podded mustard
Brassica arvensis—Wild mustard
Brassica campestris—Common yellow mustard
Brassica nigra—Black mustard
Bromus mollis—Soft chess
Bromus rigidus—Ripgut grass
Bromus spp.—Bromegrass
Calandrinia spp.—Red maids
Capsella Bursa-pastoris—Shepherd's purse
Centaurea melitensis—Tocalote
Centaurea solstitialis—Yellow star thistle
Centromadia pungens—Common spikeweed
Chenopodium album—Lambs'-quarters
Chenopodium murale—Nettle-leaf goosefoot
Chenopodium spp.—Goosefoot
Convolvulus arvensis—Wild morning-glory
Echinochloa Crusgalli—Watergrass
Erodium cicutarium—Red-stem filaree
Eschscholtzia californica—California poppy
Festuca Myuros—Rat's-tail fescue
Festuca spp.—Fescue
Helianthus spp.—Sunflower
Holcus helepensis—Johnson grass
Hookera spp.—Brodiaea
Hodeum spp.—Wild barley
Hypochoeris radicata—Hairy cat's-ear
Lactuca scariola—Prickly lettuce
Lepidium nitidum—Common peppergrass
Lepturas cylindricus—Thintail
Lolium temulentum—Darnel
Lupinus spp.—Lupine
Lythrum hyssopifolia—Grass poly
Malva parviflora—Cheese weed
Medicago hispida—California bur clover
Melilotus indica—Sour clover
Montia spp.
Phacelia spp.—Curly bloom, fiddle-neck
Phalaris Lemmoni
Phalaris minor—Mediterranean canary grass
Phalaris paradoxa—Gnawed canary grass
Plagiobothrys spp.—Popcorn flower
Polygonum argyrocoleon—Silver-sheathed knotweed
Polygonum aviculare—Knotweed

Polypogon monspeliensis—Rabbitfoot grass
Raphanus sativus—Wild radish
Rumex spp.—Dock
Silene gallica—Windmill pink
Sisymbrium officinale—Hedge mustard
Sonchus oleraceus—Common sow thistle
Thelypodium spp.
Torilis nodosa—Hedge parsley
Trifolium bifidum—Pinole clover
Trifolium spp.—Clover

WEEDS OF RICE

Alisma plantago—Water plantain
Amaranthus spp.—Pigweed
Ammannia coccinea—Redstem
Anthemis cotula—Mayweed
Aster exilis—Slender aster
Avena fatua—Wild oats
Bacopa rotundifolia—Water hyssop
Brassica nigra—Black mustard
Centaurea solstitialis—Yellow star thistle
Cyperus spp.—Nutgrass
Dopatrium junceum—Dopatrium
Echinochloa Crusgalli—Watergrass
Echninodorus cordifolius—Upright burhead
Eclipta alba—Burhead
Eleocharis spp.—Spikerush
Helianthus spp.—Wild sunflower
Leptochloa fascicularis—Scale grass
Leptochloa imbricata—Sprangletop
Leersia oryzoides—Rice cut-grass
Lolium temulentum—Darnel
Lycopus americana—Water horehound
Lythrum hyssopifolia—Loosestrife
Melilotus indica—Sour clover
Oryza sativa—Red rice
Paspalum distichum—Joint grass
Phalaris spp.—Canary grass
Physalis spp.—Ground cherry
Polygonum spp.—Smartweed
Rumex crispus—Curled dock
Sagittaria spp.—Arrowhead lily
Scirpus spp.—Bulrush
Sesbania macrocarpa—Sesbania
Solanum spp.—Nightshade
Sparganium sp.—Bur-reed
Typha spp.—Cattail

IMPORTANT WEEDS OF LAWNS AND GOLF COURSES

There has been pronounced increased in interest in weeds of lawns and golf courses during recent years. Many such weeds, new to the State, have made their appearance. Usually these new infestations can be traced to weed seed impurities in lawn seed. The principal weeds of California lawns and golf courses are as follows:

Arenaria serpyllifolia—Sandwort
Capsella Bursa-pastoris—Shepherd's purse
Cerastium arvense—Field chickweed
Cerastium viscosum—Annual mouse-ear chickweed
Cerastium vulgatum—Large mouse-ear chickweed
Cynodon Dactylon—Bermuda grass
Dichondra repens—Dichondra
Digitaria Ischaemum—Smooth crabgrass

Digitaria sanguinalis—Hairy crabgrass
Eleusine indica—Goosegrass
Euphorbia supina—Spurge
Geranium spp.—Geranium
Helxine—Baby-tears
Holcus mollis—Creeping velvet grass
Hydrocotyle sp.—Pennywort
Malva rotundifolia—Dwarf mallow
Medicago hispida—Bur clover
Medicago lupulina—Black medick
Molluga verticillata—Carpet-weed
Nepeta hederacea—Ground ivy
Oxalis corniculata—Yellow oxalis
Paspalum dilatatum—Dallis grass
Plantago spp.—Plantain
Poa annua—Annual bluegrass
Prunella vulgaris—Self heal
Scleranthus annuus—Knawel
Sherardia arvensis—Field madder
Sida hederacea—Alkali mallow
Silene noctiflora—Night-blooming catchfly
Soliva sessilis—Soliva
Stellaria graminea—Grassy starwort
Stellaria media—Common chickweed
Taraxacum vulgare—Common dandelion
Trifolium repens—White clover
Verbena bracteosa—Bracted vervain

IMPORTANT LIVESTOCK POISONING PLANTS *

Aconitum columbianum—Monkshood or aconite
Asclepias cordifolia—Purple milkweed
Asclepias eriocarpa—Woolly-pod milkweed
Asclepias Fremontii—Kotolo milkweed
Asclepias mexicana—Mexican whorled or narrow-leaved milkweed
Asclepias speciosa—Showy or creek milkweed
Astragalus Hornii—Sheep loco
Astragalus leucophyllus—Woolly-leaved loco
Astragalus lentiginosus—Spotted loco
Astragalus Menziesii—Gray loco
Astragalus Mortoni—Morton loco
Astragalus oocarpus—Smooth loco
Astragalus Purshii—Tufted loco
Chenopodium ambrosioides—Mexican tea
Chenopodium anthelminticum—California wormseed
Chenopodium Botrys—Jerusalem oak
Cicuta Bolanderi—Salt-marsh hemlock
Cicuta californica—California water hemlock
Cicuta Douglasii—Douglas water hemlock
Cicuta vagans—Oregon water hemlock
Conium maculatum—Poison hemlock
Corydalis caseana—Fitweed
Datura meteloides—Tolguacha
Datura Stramonium—Jimson weed
Datura Tatula—Purple thorn apple
Delphinium Andersonii—Anderson larkspur
Delphinium californicum—Coast larkspur
Delphinium decorum—Smooth larkspur
Delphinium hesperium—Western larkspur
Delphinium Menziesii—Menzies larkspur
Delphinium Parryi—Parry larkspur
Delphinium scopulorum—Mountain larkspur
Delphinium trolliifolium—Cow poison
Equisetum arvense—Common horsetail
Equisetum hyemale—Common scouring rush

Equisetum laevigatum—Smooth scouring rush
Equisetum palustre—Marsh horsetail
Helenium Hoopesii—Western sneezeweed
Halogeton glomeratus—Halogeton
Hypericum perforatum—Klamath weed, St. Johnswort
Kalmia polifolia—Pale laurel
Kalmia polifolia var. *microphylla*—Alpine laurel
Ledum glandulosum—Labrador tea
Leucothoe Davisiae—Black laurel
Lupinus laxiflorus—Grassland lupine
Lupinus leucophyllus—Western lupine
Lupinus onustus—Woodland lupine
Lupinus pusillus—Low lupine
Menziesia ferruginea—Rustyleaf
Monotropo uniflora—Indian pipe
Nicotiana attenuata—Coyote tobacco
Nicotiana glauca—Tree tobacco
Nicotiana trigonophylla—Desert tobacco
Prunus demissa—Western chokecherry
Pteris aquilina var. *lanuginosa*—Bracken fern
Rhododendron californicum—California rose bay
Rhododendron occidentale—Western azalea
Sarcobatus vermiculatus—Black greasewood
Solanum nigrum—Black nightshade
Solanum villosum—Villous nightshade
Tetradymia glabrata—Spring rabbit-brush
Triglochin maritima—Arrow grass
Veratrum californicum—False hellebore
Xanthium calvum—Cocklebur
Xanthium campestre—Cocklebur
Xanthium canadense—Cocklebur
Xanthium spinosum—Spiny clotbur

POISONOUS WEEDS OF MINOR OR LOCAL IMPORTANCE

Achillea spp.—Yarrow
Actaea spicata var. *arguta*—Baneberry
Aesculus californica—Buckeye
Agrostemma Githago—Corn cockle
Ammi majus—Bishop's weed
Anagallis arvensis—Red pimpernel
Anthemis Cotula—Mayweed
Apocynum andro saemifolium—Mountain hemp
Apocynum cannabinum—Dogbane, Indian hemp
Arctium minus—Common burdock
Artemisia tridentata—Common or black sagebrush
Balsamorrhiza sigittata—Balsam root
Berula erecta—Cut-leaved water parsnip
Caltha biflora—Marsh marigold
Cephalanthus occidentalis—Button-bush
Chrysothamnus nauseosus—Yellowbrush
Datisca glomerata—Durango root
Digitalis purpurea—Purple foxglove
Eragrostis cilianensis—Link grass
Eremocarpus setigerus—Turkey mullein
Erigeron canadensis—Horseweed
Euphorbia Lathyrus—Spurge
Leucocrinum montanum—Sand lily
Lolium temulentum—Darnel
Nepeta hederacea—Ground ivy
Nerium oleander—Oleander
Pedicularis spp.—Lousewort
Polygonum aviculare—Knotweed
Polygonum hydropiperoides—Water pepper

Polygonum Persicaria—Lady's thumb
Quercus spp.—Oaks
Ranunculus scleratus—Cursed crowfoot
Rhamnus spp.—Buckthorns
Ricinus communis—Castor bean
Rudbeckia spp.—Coneflower
Rumex Acetosella—Sheep sorrel
Rumex crispus—Curled dock
Saponaria officinalis—Bouncing Bet, soapwort
Sanicula bipinnata—Poison sanicle
Sium cicutaefolium—Water parsnip
Solidago spp.—Goldenrods
Stipa robusta—Sleepy grass
Taxus brevifolia—Western yew
Typha latifolia—Cat-tail

* FOOTNOTE.—List largely from Agricultural Experimental Station Bulletin 593, Stock-Poisoning Plants of California, Arthur W. Sampson and Harry E. Malmsten. 1935.

IMPORTANT WEEDS OF PASTURE LANDS AND MEADOWS

The following list includes weeds of artificial pastures and of low natural meadows and not those peculiar to open range lands.

Anagallis arvensis—Red pimpernel
Anthemis Cotula—Mayweed
Anthoxanthum odoratum—Sweet vernalgrass
Apocynum cannabinum—Dogbane
Artemisia vulgaris var. *heterophylla*—Mugwort
Asclepias mexicana—Mexican whorled milkweed
Asclepias speciosa—Showy milkweed
Bidens laevis—Bur marigold
Bromus tectorum—Downy Chess
Capsella Bursa-pastoris—Shepherd's purse
Cicuta sp.—Water hemlock
Cirsius arvense—Canada thistle
Cirsius lanceolatum—Bull thistle
Conium maculatum—Poison hemlock
Crepis capillar—Smooth hawksbeard
Daucus carota—Wild carrot
Dispsacus fullonum—Fuller's teasel
Echninochloa Crusgalli—Watergrass
Equisetum sp.—Horsetail
Eryngium spp.—Button snakeroot
Heracleum lanatum—Cow parsnip
Helianthus californicus—California sunflower
Hibiscus Trionum—Flower-of-an-hour
Hordeum jubatum—Squirrel-tail barley
Hodeum murium—Common foxtail
Hordeum nodosum—Meadow barley
Hypochoeris radicata—Hairy cat's-ear
Isatis tinctoria—Dyers woad
Lepidium virginicum—Tall peppergrass
Lolium temulentum—Darnel
Lycopus americanus—Small bugloss
Malva spp.—Mallow
Marrubium vulgare—Horehound
Matricaria suaveolens—Pineapple weed
Nepeta cataria—Catnip
Paspalum distichum—Joint grass
Plantago spp.—Plantain
Polygonum acre—Dotted smartweed
Polypogon monspeliensis—Rabbitfoot grass
Pteris aquilina var. *lanuginosa*—Bracken fern
Ranunculus scleratus—Cursed crowfoot
Roripa austriaca—Austrian field cress

Rudbeckia hirta—Black-eyed Susan
Rumex crispus—Curly dock
Rumex obtusifolius—Bitter dock
Rumex pulcher—Fiddle dock
Salvia aethiopis
Setaria lutescens—Yellow bristlegrass
Sherardia arvensis—Field madder
Silybum marianum—Milk thistle
Sisymbrium officinale—Hedge mustard
Solanum rostratum—Buffalo bur
Taraxacum vulgare—Common dandelion
Verbascum spp.—Mullein
Verbena bracteosa—Bracted vervain
Verbena prostrata—Prostrate vervain
Xanthium canadense—Cocklebur
Xanthium spinosum—Clotbur

IMPORTANT WEEDS OF RANGE LANDS

In many parts of the State, alien plants have replaced much of the native grassland of stock ranges. Changes in the original plant cover have been marked in sections where man has carried on his various operations.

Some time between 1890 and 1900, Klamath weed made its appearance here and there on the northwest ranges, and today this weed infests some 100,000 acres of land, in many places seriously reducing the carrying capacity of the range. In the last decade Halogeton from Eurasia has invaded thousands of acres of range land in Lassen County. Every year sees the appearance of new introductions.

Achillea millefolium—Yarrow
Aconitum spp.—Monkshood
Aegilops triuncialis—Barb goatgrass
Aristida purpurea—Needlegrass
Asclepias spp.—Milkweed
Astragalus spp.—Loco weed
Avena fatua—Wild oat
Bromus mollis—Soft chess
Bromus rigidus—Ripgut grass
Bromus rubens—Red brome
Bromus sterilis—Barren brome
Centaurea melitensis—Tocalote
Chrysanthemum segetum—Corn chrysanthemum
Cynara Cardunculus—Artichoke thistle
Datisca glomerata—Durango root
Delphinium spp.—Larkspur
Elymus Caput-Medusae—Medusa-head
Erodium spp.—Filaree
Festuca Myuros—Rat's-tail fescue
Halogeton glomeratus—Halogeton
Hordeum Gussoneanum—Mediterranean barley
Hordeum murinum—Common foxtail
Hordeum nodosum—Meadow barley
Hypericum concinnum—Gold-wire
Hypericum perforatum—Klamath weed
Lupinus spp.—Lupine
Polygala californica—Milkwort
Prunus demissa—Chokecherry
Salvia aethiopis—Mediterranean sage
Sida hederacea—Alkali mallow
Stipa spp.—Needle-and-thread
Ulex europeus—Gorse

SOME WEEDS OF RIGHTS OF WAYS

Amsinckia intermedia—Buckthorn
Atriplex sp.—Saltbush
Avena barbata—Wild oats
Bromus carinatus—California brome
Bromus mollis—Soft chess
Bromus rigidus—Ripgut grass
Bromus rubens—Red brome
Centaurea solstitialis—Yellow starthistle
Cucurbita spp.—Wild gourd
Eriogonum sp.—Wild buckwheat
Erodium botrys—Broadleaf filaree
Erodium cicutarium—Redstem filaree
Erodium moschatum—Whitestem filaree
Festuca confusa—Fescue
Festuca megalura—Foxtail fescue
Glycyrrhiza lepidota—Wild licorice
Grindelia camporum—Gumweed
Hordeum murinum—Common foxtail
Hordeum nodosum—Meadow barley
Lactuca scariola—Prickly lettuce
Lactura scariola var. *integrata*—Prickly lettuce
Lolium multiflorum—Rye grass
Lotus americanus—Trefoil
Lupinus benthami—Lupine
Lupinus bicolor—Lupine
Melacothrix Coulteri—Snake's head
Matricaria suaveolens—Pineapple weed
Melilotus indica—Sour clover
Polygonum aviculare—Common knotweed
Polycarpon tetraphyllum—Four leaved all-seed
Sisymbrium Irio—London rocket
Sisymbrium pinnatum—Tansy mustard
Sorghum halepense—Johnson grass
Spergularia rubra—Sand spurry
Stillingia linearifolia—Queens-root

IMPORTANT WEEDS OF SALINE AND MARITIME SOILS

Anemopsis californica—Yerba mansa
Aster exilis—Slender aster
Atriplex spp.—Saltbush
Bassia hyssopifolia—Five-hook bassia
Capsella procumbens—Nannie's purse
Centromadia pungens—Common spikeweed
Chenopodium ambrosioides—Mexican tea
Cressa cretica—Alkali clover
Cotula coronopifolia—Common brass buttons
Cycloloma atriplicifolium—Winged pigweed
Distichlis spicata—Saltgrass
Eremocarpus setigerus—Turkey mullein
Franseria bipinnatifida—Franseria
Frankenia grandifolia—Alkali heath
Heliotropium curassavicum—Alkali heliotrope
Iva axillaris—Poverty weed
Lepidium acutiden—Peppergrass
Leptochloa fascicularis—Sprangle-top
Lepturus cylindricus—Thintail
Pholiurus incurvus—Sicklegrass
Polypogon monspeliensis—Rabbitfoot grass
Polypogon maritima—Maritime beardgrass
Salicornia ambigua—Pickle-weed
Sarcobatus vermiculatus—Greasewood
Sesuvium sessile—Lowland purslane

Scirpus spp.—Bulrush
Sida hederacea—Alkali mallow
Suaeda spp.—Sea blite and alkali blite
Tetragonia expansa—New Zealand spinach

IMPORTANT WEEDS OF VINEYARDS AND ORCHARDS

Abutilon Theophrasti—Velvetleaf
Amaranthus retroflexus—Rough pigweed
Avena fatua—Wild oat
Calandrina caulescens var. *Menziesii*—Red maids
Cenchrus pauciflorus—Sandbur
Convolvulus arvensis—Wild morning-glory
Cynodon Dactylon—Bermuda grass
Cytisus scoparius—Scotch broom
Echinochloa Crusgalli—Watergrass
Epilobium paniculatum—Willow herb
Holcus halepensis—Johnson grass
Hordeum murinum—Common foxtail
Lactuca scariola—Prickly lettuce
Lepidium nitidum—Common peppergrass
Malva parviflora—Cheeseweed
Montia perfoliata—Miner's lettuce
Montia spathulata
Physalis spp.—Husk-tomato, ground cherry
Portulaca oleracea—Purslane
Pteris aquilina var. *lanuginosa*—Bracken fern
Stellaria media—Common chickweed
Tribulus terrestris—Puncture vine.

GENERAL INDEX *

(Numbers in **bold-face** type indicate pages bearing illustrations)

---

* See Weed Control Index p. 546.

(519)

528 INDEX

WEED CONTROL INDEX